Glenn Harkleroad

ELECTROMAGNETICS

McGraw-Hill Electrical and Electronic Engineering Series

Frederick Emmons Terman, Consulting Editor

W. W. Harman and J. G. Truxal, *Associate Consulting Editors*

ELECTROMAGNETICS

John D. Kraus, Ph.D.

Professor of Electrical Engineering
The Ohio State University

New York   Toronto   London

McGRAW-HILL BOOK COMPANY, INC.

1953

ELECTROMAGNETICS

Library of Congress Catalog Card Number: 52–7440

VIII

PREFACE

It is the purpose of this book to present the basic principles of electromagnetic-field theory with approximately equal emphasis on the various branches that find application in such divers areas as electronics, power, radiation, and propagation. Although the field point of view is stressed, the close interrelation of field and circuit theory is also pointed out, as, for example, in the development of field equations from circuit theory and by the very useful concept of the curvilinear square volume or field cell.

The first seven chapters are written for an introductory field-theory course in physics or electrical engineering at about the third- or fourth-year college level. The subjects covered include static electric and magnetic fields, steady currents, and changing electric and magnetic fields. The last seven chapters form a continuation and are written for a somewhat more advanced field-theory course at about senior or first-year-graduate level. These chapters treat plane waves in dielectric and conducting media, transmission lines, wave guides, antennas, and boundary-value problems. Each set of seven chapters includes enough material for a course of about one semester.

The material in the book has been used in courses in electrical engineering at the Ohio State University for several years. The first seven chapters are covered in a course given in the last part of the junior year, while the last seven chapters are treated in a course given in the first part of the first year of the graduate program.

As a prerequisite for the introductory field course the student should have completed a first course in general physics and mathematics through the differential and integral calculus. A course in vector analysis is desirable either beforehand or concurrently, but is not a necessity since most of the vector concepts are developed as they are needed.

The rationalized mksc system of units is used. This system is rapidly coming into almost universal use and has many practical advantages. Throughout the book the dimensional equality of equations is stressed as a necessary condition for correctness. In this connection the dimensional relations are frequently expressed in the appropriate mksc units. A complete table of units is given in the Appendix.

A feature of the book is the large number of worked examples. These examples are stated in problem form, and many of them serve not only to apply the theory but also to develop it further. Complete problem sets are to be found at the end of each chapter. Many important results not given in the text are stated as exercises in these problem sets. Answers are also included for many of the odd-numbered problems.

The presentation of magnetic fields is based on the actual physical situation rather than on fictitious magnetic charges. Furthermore, particular attention is given to the fact that it is the flux density **B** that occurs in the force relations involving the magnetic field.

Space vectors are always indicated by boldface symbols. Complex quantities, or phasors, are sometimes indicated by a dot (˙) over the symbol where it is desired to indicate explicitly that a quantity is complex. However, for simplicity of notation the dot is usually omitted where it is obvious that the quantity is complex.

An aim throughout the book has been to approach a new subject gradually. For example, wherever possible, simple special cases are considered first, and then with these as background the general case is developed.

Although great care has been exercised, some errors in the text or figures will inevitably occur. Anyone finding them would do the author a great service to write him about them so that they can be corrected in subsequent printings.

In conclusion the author wishes to express his appreciation to many of his associates and students for numerous helpful suggestions and also for confirming the answers to many of the problems.

JOHN D. KRAUS

COLUMBUS, OHIO
October, 1952

CONTENTS

CHAPTER 3   The Steady Electric Current

CHAPTER 6 Charged Particles in Electric and Magnetic Fields

CHAPTER 7 Time-changing Electric and Magnetic Fields

CHAPTER 1

THE STATIC ELECTRIC FIELD. PART 1

1-1. Dimensions and Units. Lord Kelvin is reported to have said: "When you can measure what you are speaking about and express it in numbers you know something about it; but when you cannot measure it, when you cannot express it in numbers your knowledge is of a meagre and unsatisfactory kind; it may be the beginning of knowledge but you have scarcely progressed in your thoughts to the stage of science whatever the matter may be."   To this it might be added that before we can measure something we must define its dimensions and provide some standard, or reference, unit in terms of which the quantity can be expressed numerically.

A *dimension* defines some physical characteristic.   For example, length, mass, time, velocity, and force are dimensions.[1] The dimensions of length, mass, time, and electric charge will be considered as the *fundamental dimensions* since other dimensions can be defined in terms of these four.   This choice is arbitrary but convenient.   Let the letters L, M, T, and Q represent the dimensions of length, mass, time, and electric charge, respectively.   Other dimensions are then secondary dimensions.   For example, area is a secondary dimension which may be expressed in terms of the fundamental dimension of length squared (L^2).   As other examples, the fundamental dimensions of velocity are L/T and of force are ML/T^2.

A *unit* is a standard, or reference, by which a dimension can be expressed numerically.   Thus, the meter is a unit in terms of which the dimension of length can be expressed, and the kilogram is a unit in terms of which the dimension of mass can be expressed.   For example, the length dimension of steel rod might be 2 meters and its mass dimension 5 kg.

1-2. Fundamental and Secondary Units. The units for the fundamental dimensions are called the *fundamental units*.   In the meter-kilogram-second, or Giorgi, system of units (abbreviated mks) the meter, kilogram, and second are the fundamental units.   Taking the coulomb as the fourth fundamental unit, the complete system of fundamental units is the meter-kilogram-second-coulomb system (mksc system). The definitions of these four fundamental units are:

---

[1] The term *quantity* is often used synonymously with dimension.

1

Meter: Length between two marks on the international prototype meter, a platinum-iridium bar. (39.37 in. = 1 meter.)

Kilogram: Mass of international prototype kilogram, a platinum-iridium mass. (2.2 lb $\simeq$ 1 kg.)

Second: 1/86,400 part of a mean solar day.

Coulomb: 1 international ampere-second, where 1 international ampere is the current that, flowing steadily through a solution of silver nitrate, will deposit silver at the rate of 1.11800×10^{-6} kg per sec.

The units for dimensions other than mass, length, time, and charge are called *secondary*, or *derived*, *units* and are based on the above fundamental units.

In this book the *rationalized* mksc system of units is used. The rationalized system has the advantage that the factor 4π does not appear in Maxwell's equations although it does appear in certain other relations. A complete table of units in this system is given in the Appendix. In the table there is an alphabetical listing of dimensions or quantities under each of the following headings: Fundamental, Mechanical, Electrical, and Magnetic. For each quantity the symbol, description, mksc unit, equivalent units, and fundamental dimensions are listed.

It is suggested that as each new quantity and unit is discussed the student refer to the table and, in particular, become familiar with the fundamental dimensions for the quantity.

1-3. Dimensional Analysis. It is a necessary condition for correctness that every equation be balanced dimensionally. For example, consider the hypothetical formula

$$\frac{M}{L} = DA \tag{1-1}$$

where M = mass

L = length

D = density (mass per unit volume)

A = area

The dimensional symbols for the left side of (1-1) are M/L, the same as those used. The dimensional symbols for the right side are

$$\frac{M}{L^3} L^2 = \frac{M}{L}$$

Therefore, both sides of this equation have the dimensions of mass per length, and the equation is balanced dimensionally. This is not a guarantee that the equation is correct, that is, it is not a *sufficient* condition for correctness. It is, however, a *necessary* condition for correctness, and it is frequently helpful to analyze equations in this way to determine whether or not they are dimensionally balanced.

Such *dimensional analysis* is also useful for determining what the dimensions of a quantity are. For example, to find the dimensions of force, we make use of Newton's second law that

$$\text{Force} = \text{mass} \times \text{acceleration}$$

Now acceleration has the dimensions of length per time squared so that the dimensions of force are

$$\frac{\text{Mass} \times \text{length}}{\text{Time}^2}$$

or in dimensional symbols

$$\text{Force} = \frac{ML}{T^2}$$

1-4. Electric Charge. The fourth fundamental dimension, or quantity, in the mksc system is *electric charge*. Whereas mass is only of one type (positive mass), electric charge is of two kinds, *positive* and *negative*. The natural elemental unit of negative electric charge is that possessed by an electron and is equal to -1.6×10^{-19} coulomb. The designation of the electron charge as negative is entirely arbitrary and is the result of definition.

A neutral, or normal, atom consists of one or more orbital electrons (negatively charged) and a much heavier nucleus of equal positive charge. The total, or net, charge of the normal atom is zero. If one or more orbital electrons is removed, the atom is ionized. A singly ionized atom (one electron removed) has a net charge of $+1.6 \times 10^{-19}$ coulomb. A doubly ionized atom (two electrons removed) has a net charge of $+3.2 \times 10^{-19}$ coulomb, etc. While negative charge is associated with electrons, positive charge may be associated with atoms having a deficiency of electrons. Thus, an object with an excess of electrons possesses a negative charge and an object with a deficiency of electrons a positive charge.

1-5. The Force between Point Charges and Coulomb's Law. A group of charged particles, that is, atoms or electrons, occupies a finite[1] volume. Even a single electron has a finite size. However, it is often convenient to regard a small, concentrated region of charged particles as a *point charge*. This assumption leads to no appreciable error provided the size of the volume occupied by the charged particles is small compared with the other distances involved.

The basic experiment of electrostatics was first performed by Coulomb about 1785, using small charged bodies which may be regarded as point charges. The results of this experiment are given by *Coulomb's law*, which states that the force F between two point charges Q_1 and Q_2 is proportional to the product of the charges and inversely proportional to the square of the distance r between them. That is,

$$F = k \frac{Q_1 Q_2}{r^2} \quad \text{newtons} \tag{1-2}$$

---

[1] By "finite" is meant "not infinitesimal."

where k = a constant of proportionality. Because of the inverse-square effect of distance this law is said to be an inverse-square law. The force is in the direction of the line connecting the charges. As suggested in Fig. 1-1a the force is outward (repulsive force) if the two charges are of the same sign, but as suggested in Fig. 1-1b the force is inward (attrac-

tive force) if the two charges are of opposite sign.

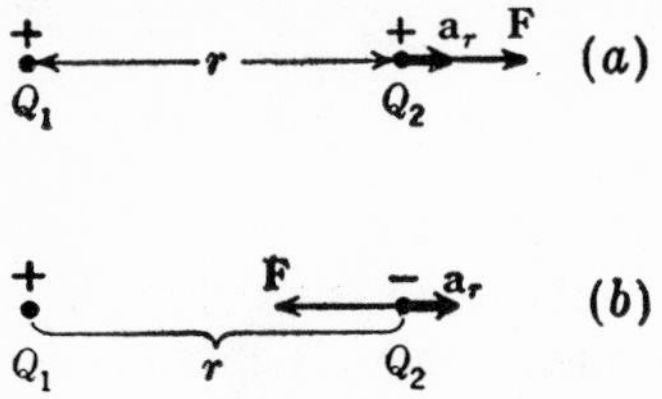

In the mksc system the constant of proportionality is given by

$$k = \frac{1}{4\pi\epsilon}$$

FIG. 1-1. Two point charges of same sign (a) and of opposite sign (b).

where ϵ = permittivity[1] of the medium in which the charges are situated. By dimensional analysis of (1-2) we find that ϵ has the dimensions of capacitance† per length, or in dimensional symbols T^2Q^2/ML^3. The mksc unit for permittivity is the farad per meter. The permittivity of vacuum is designated ϵ_0 and has a value of

$$8.85 \times 10^{-12} \simeq \frac{1}{36\pi} 10^{-9} \quad \text{farads/meter}$$

The permittivity of air is substantially the same as for vacuum.

Force is a vector, that is, it has both magnitude and direction. In this book boldface letters designate vectors. Thus, the vector force is indicated by $\mathbf{F}$ and its scalar magnitude by the lightface italic quantity F, that is, $F = |\mathbf{F}|$. Rewriting (1-2) as a vector equation and also substituting the value of k, we have

$$\mathbf{F} = \mathbf{a}_r \frac{Q_1 Q_2}{4\pi\epsilon r^2} \tag{1-3}$$

where $\mathbf{F}$ = force (newtons‡)

$\mathbf{a}_r$ = unit vector (see Fig. 1-1) pointing in direction of line joining the charges (thus, $\mathbf{F} = \mathbf{a}_r F$)

Q_1 = charge 1 (coulombs)

Q_2 = charge 2 (coulombs)

ϵ = permittivity of medium (farads/meter)

r = distance between point charges (meters)

[1] Also called the *dielectric constant*. For a further discussion of permittivity see Sec. 2-2. The term *capacitivity* is also used for permittivity.

† For a discussion of capacitance see Sec. 2-7. The significance of ϵ should become clearer after reading the portion of Sec. 2-26 on the field cell capacitor.

‡ One *newton* equals the force required to accelerate 1 kg 1 meter per sec per sec.

$$1 \text{ newton} = 10^5 \text{ dynes} = \text{weight of } 0.102 \text{ kg}$$
$$= \text{weight of } 0.224 \text{ lb avoirdupois}$$
$$= \text{weight of } 3.6 \text{ oz avoirdupois}$$

This is the complete vector expression for Coulomb's law as expressed in the rationalized mksc system. To demonstrate the application of this law let us consider the following problem.

Example. A negative point charge of 10^{-6} coulomb is situated in air at the origin of a rectangular coordinate system. A second negative point charge of 10^{-4} coulomb is situated on the positive x axis at a distance of 50 cm from the origin. What is the force on the second charge?

Solution. By Coulomb's law the force

$$\mathbf{F} = \mathbf{i}\,\frac{(-10^{-6})(-10^{-4})}{4\pi \times 0.5^2 \times 10^{-9}/36\pi}$$

$$= +\mathbf{i}3.6 \qquad \text{newtons}$$

That is, there is a force of 3.6 newtons (0.8 lb) in the positive x direction on the second charge.

1-6. Electric Field Intensity. Consider a positive electric point charge Q_1 situated at the origin of a polar coordinate system. If another positive point charge Q_2 is brought into the vicinity of Q_1, it is acted upon by a force. This force is directed radially outward and becomes greater as Q_2 approaches Q_1. It is said that Q_1 is surrounded by a *field*, that is, a region in which forces may act. The nature of this field is indicated by the vector diagram of Fig. 1-2, the length of the vector being proportional to the force at the point.

Dividing (1-3) by Q_2 puts the equation in the dimensional form of force per charge, that is,

$$\frac{F}{Q_2} = \frac{\text{force}}{\text{charge}}$$

which has the dimensional symbols

$$\frac{ML}{T^2Q}$$

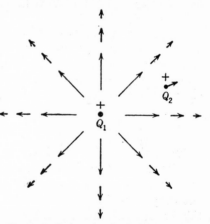

Fig. 1-2. Point charge Q_1 with vectors indicating magnitude and direction of associated electric field.

Now if Q_2 is a positive test charge, the resulting *force per unit charge* is defined as the *electric field intensity*[1] **E**. Thus, from (1-3)

$$\mathbf{E} = \frac{\mathbf{F}}{Q_2} = \mathbf{a}_r\,\frac{Q_1}{4\pi\epsilon r^2} \tag{1-4}$$

where Q_2 = positive test charge. The mksc unit of electric field intensity is the newton per coulomb. As will appear after the discussion of electric potential (Sec. 1-8), an equivalent unit for the electric field intensity is the volt per meter.

[1] Also called the *electric field strength*.

According to (1-4) the point charge Q_1 is surrounded by an *electric field* of intensity $\mathbf{E}$ which is proportional to Q_1 and is inversely proportional to r^2. The electric field intensity $\mathbf{E}$ is a vector having the same direction as the force $\mathbf{F}$ but differs in numerical magnitude and in dimensions.

It is not implied by (1-4) that the positive test charge has a value of 1 coulomb. It may have any convenient value since the ratio of the force (newtons) to the test charge (coulombs) is independent of the size of the charge provided the test charge does not disturb the field being measured. Now 1 coulomb represents a much larger charge than is ordinarily encountered in static problems. For example, we note by Coulomb's law that the repulsive force of two positive charges of 1 coulomb separated by 1 meter is 9×10^9 newtons (or 1 million tons). This is an enormous force, and it follows that if we attempted to use a test charge of 1 coulomb we should tend to disturb the charges whose field we seek to measure. Therefore, it is necessary to use small test charges; in fact, the test charge should be sufficiently small that it does not appreciably disturb the charge configuration whose field is to be measured.

If the test charge is made small enough, it may be regarded as of infinitesimal size so that the ultimate value of the electric field intensity at a point becomes the force $\Delta\mathbf{F}$ on a positive test charge ΔQ divided by the charge with the limit taken as the charge approaches zero. That is,

$$\mathbf{E} = \lim_{\Delta Q \to 0} \frac{\Delta\mathbf{F}}{\Delta Q} \qquad (1\text{-}5)$$

Actually the smallest available test charge is an electron. Since this is a finite charge, it follows that $\mathbf{E}$ cannot be measured with unlimited accuracy. Although this is of importance in atomic problems, it need not concern us in the large-scale, or macroscopic, problems treated in this book. In practice, $\mathbf{E}$ would be measured with a small but finite test charge, and if this charge is small enough, $\mathbf{E}$ would differ inappreciably from that measured with an infinitesimal or vanishingly small test charge as implied in (1-5).

A sample calculation of electric field intensity is given in the following problem.

Example. A negative point charge 10^{-8} coulomb is situated in air at the origin of a rectangular coordinate system. What is the electric field intensity at a point on the positive x axis 3 meters from the origin?

Solution. By (1-4) the field intensity is given by

$$\mathbf{E} = -\mathbf{i}\frac{10^{-8}}{4\pi \times 3^2 \times 10^{-9}/36\pi}$$
$$= -\mathbf{i}10 \quad \text{newtons/coulomb}$$

That is, the electric field intensity is 10 newtons per coulomb (or 10 volts per meter) and is in the negative x direction.

1-7. The Electric Field of Several Point Charges and the Principle of Superposition of Fields. Since the electric field of a point charge is a linear function of the value of the charge, it follows that the fields of more than one point charge are linearly superposable by vector addition. As a generalization, this fact may be stated as the *principle of superposition* applied to electric fields as follows:

The total or resultant field at a point is the vector sum of the individual component fields at the point.

Thus, referring to Fig. 1-3, the field intensity of the point charge Q_1 at the point P is $\mathbf{E}_1$ and of the point charge Q_2 is $\mathbf{E}_2$. The total field at P due to both point charges is the vector sum of $\mathbf{E}_1$ and $\mathbf{E}_2$, or $\mathbf{E}$ as indicated in the figure.

A further illustration is given in the following example.

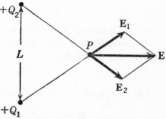

FIG. 1-3. Vector addition of fields due to two equal point charges of the same sign to give resultant or total field **E**.

Example. A positive point charge of 10^{-9} coulomb is situated in air at the origin ($x = 0$, $y = 0$), and a negative point charge of -2×10^{-9} coulomb is situated on the y axis 1 meter from the origin ($x = 0$, $y = 1$) as shown in Fig. 1-4. Find the total

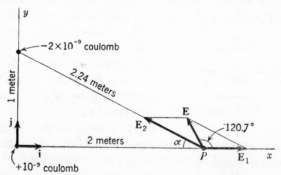

FIG. 1-4. Vector addition of fields due to two unequal point charges of opposite sign to give resultant or total field **E**.

electric field intensity at the point P on the x axis 2 meters from the origin ($x = 2$, $y = 0$).

Solution. The vector value of the electric field $\mathbf{E}_1$ due to the charge at $(0, 0)$ is, from (1-4),

$$\mathbf{E}_1 = \mathbf{i} \frac{10^{-9}}{4\pi \times 2^2 \times 10^{-9}/36\pi}$$
$$= \mathbf{i} 2.25 \quad \text{newtons/coulomb}$$

The magnitude of the field $\mathbf{E}_2$ due to the charge at $(0,1)$ is

$$E_2 = \frac{-2 \times 10^{-9}}{4\pi \times 2.24^2 \times 10^{-9}/36\pi}$$
$$= -3.58 \text{ newtons/coulomb}$$

The vector value of $\mathbf{E}_2$ is given by

$$\mathbf{E}_2 = -\mathbf{i}3.58 \cos \alpha + \mathbf{j}3.58 \sin \alpha$$
$$= -\mathbf{i}3.58 \frac{2}{2.24} + \mathbf{j}3.58 \frac{1}{2.24}$$
$$= -\mathbf{i}3.2 + \mathbf{j}1.6 \quad \text{newtons/coulomb}$$

where $\mathbf{i}$ is a unit vector in the x direction and $\mathbf{j}$ a unit vector in the y direction. The total vector field $\mathbf{E}$ may be obtained by graphical vector addition of $\mathbf{E}_1$ and $\mathbf{E}_2$ or analytically as follows:

$$\mathbf{E} = \mathbf{i}(2.25 - 3.2) + \mathbf{j}1.6$$

and in both rectangular and polar forms

$$\mathbf{E} = -\mathbf{i}0.95 + \mathbf{j}1.6 = 1.86\underline{/120.7°} \text{ newtons/coulomb}$$

1-8. The Electric Scalar Potential. It has been shown that an electric charge produces an electric field and that a test charge brought into this field is acted on by a force. Let us now consider the work or energy required to move the test charge from one point to another in the electric field.

A point charge produces a nonuniform field since its magnitude varies inversely as the distance squared. However, if we confine our attention to a small portion of the field at a great distance from the charge, the field is substantially uniform. Con-

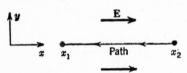

FIG. 1-5. Linear path in uniform electric field.

sider two points, x_1 and x_2, situated in such a uniform electric field $\mathbf{E}$ parallel to the x direction. Let a positive test charge at x_2 be moved in the negative x direction to x_1 as in Fig. 1-5. The field exerts a force on the charge so that it requires work to move the charge against the force. The amount of work per unit charge is equal to the force per unit charge (or field intensity $\mathbf{E}$) times the distance through which the charge is moved. Thus,

$$\mathbf{E}(x_2 - x_1) = \text{work per unit charge} \quad \text{(joules/coulomb)} \quad (1\text{-}6)$$

The dimensions of (1-6) are

$$\frac{\text{Force}}{\text{Charge}} \times \text{length} = \frac{\text{work}}{\text{charge}}$$

or

$$\frac{ML}{T^2} \frac{L}{Q} = \frac{ML^2}{T^2Q}$$

In mksc units the relation is

$$\frac{\text{Newtons}}{\text{Coulomb}} \times \text{meters} = \frac{\text{joules}}{\text{coulomb}} \qquad (1\text{-}7)$$

The dimensions of work per charge are those of potential. In our example (Fig. 1-5), the work or energy per unit charge required to transport the test charge from x_2 to x_1 is called the difference in *electric potential*[1] of the points x_2 and x_1. The point x_1 has the higher potential since it requires work to reach it from point x_2. Thus, moving from x_2 to x_1 (opposite to **E**), we experience a *rise* in potential. The unit of electric potential V in the mksc system is the volt and is equal to 1 joule per coulomb. Hence, electric potential is expressible either in joules per coulomb or in volts. The relation of (1-7) can then be extended to

$$\frac{\text{Newtons}}{\text{Coulomb}} \times \text{meters} = \frac{\text{joules}}{\text{coulomb}} = \text{volts}$$

Dividing by meters, we obtain

$$\frac{\text{Newtons}}{\text{Coulomb}} = \frac{\text{volts}}{\text{meter}} = \text{electric field intensity}$$

Thus, the electric field intensity **E** is expressible in either newtons per coulomb or in volts per meter. With **E** expressed in volts per meter the dimensional form of (1-6) becomes

$$\frac{\text{Volts}}{\text{Meter}} \times \text{meters} = \text{volts} \qquad (1\text{-}8)$$

Example. Let the uniform electric field in Fig. 1-5 have an intensity **E** of 10 volts/meter. If the distance $x_2 - x_1$ is 10 cm what is the potential difference of the two points?

Solution. From (1-6) the electric potential is given by

$$V = 10 \times 0.1 = 1 \text{ volt}$$

That is, the potential of x_1 is 1 volt higher than the potential of x_2.

Consider next the case of a nonuniform field such as exists in the vicinity of the positive point charge Q (Fig. 1-6). The electric field **E** is radial and is inversely proportional to the square of the distance r from the charge Q. The energy per coulomb required to move a positive test charge from r_2 to r_1 along a radial path equals the potential differ-

---

[1] *Potential*, in general, is a measure of energy per some kind of unit quantity. For example, the difference in gravitational potential at sea level and 100 meters above sea level is equal to the work required to raise a 1-kg mass from sea level to a height of 100 meters against the earth's gravitational field. Potential is a scalar quantity, that is, it has magnitude but no direction.

ence or rise V_{21} between the points. This is given by

$$V_{21} = \int_{r_2}^{r_1} dV = - \int_{r_2}^{r_1} E \, dr \qquad \text{volts} \qquad (1\text{-}9)$$

The negative sign takes into account the fact that the motion from r_2 to r_1 is opposite to the direction of the field. Substituting the value of E from (1-4) yields

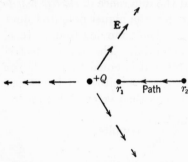

$$V_{21} = V_1 - V_2 = - \int_{r_2}^{r_1} \frac{Q}{4\pi\epsilon r^2} \, dr$$

$$= -\frac{Q}{4\pi\epsilon} \int_{r_2}^{r_1} \frac{dr}{r^2} = \frac{Q}{4\pi\epsilon} \left(\frac{1}{r_1} - \frac{1}{r_2} \right)$$

$$(1\text{-}10)$$

where V_1 = potential at point r_1

V_2 = potential at point r_2

The potential difference or rise in (1-10) is positive since work must be expended to move the test charge from r_2 to r_1 against the field. However,

FIG. 1-6. Linear path in nonuniform electric field.

if the motion is from r_1 to r_2, the field does work on the charge and there is a fall in potential (negative potential difference).

If the point r_2 (Fig. 1-6) is removed to infinity, we can consider that it is at zero potential. Thus, (1-10) becomes

$$V_1 = \frac{Q}{4\pi\epsilon r_1} \qquad \text{volts} \qquad (1\text{-}11)$$

This potential is called the *absolute potential* of the point r_1 due to the charge Q. It is inversely proportional to the distance from Q to the point r_1 and is, by definition, the work per coulomb required to bring a positive test charge from infinity to the point r_1. For the sake of brevity the potential at a point will hereafter be understood, unless otherwise specified, to mean the absolute potential of the point.

1-9. The Electric Scalar Potential as a Line Integral of the Electric Field. In Sec. 1-8 the test charge is moved via the shortest path between two points. Actually, the path followed is immaterial since the potential difference is determined solely by the difference in potential of the two end points of the path. Thus, referring to Fig. 1-6, the potential at the point r_1 with respect to the potential at r_2 is said to be *single-valued*, that is, it can have only one value regardless of the path taken from r_2 to r_1. In Sec. 1-8 the test charge is moved parallel to the electric field **E**. When the path of the test charge is not parallel to **E** but at an angle θ, as in Fig. 1-7, the potential difference V_{21} between the points x_2 and x_1 is equal to the path length $(x_2 - x_1)$ multiplied by the component of **E**

parallel to it. Thus,

$$V_{21} = (x_2 - x_1)E \cos \theta \qquad (1\text{-}12)$$

It is assumed here that $\mathbf{E}$ is uniform.

If the test charge is moved perpendicular to the direction of the field ($\theta = 90°$), no work is performed and hence this path is said to be an *equipotential* line.   It is an important property of fields that equipotential and field lines
are orthogonal.

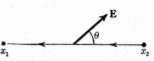

Let us consider next the case where the
path of the test charge is curved.   Then the
potential difference between the end points

FIG. 1-7. Linear path in uniform electric field at angle θ.

of the path is given by the product of the infinitesimal element of path
length dl and the component of $\mathbf{E}$ parallel to it, integrated over the length
of the path.   Referring to the path in the uniform field $\mathbf{E}$ in Fig. 1-8, the

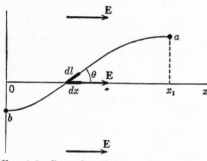

infinitesimal potential rise dV between the ends of the path element
dl is given by

$$dV = -E \cos \theta \, dl \quad (1\text{-}13)$$

where θ = angle between the path
element and the field ($0 \leq \theta \leq 90°$).
A potential rise (positive potential
difference dV) requires that the
component of the motion parallel to
$\mathbf{E}$ be opposed to the field.   Hence
the negative sign in (1-13).   By integrating (1-13) between the limits

FIG. 1-8. Curved path in a uniform electric field.

a and b, we obtain the potential rise V_{ab} between the points a and b.
Thus,

$$V_{ab} = \int_a^b dV = V_b - V_a = - \int_a^b E \cos \theta \, dl \qquad (1\text{-}14)$$

The integral involving dl in (1-14) is called a *line integral*.   Hence the
potential rise between a and b equals the line integral of $\mathbf{E}$ along the
curved path between a and b.

Example 1.   In Fig. 1-8 let $\mathbf{E}$ be everywhere in the $+x$ direction and equal to
10 volts/meter (a uniform field).   Let $x_1 = 1$ meter.   Find V_{ab}.
Solution.   From (1-14)

$$V_{ab} = - \int_a^b E \cos \theta \, dl = - \int_{x_1}^0 E \, dx = Ex_1 = +10 \text{ volts}$$

As a variation of the above example, suppose that the path is from
b to a.   Then $V_{ba} = -10$ volts.   As a third variation, let the direction

of $\mathbf{E}$ be reversed (negative x direction) but the path be from a to b.   Then,

$$V_{ab} = - \int_a^b (-E) \cos \theta \, dl = \int_{x_1}^0 E \, dx = -10 \text{ volts}$$

Finally, let us consider the situation where the path of the test charge is curved and also where the electric field is nonuniform.   For instance, let the nonuniform field be produced by a point charge $+Q$ as in Fig. 1-9. The field intensity due to a point charge is given by (1-4).   Substituting this in (1-14) and also putting $dr = \cos \theta \, dl$, where dr is an infinitesimal element of radial distance,

$$V_{ab} = - \frac{Q}{4\pi\epsilon} \int_{r=a}^{r=b} \frac{dr}{r^2} = \frac{Q}{4\pi\epsilon}\left(\frac{1}{b} - \frac{1}{a}\right) \qquad \text{volts} \qquad (1\text{-}15)$$

Putting $b = r_1$ and $a = r_2$ makes this result identical with (1-10) where the path is along a radial line.

Example 2.   Let the positive charge Q, Fig. 1-9, be equal to 2.23×10^{-10} coulomb. Also let $a = 40$ cm and $b = 10$ cm.   The medium is air.   Find the absolute potential V_a at a, the absolute potential V_b at b, and the potential rise V_{ab}.

Solution:

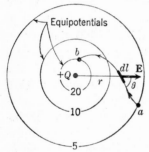

FIG. 1-9. Curved path in a nonuniform electric field.

$$V_a = \frac{Q}{4\pi\epsilon_0}\frac{1}{a} = 5 \text{ volts}$$

$$V_b = \frac{Q}{4\pi\epsilon_0}\frac{1}{b} = 20 \text{ volts}$$

$$V_{ab} = V_b - V_a = 15 \text{ volts}$$

In the above example the potential at any point 10 cm from Q has an absolute potential of 20 volts.   Therefore, a circle of 10 cm radius around Q is a 20-volt *equipotential contour* (see Fig. 1-9).   In three dimensions a sphere of 10 cm radius around Q is a 20 volt *equipotential surface*.   Likewise, a sphere of 40 cm radius around Q is a 5-volt equipotential surface. It follows that the equipotential surfaces around a point charge are concentric spheres.

The work to move a test charge along an equipotential contour or surface is zero ($\theta = 90°$).   The maximum amount of work per unit distance is performed by moving normal to an equipotential surface.   This coincides with the direction of the field.

The work to transport a test charge around any *closed path* in a static field is zero since the path starts and ends at the same point.   Thus, the upper and lower limits of the integrals in (1-14) become the same, and the result is zero.   Suppose the path starts and ends at a (Fig. 1-9).

Then[1]

$$\int_a^a dV = -\int_a^a E \cos\theta\, dl = -\oint E \cos\theta\, dl = 0 \text{ volts} \quad (1\text{-}16)$$

A property of the *static electric field* is, then, that *the line integral of this field around a closed path is zero.* It follows that the potential difference between any two points is independent of the path, as was mentioned at the beginning of this section.

1-10. Scalar, or Dot, Product. In vector analysis the *scalar*, or *dot*, product of two vectors is a scalar and is equal to the product of the vector magnitudes times the cosine of the angle θ between the vectors.

Referring to Fig. 1-10, the dot product of **A** and **B** is

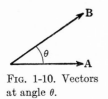

FIG. 1-10. Vectors at angle θ.

$$\mathbf{A} \cdot \mathbf{B} = AB \cos\theta \quad (1\text{-}17)$$

where **A** = vector
$A = |\mathbf{A}|$ = scalar magnitude of **A**
B = vector
$B = |\mathbf{B}|$ = scalar magnitude of **B**
θ = angle between **A** and **B**

If $\mathbf{A} \cdot \mathbf{B} = 0$, the two vectors are perpendicular, provided, of course, that neither is zero.

Introducing the vector notation of the dot product into (1-14), we obtain

$$V_{ab} = \int_a^b dV = -\int_a^b E \cos\theta\, dl = -\int_a^b \mathbf{E} \cdot d\mathbf{l} \quad (1\text{-}18)$$

where **E** = electric field intensity (vector)
$E = |\mathbf{E}|$ = scalar magnitude of **E**
$d\mathbf{l}$ = infinitesimal element of path length (vector)
$dl = |d\mathbf{l}|$ = scalar magnitude of $d\mathbf{l}$

In vector notation the line integral (1-16) around a closed path is written

$$\oint E \cos\theta\, dl = \oint \mathbf{E} \cdot d\mathbf{l} = 0 \quad (1\text{-}19)$$

1-11. Relation of Electric Field Lines and Equipotential Contours. A field line indicates the direction of the force on a positive test charge introduced into the field. If the test charge were released, it would move in the direction of the field line.

In a uniform field the field lines are parallel as in Fig. 1-11. A single field line gives no information as to the intensity of the field. It indicates only the direction. However, by measuring the work per coulomb required to move a positive test charge along a field line the potential differences along the line can be determined. The larger the potential difference between two points a unit distance apart, the stronger the field.

---

[1] The symbol $\oint$ indicates a line integral around a closed path.

In a uniform field the potential difference per unit length is constant so that the equipotential lines (which are orthogonal to the field lines) are equally spaced. In the example of Fig. 1-11, the electric field intensity is 2 volts per cm so that the equipotential contours at 1-volt intervals are parallel lines spaced $\frac{1}{2}$ cm apart. One of the lines is arbitrarily taken as

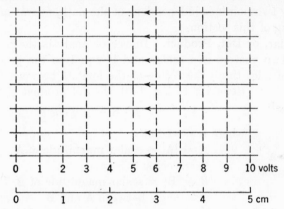

Fig. 1-11. Field lines (solid) and equipotential lines (dashed) of a uniform electric field.

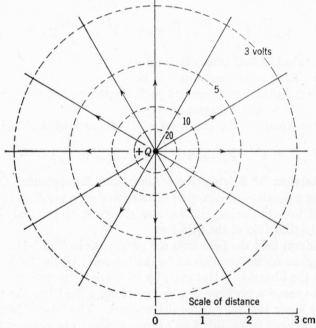

Fig. 1-12. Field lines (solid) and equipotential lines (dashed) of a nonuniform electric field.

having a zero potential so that the potentials shown are relative to this line.

Consider now the case of a nonuniform field such as exists in the vicinity of the positive point charge Q in Fig. 1-12. If a positive test charge were released in this field, it would move radially away from Q, so that the field lines are radial. The field intensity varies inversely as the square of the distance as given by (1-4). In Fig. 1-12 this is suggested by the fact that the field lines become more widely separated as the distance from Q increases. The absolute potential is inversely proportional to the distance from Q as given by (1-11). If $Q = 10^{-11}$ coulomb, the equipotential contours for 20, 10, 5, and 3 volts are then as shown by the concentric circles in Fig. 1-12.

It is to be noted (Figs. 1-11 and 1-12) that a potential *rise* is always in the opposite direction to **E**.

1-12. Charge Density and Continuous Distributions of Charge. The electric *charge density* ρ is equal to the total charge Q in a volume v divided by the volume. Thus,

$$\rho = \frac{Q}{v} \tag{1-20}$$

The value of ρ in (1-20) is an *average* charge density.

Electric charge density has the dimensions of charge per unit volume, or in dimensional symbols Q/L^3. In the mksc system the unit of charge density is the *coulomb per cubic meter*.

By assuming that electric charge may be continuously distributed throughout a region we can also define the value of the charge density ρ at a point P as the charge ΔQ in a small volume element Δv divided by the volume, with the limit of this ratio taken as the volume shrinks to zero around the point P. In symbols,

$$\rho = \lim_{\Delta v \to 0} \frac{\Delta Q}{\Delta v} \tag{1-21}$$

This gives the value of ρ at a point and hence defines ρ as a point function.

It will be convenient to use this definition of ρ, but it is to be noted that it is based on the assumption that the electric charge is continuously distributed. Actually electric charge is not continuously distributed but is associated with discrete particles (electrons or atoms) separated by finite atomic distances. Nevertheless, the assumption of a continuous charge distribution leads to no appreciable error provided the region contains many atoms or electrons and the distances involved are large compared with atomic dimensions. The assumption of continuous charge distribution can be applied to the large-scale, or macroscopic, problems treated in this book but would not be applicable to problems on atomic structure, where the noncontinuous nature of the charge distribution must be taken into account.

The charge density ρ, discussed above, is sometimes called a *volume charge density* to distinguish it from surface charge density and linear charge density. The *surface charge density* ρ_S gives the charge per unit area (coulombs per square meter) at a point in a continuous surface distribution of charge. The *linear charge density* ρ_L gives the charge per unit length (coulombs per meter) at a point on a continuous line distribution of charge. Both ρ_S and ρ_L are point functions which can be defined as in (1-21), with a surface or line element substituted for the volume element.

1-13. Electric Potential of Charge Distributions and the Principle of Superposition of Potential. Since the electric scalar potential due to a single point charge is a linear function of the value of its charge, it follows that the potentials of more than one point charge are linearly superposable by scalar (algebraic) addition. As a generalization, this fact may be stated as the *principle of superposition* applied to electric potential[1] as follows:

The total electric potential at a point is the algebraic sum of the individual component potentials at the point.

Thus, if only the three point charges Q_1, Q_2, and Q_3 are present in Fig. 1-13, the total electric potential (work per unit charge) at the point P is given by

$$V_p = \frac{1}{4\pi\epsilon}\left(\frac{Q_1}{r_1} + \frac{Q_2}{r_2} + \frac{Q_3}{r_3}\right) \tag{1-22}$$

where r_1 = distance from Q_1 to P
r_2 = distance from Q_2 to P
r_3 = distance from Q_3 to P
This may also be expressed with a summation sign. Thus,

$$V_p = \frac{1}{4\pi\epsilon}\sum_{n=1}^{n=3}\frac{Q_n}{r_n} \tag{1-23}$$

If the charge is not concentrated at a point but is distributed along a line as in Fig. 1-13, the potential at P due to this linear charge distribution is

$$V_L = \frac{1}{4\pi\epsilon}\int \frac{\rho_L}{r}\,dl \tag{1-24}$$

where ρ_L = linear charge density (coulombs/meter)
dl = element of length of line (meters)
The integration is carried out over the entire line of charge.

[1] Although "electric *scalar* potential" is implied, the word "scalar" will usually be omitted for brevity.

When the charge is distributed over a surface as in **Fig.** 1-13, the potential at P caused by this surface charge distribution is

$$V_s = \frac{1}{4\pi\epsilon} \iint \frac{\rho_s}{r} \, ds \qquad \text{volts} \qquad (1\text{-}25)$$

where ρ_s = surface charge density (coulombs/meter²)
  ds = element of surface (meters²)
The integration is carried out over the entire surface of charge.

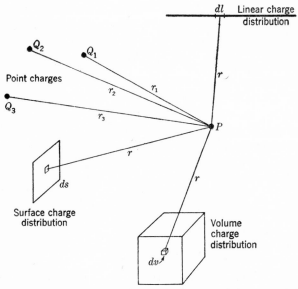

FIG. 1-13. Electric potential at P is the algebraic sum of the potentials due to the point, line, surface, and volume distributions of charge.

For a volume charge distribution as in Fig. 1-13

$$V_v = \frac{1}{4\pi\epsilon} \iiint \frac{\rho}{r} \, dv \qquad \text{volts} \qquad (1\text{-}26)$$

where ρ = (volume) charge density (coulombs/meter³)
  dv = element of volume (meters³)
The integration is taken throughout the volume containing charge.
  If the point charges, the line charge distribution, the surface charge distribution, and the volume charge distribution of Fig. 1-13 are all present simultaneously, the total electric potential at the point P due to all of these distributions is by the superposition principle the algebraic sum of the individual component potentials. Thus,

$$V = V_p + V_L + V_s + V_v$$

or

$$V = \frac{1}{4\pi\epsilon} \left(\sum_{n=1}^{n=3} \frac{Q_n}{r_n} + \int \frac{\rho_L}{r} \, dl + \iint \frac{\rho_s}{r} \, ds + \iiint \frac{\rho}{r} \, dv \right) \quad (1\text{-}27)$$

If all of the charge distributions are considered to occupy finite volumes instead of being idealized to points, lines, and surfaces, then (1-27) reduces to (1-26).

Example. As shown in Fig. 1-14 a square 1 meter on a side in air has a point charge $Q_1 = +10^{-12}$ coulomb at the upper left corner, a point charge $Q_2 = -10^{-11}$ coulomb at the lower left corner, and a line distribution of charge of uniform density

$$\rho_L = +10^{-11} \text{ coulomb/meter}$$

along the right edge. Find the potential at the point P at the center of the square.

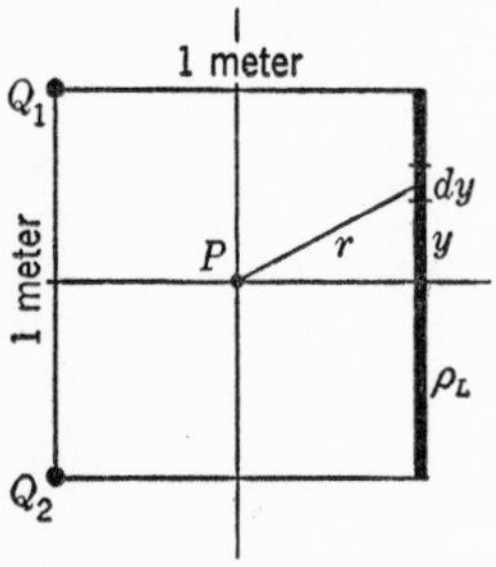

Solution. The potential at P due to the point charges is

$$V_p = \frac{1}{4\pi\epsilon_0} \left(\frac{10^{-12}}{0.707} - \frac{10^{-11}}{0.707} \right) = -0.115 \text{ volt}$$

The potential at P caused by the line distribution of charge is

$$V_L = \frac{1}{4\pi\epsilon_0} \int_{y=-0.5}^{y=0.5} \frac{10^{-11}}{\sqrt{0.5^2 + y^2}} \, dy = +0.158 \text{ volt}$$

FIG. 1-14. Line and point charges for example illustrating superposition of electric potential.

The total potential at P is then

$$V = V_p + V_L = +0.043 \text{ volt}$$

The principle of superposition stated for the special cases of potential in this section and for fields in Sec. 1-7 can be applied, in general, to any quantity which is linearly related to its cause. The electric fields or potentials at a point are linear functions of the charge producing them and hence are superposable (by vector addition for fields and scalar addition for potential).

1-14. Gradient. The potential rise between **two** points along an electric field line is a measure of the *gradient* of the potential in the same way that the elevation rise between two points on a slope is a measure of the gradient of the slope. More specifically the gradient of the potential at a point is defined as the potential rise ΔV across an element of length Δl along a field line divided by Δl, with the limit of this ratio taken as Δl approaches zero. In symbols

$$\text{Gradient of } V = \lim_{\Delta l \to 0} \frac{\Delta V}{\Delta l}. \quad (1\text{-}28)$$

By definition this is also the ratio of the infinitesimal potential rise dV to the infinitesimal length dl. Thus,

$$\text{Gradient of } V = \frac{dV}{dl} = \lim_{\Delta l \to 0} \frac{\Delta V}{\Delta l} \qquad (1\text{-}29)$$

The gradient of V expressed as dV/dl is said to be in differential or infinitesimal notation.

If the element of length dl is at an angle θ with respect to the electric field **E**, we have from (1-13) that

$$\frac{dV}{dl} = -E \cos \theta \qquad (1\text{-}30)$$

If $\theta = 0$, dl is along a field line and the ratio dV/dl is a maximum. Thus, from (1-29) and (1-30) we have, when $\theta = 0$, that

$$\text{Gradient of } V = \frac{dV}{dl} = -\mathbf{E} \qquad (1\text{-}31)$$

Hence, the gradient of the potential (or maximum rise in potential with distance) is equal in magnitude to the electric field intensity and has a direction opposite to the electric field. Since the gradient has both magnitude and direction, it is a vector equal to $-\mathbf{E}$. Thus,

$$\text{grad } V = -\mathbf{E} \qquad (1\text{-}32)$$

where "grad" stands for the gradient of V. As will be shown in the next section, (1-32) can also be written with the operator del, or nabla ($\mathbf{\nabla}$), as

$$\mathbf{\nabla} V = -\mathbf{E} \qquad (1\text{-}33)$$

The significance of the negative sign in (1-32) and (1-33) is that to experience a *rise* in potential a positive test charge must be moved *opposite* to the electric field direction.

Example. Let the potential along a field line vary with x as shown in Fig. 1-15a. The potential rises uniformly with distance from a to b, is constant from b to c, decreases uniformly from c to d (but at a more rapid rate than the increase from a to b), and is zero from d to e. Find the gradient of V and the electric field intensity **E** from a to e.

Solution. From (1-29)

$$\text{grad } V = \frac{dV}{dx}$$

Therefore,

From a to b: grad $V = +\frac{10}{8} = +1.25$ volts/meter
From b to c: grad $V = 0$
From c to d: grad $V = -\frac{10}{2} = -5$ volts/meter
From d to e: grad $V = 0$

The variation of grad V with x is illustrated in Fig. 1-15b. From (1-31), $\mathbf{E} = -\text{grad } V$. Thus, the variation of the field is as shown in Fig. 1-15c.

The analogy between electric potential V and elevation and between grad V and the gradient of the slope may also be illustrated with the aid of Fig. 1-15. Thus, if the ordinate in Fig. 1-15a were elevation in meters instead of V in volts, the ordinate in Fig. 1-15b would become the gradient of the slope in meters elevation per meter of horizontal distance. From a to b the gradient is positive (uphill), while from c to d the gradient is negative (downhill).

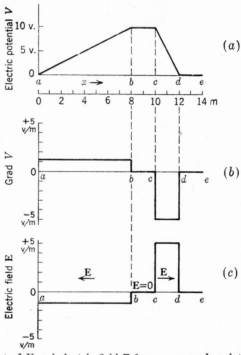

Fig. 1-15. Gradient of V and electric field $\mathbf{E}$ for an assumed variation of the electric potential V.

1-15. Gradient in Rectangular Coordinates. In this section a relation for gradient will be developed in rectangular coordinates. To do this, consider the electric potential distribution of Fig. 1-16. The work per coulomb to bring a positive test charge to the point P (at origin of coordinates) is 104 volts. This is the absolute potential V at P. The potential elsewhere is a function of both x and y, and its variation is indicated by the equipotential contours. The field is uniform. Thus, the contours are straight, parallel, and equally spaced. There is no variation with respect to z (normal to page). At P the electric field is as indicated by the vector $\mathbf{E}$, perpendicular to the equipotential line.

Consider now the change in potential along an infinitesimal element of

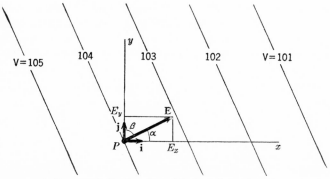

FIG. 1-16. Potential distribution with electric field **E** at a point P.

path length in the x direction (y = constant).   Then

$$-\frac{\partial V}{\partial x} = E \cos \alpha = E_x \qquad (1\text{-}34)$$

where α = angle between **E** and the x axis
   E_x = component of **E** in x direction
Likewise, for an infinitesimal element of path length in the y direction,

$$-\frac{\partial V}{\partial y} = E \cos \beta = E_y \qquad (1\text{-}35)$$

where β = angle between **E** and the y axis
   E_y = component of **E** in y direction
   The relation of (1-34) is a scalar equation.   It may also be expressed
as a vector equation.   Thus,

$$-\mathbf{i}\,\frac{\partial V}{\partial x} = \mathbf{i}E_x \qquad (1\text{-}36)$$

where **i** = unit vector in x direction.   Likewise (1-35) may be written

$$-\mathbf{j}\,\frac{\partial V}{\partial y} = \mathbf{j}E_y \qquad (1\text{-}37)$$

where **j** = unit vector in y direction.
   By the principle of superposition the total field **E** at the point P is the
vector sum of the component fields at the point.   Hence,

$$\mathbf{E} = \mathbf{i}E_x + \mathbf{j}E_y = -\left(\mathbf{i}\,\frac{\partial V}{\partial x} + \mathbf{j}\,\frac{\partial V}{\partial y}\right) \qquad (1\text{-}38)$$

Comparing (1-38) with (1-32), it follows that

$$\mathbf{i}\,\frac{\partial V}{\partial x} + \mathbf{j}\,\frac{\partial V}{\partial y} = \text{grad } V \qquad (1\text{-}39)$$

Thus, the gradient in this rectangular two-dimensional case is equal to the x and y derivatives of the potential added vectorially.

Example 1. Suppose that in Fig. 1-16 the potential decreases by 2 volts/meter in the x direction and by 1 volt/meter in the y direction. Find the electric field **E**.
Solution:

$$\text{grad } V = -\mathrm{i}2 - \mathrm{j}1 \qquad \text{volts/meter}$$

and

$$\mathbf{E} = -\text{grad } V = \mathrm{i}2 + \mathrm{j}1 = 2.24\underline{/27^\circ} \text{ volts/meter}$$

Therefore, **E** has a magnitude of 2.24 volts per meter and is directed at an angle of 27° with respect to the positive x axis ($\alpha = 27^\circ$).

The two-dimensional case discussed above can readily be extended to three dimensions. Thus, as shown in Fig. 1-17 there are field components at the origin in the three coordinate directions as follows

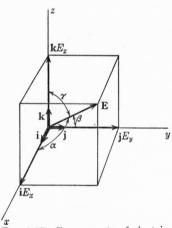

$$\left.\begin{aligned} \mathrm{i}E_x &= \mathrm{i}E \cos \alpha = -\mathrm{i}\frac{\partial V}{\partial x} \\ \mathrm{j}E_y &= \mathrm{j}E \cos \beta = -\mathrm{j}\frac{\partial V}{\partial y} \\ \mathbf{k}E_z &= \mathbf{k}E \cos \gamma = -\mathbf{k}\frac{\partial V}{\partial z} \end{aligned}\right\} \quad (1\text{-}40)$$

By the principle of superposition the total field **E** at the origin is the vector sum of the component fields, or

$$\mathbf{E} = -\left(\mathrm{i}\frac{\partial V}{\partial x} + \mathrm{j}\frac{\partial V}{\partial y} + \mathbf{k}\frac{\partial V}{\partial z} \right) \quad (1\text{-}41)$$

Fig. 1-17. Components of electric field in rectangular coordinates.

where the relation in the parentheses is the complete expression in rectangular coordinates for the gradient of V.† It is often convenient to consider that this expression is the product of V and an operator del (**∇**). Thus, in rectangular coordinates

$$\mathbf{\nabla} = \mathrm{i}\frac{\partial}{\partial x} + \mathrm{j}\frac{\partial}{\partial y} + \mathbf{k}\frac{\partial}{\partial z} \quad (1\text{-}42)$$

The operator **∇** is a quasi vector. It is meaningless until applied. Taking the product of **∇** and V yields the gradient of V. That is,

$$\mathbf{\nabla}V = \mathrm{i}\frac{\partial V}{\partial x} + \mathrm{j}\frac{\partial V}{\partial y} + \mathbf{k}\frac{\partial V}{\partial z} = -\mathbf{E} \quad (1\text{-}43)$$

or we can write

$$\mathbf{\nabla}V = \text{grad } V = -\mathbf{E} \quad (1\text{-}44)$$

† The two-dimensional example of Fig. 1-16 is a special case of (1-41) where $\frac{\partial V}{\partial z} = 0$.

The electric potential is a *scalar* function.   Taking its gradient results in a *vector* that indicates the magnitude and direction of the maximum rate of change of the potential with distance.   This vector is equal and opposite to the electric field E.   In general, taking the gradient of a scalar function yields a vector that indicates the magnitude and direction of the maximum rate of change with distance of the scalar function.

Equation (1-44) is expressed in a concise vector notation that implies no particular coordinate system.   In rectangular coordinates it has the form of (1-43).

A further illustration of gradient is provided by the following example.

Example 2.   Consider a nonuniform field with a potential distribution given by

$$V = \frac{10}{x^2 + y^2}$$

where V is in volts and x and y are in centimeters.   There is no variation of V with respect to z.   Hence the distribution is two-dimensional.   The potential variation is illustrated by the equipotential contours in Fig. 1-18.   Find (*a*) the expression for the gradient of the potential; (*b*) the value of the gradient at the point $(2, 1)$ cm; (*c*) the electric field intensity at this point.

Solution.   *a.* Since the potential distribution is independent of z, $\partial V/\partial z = 0$ and

$$\text{grad } V = \boldsymbol{\nabla}V = \mathbf{i}\frac{\partial V}{\partial x} + \mathbf{j}\frac{\partial V}{\partial y}$$

$$= -\frac{20}{(x^2 + y^2)^2}(\mathbf{i}x + \mathbf{j}y)$$

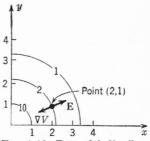

FIG. 1-18. Potential distribution showing gradient of V and electric field **E** at a point P.

b. At the point $(2, 1)$

$$\boldsymbol{\nabla}V = -\tfrac{20}{25}(\mathbf{i}2 + \mathbf{j}1) = 1.79\underline{/206°}\text{ volts/cm}$$

c. The electric field has the opposite direction.   Thus

$$\mathbf{E} = -\boldsymbol{\nabla}V = -1.79\underline{/206°} = 1.79\underline{/26°}\text{ volts/cm}$$

1-16. Electric Flux.   A point charge is surrounded by an electric field as discussed in Sec. 1-6.   Thus, an isolated, positive point charge Q has a radial field as indicated by the lines radiating from Q in Fig. 1-19.   These lines indicate the direction of the electric field, that is, the direction of the force on a positive test charge.

The electric field intensity **E** at the radius r from Q (see Fig. 1-19) is, by (1-4),

$$\mathbf{E} = \mathbf{a}_r \frac{Q}{4\pi\epsilon r^2} \tag{1-45}$$

where $\mathbf{a}_r$ = unit vector in radial direction.   Multiplying (1-45) by ϵ, we obtain

$$\mathbf{a}_r \frac{Q}{4\pi r^2} = \epsilon\mathbf{E} \tag{1-46}$$

The dimensions of (1-46) are

$$\frac{\text{Charge}}{\text{Area}} = \text{surface charge density}$$

Hence, the product ϵE has the dimensions of surface charge density. (Q/L^2). The product ϵE may be designated by the symbol $\mathbf{D}$, called the *electric flux density*. Thus

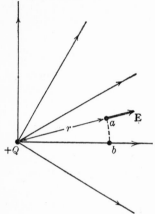

$$\mathbf{D} = \epsilon \mathbf{E} \qquad \text{coulombs/meter}^2 \quad (1\text{-}47)$$

where $\mathbf{D}$ = electric flux density (coulombs/meter²)

ϵ = permittivity of medium (farads/meter)

$\mathbf{E}$ = electric field intensity (volts/meter)

According to (1-47) the flux density and field intensity are vectors with the same direction. This is true for all isotropic media, that is, media whose properties do not depend on direction.

Fig. 1-19. Electric field lines originating on a charge Q.

Now the integral of the normal component of a vector over a surface is defined as the *flux* of the vector over that surface. Let us apply this definition to $\mathbf{D}$ by integrating it over a surface S at a constant radius r from the point charge Q (Fig. 1-20). $\mathbf{D}$ everywhere on the surface S is a constant and is normal to S; so the flux of $\mathbf{D}$ over S is simply S times the magnitude of $\mathbf{D}$. That is,

Fig. 1-20. Electric flux over surface S due to a point charge Q is equal to SD.

$$\text{Flux (of } \mathbf{D} \text{ over } S) = SD \qquad (1\text{-}48a)$$

Since $\mathbf{D}$ has the dimensions of charge density (Q/L^2), the flux of $\mathbf{D}$ has the dimensions of charge density times area or the dimensions of charge (Q).[1] Thus, the dimensional form of (1-48a) is

$$\text{Charge} = \text{area} \frac{\text{charge}}{\text{area}}$$

[1] As a nonelectrical example, consider the case of the frictionless flow of water through a pipe of uniform cross section. Let the velocity of the water in the pipe be the same everywhere and equal to $\mathbf{v}$. A cross section through the pipe has an area A and is normal to $\mathbf{v}$. Hence the *flux of the velocity vector* over the cross-sectional area is the integral of $\mathbf{v}$ over the surface or in this case simply the product of A and $\mathbf{v}$. Thus

$$\text{Flux (of } \mathbf{v} \text{ over } A) = Av$$

which is equal to the total flow of water through the pipe in cubic meters per second if A is in square meters and $\mathbf{v}$ in meters per second.

The flux of **D** over a surface is called the *electric flux*, designated by ψ. Thus

$$\psi = \text{flux (of } \mathbf{D} \text{ over } S) = SD \tag{1-48b}$$

Electric flux has the dimensions of charge.   The mksc unit is the coulomb.

The electric flux per unit area is the *electric flux density* designated by **D**. Thus, from (1-48b)

$$D = \frac{\psi}{S} = \text{flux density} \tag{1-49}$$

Electric flux density has the dimensions of charge per area.   The mksc unit is the coulomb per square meter.

Substituting **E** from (1-45) into (1-47), we obtain the flux density **D** for a point charge Q.   That is,

$$\mathbf{D} = \epsilon \mathbf{E} = \mathbf{a}_r \frac{\epsilon Q}{4\pi\epsilon r^2} = \mathbf{a}_r \frac{Q}{4\pi r^2} \tag{1-50}$$

Hence the flux density depends on the charge and the radius but is independent of the permittivity of the medium.

Since $4\pi r^2$ equals the area of a sphere of radius r, it follows from (1-50) that the magnitude of **D** at the radius r is identical with the surface charge density which would occur if the charge Q were distributed uniformly over a sphere of radius r instead of concentrated at the center.[1] This is illustrated by Fig. 1-21.   From this example it is evident that

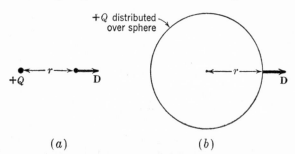

(a) (b)

Fig. 1-21. Flux density **D** at radius r is the same for the charge Q concentrated at a point as in (a) or distributed uniformly over a sphere as in (b).

the term "apparent surface charge density" might be appropriate for **D** since it represents the surface charge density which would be present if Q were redistributed.   However, the term "flux density" is used.

1-17. Flux Lines.   Referring to Fig. 1-19, the lines in this diagram may now be given another interpretation.   Thus, each line may be imagined as emanating from a certain amount of positive charge and ending on an equal amount of negative charge.   In the figure the lines

[1] The surface charge density $\rho_s = Q/4\pi r^2 = D$.

all emanate from a positive point charge and end on an equal negative charge situated on a sphere at infinity. The number of lines passing through a normal surface (Fig. 1-22) then indicates the flux density **D**, and the individual lines are *flux lines*, each associated with a certain fraction of the charge Q. The number of flux lines used is arbitrary, but it is always proportional to the charge Q.

Example. A point charge has a value $Q = +10^{-10}$ coulomb. Arbitrarily taking 10^{20} flux lines per coulomb of charge, find the number of lines per square meter at a distance of 10 meters. Find also the flux density **D** at this distance.

Solution:

Total no. of lines $= 10^{-10} \times 10^{20} = 10^{10}$

FIG. 1-22. Number of flux lines per unit area normal to the field equals the flux density.

$$\text{Lines/meter}^2 \text{ at 10 meters} = \frac{10^{10}}{4\pi r^2} = 7.95 \times 10^6$$

$$\mathbf{D} = 7.95 \times 10^6 \times \text{charge/line} = 7.95 \times 10^6 \times 10^{-20}$$
$$= 7.95 \times 10^{-14} \text{ coulomb/meter}^2$$

or, directly from (1-50),

$$\mathbf{D} = \frac{Q}{4\pi r^2} = \frac{10^{-10}}{4\pi 10^2} = 7.95 \times 10^{-14} \text{ coulomb/meter}^2$$

1-18. Flux Tubes. It should be noted that the field intensity at a constant radius from a point charge as in Fig. 1-19 is the same between the lines (point a) as it is on a line (point b). The field intensity **E** and the flux density **D** are continuous functions of position around the point charge, and both are constant for a fixed radius. Thus, if no flux lines pass through a certain area in a diagram, this does not necessarily imply that the flux density there is zero. It may be that some lines would pass through the area if a larger number of flux lines had been assumed. This difficulty can be avoided by a simple extension of the concept of the *flux line* to the *flux tube*.

A *flux tube* is defined as an imaginary tube with walls that are everywhere parallel to **D** and with a constant electric flux over any cross section. The requirement that the flux over any cross section be a constant actually is a necessary consequence of the fact that **D** is parallel to the sides of the tube and, therefore, that the flux over the side walls is zero. Using a flux-tube representation, we have the flux tubes of Fig. 1-23b instead of the flux lines of Fig. 1-23a. Each tube in Fig. 1-23b has the same total flux as represented by each line in Fig. 1-23a. The cross section of a tube may be of any convenient shape. However, tubes of triangular, square, or hexagonal cross section have the advantage that their walls can be made to coincide, and hence all of space can be filled with tubes of the same kind.

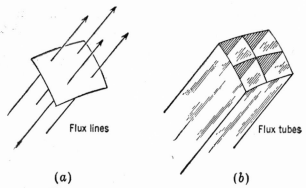

FIG. 1-23. Flux lines (a) and flux tubes (b).

In Fig. 1-24 a single flux tube of square cross section is shown which originates on a certain fraction of the charge $+Q$ and ends on an equal fraction of the charge $-Q$. The magnitude of the flux density **D** varies along the tube, but the integral of the normal component of **D** over any cross section of the tube is constant. In Fig. 1-24 the flux density **D** is indicated at three points along the tube. Where the magnitude of **D** is large, the cross-sectional area is small, and where **D** is small, the area is large, the integral of **D** over each cross-sectional area being a constant.

All of space can be divided up into tubes of equal flux originating on the positive charge of Fig. 1-24 and ending on the negative. The tubes never cross. The number of tubes into which space is divided is arbitrary. As a matter of convenience the number is sometimes taken as 4π so that near each charge a single tube subtends a solid angle of 1 rad².

FIG. 1-24. Flux tube extending from a positive charge Q to an equal negative charge.

Near a charge the field is not appreciably affected by the remote charge, and hence near a charge each tube is like a pyramid. The number of tubes might, on the other hand, be taken as 100. Or the number could be 41,253 so that near each charge a single tube subtends a solid angle of 1 square degree.†

1-19. Electric Flux over a Closed Surface. Gauss's Law. Consider an infinitesimal surface element ds as in Fig. 1-25a. The infinitesimal amount of electric flux $d\psi$ over this surface element is, by an extension of (1-48b),

$$d\psi = D \cos \alpha \, ds = \mathbf{D} \cdot \mathbf{n} \, ds \qquad \text{coulombs} \qquad (1\text{-}51a)$$

† In two dimensions a circle subtends an angle of 2π rad or 360° with respect to a point inside; so 1 rad $= 360°/2\pi = \mathbf{57.3°}$. In three dimensions, a sphere subtends, with respect to a point inside, a solid angle of 4π square radians (steradians) or $4\pi(57.3)^2 = 41,253$ square degrees.

where $\mathbf{D}$ = flux density at the surface element (coulombs/meter²)

α = angle between $\mathbf{D}$ and normal to surface element (dimensionless)

$\mathbf{n}$ = unit vector normal to the surface element (dimensionless)

ds = area of surface element (meters²)

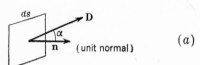

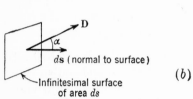

(a)

This notation may be shortened if we write

$$ds = \mathbf{n}\, ds$$

where ds (see Fig. 1-25b) is considered to be a vector having a direction normal to the surface and a magnitude equal to ds. Introducing this notation into (1-51a), we have

(b)

$$d\psi = \mathbf{D} \cdot d\mathbf{s} \qquad (1\text{-}51b)$$

FIG. 1-25. Relation of vectors to infinitesimal surface element.

Referring now to Fig. 1-26, let a positive point charge Q be situated at the center of an imaginary sphere of radius r. The infinitesimal amount of electric flux $d\psi$ over the surface element ds is as given by (1-51b). Integrating this over the sphere of radius

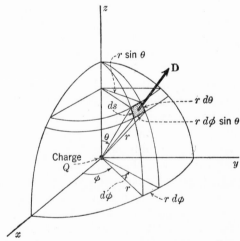

FIG. 1-26. Point charge Q at origin of spherical coordinate system.

r then gives the total flux over the sphere, or

$$\psi = \iint \mathbf{D} \cdot d\mathbf{s} \qquad (1\text{-}52)$$

Since $\mathbf{D}$ everywhere on the sphere is normal to ds, $\cos \alpha = 1$, and therefore, in this case,

$$\mathbf{D} \cdot d\mathbf{s} = D\, ds \qquad (1\text{-}53)$$

where $D = |\mathbf{D}|$ = scalar magnitude of the vector $\mathbf{D}$

$ds = |d\mathbf{s}|$ = scalar magnitude of the vector $d\mathbf{s}$

Introducing (1-53) into (1-52) and also the magnitude of $\mathbf{D}$ from (1-50) yields

$$\psi = \iint \frac{Q}{4\pi r^2}\, ds \qquad (1\text{-}54)$$

From Fig. 1-26

$$ds = (r\, d\theta)(r\, d\phi \sin \theta) = r^2 \sin \theta\, d\theta\, d\phi \qquad (1\text{-}55)$$

The surface area divided by the square of its radius yields the solid angle subtended by the surface area in square radians (steradians). Thus, the solid angle $d\Omega$ subtended by the spherical element of surface area ds is

$$\frac{ds}{r^2} = d\Omega = \sin \theta\, d\theta\, d\phi \qquad (1\text{-}56)$$

Substituting (1-56) in (1-54), we obtain[1]

$$\psi = \frac{Q}{4\pi} \iint d\Omega = \frac{Q}{4\pi} \int_0^{2\pi} \int_0^{\pi} \sin \theta\, d\theta\, d\phi$$

$$= \frac{Q}{4\pi} [-\cos \theta]_0^{\pi} \int_0^{2\pi} d\phi = \frac{Q}{4\pi} \times 2 \times 2\pi = Q \qquad (1\text{-}57)$$

Thus, the total electric flux over the sphere (obtained by integrating the normal component of the flux density $\mathbf{D}$ over the sphere) is equal to the charge Q enclosed by the sphere. We could have obtained the result in this case more simply by multiplying $D = Q/4\pi r^2$ by the area of the sphere $(4\pi r^2)$. However, the above development serves to illustrate a more general procedure which can also be applied to cases where $\mathbf{D}$ is not constant as a function of angle.

The result in the above example is a statement of Gauss's law for a special case. A general statement of Gauss's law for electric fields is:

The surface integral of the normal component of the electric flux density $\mathbf{D}$ *over any closed surface equals the charge enclosed.*†

Thus, in symbols

$$\iint D \cos \theta\, ds = \iint \mathbf{D} \cdot d\mathbf{s} = Q \qquad (1\text{-}58a)$$

where Q is the total or net charge enclosed. This charge may also be expressed as the volume integral of the charge density ρ so that (1-58a)

---

[1] The first integral with limits 0 and 2π is associated with the second differential $d\phi$ and the second integral with the first differential.

† This statement of Gauss's law applies specifically to the rationalized mksc system. In general, Gauss's law states that the surface integral of the normal component of the electric flux density over a closed surface is proportional to the charge enclosed (or equal to the charge times a constant, this constant being unity in the rationalized mksc system).

becomes

$$\iint \mathbf{D} \cdot d\mathbf{s} = \iiint \rho \, dv = Q \tag{1-58b}$$

where the surface integration is carried out over a closed surface and the volume integration throughout the region enclosed.   An alternative notation for (1-58b) is

$$\oint_s \mathbf{D} \cdot d\mathbf{s} = \oint_v \rho \, dv = Q \tag{1-59}$$

where $\oint_s$ indicates a double, or surface, integral over a closed surface and $\oint_v$ indicates a triple, or volume, integral throughout the region enclosed.

From (1-47) Gauss's law may also be expressed as

$$\epsilon \oint_s \mathbf{E} \cdot d\mathbf{s} = Q \qquad \text{coulombs} \tag{1-60}$$

where $\mathbf{E}$ = electric field intensity (volts/meter)

ϵ = permittivity of medium (farads/meter)

Gauss's law is the basic theorem of electrostatics.   It is a necessary consequence of the inverse-square law (Coulomb's law).   Thus, if $\mathbf{D}$ for a point charge did not vary as $1/r^2$, the total flux over a surface enclosing it would not equal the charge (see Sec. 2-36).

If a volume contains no charge, the electric flux over the surface of the volume is always zero, even though the volume may be in an electric field.   In such a case, the inward flux equals the outward flux (net flux zero); in other words, the number of flux tubes entering equals the number leaving.

To illustrate the utility of Gauss's law, several situations will be analyzed with its aid in the next sections.

1-20. Single Shell of Charge.   Referring to Fig. 1-27a, suppose that a positive charge Q is uniformly distributed over an imaginary spherical shell of radius r_1.   It is assumed that the medium everywhere is air ($\epsilon = \epsilon_0$).   Applying Gauss's law by integrating $\mathbf{D}$ over a spherical surface (radius $r_1 - dr$) just inside the shell of charge, we have

$$\epsilon \oint_s \mathbf{E} \cdot d\mathbf{s} = 0 \tag{1-61}$$

since the charge enclosed is zero.   It follows that $\mathbf{E}$ inside the shell is zero.   Applying Gauss's law to a spherical shell (radius $r_1 + dr$) just outside the shell of charge, we have, neglecting infinitesimals,

$$\epsilon \oint_s \mathbf{E} \cdot d\mathbf{s} = \epsilon_0 E 4 \pi r_1{}^2 = Q \tag{1-62}$$

or

$$E = \frac{Q}{4\pi\epsilon_0 r_1{}^2} \tag{1-63}$$

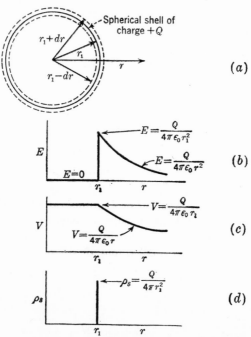

FIG. 1-27. Uniformly charged spherical shell with graphs showing variation of electric field intensity E, electric potential V, and surface charge density ρ_s as a function of radial distance r.

This value of field intensity is identical with that at a radius r_1 from a point charge Q. We can therefore conclude that the field outside the shell of charge is the same as if the charge Q were concentrated at the center. Summarizing, the field everywhere due to a spherical shell of charge is

$$E = 0 \text{ inside } (r \le r_1) \tag{1-64}$$

$$E = a_r \frac{Q}{4\pi\epsilon_0 r^2} \text{ outside } (r \ge r_1) \tag{1-65}$$

The variation of E as a function of r is illustrated by Fig. 1-27b.[1]

The absolute potential at a radius r outside the shell is given by

$$V = - \int_\infty^r \mathbf{E} \cdot d\mathbf{r} \tag{1-66}$$

Introducing the value of $\mathbf{E}$ from (1-65),

$$V = - \frac{Q}{4\pi\epsilon_0} \int_\infty^r \frac{dr}{r^2} = \frac{Q}{4\pi\epsilon_0 r} \tag{1-67}$$

[1] Note that a point charge at the origin gives an infinite E as $r \to 0$ but a surface charge of finite area at a radius r_1 gives a finite E as $r \to r_1$. This is because the volume charge density ρ of a point charge is infinite, whereas the surface charge density ρ_s of the shell of charge is finite. In the present case $\rho_s = Q/4\pi r_1^2$.

At the shell where $r = r_1$ we have

$$V = \frac{Q}{4\pi\epsilon_0 r_1} \tag{1-68}$$

Since **E** inside the shell is zero, it requires no work to move a test charge inside and therefore the potential is constant, being equal to the value at the shell. Summarizing, the electric potential everywhere due to a spherical shell of charge of radius r_1 is

$$V = \frac{Q}{4\pi\epsilon_0 r_1} \text{ inside } (r \leq r_1) \tag{1-69}$$

$$V = \frac{Q}{4\pi\epsilon_0 r} \text{ outside } (r \geq r_1) \tag{1-70}$$

The variation of V as a function of r is illustrated by Fig. 1-27c. The variation of the surface charge density ρ_s is shown by Fig. 1-27d. The surface density is zero everywhere except at $r = r_1$, where it has the value $Q/4\pi r_1{}^2$ as indicated by the vertical line, or spike.

It is to be noted that the potential is continuous, both (1-69) and (1-70) being equal *at* the shell ($r = r_1$). However, the electric field is discontinuous, jumping abruptly from zero just inside the shell to a value $Q/4\pi\epsilon_0 r_1{}^2$ just outside the shell. This results from the assumption that the shell of charge has zero thickness. If a shell of finite thickness is assumed, the field is also continuous (see Prob. 1-15). As the shell thickness is decreased, the change in **E** becomes very rapid, ultimately becoming an abrupt change as the shell thickness approaches zero.

1-21. Two Concentric Spherical Shells of Charge. Let two imaginary concentric spherical shells have radii r_1 and r_2 with a charge Q_1 uniformly distributed over the shell of radius r_1 and a charge Q_2 uniformly distributed over the shell of radius r_2, as suggested in Fig. 1-28a. It is assumed that the medium everywhere is air. Applying Gauss's law in a similar manner to that used for the single shell, it may be shown that the electric field intensity everywhere is given by

$$\mathbf{E} = 0 \text{ inside both shells } (r \leq r_1) \tag{1-71}$$

$$\mathbf{E} = \mathbf{a}_r \frac{Q_1}{4\pi\epsilon_0 r^2} \text{ between shells } (r_1 \leq r \leq r_2) \tag{1-72}$$

$$\mathbf{E} = \mathbf{a}_r \frac{Q_1 + Q_2}{4\pi\epsilon_0 r^2} \text{ outside both shells } (r \geq r_2) \tag{1-73}$$

The variation of **E** as a function of the radius r is shown by Fig. 1-28b. The potential everywhere is

$$V = \frac{1}{4\pi\epsilon_0}\left(\frac{Q_2}{r_2} + \frac{Q_1}{r_1}\right) \quad \text{for } r \leq r_1 \tag{1-74}$$

$$V = \frac{1}{4\pi\epsilon_0}\left(\frac{Q_2}{r_2} + \frac{Q_1}{r}\right) \quad \text{for } r_1 \leq r \leq r_2 \tag{1-75}$$

$$V = \frac{1}{4\pi\epsilon_0} \frac{Q_2 + Q_1}{r} \qquad \text{for } r \geq r_2 \qquad (1\text{-}76)$$

The variation of V as a function of r is illustrated by Fig. 1-28c and of the surface charge density ρ_s by Fig. 1-28d. It is again to be noted that V is continuous, since (1-74) equals (1-75) when $r = r_1$ and (1-75) equals (1-76) when $r = r_2$. The verification of the above results (1-71) through (1-76) is left to the reader as an exercise (see Prob. 1-22).

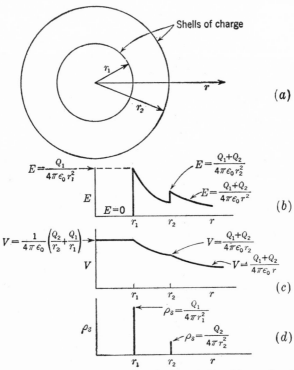

FIG. 1-28. Uniformly charged concentric spherical shells with graphs showing variation of electric field E, potential V, and surface charge density ρ_s as a function of radial distance r. It is assumed that the total charge on each sphere is the same ($Q_1 = Q_2$) and that $r_2 = 2r_1$.

1-22. n Shells and Volume Distributions of Charge. Proceeding a step further, let us consider the situation for a large number n of imaginary concentric spherical shells as suggested in Fig. 1-29. The charge on each shell is uniformly distributed, so that it is not a function of angle, but the charge on each shell may be any function of the radius. It follows from Gauss's law that between two shells, say between shells 2 and 3 ($r_2 \leq r \leq r_3$), the electric field is independent of the charge on all spheres of radius r_3 or larger and depends only on the charges on shells 1 and 2.

Furthermore, the electric field between shells 2 and 3 is the same as if the charges on shells 1 and 2 were concentrated at the center.

It is but a small additional step to consider an infinite number of imaginary concentric shells with uniformly distributed charge, each of slightly different radius. The charge on each shell may be any function of the radius. If the spacing between shells is made as small as we please, a volume charge distribution is obtained which is some function of r but is independent of angle (latitude and longitude). At a radius r_1 the electric field intensity then depends only on the charge at radii for which $r \leq r_1$ and is independent of the charge at radii for which $r \geq r_1$.

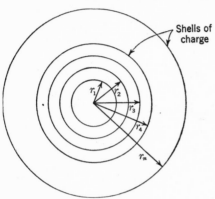

Shells of charge

Thus, for any spherical volume distribution of charge (which is a function only of r) the electric field intensity $\mathbf{E}$ everywhere is given by

$$\mathbf{E} = \mathbf{a}_r \frac{Q_R}{4\pi\epsilon_0 r^2} \qquad \text{for } r \geq R \quad (1\text{-}77)$$

$$\mathbf{E} = \mathbf{a}_r \frac{Q_r}{4\pi\epsilon_0 r^2} \qquad \text{for } r \leq R \quad (1\text{-}78)$$

Fig. 1-29. n concentric shells of charge.

where R = radius of spherical volume distribution of charge

Q_R = total charge in the spherical volume of radius R

Q_r = charge within a radius r $(r \leq R)$

For the case where the charge is uniformly distributed throughout the sphere so that the volume charge density ρ is constant,[1] the electric field intensity outside the sphere $(r \geq R$, Fig. 1-30a) is the same as given by (1-77). To find the field intensity inside the sphere $(r \leq R)$, we use (1-78) where for Q_r we have

$$Q_r = Q_R \left(\frac{r}{R}\right)^3 \tag{1-79}$$

Thus

$$\mathbf{E} = \mathbf{a}_r \frac{Q_R r}{4\pi\epsilon_0 R^3} \qquad \text{for } r \leq R \tag{1-80}$$

The variation of ρ as a function of r is shown in Fig. 1-30d, and the variation of $\mathbf{E}$ as a function of r is illustrated by the solid curve in Fig. 1-30b. It is to be noted that if Q_R were concentrated at the center of the sphere the field at radii less than R would follow the dashed curve to an infinite $\mathbf{E}$, while if Q_R were all uniformly distributed over an imaginary

[1] In this case

$$\rho = \frac{Q_R}{\frac{4}{3}\pi R^3}$$

shell of radius R the field at radii less than R would be zero, as indicated by the dash-dot curve.   The variation of E for the uniform volume distribution of charge (solid curve) lies between these extremes.

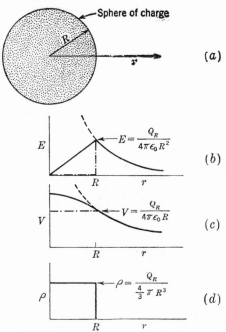

FIG. 1-30. Solid sphere of charge with graphs showing variation of electric field E, potential V, and volume charge density ρ as a function of radial distance r.

The absolute potential at any radius r is given by integrating the work per unit charge required to bring a positive test charge from infinity to the radius r.   Hence, integrating (1-77), we obtain

$$V = \frac{Q_R}{4\pi\epsilon_0 r} \qquad \text{for } r \geq R \qquad (1\text{-}81)$$

Inside the sphere $(r \leq R)$ the potential is equal to that at the sphere, as given by (1-81) where $r = R$, plus the additional work required to move the test charge from R to a radius r inside.   This extra work is given by integrating the negative of (1-80) from R to r.   Thus,

$$V = \frac{Q_R}{4\pi\epsilon_0 R} - \frac{Q_R}{4\pi\epsilon_0 R^3} \int_R^r r \, dr$$

$$= \frac{Q_R}{4\pi\epsilon_0 R} + \frac{Q_R}{8\pi\epsilon_0 R^3} (R^2 - r^2) \qquad (1\text{-}82)$$

The variation of V as a function of r is presented by the solid curve in Fig. 1-30c.   It is to be noted that if Q_R were concentrated at the center the potential at radii less than R would follow the dashed curve to an infinite V, while if Q_R were all uniformly distributed over an imaginary shell of radius R the potential at radii less than R would be a constant, as shown by the dash-dot curve. The variation of V for the uniform volume distribution of charge (solid curve) lies between these extremes.

1-23. Conductors and Induced Charges. A conductor can conduct, or convey, electric charge. In static situations a conductor may be defined as a medium in which the electric field is always zero. It follows that all parts of a conductor must be at the same potential. Metals such as copper, brass, aluminum, and silver are examples of conductors.

When a metallic conductor is brought into an electric field, different parts of the conductor would assume different potentials were it not for the fact that electrons flow in the conductor until a surface charge distribution is built up that reduces the total field in the conductor to zero.[1] This surface charge distribution is said to consist of *induced charges*. The field in which the conductor is placed may be called the *applied field* $\mathbf{E}_a$, while the field produced by the surface charge distribution may be called the *induced field* $\mathbf{E}_i$. The sum of the applied and induced fields yields a total field in the conductor equal to zero. Although the total field inside the conductor is zero after the static situation has been reached, the total field is not zero while the induced charges are in motion, that is, while currents are flowing.

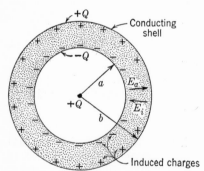

FIG. 1-31. Conducting shell of wall thickness $b - a$ with point charge Q at center.

To summarize, under static conditions the electric field in a conductor is zero, and its potential is a constant. Charge may reside on the surface of the conductor, and, in general, the surface charge density need not be constant.

1-24. Conducting Shell. An initially uncharged conducting shell of inner radius a and outer radius b (wall thickness $b - a$) is shown in cross section in Fig. 1-31. Let a point charge $+Q$ be placed at the center of the shell. This might be done by introducing the charge through a hole in the shell which is plugged after the charge is inside.[2] The point charge has a radial electric field. Let this be called the applied field $\mathbf{E}_a$. For

[1] The electrons in the outermost shell of the atoms of a conductor are so loosely held that they migrate readily from atom to atom under the influence of an electric field.

[2] This is an idealized version of an experiment first performed by Faraday, using an ice pail.

the total field **E** in the conducting wall to be zero requires an induced field $\mathbf{E}_i$ inside the wall such that

$$\mathbf{E}_a + \mathbf{E}_i = \mathbf{E} = 0 \qquad (1\text{-}83)$$

or

$$\mathbf{E}_i = -\mathbf{E}_a \qquad (1\text{-}84)$$

The induced field $\mathbf{E}_i$ is produced by a distribution of induced negative charges on the inner shell wall and induced positive charges on the outer shell wall as suggested in Fig. 1-31. Let us apply Gauss's law to this situation to determine quantitatively the magnitude of these induced charges.

Suppose that an imaginary sphere designated S_1 with a radius $a - dr$ is situated just inside the inner wall of the shell as in Fig. 1-32. By Gauss's law the surface integral of the normal component of **D** over this sphere must equal $+Q$. That is,

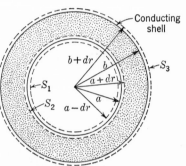

$$\oint_{S_1} \mathbf{D} \cdot d\mathbf{s} = +Q \qquad (1\text{-}85)$$

FIG. 1-32. Conducting shell of wall thickness $b - a$ with surfaces of integration.

Applying Gauss's law to the sphere S_2 of radius $a + dr$ just inside the conductor, we have, since the total field **E** in the conductor is zero,

$$\oint_{S_2} \mathbf{D} \cdot d\mathbf{s} = \epsilon \oint_{S_2} \mathbf{E} \cdot d\mathbf{s} = 0 \qquad (1\text{-}86)$$

Thus, the total charge inside the sphere S_2 must be zero. It follows that a charge $-Q$ is situated on the inner surface of the shell wall. Since the shell was originally uncharged, this negative charge Q, produced by a migration of electrons to the inner surface, must leave a deficiency of electrons or positive charge Q on the outer surface of the shell. It is assumed that the surface charges reside in an infinitesimally thin layer.

Applying Gauss's law to the sphere S_3 of radius $b + dr$ just outside the outer surface of the shell, we then have

$$\oint_{S_3} \mathbf{D} \cdot d\mathbf{s} = +Q \qquad (1\text{-}87)$$

To summarize, the charge $+Q$ at the center of the shell induces an exactly equal but negative charge $(-Q)$ on the inner surface of the shell, and this in turn results in an equal positive charge $(+Q)$ distributed over the outer surface of the shell. The flux tubes originating on $+Q$ at the center end on the equal negative charge on the inside of the shell. There is no total field and no flux in the shell wall.   Outside the shell the flux tubes continue from the charge $+Q$ on the outer surface as though no shell were present.   The variation of the component fields $\mathbf{E}_a$ (applied) and $\mathbf{E}_i$ (induced) as a function of r is illustrated by Fig. 1-33b.   The variation of the total field $\mathbf{E}$ is shown in Fig. 1-33c.   For $r \leq a$ and $r \geq b$, $\mathbf{E} = \mathbf{E}_a$, while for $a \leq r \leq b$, $\mathbf{E}_a + \mathbf{E}_i = \mathbf{E} = 0$.

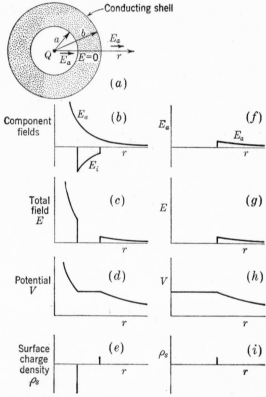

FIG. 1-33. Conducting shell of wall thickness $b - a$ with graphs showing variation of applied field E_a, induced field E_i, total field E, potential V, surface charge density ρ_s, with charge Q at center (b, c, d, and e) and with charge only on outside of shell (f, g, h, and i).

If a conducting wire is connected from the inner surface of the shell to the charge $+Q$ at the center, electrons will flow and reduce the charge at the center and on the inner surface to zero.   However, the charge $+Q$ remains on the outer surface of the shell.   This results in an applied field only external to the shell ($r \geq b$) and of the same value as before.   There is no induced field whatsoever.   Thus, the total field is identical with the applied field, as shown by Figs. 1-33f and g, and is zero for $r \leq b$.   This final result might have been achieved more simply in the first place by applying the charge $+Q$ to the outside of the originally uncharged conducting sphere.

The variation of V and ρ_s as a function of r when the charge $+Q$ is at the center of the sphere is indicated in Figs. 1-33d and e, while the variation when the charge is only on the outside of the shell is shown by Figs. 1-33h and i.

1-25. Conducting Box and Plates.   Instead of the spherical conducting enclosure discussed in the previous section, let us consider an initially uncharged conducting enclosure of the shape shown by the cross section of Fig. 1-34a.   This enclosure consists of two large flat parallel con-

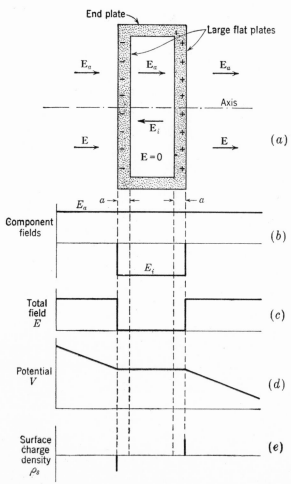

FIG. 1-34. Cross section through rectangular metal box with large flat sides in uniform applied field E_a. Graphs show variation of applied field E_a, induced field E_i, total field E, potential V, and surface charge density ρ_s as a function of distance along axis through center of box.

ducting plates of thickness a with conducting plates along all four edges so as to make a complete enclosure, or box. Let this box be placed in a uniform applied field $\mathbf{E}_a$.   This field induces negative charges on the left side of the left plate and positive charges on the right side of the right

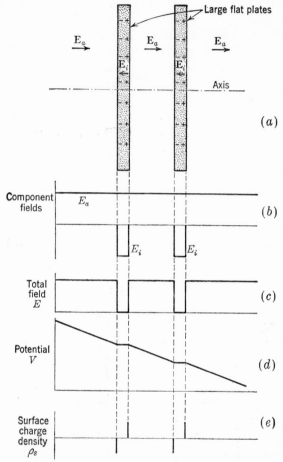

(a)

(b)

(c)

(d)

(e)

Fig. 1-35. Cross section through two large flat metal plates in uniform applied field E_a.   Graphs show variation of applied field E_a, induced field E_i, total field E, potential V, and surface charge density ρ_s as a function of distance along axis through center of plates.

plate, producing an induced field $\mathbf{E}_i$ opposite to $\mathbf{E}_a$. Since no charge is enclosed by a surface just inside the walls of the box, it follows from Gauss's law that the total field $\mathbf{E}$ inside the box is zero and hence that $\mathbf{E}_i = -\mathbf{E}_a$.   In general, the field inside of any hollow conducting enclosure is always zero under static conditions provided no charge is present inside the shell.

The variation of the applied field $\mathbf{E}_a$ and induced field $\mathbf{E}_i$ along the axis (normal to the center of the large flat sides of the box) is illustrated by Fig. 1-34b and of the total field $\mathbf{E}$ by Fig. 1-34c. The variation of the potential V and surface charge density is presented in Figs. 1-34d and e.

Let us consider next two large flat parallel conducting plates as in Fig. 1-35a. The two plates are initially uncharged and are not connected. Let the plates be introduced into a uniform applied field $\mathbf{E}_a$. This field induces negative charges on the left side and positive charges on the right side of each plate so that the variation of the induced field $\mathbf{E}_i$ along the axis is as shown in Fig. 1-35b and the variation of the total field as in Fig. 1-35c. The potential and surface-charge-density variations are presented in Figs. 1-35d and e.

If now a wire is connected between the plates, the electrons on the inside surface of the right plate can flow to the left plate, reducing the charge on the inside surfaces to zero. The induced field now extends from the right side of the right plate to the left side of the left plate, and the total field between the plates vanishes like inside a conducting

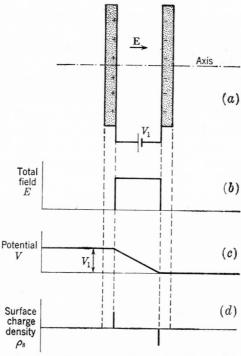

FIG. 1-36. Cross section through two large flat metal plates with applied potential difference V_1. Graphs show variation of total field E, potential V, and surface charge density ρ_s as a function of distance along axis through center of plates.

enclosure.[1] If the wire is disconnected again after the flow of charge has ceased, the total field inside remains equal to zero, unless the applied field is removed, in which case the induced field remains. However, when the external field is removed, the charges migrate from the outer to the inner surfaces of the plates so that the induced field extends only between the inner surfaces of the plates.

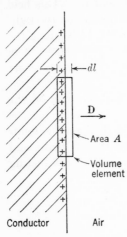

FIG. 1-37. Conductor-air boundary with cross section through small volume element half in the conductor and half in air.

Let us consider finally two large flat parallel conducting plates, initially uncharged, and placed in a field-free region. If the plates are charged, as shown in Fig. 1-36a, by a battery, charges appear on the inner surfaces of the plates and an electric field is applied between the plates.[2] If the plates are large compared with their spacing, the field outside is negligibly small. The total field variation along the axis would then be as indicated in Fig. 1-36b, the potential variation as in Fig. 1-36c, and the surface charge density as in Fig. 1-36d.

1-26. Boundary Relations at a Conducting Surface. Referring to Fig. 1-37, let a thin imaginary volume element be constructed at the surface of a conductor. The medium outside the conductor may, for example, be air. The volume element is half in the conductor and half in air. The volume element has an area A parallel to the conductor surface but has an infinitesimal thickness dl normal to the surface. According to Gauss's law the normal component of the flux density $\mathbf{D}$ over the volume element must equal the total charge Q enclosed. Thus, if ρ_s is the surface-charge density, we have

$$\oint_s \mathbf{D} \cdot d\mathbf{s} = Q = \rho_s A \qquad (1\text{-}88)$$

Now $\mathbf{D}$ in the conductor is zero, and so the integral reduces to the normal component D_n of the flux density in air multiplied by the area A. Hence

$$D_n A = \rho_s A$$

or

$$D_n = \rho_s \qquad (1\text{-}89)$$

This important boundary relation states that the normal component of the flux density $\mathbf{D}$ at a conducting surface equals the surface-charge

---

[1] This is not strictly true because of fringing of the field around the edges, but provided the plates are sufficiently large the field at the center will be substantially zero.

[2] Here $\mathbf{E} = \mathbf{E}_a$, and $\mathbf{E}_i = 0$.

density.   Both D_n and ρ_s have the dimensions of charge per area and are expressed in coulombs per square meter.

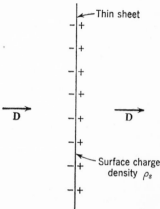

If a thin conducting sheet is introduced normal to an electric field, surface charges are induced on the sheet so that the original field external to the sheet is undisturbed.   The value of the induced surface charge density ρ_s is, by (1-89), equal to the flux density D at the sheet.   Hence, one can interpret the flux density D at a point as equal to the charge density ρ_s which would appear on a thin conducting sheet introduced normal to D at the point. Referring, for example, to the thin conducting sheet normal to the field in Fig. 1-38, the relation of D and ρ_s is as follows:

Fig. 1-38. Thin conducting sheet placed normal to field has an induced surface charge density ρ_s equal to the flux density D of the field at the sheet. The surface charge densities on the two sides of the sheet are equal in magnitude but opposite in sign.

On left side: $D = -n\rho_s$
On right side: $D = +n\rho_s$

where n = unit vector normal to the surface.   Thus D is normally inward on the left side and normally outward on the right.   The magnitude of the flux density on each side is equal to the charge density ρ_s.

PROBLEMS

1-1. What are (a) the dimensional description, (b) the dimensional formulas in terms of the symbols M, L, T, and Q, (c) the mksc units for each of the following:

$$\frac{dl}{dt} \text{ where } l = \text{length} \qquad Ans.:\ \text{Velocity};\ \frac{L}{T};\ \frac{\text{meters}}{\text{second}}.$$
$$t = \text{time}$$

$$\int (\text{force})\ dl \qquad Ans.:\ \text{Work};\ \frac{ML^2}{T^2};\ \text{joules}.$$

$$\frac{dl}{dx} \qquad Ans.:\ \text{Ratio};\ \text{dimensionless}.$$

1-2. Give the same information as requested in Prob. 1-1 for each of the following:

$$\int_v \rho\ dv;\ \rho_s;\ V;\ \epsilon E;\ \int_s D \cdot ds$$
$$\int E \cdot dl;\ \psi;\ \nabla V;\ \frac{1}{4\pi\epsilon};\ E$$

1-3. Find the force F on a positive point charge of 10^{-10} coulomb at a distance of 10 cm in air from a positive point charge of 10^{-8} coulomb.

$$Ans.:\ 9 \times 10^{-7} \text{ newton} = 0.09 \text{ dyne (repulsive)}.$$

1-4. A positive point charge of 10^{-10} coulomb is located in air at $x = 0$, $y = 0.1$ meter and another such charge at $x = 0$, $y = -0.1$ meter. Find the magnitude and direction of the force $\mathbf{F}$ on a positive point charge of 10^{-8} coulomb at $x = 0.2$ meter, $y = 0$.

1-5. Find the electric field strength E and the absolute potential V at a distance of 10 cm in air from a positive point charge of 10^{-8} coulomb.

$Ans.$: $E = 9 \times 10^3$ volts/meter; $V = 900$ volts.

1-6. Repeat Prob. 1-4 for the case where the positive charge at $x = 0$, $y = -0.1$ meter is replaced by an equal but negative charge.

1-7. A positive point charge of 10^{-10} coulomb is located in air at $x = 0$, $y = 0.1$ meter and another such charge at $x = 0$, $y = -0.1$ meter. What are the magnitude and direction of the electric field intensity $\mathbf{E}$, and what is the absolute potential V, at $x = 0.2$ meter, $y = 0$?

1-8. Repeat Prob. 1-7 for the case where the positive charge at $x = 0$, $y = -0.1$ meter is replaced by an equal but negative charge.

1-9. A potential distribution is given by $V = 5x + 2$. What is the expression for the gradient of V? What is its vector value (magnitude and direction) at the point $(0, 0)$ and at $(10, 0)$, that is, $(x = 0, y = 0)$ and $(x = 10, y = 0)$?

1-10. A potential distribution is given by $V = 2y^{\frac{1}{2}}$. What is the expression for the electric field intensity $\mathbf{E}$? What is its vector value (magnitude and direction) at the points $(0, 0)$, $(4, 0)$, and $(0, 4)$?

1-11. A potential distribution is given by $V = 5y^2 + 10x$. What is the expression for the electric field intensity $\mathbf{E}$? What is its vector value (magnitude and direction) at the points $(0, 0)$, $(10, 0)$, $(0, 2)$, and $(10, 2)$?

1-12. A potential distribution is given by $V = 10/(x + y^2 + z^3)$. What is the expression for the electric field intensity $\mathbf{E}$? What is its vector value at the points $(0, 0, 2)$ and $(5, 3, 2)$?

1-13. A spherical conducting shell 20 cm in diameter has a positive charge of 10^{-10} coulomb. Calculate and plot the absolute potential V (ordinate) as a function of the distance from the center of the sphere (abscissa) to a distance of 1 meter. Do the same for the magnitude of the electric field intensity $\mathbf{E}$.

1-14. A positive charge of 10^{-10} coulomb is uniformly distributed throughout a spherical volume 30 cm in diameter. Calculate and plot the variation of the electric field intensity $\mathbf{E}$ and the absolute potential V as a function of the radius r from the center of the sphere to a distance of 1 meter.

1-15. An electric charge Q is distributed with uniform volume density between two imaginary spherical shells of radius a (inner shell) and b (outer shell). Find the expressions for $\mathbf{E}$ and V everywhere $(0 \leq r \leq \infty)$. Plot the variation of $\mathbf{E}$ and V as a function of the radial distance r for $0 \leq r \leq 5b$.

1-16. Positive electric charge of density 10^{-6} coulomb/meter^3 is distributed uniformly over a volume located between two concentric imaginary shells with diameters of 10 and 20 cm. What are the magnitude and direction of $\mathbf{D}$ at a distance of 50 cm from the center of the shells?

1-17. Calculate and plot the variation of $\mathbf{E}$ and V as a function of the radius r from the center to a distance of 1 meter from the shells of Prob. 1-16.

1-18. A spherical volume of radius R has a volume charge density given by $\rho = kr$, where r = radial distance and k = constant. Find the expressions for $\mathbf{E}$ and V everywhere $(0 \leq r \leq \infty)$. Plot the variation of $\mathbf{E}$, V, and ρ as a function of r for $0 \leq r \leq 5R$.

1-19. Repeat Prob. 1-18 for the case where $\rho = k/r^2$.

1-20. A spherical volume of $r = 1$ meter has a uniform charge density $\rho = 1$ coulomb/meter^3. What is V at $r = 50$ cm? $Ans.$: $V = 11/24\epsilon$ volts.

1-21. Find the field strength $\mathbf{E}$ if $V = Q/4\pi\epsilon r$ by taking the gradient of V in rectangular coordinates ($r = \sqrt{x^2 + y^2 + z^2}$) and also by taking the gradient in spherical coordinates. (See expression for $\boldsymbol{\nabla} V$ in spherical coordinates in Appendix.)

1-22. Verify Eqs. (1-71) to (1-76) inclusive.

1-23. At the surface of the earth the gravitational field $\mathbf{G}$ (force per unit mass) has a value of 9.8 newtons/kg. The field is normal to the earth's surface. A gravitational vector $\mathbf{W}$ analogous to $\mathbf{D}$ in the electric case ($\epsilon\mathbf{E} = \mathbf{D}$) is obtained by multiplying the gravitational field $\mathbf{G}$ by the universal gravitational constant γ. The value of γ is 1.2×10^9 kg-sec^2/meter^3. Thus $\gamma\mathbf{G} = \mathbf{W}$. The direction of $\mathbf{W}$ is normal to the earth's surface. The dimensions of $\mathbf{W}$ are

$$\frac{MT^2}{L^3}\frac{L}{T^2} = \frac{M}{L^2}$$

These are expressed in mksc units as kilograms per square meter. Thus $\mathbf{W}$ has the dimensions of mass surface density and in this example has a value equal to the mass per unit area which would result if the mass of the earth were distributed uniformly in a thin spherical shell of the same diameter as the earth. The magnitude of $\mathbf{W}$ in our example is $W = \gamma G = 1.2 \times 10^9 \times 9.8 = 1.17 \times 10^{10}$ kg/meter^2. Assume that the earth is spherical with a radius $R = 6.36 \times 10^6$ meters. Apply Gauss's law to this gravitational problem to show that the mass of the earth is 5.98×10^{24} kg.

1-24. An imaginary cubical volume element is oriented with its sides parallel to a uniform field $\mathbf{E}$ in a charge-free region. Prove that the net flux over the volume is zero.

1-25. Point charges in air are located as follows: $+5 \times 10^{-8}$ coulomb at $(0, 0)$ meters; $+4 \times 10^{-8}$ coulomb at $(3, 0)$ meters; -6×10^{-8} coulomb at $(0, 4)$ meters. (a) Find V, $\mathbf{E}$, and $\mathbf{D}$ at $(3, 4)$. (b) What is the total electric flux over a sphere of 5-meter radius with center at $(0, 0)$?

1-26. Four positive point charges are situated at $(0, 0)$, $(0, 1)$ $(1, 1)$, and $(1, 0)$ meters, that is, at the corners of a square 1 meter on a side. (a) Find $\mathbf{E}$ and V at $(\frac{1}{2}, \frac{1}{2})$ (at center of the square). (b) Find $\mathbf{E}$ and V at $(1, \frac{1}{2})$.

CHAPTER 2

THE STATIC ELECTRIC FIELD. PART 2

2-1. The Electric Dipole and Electric Dipole Moment. When two point charges $+Q$ and $-Q$ are superposed, the resultant field is zero. However, when the charges are separated by a small distance l, there is a finite resultant field. This combination of two point charges of opposite sign separated by a small distance is called an *electric dipole*, and the product Ql is called the *electric dipole moment*. By regarding the separation between the charges as a vector $\mathbf{l}$, pointing from the negative to the positive charge[1] as in Fig. 2-1, the dipole moment can be expressed as a vector $Q\mathbf{l}$ with the magnitude Ql and the direction of $\mathbf{l}$.

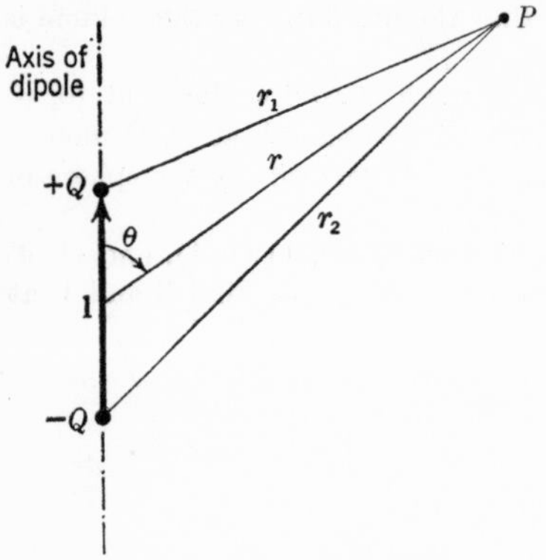

Fig. 2-1. Electric dipole.

Referring to Fig. 2-1, the potential of the positive charge at a point P is

$$V_1 = \frac{Q}{4\pi\epsilon r_1} \qquad (2\text{-}1)$$

The potential of the negative charge at P is

$$V_2 = \frac{-Q}{4\pi\epsilon r_2} \qquad (2\text{-}2)$$

The total potential V at P is then

$$V = V_1 + V_2 = \frac{Q}{4\pi\epsilon}\left(\frac{1}{r_1} - \frac{1}{r_2}\right) \qquad (2\text{-}3)$$

If the point P is at a large distance compared with the separation l, so that the radial lines r_1, r, and r_2 are essentially parallel, we have very nearly that

$$r_1 = r - \frac{l}{2}\cos\theta \qquad (2\text{-}4)$$

and

$$r_2 = r + \frac{l}{2}\cos\theta \qquad (2\text{-}5)$$

---

[1] The vector $\mathbf{l}$ may be regarded as a unit vector $\mathbf{a}_l$ pointing in the direction from the negative to the positive charge multiplied by the magnitude of the separation l. Thus, $\mathbf{l} = \mathbf{a}_l l$. The symbol $\mathbf{p}$ is often used to designate the electric dipole moment. Thus, $\mathbf{p} = Q\mathbf{l}$.

where r = distance from center of dipole to the point P

  θ = angle between axis of dipole and r

Substituting (2-4) and (2-5) into (2-3), we obtain for the potential V at a distance r from an electric dipole the expression

$$V = \frac{Ql \cos \theta}{4\pi\epsilon r^2} \tag{2-6}$$

where it is assumed that r is much greater than l ($r \gg l$) so that terms in l^2 can be neglected compared with those in r^2. V is in volts if Q is in coulombs, l and r in meters, and ϵ in farads per meter.

According to (2-6) the potential of a dipole varies as the inverse square of the distance, whereas according to (2-1) the potential of a single point charge varies as the inverse distance. The potential of the dipole is also a function of the angle θ. At a fixed radius the potential is a maximum on the axis of the dipole ($\theta = 0$) and is zero normal to the axis ($\theta = 90°$). This could have been anticipated since, when $\theta = 90°$, the point P is *exactly* equidistant from the two charges so that their effects cancel.

To find the electric field intensity **E** at the point P, we take the negative gradient of the potential given by (2-6), obtaining[1]

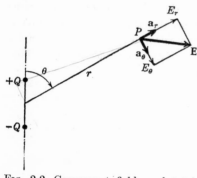

Fig. 2-2. Component fields and total field **E** at a distance r from an electric dipole.

$$\mathbf{E} = -\mathbf{a}_r \frac{\partial V}{\partial r} - \mathbf{a}_\theta \frac{1}{r} \frac{\partial V}{\partial \theta}$$

$$= \mathbf{a}_r \frac{Ql \cos \theta}{2\pi\epsilon r^3} + \mathbf{a}_\theta \frac{Ql \sin \theta}{4\pi\epsilon r^3} \tag{2-7}$$

where $\mathbf{a}_r$ = unit vector in r direction (see Fig. 2-2)

  $\mathbf{a}_\theta$ = unit vector in θ direction

  l = separation of dipole charges Q

According to (2-7) the electric field has two components as shown in Fig. 2-2, one in the r direction (E_r) and one in the θ direction (E_θ). Thus

$$\mathbf{E} = \mathbf{a}_r E_r + \mathbf{a}_\theta E_\theta \tag{2-8}$$

or

$$E_r = \frac{Ql \cos \theta}{2\pi\epsilon r^3} \tag{2-9}$$

and

$$E_\theta = \frac{Ql \sin \theta}{4\pi\epsilon r^3} \tag{2-10}$$

[1] See Appendix for gradient in spherical coordinates. Equation (2-7) can also be expressed with the dot-product notation as follows:

$$\mathbf{E} = \frac{Q}{4\pi\epsilon r^3} (2\mathbf{a}_r \cdot 1 - \mathbf{a}_\theta \cdot 1)$$

The field components of a dipole vary as the inverse cube of the distance, whereas the field of a point charge varies as the inverse square of the distance.

In (2-9) and (2-10) the restriction applies that $r \gg l$ since this condition is implicit in the potential expression (2-6) used in obtaining the field.

2-2. Dielectrics and Permittivity. A *conductor* is a substance in which the outer electrons of an atom are easily detached and migrate readily from atom to atom under the influence of an electric field. A *dielectric*, on the other hand, is a substance in which the electrons are so well bound or held near their equilibrium positions that they cannot be detached by the application of ordinary electric fields. Hence, an electric field produces no migration of charge in a dielectric, and, in general, this property makes dielectrics act as good insulators. Paraffin, glass, and mica are examples of dielectrics.

An important characteristic of a dielectric is its *permittivity*[1] ϵ. Since the permittivity of a dielectric is always greater than the permittivity of vacuum, it is often convenient to use the relative permittivity ϵ_r of the dielectric, that is, the ratio of its permittivity to that of vacuum. Thus

$$\epsilon_r = \frac{\epsilon}{\epsilon_0} \tag{2-11}$$

where ϵ_r = relative permittivity of dielectric

ϵ = permittivity of dielectric

ϵ_0 = permittivity of vacuum

As mentioned earlier,

$$\epsilon_0 = 8.85 \times 10^{-12} \simeq \frac{10^{-9}}{36\pi} \qquad \text{farads/meter}$$

Whereas ϵ or ϵ_0 is expressed in farads per meter, the relative permittivity ϵ_r is a dimensionless ratio.

The relative permittivity is the value ordinarily given in tables. The relative permittivity of a few media is given in Table 2-1, with media arranged in order of increasing permittivity. The values are for static (or low-frequency) fields and, except for vacuum or air, are approximate.

2-3. Polarization. Although there is no migration of charge when a dielectric is placed in an electric field, there does occur a slight displacement of the electrons with respect to their nuclei so that individual atoms behave as very small, or *atomic, dipoles*.[2] When these atomic dipoles are

---

[1] The term *dielectric constant* is also used synonymously with permittivity. However, the permittivity is not always a constant as might be inferred from the term "dielectric constant" but may depend on the temperature and, as discussed later, on the frequency. The term *capacitivity* is also used for permittivity.

[2] The dipoles may also be of molecular size. In a liquid the molecules are free to turn when a field is applied, and this may result in a relatively large permittivity. Water is an example.

TABLE 2-1
PERMITTIVITIES OF DIELECTRIC MEDIA

Medium	Relative permittivity ϵ_r
Vacuum	1 (by definition)
Air (atmospheric pressure)	1.0006
Paraffin	2.1
Polystyrene	2.7
Amber	3
Rubber	3
Sulfur	4
Quartz	5
Bakelite	5
Lead glass	6
Mica	6
Marble	8
Flint glass	10
Ammonia (liquid)	22
Glycerin	50
Water (distilled)	81
Rutile (TiO_2)	89–173†
Barium titanate ($BaTiO_3$)	1,200‡
Barium strontium titanate ($2BaTiO_3$: $1SrTiO_3$)	10,000‡

† Crystals, in general, are nonisotropic, that is, their properties vary with direction. Rutile is an example of such a nonisotropic crystalline substance. Its relative permittivity depends on the direction of the applied electric field with relation to the crystal axes, being 89 when the field is perpendicular to a certain crystal axis and 173 when the field is parallel to this axis. For an aggregation of randomly oriented rutile crystals $\epsilon_r = 114$. All crystals, except those of the cubic system, are nonisotropic to electric fields, that is, their properties vary with direction. Thus, the permittivity of many other crystalline substances may vary with direction. However, in many cases the difference is slight. For example, a quartz crystal has a relative permittivity of 4.7 in one direction and 5.1 at right angles. The average value is 4.9. The nearest integer is 5 and this is the value given in the table.

‡ The permittivity of these titanates is highly temperature-sensitive. The above values are for 25°C. See, for example, E. Wainer, High Titania Dielectrics, *Trans. Electrochem. Soc.*, **89**, 1946.

present, the dielectric is said to be *polarized* or in a state of *polarization*. When the field is removed and the atoms return to their normal, or unpolarized, state, the dipoles disappear.[1]

Consider the dielectric slab of permittivity ϵ in Fig. 2-3 situated in vacuum. Let a uniform field E_0 be applied normal to the slab. This polarizes the dielectric, that is, induces atomic dipoles throughout the slab. In the interior the positive and negative charges of adjacent dipoles annul each other's effects. The net result of the polarization is to produce

[1] When polarization in a dielectric persists in the absence of an applied electric field, the substance is permanently polarized and is called an *electret*. A strained piezoelectric crystal is an example of an electret.

a layer of negative charge on one surface of the slab and a layer of positive charge on the other as suggested in Fig. 2-3.

The effect of the atomic dipoles can be described by the polarization **P**

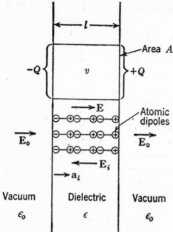

or dipole moment per unit volume. Thus,

$$\mathbf{P} = \frac{\mathbf{p}}{v} = \frac{Ql}{v} \qquad (2\text{-}12)$$

where $\mathbf{p} = Ql$ = net dipole moment in volume v. For example, consider the rectangular volume of surface A and thickness l ($v = Al$) in Fig. 2-3. For this volume

$$P = \frac{Ql}{Al} = \frac{Q}{A} \qquad (2\text{-}13)$$

FIG. 2-3. Dielectric slab in uniform field.

where Q = charge on area A of one face of volume v. But Q/A is charge per area. Hence P has the dimensions both of dipole moment per volume and charge per area ($QL/L^3 = Q/L^2$). The charge per area equals the surface charge density ρ_{sp} of polarization charge appearing on the slab face. Thus

$$P = \frac{Q}{A} = \rho_{sp} \qquad (2\text{-}14)$$

The value of **P** in (2-12) is an average for the volume v. To define the meaning of **P** at a point, it is convenient to assume that a dielectric in an electric field has a continuous distribution of infinitesimal dipoles, that is, a continuous polarization, whereas the dipoles actually are discrete polarized atoms. Nevertheless, the assumption of a continuous distribution leads to no appreciable error provided that we restrict our attention to volumes containing many atoms or dipoles, that is, to macroscopic regions.[1] Assuming now a continuously polarized dielectric, the value of **P** at a point can be defined as the net dipole moment **p** of a small volume Δv divided by the volume, with the limit taken as Δv shrinks to zero around the point. Thus,

$$\mathbf{P} = \lim_{\Delta v \to 0} \frac{\mathbf{p}}{\Delta v} \qquad (2\text{-}15)$$

In a dielectric the flux density **D** is related to the polarization **P** by the equation

$$\mathbf{D} = \epsilon_0 \mathbf{E} + \mathbf{P} \qquad (2\text{-}16)$$

[1] The reasoning here is similar to that in connection with continuous distributions of charge (Sec. 1-12).

where ϵ_0 = permittivity of vacuum

$\quad$ $\mathbf{E}$ = field in dielectric

From (2-16) we have

$$\mathbf{D} = \left(\epsilon_0 + \frac{\mathbf{P}}{\mathbf{E}}\right)\mathbf{E} \qquad (2\text{-}17)$$

Comparing (2-17) with the relation given in (1-47) that

$$\mathbf{D} = \epsilon\mathbf{E} \qquad (2\text{-}18)$$

it follows that[1]

$$\epsilon = \epsilon_0 + \frac{\mathbf{P}}{\mathbf{E}} \qquad (2\text{-}19)$$

where ϵ = permittivity of dielectric.   In isotropic media $\mathbf{P}$ and $\mathbf{E}$ are in the same direction so that their quotient is a scalar, and hence ϵ is a scalar.   In nonisotropic media, such as crystals, $\mathbf{P}$ and $\mathbf{E}$ are, *in general*, not in the same direction so that ϵ is no longer a scalar but becomes a nine-component quantity called a tensor.[2]   If $\mathbf{E}$ is applied parallel to certain crystal axes, $\mathbf{P}$ and $\mathbf{E}$ may be in the same direction and for this direction ϵ is also a scalar quantity.[3]   Thus, it appears that (2-16) is a general relation, while (2-18) is a more concise expression, which, however, has a simple significance only for isotropic media or certain special cases in nonisotropic media.

$\quad$ The flux density $\mathbf{D}$, which is normal to the slab face (Fig. 2-3), is the same in the vacuum as in the dielectric.[4]   Hence (2-16) can be expressed

$$\epsilon_0\mathbf{E}_0 = \epsilon_0\mathbf{E} + \mathbf{P}$$

or

$$\mathbf{P} = \epsilon_0(\mathbf{E}_0 - \mathbf{E}) \qquad (2\text{-}20)$$

where $\mathbf{E}_0$ = field in vacuum (applied field)

$\quad$ $\mathbf{E}$ = field in dielectric (resultant field)

According to (2-20) the polarization $\mathbf{P}$ equals the difference of the applied and resultant fields multiplied by ϵ_0.   This difference is due to the induced field $\mathbf{E}_i$ opposing $\mathbf{E}_0$ which is produced by the polarization charge on the slab surfaces.   Thus,

$$\mathbf{E}_0 - \mathbf{E} = -\mathbf{E}_i \qquad \text{or} \qquad \mathbf{E} = \mathbf{E}_0 + \mathbf{E}_i \qquad (2\text{-}21)$$

and

$$\mathbf{P} = -\epsilon_0\mathbf{E}_i \qquad (2\text{-}22)$$

[1] The ratio $\mathbf{P}/\mathbf{E}$ may be written as $\chi\epsilon_0$, where χ is called the *electric susceptibility* (dimensionless).   Thus, from (2-19) $\epsilon = \epsilon_0(1 + \chi)$.

[2] A vector is expressable by three components.

[3] See footnote for rutile in Table 2-1.

[4] This is demonstrated in Sec. 2-4 on Boundary Relations.

But from (2-14) **P** also has the same value as the polarization charge surface density ρ_{sp}; so

$$P = -\epsilon_0 E_i = \rho_{sp} \qquad (2\text{-}23)$$

In a conductor the induced field equals the applied field so that the resultant field is zero. On the other hand, in a dielectric the induced field $\mathbf{E}_i$ is always less than the applied field $\mathbf{E}_0$ so that the resultant field $\mathbf{E}$ is not zero. This may be illustrated by expressing (2-19) as

$$\mathbf{E} = \frac{\mathbf{P}}{\epsilon - \epsilon_0} = \frac{\mathbf{P}/\epsilon_0}{\epsilon_r - 1} \qquad (2\text{-}24)$$

If the relative permittivity of the dielectric is large, **E** may be small, but not zero. For **E** to be zero would require an infinite ϵ_r. However, no dielectrics of infinite ϵ_r are known.

Although the polarization **P** is based on the actual polarization phenomenon, it is usually simpler and more convenient in most practical problems with isotropic dielectrics to ignore the mechanism of the phenomenon and employ only the permittivity ϵ to describe the characteristics of the dielectric. In this case, ϵ is determined experimentally from a slab of the dielectric, and it is not necessary to consider the polarization. If we wish to calculate ϵ, however, we must consider the polarization. An example of such a calculation is given in Sec. 2-6 on Artificial Dielectrics.

2-4. Boundary Relations. In a single medium the electric field is continuous. That is, the field, if not constant, changes only by an infinitesimal amount in an infinitesimal distance. However, at the boundary between two different media the electric field may change abruptly both in magnitude and direction. It is of great importance in many problems to know the relations of the fields at such boundaries. These boundary relations are discussed in this section.

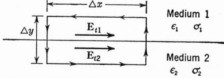

Fig. 2-4. The tangential electric field is continuous across a boundary.

It is convenient to analyze the boundary problem in two parts, considering first the relation between the fields *tangent* to the boundary and second the fields *normal* to the boundary.

Taking up first the relation of the fields tangent to the boundary, let two dielectric media of permittivities ϵ_1 and ϵ_2 be separated by a plane boundary as in Fig. 2-4. It is assumed that both media are perfect insulators, that is, the conductivities[1] σ_1 and σ_2 of the two media are zero.

[1] For discussion of conductivity see Sec. 3-7.

Consider a rectangular path, half in each medium, of length Δx parallel to the boundary and of length Δy normal to the boundary. Let the average electric field intensity tangent to the boundary in medium 1 be E_{t1} and the average field intensity tangent to the boundary in medium 2 be E_{t2}. The work per unit charge required to transport a positive test charge around this closed path is the line integral of $\mathbf{E}$ around the path ($\oint \mathbf{E} \cdot d\mathbf{l}$). By making the path length Δy approach zero, the work along the segments of the path normal to the boundary is zero even though a finite electric field may exist normal to the boundary. The line integral of $\mathbf{E}$ around the rectangle in the direction of the arrows is then

$$E_{t1}\,\Delta x \,-\, E_{t2}\,\Delta x \,=\, 0 \qquad (2\text{-}25)$$

or

$$E_{t1} \,=\, E_{t2} \qquad (2\text{-}26)$$

According to (2-26) *the tangential components of the electric field are the same on both sides of a boundary between two dielectrics.* In other words, the tangential electric field is *continuous* across such a boundary.

If medium 2 is a conductor ($\sigma_2 \neq 0$), the field E_{t2} in medium 2 must be zero under static conditions and hence (2-25) reduces to

$$E_{t1} \,=\, 0 \qquad (2\text{-}27)$$

According to (2-27) *the tangential electric field at a dielectric-conductor boundary is zero.*[1]

Turning our attention next to the fields normal to the boundary, consider two dielectric media of permittivities ϵ_1 and ϵ_2 separated by the x-y plane as shown in Fig. 2-5. It is assumed that both media are perfect insulators ($\sigma_1 = \sigma_2 = 0$). Suppose that an imaginary box is constructed, half in each medium, of area $\Delta x\,\Delta y$ and height Δz. Let D_{n1} be the average flux density normal to the top of the box in medium 1 and D_{n2} the average flux density normal to the bottom of the box in medium 2. D_{n1} is an outward normal (positive), while D_{n2} is an inward normal (negative). By Gauss's law the electric flux or surface integral of the normal component of $\mathbf{D}$ over a closed surface equals the charge enclosed. By making the height of the box Δz approach zero the contribution of the sides to the

---

[1] This assumes that no currents are flowing. If currents are present, then $\mathbf{E}$ in the conductor is not zero, unless the conductivity is infinite, and (2-26) applies rather than (2-27). In Chap. 7 the relations of (2-26) and (2-27) are extended to include *time-changing fields*, and it is shown that the relation $E_{t1} = E_{t2}$ of (2-26) holds with static or changing fields for the boundary between *any* two media of permittivities, permeabilities, and conductivities ϵ_1, μ_1, σ_1 and ϵ_2, μ_2, σ_2. Furthermore, for changing fields the relation $E_{t1} = 0$ of (2-27) is restricted to the case where the conductivity of medium 2 is infinite ($\sigma_2 = \infty$). This follows from the fact that a time-changing electric field in a conductor is zero only if the conductivity is infinite.

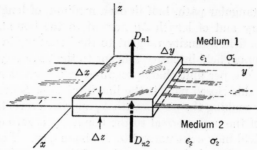

Fig. 2-5. The normal component of the flux density is continuous across a charge-free boundary.

surface integral is zero. The total flux over the box is then due entirely to flux over the top and bottom surfaces. If the average surface charge density on the boundary is ρ_s, we have on applying Gauss's law

$$D_{n1} \, \Delta x \, \Delta y - D_{n2} \, \Delta x \, \Delta y = \rho_s \, \Delta x \, \Delta y$$

or

$$D_{n1} - D_{n2} = \rho_s \tag{2-28}$$

According to (2-28) *the normal component of the flux density changes at a charged boundary between two dielectrics by an amount equal to the surface charge density.* This is usually zero at a dielectric-dielectric boundary unless charge has been placed there by mechanical means, as by rubbing.

If the boundary is free from charge, $\rho_s = 0$ and (2-28) reduces to

$$D_{n1} = D_{n2} \tag{2-29}$$

According to (2-29) *the normal component of the flux density is continuous across the charge-free boundary between two dielectrics.*

If medium 2 is a conductor, $D_{n2} = 0$ and (2-28) reduces to

$$D_{n1} = \rho_s \tag{2-30}$$

According to (2-30) *the normal component of the flux density at a dielectric-conductor boundary is equal to the surface charge density on the conductor.*[1]

It is important to note that ρ_s in these relations refers to actual electric charge separated by finite distances from equal quantities of opposite charge and *not* to surface charge ρ_{sp} due to polarization. The polarization surface charge is produced by atomic dipoles having equal and opposite charges separated by what is assumed to be an infinitesimal distance. It is not permissible to separate the positive and negative charges of such

[1] At a conductor-conductor boundary with currents present **E** is not zero in either medium unless the conductivity is infinite so that (2-28) applies rather than (2-30). In Chap. 7 it is pointed out that the relation $D_{n1} - D_{n2} = \rho_s$ of (2-28) and $D_{n1} = D_{n2}$ of (2-29) hold with static *or* time-changing fields for *any* two media of permittivities, permeabilities, and conductivities $\epsilon_1, \mu_1, \sigma_1$ and $\epsilon_1, \mu_2, \sigma_2$.

a dipole by a surface of integration, and hence the volume must always contain an integral (whole) number of dipoles and, therefore, zero net charge.   Only when the positive and negative charges are separated by a macroscopic distance (as on the opposite surfaces of a conducting sheet) can we separate them by a surface of integration.   This emphasizes a fundamental difference between the polarization, or so-called "bound," charge on a dielectric surface and the true charge on a conductor surface.

To illustrate the application of these boundary relations, two examples will be considered.

Example 1.   *Boundary between two dielectrics.*   Let two isotropic dielectric media 1 and 2 be separated by a charge-free plane boundary as in Fig. 2-6.   Let the permittivities be ϵ_1 and ϵ_2, and let the conductivities $\sigma_1 = \sigma_2 = 0$.   Referring to Fig. 2-6 the problem is to find the relation between the angles α_1 and α_2 of a static field line or flux tube which traverses the boundary.   For example, given α_1, to find α_2.

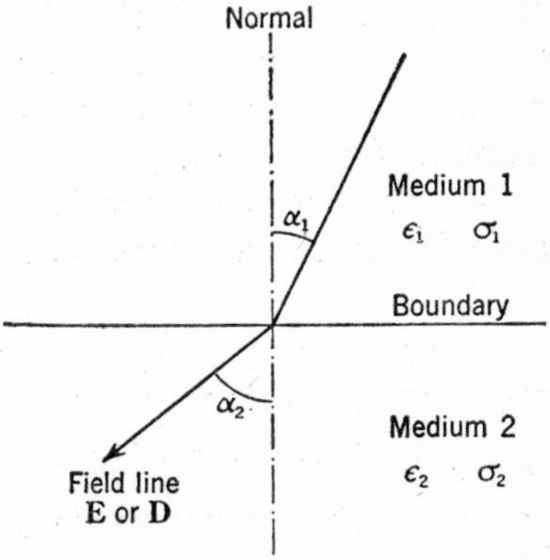

FIG.   2-6.   Boundary   between   two dielectric media showing change in direction of field line.

Solution.   Let

D_1 = magnitude of **D** in medium 1
D_2 = magnitude of **D** in medium 2
E_1 = magnitude of **E** in medium 1
E_2 = magnitude of **E** in medium 2

In an isotropic medium, **D** and **E** have the same direction.   According to the boundary relations,

$$D_{n1} = D_{n2} \quad \text{and} \quad E_{t1} = E_{t2} \tag{2-31}$$

Referring to Fig. 2-6

$$D_{n1} = D_1 \cos \alpha_1 \quad \text{and} \quad D_{n2} = D_2 \cos \alpha_2 \tag{2-32}$$

while

$$E_{t1} = E_1 \sin \alpha_1 \quad \text{and} \quad E_{t2} = E_2 \sin \alpha_2 \tag{2-33}$$

Substituting (2-32) and (2-33) into (2-31) and dividing the resulting equations yields

$$\frac{D_1 \cos \alpha_1}{E_1 \sin \alpha_1} = \frac{D_2 \cos \alpha_2}{E_2 \sin \alpha_2} \tag{2-34}$$

But $D_1 = \epsilon_1 E_1$, and $D_2 = \epsilon_2 E_2$, so that (2-34) becomes

$$\frac{\tan \alpha_1}{\tan \alpha_2} = \frac{\epsilon_1}{\epsilon_2} = \frac{\epsilon_{r1}\epsilon_0}{\epsilon_{r2}\epsilon_0} = \frac{\epsilon_{r1}}{\epsilon_{r2}} \tag{2-35}$$

where ϵ_{r1} = relative permittivity of medium 1
ϵ_{r2} = relative permittivity of medium 2
ϵ_0 = permittivity of vacuum

Suppose, for example, that medium 1 is air ($\epsilon_{r1} = 1$), while medium 2 is a slab of sulfur ($\epsilon_{r2} = 4$).   Then when $\alpha_1 = 30°$, the angle α_2 in medium 2 is 66.6°.

Example 2.   *Boundary between a conductor and a dielectric.*   Suppose that medium 2 in Fig. 2-6 is a conductor.   Find α_1.

Solution. Since medium 2 is a conductor, $D_2 = E_2 = 0$ under static conditions. According to the boundary relations,

$$D_{n1} = \rho_s \quad \text{or} \quad E_{n1} = \frac{\rho_s}{\epsilon_1}$$

and

$$E_{t1} = 0$$

Therefore

$$\alpha_1 = \tan^{-1}\frac{E_{t1}}{E_{n1}} = \tan^{-1} 0 = 0$$

It follows that a static electric field line or flux tube at a dielectric-conductor boundary is always perpendicular to the conductor surface (when no currents are present). This fact is of fundamental importance in field mapping (see Sec. 2-27).

2-5. Table of Boundary Relations. Table 2-2 summarizes the boundary relations for static fields developed in the preceding section.

TABLE 2-2
BOUNDARY RELATIONS FOR STATIC ELECTRIC FIELDS†

Field component	Boundary relation	Condition
Tangential	$E_{t1} = E_{t2}$ (1)	Any two media
Tangential	$E_{t1} = 0$ (2)	Medium 1 is a dielectric Medium 2 is a conductor
Normal	$D_{n1} - D_{n2} = \rho_s$ (3)	Any two media with charge at boundary
Normal	$D_{n1} = D_{n2}$ (4) $(\epsilon_1 E_{n1} = \epsilon_2 E_{n2})$	Any two media with no charge at boundary
Normal	$D_{n1} = \rho_s$ (5) $(\epsilon_1 E_{n1} = \rho_s)$	Medium 1 is a dielectric Medium 2 is a conductor with surface charge

† Relations (1), (3), and (4) apply in the presence of currents and also for time-varying fields (Chap. 7). The other relations, (2) and (5), also apply for time-changing situations provided $\sigma_2 = \infty$.

2-6. Artificial Dielectrics. Certain of the properties of a dielectric material may be simulated with *artificial dielectrics*. These were developed as a material for lenses for focusing short-wavelength radio waves.[1] Whereas the true dielectric consists of atomic or molecular particles of microscopic size, the artificial dielectric consists of discrete metal particles of macroscopic size. For example, the artificial dielectric may consist of

[1] W. E. Kock, Metallic Delay Lens, *Bell System Tech. J.*, **27**, 58–82, January, 1948. See also discussion by J. D. Kraus, "Antennas," McGraw-Hill Book Company, Inc., New York, 1950, p. 390.

a large number of metal spheres, as in Fig. 2-7, arranged in a three-dimensional or lattice structure which simulates the arrangement of the atoms of a true dielectric *but on a much larger scale.*[1]

The permittivity of an artificial dielectric made of metal spheres will now be calculated. This calculation is approximate but provides a good illustration of the significance of polarization and its application in a practical problem. Let a uniform electric field **E** be applied, as in Fig. 2-7, to a slab of artificial dielectric consisting of many metal spheres. The field **E** induces charges on the individual spheres as suggested in Fig. 2-8a. Thus, the spheres become analogous to the polarized atoms of a true dielectric, and each sphere may be represented by an equivalent dipole of charge q and length l as in Fig. 2-8b.

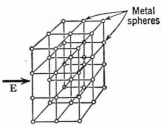

Fig. 2-7. Slab of artificial dielectric consisting of metal spheres in lattice arrangement.

The polarization **P** of the artificial dielectric is by (2-12) equal to the net dipole moment per unit volume, or

$$\mathbf{P} = Nq\mathbf{l} \qquad (2\text{-}36)$$

where N = number of spheres per unit volume (meters^{-3})

$q\mathbf{l}$ = dipole moment of individual sphere (coulomb-meters)

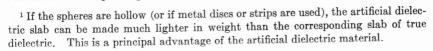

(a)

(b)

Fig. 2-8. Individual sphere of artificial dielectric (a) and equivalent dipole (b).

From (2-19) the permittivity is given by

$$\epsilon = \epsilon_0 + \frac{\mathbf{P}}{\mathbf{E}} \qquad (2\text{-}37)$$

Introducing the value of **P** from (2-36) into (2-37),

$$\epsilon = \epsilon_0 + \frac{Nq\mathbf{l}}{\mathbf{E}} = \epsilon_0 + \frac{Nql}{E} \qquad (2\text{-}38)$$

The last step in (2-38) follows from the fact that **l** and **E** are in the same direction, and hence their ratio (as vectors) equals that of their scalar magnitudes (l and E).

According to (2-38) the permittivity of the artificial dielectric can be determined if the number of spheres per unit volume and the dipole moment of one sphere per unit applied field are known. Proceeding now

[1] If the spheres are hollow (or if metal discs or strips are used), the artificial dielectric slab can be made much lighter in weight than the corresponding slab of true dielectric. This is a principal advantage of the artificial dielectric material.

to find the dipole moment of one sphere, it is assumed that each sphere is in a uniform field. This neglects the interaction of spheres, but this is negligible provided the sphere radius is small compared with the spacing between spheres.

From (1-14) the potential V_0 at a point in a uniform field is given by

$$V_0 = - \int_0^r E \cos \theta \, dr = -Er \cos \theta \qquad (2\text{-}39)$$

where r = radial distance from origin (taken at center of dipole)

θ = angle between field direction or axis of dipole and radial line (see Fig. 2-8b)

According to (2-39), $V_0 = 0$ at all points in a plane through the origin and normal to **E**. Equation (2-39) gives the potential at a point in a uniform field. Assuming that $r \gg l$, the potential V_d of a dipole in air is, from (2-6),

$$V_d = \frac{ql \cos \theta}{4\pi\epsilon_0 r^2} \qquad (2\text{-}40)$$

The total potential V is, by superposition, the sum of (2-39) and (2-40), or

$$V = V_0 + V_d$$
$$= -Er \cos \theta + \frac{ql \cos \theta}{4\pi\epsilon_0 r^2} \qquad (2\text{-}41)$$

The metal sphere has only induced charges on its surface (equal amounts of positive and negative charge) so that its potential is zero. Thus, for $r = a$, (2-41) reduces to

$$0 = -Ea \cos \theta + \frac{ql \cos \theta}{4\pi\epsilon_0 a^2} \qquad (2\text{-}42)$$

Solving (2-42) for ql/E, we have

$$\frac{ql}{E} = 4\pi\epsilon_0 a^3 \qquad (2\text{-}43)$$

Introducing (2-43) into (2-38), we obtain

$$\epsilon = \epsilon_0 + 4\pi\epsilon_0 N a^3 \qquad (2\text{-}44)$$

or

$$\epsilon_r = 1 + 4\pi N a^3 \qquad (2\text{-}45)$$

where ϵ = permittivity of artificial dielectric

ϵ_r = relative permittivity of artificial dielectric

N = number of spheres/unit volume

a = radius of sphere

Both the unit volume and the radius are expressed in the same unit of length.

Since the volume v of the sphere is $4\pi a^3/3$, (2-45) can also be written as

$$\epsilon_r = 1 + 3vN \qquad (2\text{-}46)$$

where N = number of spheres/unit volume

$\quad\quad v$ = volume of sphere (in same units as unit volume)

Thus, the permittivity of the artificial dielectric depends on both the number of spheres per unit volume and the size of the spheres.

2-7. Capacitors and Capacitance. A *capacitor*[1] is an electrical device consisting of two conductors separated by an insulating or dielectric medium.

By definition the *capacitance* of a capacitor is the ratio of the charge on one of its conductors to the potential difference between them.   Thus, the capacitance C of a capacitor is

$$\frac{Q}{V} = C \qquad (2\text{-}47)$$

where Q = charge on one conductor

$\quad\quad V$ = potential difference of conductors

Dimensionally (2-47) is

$$\frac{\text{Charge}}{\text{Potential}} = \frac{\text{charge}}{\text{energy/charge}} = \frac{\text{charge}^2}{\text{energy}} = \text{capacitance}$$

or in dimensional symbols

$$\frac{Q^2}{ML^2/T^2} = \frac{Q^2T^2}{ML^2}$$

The mksc unit of capacitance is the *farad*.   Thus, 1 coulomb per volt equals 1 farad, or

$$\frac{\text{Coulombs}}{\text{Volt}} = \text{farads}$$

In other words, a capacitor that can store 1 coulomb of charge with a potential difference of 1 volt has a capacitance of 1 farad.   A capacitor of 1 farad capacitance is much larger than is ordinarily used in practice so that the units

$$\text{Microfarad} = 10^{-6}\,\text{farad}$$

and

$$\text{Micromicrofarad} = 10^{-12}\,\text{farad}$$

are commonly employed.

2-8. Capacitance of Isolated Sphere. A very simple capacitor of theoretical interest consists of a single isolated conducting sphere.   The sphere may be solid or hollow.   Let the radius of the sphere be r_1.   Since

[1] Also called a *condenser*.

a capacitor must have two conductors, the second conductor in this case can be regarded as a sphere of infinite radius and zero potential. Let a charge Q be placed on the sphere of radius r_1. From (1-11) the potential of the sphere (work per unit charge to bring a positive test charge from infinity to the sphere) is given by

$$V = \frac{Q}{4\pi\epsilon r_1} \tag{2-48}$$

where ϵ = permittivity of medium filling all of space surrounding sphere.

Since V in (2-48) represents the potential or voltage difference between the infinite sphere and the isolated sphere of radius r_1, the capacitance of the isolated sphere is obtained by substituting (2-48) for V in (2-47), which yields

$$C = \frac{Q}{V} = 4\pi\epsilon r_1 \tag{2-49}$$

The capacitance C of the isolated sphere is in farads if r_1 is in meters and ϵ in farads per meter.

2-9. Capacitor of Two Concentric Spherical Shells. Consider now a capacitor consisting of two spherical conducting shells of radius r_1 and r_2 arranged concentrically as in Fig. 2-9. This capacitor is similar to the isolated sphere of Sec. 2-8 but with the radius of the outer conductor reduced from infinity to r_2.

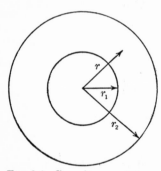

Assume that a charge Q is placed on the outer surface of the inner shell (radius r_1). There will then be induced an equal charge of opposite sign on the inner surface of the outer shell (radius r_2). The electric field extends radially between the two shells and is of the same intensity as the field at the same radius from a point charge Q. Thus, from (1-4) the radial component E_r of the field is

FIG. 2-9. Capacitor consisting of two concentric spherical shells.

$$E_r = \frac{Q}{4\pi\epsilon r^2} \tag{2-50}$$

where $r_1 \leq r \leq r_2$. The potential difference V_{21} between the shells is then the same as the work per unit charge required to bring a positive test charge from a radius r_2 to a radius r_1 in the field of an isolated point charge Q. The result is identical with that of (1-10) and is given by

$$V_{21} = -\frac{Q}{4\pi\epsilon} \int_{r_2}^{r_1} \frac{dr}{r^2} = \frac{Q}{4\pi\epsilon}\left(\frac{1}{r_1} - \frac{1}{r_2}\right) = \frac{Q}{4\pi\epsilon}\frac{r_2 - r_1}{r_1 r_2} \tag{2-51}$$

The capacitance C of the spherical shell capacitor is the ratio of the charge Q to the voltage difference V_{21}, or

$$C = \frac{Q}{V_{21}} = 4\pi\epsilon \frac{r_1 r_2}{r_2 - r_1} \tag{2-52}$$

Thus, the capacitance of the spherical shell capacitor is proportional to the product of the shell radii and inversely proportional to the difference of the radii.

2-10. Parallel-plate Capacitor. The capacitors described in the above sections are not commonly used, whereas the parallel-plate capacitor such as shown in Fig. 2-10 is a very common type. This capacitor consists of two parallel flat plates of area A separated by a distance l. The capacitor can be charged or discharged by wires connected as indicated.

Suppose that a potential V applied to the capacitor plates results in a charge $+Q$ on one plate and $-Q$ on

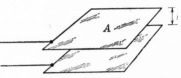

FIG. 2-10. Parallel-plate capacitor.

the other. Assuming that the charge is uniformly distributed (edge effects[1] neglected), the surface charge density ρ_s is uniform and is given by

$$\rho_s = \frac{Q}{A} \tag{2-53}$$

where A = area of plates. The flux density D between the plates is equal to ρ_s. Thus

$$Q = A\rho_s = AD = A\epsilon E = A\epsilon \frac{V}{l} \tag{2-54}$$

where E = field strength between plates
   ϵ = permittivity of medium between plates
The capacitance C of the parallel-plate capacitor equals Q/V. Introducing the value of Q from (2-54), we have

$$C = \frac{\epsilon A}{l} \tag{2-55}$$

where ϵ = permittivity of medium between capacitor plates (farads/ meter)
   A = area of plates (meters^2)
   l = separation of plates (meters)
Introducing the relative permittivity ϵ_r and the value of ϵ_0, we obtain for the capacitance of the parallel-plate capacitor

$$C = 8.85 \times 10^{-12} \frac{A\epsilon_r}{l} \qquad \text{farads}$$

or

$$C = \frac{8.85 A\epsilon_r}{l} \qquad \text{micromicrofarads } (\mu\mu\text{f})$$

$$\left. \right\} \tag{2-56}$$

[1] The edge effects decrease in importance as the size of the plates is increased compared with the spacing

where ϵ_r is the relative permittivity of the medium between the plates. As mentioned above, this formula neglects the electric field fringing the edge of the capacitor so that C by (2-56) is slightly less than the actual capacitance.

Example. A parallel-plate capacitor consists of two square metal plates 50 cm on a side and separated by 1 cm. A slab of sulfur ($\epsilon_r = 4$) 6 mm thick is placed on the lower plate as indicated in Fig. 2-11a. This leaves an air gap 4 mm thick between the

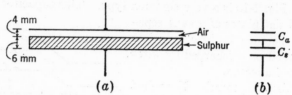

$$(a) \qquad\qquad\qquad\qquad\qquad\qquad (b)$$

Fig. 2-11. Parallel-plate capacitor with sulfur slab and air gap (a) and equivalent series capacitor (b).

sulfur slab and the upper plate. Find the capacitance of the capacitor. Neglect fringing of the field at the edges of the capacitor.

Solution. Imagine that a thin metal foil is placed on the upper surface of the sulfur slab. The foil is not connected to either plate. Since the foil is normal to **E**, and assuming that it is of negligible thickness, the field in the capacitor is undisturbed. The capacitor may now be regarded as two capacitors in series, an air capacitor of 4 mm plate spacing and capacitance C_a, and a sulfur-filled capacitor of 6 mm plate spacing and capacitance C_s, as suggested in Fig. 2-11b. The capacitance of the air capacitor is, from (2-56),

$$C_a = \frac{8.85 A \epsilon_r}{l} = \frac{8.85 \times 0.5^2 \times 1}{0.004} = 553 \ \mu\mu\text{f}$$

The capacitance of the sulfur-filled capacitor is

$$C_s = \frac{8.85 \times 0.5^2 \times 4}{0.006} = 1,475 \ \mu\mu\text{f}$$

The total capacitance of two capacitors in parallel is the sum of the individual capacitances. However, the total capacitance of two capacitors in series, as here, is the reciprocal of the sum of the reciprocals of the individual capacitances. Thus, the total capacitance C is given by

$$\frac{1}{C} = \frac{1}{C_a} + \frac{1}{C_s}$$

or

$$C = \frac{C_a C_s}{C_a + C_s} = \frac{553 \times 1,475}{553 + 1,475} = 402 \ \mu\mu\text{f}$$

2-11. Action of Dielectric in a Capacitor. In the above relations for the capacitance of capacitors it is to be noted that the capacitance is proportional to the permittivity ϵ. For example, if the capacitance of a parallel-plate capacitor with air as the dielectric medium is 1 μf then filling the space between the plates with paraffin ($\epsilon_r = 2.1$) raises the capacitance to 2.1 μf.   That is, with the paraffin dielectric the capacitor plates can store 2.1 times as much charge for a given applied potential. The reason for this increase in the charge storage capacity is to be found in the polarization of the paraffin.

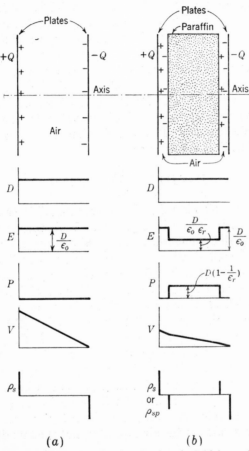

FIG. 2-12. The variation of the flux density D, electric field intensity E, polarization P, potential V, and surface charge density ρ_s along the axis between the plates of an air capacitor is shown at (a).   The variation after a paraffin slab has been introduced is illustrated at (b).

Referring to Fig. 2-12a, let the medium between the plates be air. Let a potential or voltage difference V be applied to the plates, as with a battery, resulting in charges $+Q$ and $-Q$ on the plates.   The battery is then disconnected.   The resulting variation of the flux density D, field intensity E, polarization P, potential V, and surface charge density ρ_s as a function of distance along the capacitor axis (normal to the center of the plates) is presented by the graphs in Fig. 2-12a.   Since the relative permittivity of air is nearly unity, the polarization is substantially zero. The surface charge density is due to true charge on the capacitor plates and is indicated by vertical lines in the graph.

Consider now the situation when a slab of paraffin ($\epsilon_r = 2.1$) is introduced between the capacitor plates as in Fig. 2-12b. It is assumed that the slab is substantially as thick as the spacing between the plates. However, for clarity the air gaps between the plates and the paraffin slab are exaggerated in Fig. 2-12b. Since the battery was disconnected before the paraffin was introduced, the charge on the plates is the same as previously. Therefore, the flux density D is the same as before and is constant between the plates. However, the total field intensity E in the dielectric is reduced to 0.475 of its value in the air capacitor ($E = D/\epsilon_0\epsilon_r = 0.475D/\epsilon_0$). The polarization P has a value in the paraffin such that $P + \epsilon_0 E = D$ or

$$P = D\left(1 - \frac{1}{\epsilon_r}\right) = 0.525\,D$$

Since E in the paraffin is reduced, the potential difference of the plates is also reduced as indicated in Fig. 2-12. With the paraffin dielectric there is not only the true surface charge of density ρ_s on the capacitor plates but also the polarization charge of density ρ_{sp} on the surface of the paraffin. It is to be noted that $D = \rho_s$, while $P = \rho_{sp}$. The polarization charge does not affect D, but it does reduce E in the dielectric by partially neutralizing the effect of the true surface charge on the plates. As a result the potential difference of the plates is only $1/2.1 = 0.475$ of its value for the air capacitor (the effect of the air gap in the paraffin capacitor being neglected). Therefore, if the battery with potential V that was originally applied to the air capacitor is now connected to the paraffin capacitor, the true charge stored on the plates can be increased to 2.1 times its original value. Accordingly, the capacitance (charge per unit potential) is 2.1 its value with air. The field E in the paraffin capacitor is now equal to its value in the air capacitor, but the flux density D is 2.1 times as much.

2-12. Dielectric Strength. The field intensity **E** in a dielectric cannot be increased indefinitely. If a certain value is exceeded, sparking occurs and the dielectric is said to break down.[1] The maximum field intensity that a dielectric can sustain without breakdown is called its *dielectric strength.*

---

[1] As **E** is gradually increased, sparking occurs in air almost immediately when a critical value of field is exceeded if the field is uniform (**E** everywhere parallel), but a glowing, or corona, discharge may occur first if the field is nonuniform (diverging) with spark-over following as **E** is increased further. For a detailed discussion see, for example, F. W. Peek, Jr., "Dielectric Phenomena in High Voltage Engineering," 3d ed., McGraw-Hill Book Company, Inc., New York, 1929.

In the design of capacitors it is important to know the maximum potential difference that can be applied before breakdown occurs.   For a given plate spacing this breakdown is proportional to the dielectric strength of the medium between the plates.   The radius of curvature of the edge of the capacitor plate is another factor, since this curvature largely determines the maximum field intensity that occurs for a given potential difference (see Sec. 2-28).

Many capacitors have air as the dielectric.   These types have the advantage that if breakdown occurs the capacitor is not permanently damaged.   For applications requiring large capacitance or small physical size or both, other dielectrics are employed.   The dielectric strength of a number of common dielectric materials is listed in Table 2-3.   The dielectric strengths are for a uniform field.   The materials are arranged in order of increasing strength.

TABLE 2-3

Material	Dielectric strength, volts/meter
Air (atmospheric pressure)	3×10^6
Oil (mineral)	15×10^6
Paper (impregnated)	15×10^6
Polystyrene	20×10^6
Rubber (hard)	21×10^6
Bakelite	25×10^6
Glass (plate)	30×10^6
Paraffin	30×10^6
Quartz (fused)	30×10^6
Mica	200×10^6

2-13. Energy in a Capacitor.   It requires work to charge a capacitor. Hence energy is stored by a charged capacitor.

To determine the magnitude of this energy, consider a capacitor of capacitance C charged to a potential difference V between the two conductors.   Then from (2-47)

$$q = CV \qquad (2\text{-}57)$$

where q = charge on each conductor.   Now potential is work per charge.   In terms of infinitesimals it is the infinitesimal work dW per infinitesimal charge dq.   That is,

$$V = \frac{dW}{dq} \qquad (2\text{-}58)$$

Introducing the value of V from (2-58) in (2-57), we have

$$dW = \frac{q}{C}\, dq \qquad (2\text{-}59)$$

If the charging process starts from a zero charge and continues until a final charge Q is delivered, the total work W is the integral of (2-59), or

$$W = \frac{1}{C} \int_0^Q q \, dq = \frac{1}{2} \frac{Q^2}{C} \qquad (2\text{-}60)$$

This is the energy stored in the capacitor. By (2-47) this relation can be variously expressed as

$$W = \frac{1}{2} \frac{Q^2}{C} = \frac{1}{2} CV^2 = \frac{1}{2} QV \qquad (2\text{-}61)$$

where W = energy (joules)

C = capacitance (farads)

V = potential difference (volts)

Q = charge on one conductor (coulombs)

2-14. Energy Density in a Static Electric Field. Consider the parallel-plate capacitor of capacitance C shown in Fig. 2-13. When it is charged to a potential difference V between the plates, the energy stored is

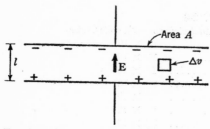

$$W = \tfrac{1}{2}CV^2 = \tfrac{1}{2}QV \quad (2\text{-}62)$$

The question may now be asked: In what part of the capacitor is the energy stored? The answer is: The energy is stored in the electric field *between* the plates. To demonstrate this, let us proceed as follows: Consider the small cu-

FIG. 2-13. Energy is stored in the electric field between the capacitor plates.

bical volume $\Delta v (= \Delta l^3)$ between the plates as indicated in Fig. 2-13. This volume is shown to a larger scale in Fig. 2-14. The length of each side is Δl, and the top and bottom faces (of area Δl^2) are parallel to the capacitor plates (normal to the field $\mathbf{E}$). If thin sheets of metal foil are placed coincident with the top and bottom faces of the volume, the field will be undisturbed provided the sheets are sufficiently thin. The volume Δv now constitutes a small capacitor of capacitance

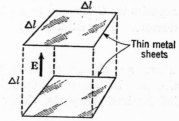

$$\Delta C = \frac{\epsilon \, \Delta l^2}{\Delta l} = \epsilon \, \Delta l \qquad (2\text{-}63)$$

FIG. 2-14. Small cubical volume of capacitance $\epsilon \Delta l$.

The potential difference ΔV of the thin sheets is given by

$$\Delta V = E \, \Delta l \qquad (2\text{-}64)$$

Now the energy ΔW stored in the volume Δv is, from (2-61),

$$\Delta W = \tfrac{1}{2} \Delta C \, \Delta V^2 \qquad (2\text{-}65)$$

Substituting (2-63) for ΔC and (2-64) for ΔV in (2-65), we have

$$\Delta W = \tfrac{1}{2}\epsilon E^2\,\Delta v \qquad (2\text{-}66)$$

Dividing (2-66) by Δv and taking the limit of the ratio $\Delta W/\Delta v$ as Δv approaches zero, we obtain the energy per volume, or *energy density*, w at the point around which Δv shrinks to zero. Thus[1]

$$w = \lim_{\Delta v \to 0} \frac{\Delta W}{\Delta v} = \frac{1}{2}\,\epsilon E^2 \qquad (2\text{-}67a)$$

Now the total energy W stored by the capacitor of Fig. 2-13 will be given by the integral of the energy density w over the entire region in which the electric field $\mathbf{E}$ has a value.

$$W = \int_v w\,dv = \tfrac{1}{2}\int_v \epsilon E^2\,dv \qquad (2\text{-}68)$$

where the integration is taken throughout the region between the plates. For simplicity it is assumed that the field is uniform between the plates and that there is no fringing of the field at the edges of the capacitor. Thus, evaluating (2-68),

$$W = \tfrac{1}{2}\epsilon E^2 Al = \tfrac{1}{2}DA\,El = \tfrac{1}{2}QV \qquad \text{joules} \qquad (2\text{-}69)$$

where A = area of one capacitor plate (meters^2)

l = spacing between capacitor plates (meters)

This result, obtained by integrating the energy density throughout the volume between the plates of the capacitor, is identical with the relation given by (2-61).

2-15. Fields of Simple Charge Configurations. In many problems it is desirable to know the distribution of the electric field and the associated potential. For example, if the field intensity exceeds the breakdown value for the dielectric medium, sparking, or corona, can occur. From a knowledge of the field distribution, the charge surface density on conductors bounding the field and the capacitance between them can also be determined.

In Secs. 2-16 to 2-25 the field and potential distributions for a number of simple geometric forms are discussed. The field and potential distributions around point charges, charged spheres, line charges, and charged cylinders are considered first. The field and potential distributions of these configurations can be expressed by relatively simple equations. The extension of these relations by the method of images to situations involving large conducting sheets or ground planes is then considered. Finally, in Sec. 2-26, the field and potential distributions for some conductor configurations, which are not easily treated mathe-

---

[1] For the more general case of a nonisotropic medium in which $\mathbf{D}$ and $\mathbf{E}$ may not be in the same direction,

$$w = \tfrac{1}{2}\mathbf{D}\cdot\mathbf{E} \qquad (2\text{-}67b)$$

matically, are found by a simple graphical method known as *field mapping*.

2-16. Fields of Point Charges and Conducting Spheres. The fields of point charges and conducting spheres have already been discussed, but the relations will be summarized in this section.

The electric field of an *isolated point charge* is everywhere radial and is given in volts per meter by

$$E_r = \frac{Q}{4\pi\epsilon r^2} \tag{2-70}$$

where Q is the charge in coulombs and r is the distance from the charge in meters.

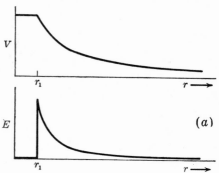

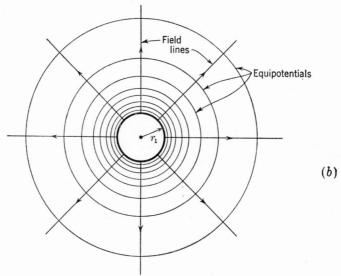

Fig. 2-15. Variation of electric field E and potential V for an isolated charged conducting sphere of radius r_1.

The absolute electric potential V of an isolated point charge is given in volts by

$$V = \frac{Q}{4\pi\epsilon r} \qquad (2\text{-}71)$$

The electric field of an *isolated conducting sphere* (hollow or solid) of radius r_1 with a total charge Q is everywhere radial and is also given by (2-70) for all values of r larger than r_1. For values of r less than r_1 (inside sphere) $\mathbf{E} = 0$.

The electric potential V of such an isolated conducting sphere is given by (2-71) for all values of r larger than r_1. For values of r less than r_1 (inside sphere) the potential is constant and has the same value as the potential of the sphere.

Field and potential distributions may be presented in various ways. For example, a graph of the variation of the magnitude of the electric field $\mathbf{E}$ and of the electric potential V along a reference line may give the desired information. This is illustrated by the curves for E and V in Fig. 2-15a for the field and potential along a radial line extending from the center of a charged conducting sphere of radius r_1. Or the field and potential distribution may be indicated by a contour map, or graph, as in Fig. 2-15b. In this map the radial lines indicate the direction of the electric field, while the circular contours are equipotential lines. In this diagram the potential difference between contours is a constant.

2-17. Field of Two Equal Point Charges of Opposite Sign (Electric Dipole). The electric field at a point P due to two point charges $+Q$ and $-Q$ is equal to the vector sum of the fields at P due to each of the charges alone. This is illustrated in Fig. 2-16. The potential V at P is equal to the algebraic sum of the potentials at P due to each charge alone. The field can also be obtained from the gradient of the potential ($\mathbf{E} = -\nabla V$) if the potential distribution is known.

A map of the field lines (solid) and equipotential contours (dashed) is shown in Fig. 2-16 for the case of point charges $+Q$ and $-Q$ separated by 12.7 cm. The equipotential contours are given in volts for $Q = 1.4 \times 10^{-10}$ coulomb. The charge configuration in Fig. 2-16 constitutes an electric dipole with a charge separation of 12.7 cm. The expressions for $\mathbf{E}$ and V of an electric dipole given by (2-7) and (2-6) would not apply to the map shown in Fig. 2-16 since these are restricted to distances that are large compared with the charge separation.

2-18. Field of Two Equal Point Charges of Same Sign. In contrast to the configuration in Sec. 2-17 let us consider the situation of two positive point charges of equal magnitude as in Fig. 2-17. A map of the field lines (solid) and equipotential contours (dashed) is shown for a charge separation of 12.7 cm. The equipotential contours are given in volts for

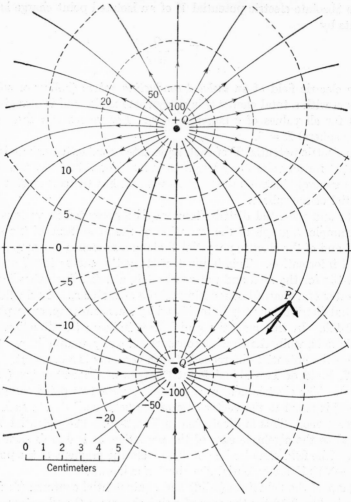

Fig. 2-16. Electric field and potential variation around an electric dipole consisting of a positive and negative charge of 1.4×10^{-10} coulomb separated by 12.7 cm (5 in.). The solid lines are field lines, and the dashed lines are equipotential contours, with their potential level indicated in volts.

$Q = 1.4 \times 10^{-10}$ coulomb. The only difference between the charge configuration of Fig. 2-17 and that in Fig. 2-16 is that the lower charge is positive.

At distances from the charges that are large compared with their separation the equipotentials become circles, while the field lines become radials as though the field were caused by a charge of $+2Q$ situated at P midway between the charges. At large distances this point appears to be the center of charge, or "center of gravity," of the charge configuration.

Near each charge the effect of the other charge is small, and the equipotentials are circles like around an isolated point charge. For intermediate distances the equipotentials have the shapes shown in Fig. 2-17. Of particular interest is the figure-eight-shaped equipotential

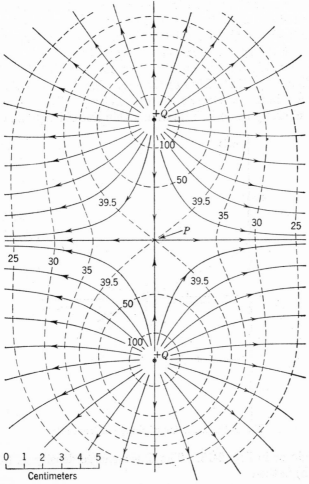

FIG. 2-17. Electric field and potential variation around two equal positive charges of 1.4×10^{-10} coulomb separated by 12.7 cm (5 in.). The solid lines are field lines, and the dashed lines are equipotential contours, with their potential level indicated in volts.

($V = 39.5$ volts) that crosses itself at the point P. At the point P the gradient of V is zero, and hence $\mathbf{E} = 0$. A point such as this is called a *singular point*.

2-19. Field of a Number of Point Charges and Conducting Spheres. The electric field $\mathbf{E}$ at a point P due to a *number of point charges* is equal to the vector sum of the fields at P due to each of the charges alone. The potential V at P is equal to the algebraic sum of the potentials at P due to each charge alone.

The electric field $\mathbf{E}$ at a point P due to a *number of charged conducting spheres* is approximately equal to the vector sum of the fields at P due to each sphere alone, while the potential V at P is approximately equal to the algebraic sum of the potentials at P due to each sphere alone. It is assumed that the spheres are small compared with their separation so that the charge distribution on each sphere is substantially uniform.

2-20. Field of a Finite Line of Charge. Consider now the field produced by a thin line of electric charge. Let a positive charge Q be distributed uniformly as an infinitesimally thin line of length $2a$ with center

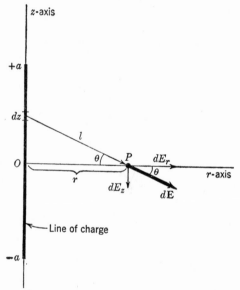

Fig. 2-18. Thin line of charge of length $2a$.

at the origin as in Fig. 2-18. The linear charge density ρ_L (charge per unit length) is then

$$\rho_L = \frac{Q}{2a} \qquad (2\text{-}72)$$

where ρ_L is in coulombs per meter when Q is in coulombs and a is in meters.

At the point P on the r axis, the infinitesimal electric field $d\mathbf{E}$ due to an infinitesimal length of wire dz is the same as from a point charge of magnitude $\rho_L \, dz$. Thus,

$$d\mathbf{E} = \mathbf{a}_l \frac{\rho_L \, dz}{4\pi\epsilon l^2} \qquad (2\text{-}73)$$

where $l = \sqrt{r^2 + z^2}$

$\mathbf{a}_l$ = unit vector in direction of l

The z axis in Fig. 2-18 is an axis of symmetry so that the field will have only z and r components.   These are

$$dE_r = dE \cos \theta = dE \frac{r}{l} \qquad (2\text{-}74)$$

and

$$dE_z = dE \sin \theta = dE \frac{z}{l} \qquad (2\text{-}75)$$

The resultant or total r component E_r of the field at a point on the r axis is obtained by integrating (2-74) over the entire line of charge.   That is,

$$E_r = \frac{\rho_L r}{4\pi\epsilon} \int_{-a}^{+a} \frac{dz}{l^3} = \frac{\rho_L r}{4\pi\epsilon} \int_{-a}^{+a} \frac{dz}{\sqrt{(r^2 + z^2)^3}}$$

and

$$E_r = \frac{\rho_L a}{2\pi\epsilon r \sqrt{r^2 + a^2}} \qquad (2\text{-}76)$$

By symmetry the resultant z component E_z of the field at a point on the r axis is zero.   Hence the total field $\mathbf{E}$ at points along the r axis is radial and is given by

$$|\mathbf{E}| = E_r = \frac{\rho_L a}{2\pi\epsilon r \sqrt{r^2 + a^2}} \qquad (2\text{-}77)$$

This relation gives the field as a function of r at points on the r axis for a *finite* line of charge of length $2a$ and uniform charge density ρ_L.   For the potential V at any point see Prob. 2-28.

2-21. Field of an Infinite Line of Charge.   Consider that the line of charge in Fig. 2-18 extends to infinity in both positive and negative z directions.   By dividing the numerator and denominator of (2-77) by a and letting a become infinite, the electric field intensity due to an *infinite line of positive charge* is found to be

$$|\mathbf{E}| = E_r = \frac{\rho_L}{2\pi\epsilon r} \qquad (2\text{-}78)$$

The potential difference V_{21} between two points at radial distances r_2 and r_1 from the infinite line of charge is then the work per unit charge required to transport a positive test charge from r_2 to r_1.   Assume that $r_2 > r_1$.   This potential difference is given by the line integral of E_r from r_2 to r_1, the potential at r_1 being higher than at r_2 if the line of charge is positive.   Thus

$$V_{21} = -\int_{r_2}^{r_1} E_r \, dr = \frac{\rho_L}{2\pi\epsilon} \int_{r_1}^{r_2} \frac{dr}{r}$$

or[1]

$$V_{21} = \frac{\rho_L}{2\pi\epsilon} \ln r \Big]_{r_1}^{r_2} = \frac{\rho_L}{2\pi\epsilon} \ln \frac{r_2}{r_1} \qquad (2\text{-}79)$$

2-22. Infinite Cylinder of Charge. If the charge is distributed uniformly along a cylinder of radius r_1 instead of concentrated along an infinitesimally thin line, the field external to the cylinder is given by (2-78) for $r \geq r_1$. Inside of the cylinder, $\mathbf{E} = 0$.

The potential difference between the cylinder and points outside the cylinder is given by (2-79), where $r_2 > r_1$ and ρ_L is the charge per unit length of the cylinder. Inside of the cylinder the potential is the same as the potential at the surface $(r = r_1)$.

2-23. Infinite Coaxial Transmission Line. A coaxial transmission line consists of two conductors arranged coaxially as shown by the cross section of Fig. 2-19a. This is a common type of transmission line, and much can be learned concerning its properties from a consideration of its

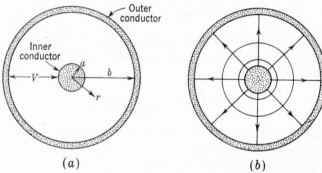

(a)   (b)

Fig. 2-19. Coaxial transmission line.

behavior under static conditions. Let a fixed potential difference be applied between the inner and outer conductors of an infinitely long coaxial line so that the charge Q per unit length l of one line is ρ_L. The field is confined to the space between the two conductors. The field lines are radial and the equipotential lines are concentric circles as indicated in Fig. 2-19b. The magnitude of the field at a radius r is given by (2-78), where $a \leq r \leq b$ and where ρ_L is the charge per unit length on the inner conductor. The potential difference V between the conductors is, from (2-79),

$$V = \frac{\rho_L}{2\pi\epsilon} \ln \frac{b}{a} \qquad (2\text{-}80)$$

[1] The abbreviation ln indicates the natural logarithm (to base e). The abbreviation log indicates the common logarithm (to base 10). That is,

$$\ln x = \log_e x = 2.3 \log_{10} x = 2.3 \log x$$

Now capacitance is given by the ratio of charge to potential. Thus

$$C = \frac{Q}{V}$$

Dividing by length l, we have

$$\frac{C}{l} = \frac{Q/l}{V}$$

The ratio Q/l equals the linear charge density ρ_L (coulombs per meter).
Hence, the capacitance per unit length, C/l, of the coaxial line is

$$\frac{C}{l} = \frac{\rho_L}{V} = \frac{2\pi\epsilon}{\ln(b/a)} \qquad \text{farads/meter} \qquad (2\text{-}81)$$

where ϵ = permittivity of medium between conductors.   With ϵ in farads
per meter, C/l is also in farads per meter.   The radii a and b are expressed
in the same units of length.

Since $\epsilon = \epsilon_0\epsilon_r$, where $\epsilon_0 = 8.85 \times 10^{-12}$ farad/meter, (2-81) can be
expressed more conveniently as

$$\frac{C}{l} = \frac{55.6\epsilon_r}{\ln(b/a)} = \frac{24.2\epsilon_r}{\log(b/a)} \qquad \mu\mu\text{f/meter} \qquad (2\text{-}82)$$

where ϵ_r = relative permittivity of medium between conductors
    $\mu\mu$f = micromicrofarads
      b = inside radius of outer conductor
      a = radius of inner conductor (in same units as b)
    $\ln$ = natural logarithm
   $\log$ = logarithm to base 10

2-24. Two Infinite Lines of Charge. Let two infinite parallel lines
of charge be separated by a distance $2s$ as in Fig. 2-20.   Assume that the
linear charge density of the two lines is equal but of opposite sign.   The
resultant electric field **E** at a point P, distant r_1 from the negative line
and r_2 from the positive line, is then the vector sum of the field of each
line taken alone.

Let the origin of the coordinates in Fig. 2-20 be the reference for
potential.   Then the potential difference between P and the origin produced by the positively charged line is

$$V_+ = \frac{\rho_L}{2\pi\epsilon} \ln \frac{s}{r_2} \qquad (2\text{-}83)$$

and the potential due to the negatively charged line is

$$V_- = - \frac{\rho_L}{2\pi\epsilon} \ln \frac{s}{r_1} \qquad (2\text{-}84)$$

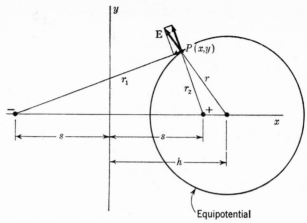

FIG. 2-20. Two infinite lines of charge separated by a distance $2s$.

The total potential difference V between P and the origin is the algebraic sum of (2-83) and (2-84), or

$$V = V_+ + V_- = \frac{\rho_L}{2\pi\epsilon} \ln \frac{r_1}{r_2} \qquad (2\text{-}85)$$

If V in (2-85) is a constant, (2-85) is the equation of an equipotential line. The form of the equipotential line will be more apparent if (2-85) is transformed in the following manner: From (2-85)

$$\ln \frac{r_1}{r_2} = \frac{2\pi\epsilon V}{\rho_L} \qquad (2\text{-}86)$$

and

$$\frac{r_1}{r_2} = e^{2\pi\epsilon V/\rho_L} \qquad (2\text{-}87)$$

Since $2\pi\epsilon V/\rho_L$ is a constant for any equipotential line, the right side of (2-87) is a constant K. Thus

$$e^{2\pi\epsilon V/\rho_L} = K \qquad \text{and} \qquad r_1 = Kr_2 \qquad (2\text{-}88)$$

The coordinates of the point P in Fig. 2-20 are (x, y) so that

$$r_1 = \sqrt{(s + x)^2 + y^2} \qquad (2\text{-}89)$$

and

$$r_2 = \sqrt{(s - x)^2 + y^2} \qquad (2\text{-}90)$$

Substituting (2-89) and (2-90) in (2-88), squaring, and rearranging yields

$$x^2 - 2xs \frac{K^2 + 1}{K^2 - 1} + s^2 + y^2 = 0 \qquad (2\text{-}91)$$

Adding $s^2(K^2 + 1)^2/(K^2 - 1)^2$ to both sides of (2-91) to complete the square on the left side, we have

$$\left(x - s\frac{K^2 + 1}{K^2 - 1}\right)^2 + y^2 = \left(\frac{2Ks}{K^2 - 1}\right)^2 \tag{2-92}$$

This is the equation of a circle having the form

$$(x - h)^2 + (y - l)^2 = r^2 \tag{2-93}$$

where x and y are the coordinates of a point on the circle, h and l are the coordinates of the center of the circle, and r is the radius of the circle. Comparing (2-92) and (2-93), it follows that the equipotential curve passing through the point (x, y) is a circle of radius

$$r = \frac{2Ks}{K^2 - 1} \tag{2-94}$$

with its center on the x axis at a distance from the origin

$$h = s\frac{K^2 + 1}{K^2 - 1} \tag{2-95}$$

An equipotential line of radius r with center at $(h, 0)$ is shown in Fig. 2-20. As K increases, corresponding to larger equipotentials, r approaches zero and h approaches s so that the equipotentials are smaller circles with their centers more nearly at the line of charge. This is illustrated by the additional equipotential circles in Fig. 2-21.

The potential is zero along the y axis. Potentials to the right of the y axis are positive and to the left are negative.

Field lines are also shown in Fig. 2-21. These are everywhere orthogonal to the potential circles and also are circles with their centers on the y axis.

2-25. Infinite Two-wire Transmission Line. The discussion of two infinite lines of charge in the previous section is easily extended to the case of an infinite line consisting of two parallel cylindrical conductors or wires. This is a type of transmission line commonly used in practice, and much can be learned concerning its properties from a consideration of its behavior under static conditions. Let a fixed potential difference be applied between the conductors so that the charge per unit length of each conductor is ρ_L.

The surface of the wire is an equipotential surface, and therefore an equipotential circle in Fig. 2-21 will coincide with the wire surface. Thus, the heavy circles of radius r and center-to-center spacing $2h$ can represent the two wires. The field and potential distributions external to the wire surfaces are the same as if the field were produced by two infinitesimally thin lines of charge with a spacing of $2s$. The field inside

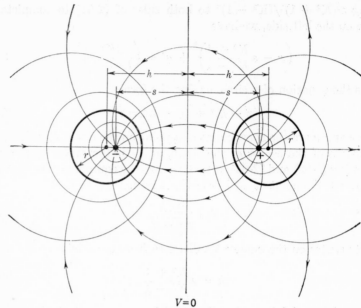

$V=0$

Fig. 2-21. Field and equipotential lines around two infinite parallel lines of charge or around an infinite two-conductor transmission line.

the wires is, of course, zero and the potential the same as on the surface. The charge is not uniformly distributed on the wire surface but has higher density on the adjacent sides of the conductors.

The potential difference V_c between one of the conductors and a point midway between them is, from (2-85) and (2-88),

$$V_c = \frac{\rho_L}{2\pi\epsilon} \ln K \tag{2-96}$$

The value of K can be expressed in terms of the radius r and half the center-to-center spacing h by eliminating s from (2-94) and (2-95) and solving for K, obtaining

$$K = \frac{h}{r} \pm \sqrt{\frac{h^2}{r^2} - 1} \tag{2-97}$$

The potential difference V_{2c} between the two conductors is then

$$V_{2c} = \frac{\rho_L}{\pi\epsilon} \ln \left(\frac{h}{r} \pm \sqrt{\frac{h^2}{r^2} - 1} \right) \tag{2-98}$$

To find the *capacitance per unit length, C/l,* of the two-conductor line, we take the ratio of the charge per unit length on one conductor to the difference of potential between the conductors.   That is,

$$\frac{C}{l} = \frac{\rho_L}{V_{2c}} = \frac{\pi\epsilon}{\ln\left[\frac{h}{r} \pm \sqrt{\left(\frac{h}{r}\right)^2 - 1}\right]} \qquad \text{farads/meter} \qquad (2\text{-}99)$$

or

$$\frac{C}{l} = \frac{12.1\epsilon_r}{\log\left[\frac{h}{r} \pm \sqrt{\left(\frac{h}{r}\right)^2 - 1}\right]} \qquad \mu\mu\text{f/meter} \qquad (2\text{-}100)$$

where ϵ_r = relative permittivity of the medium surrounding the conductors (dimensionless)

h = half center-to-center spacing

r = conductor radius (same units as h)

2-26. Infinite Single-wire Transmission Line.   Method of Images.
A single-wire transmission line with ground return is another form of line
sometimes used.   Let the conductor radius be r and the height of the
center of the conductor above ground be h.   Assume that the conductor
has a positive charge ρ_L per unit length and that the ground is at zero
potential.

The field and potential distribution of this type of line is readily found
by the *method of images*.   Thus, if the ground is removed and an identical
conductor with charge $-\rho_L$ per unit length placed as far below ground
level as the other conductor is above, the situation is the same as for a
two-conductor line (Fig. 2-21).   The conductor which replaces the
ground is called the *image* of the upper conductor.   The field and
potential distribution for the single conductor line is then as illustrated by
Fig. 2-22.

The difference in potential between the single conductor and the
ground is as given by (2-96) or by one-half of (2-98).   The capacitance
per unit length, C/l, is twice the value given by (2-99), or

$$\frac{C}{l} = \frac{2\pi\epsilon}{\ln\left[\frac{h}{r} \pm \sqrt{\left(\frac{h}{r}\right)^2 - 1}\right]} \qquad \text{farads/meter} \qquad (2\text{-}101)$$

or

$$\frac{C}{l} = \frac{24.2\epsilon_r}{\log\left[\frac{h}{r} \pm \sqrt{\left(\frac{h}{r}\right)^2 - 1}\right]} \qquad \mu\mu\text{f/meter} \qquad (2\text{-}102)$$

The surface charge density ρ_s on the conducting ground plane is not
uniform.   It is a maximum directly below the wire and is zero at an
infinite distance.   The variation of ρ_s as a function of distance along the
ground plane is given in Prob. 2-34.

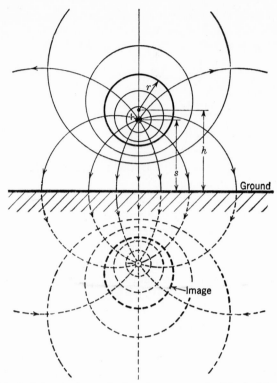

FIG. 2-22. Infinite single conductor above ground with electrical image.

2-27. Graphical Mapping of Static Electric Fields. Field Cells.
Not all conductor configurations can be treated mathematically as readily as those in the preceding sections. Although it is theoretically possible to find the potential distribution for any configuration of conductors by means of Laplace's equation, as will be discussed later, such an approach may be impractical and other methods must be used. In two-dimensional problems[1] a very effective graphical method, known as *field mapping*,[2] is applicable.

In graphical field mapping the following fundamental properties of static electric fields are useful:

1. Field and potential lines intersect at right angles.
2. The surface of a conductor is an equipotential surface.

---

[1] By a two-dimensional problem is meant one in which the conductor configuration can be shown by a single cross section, all cross sections parallel to it being the same. A uniform coaxial transmission line is an example of a two-dimensional configuration. Thus, the cross section of Fig. 2-19 is representative of any cross section of the line.

[2] A. D. Moore, "Fundamentals of Electrical Design," McGraw-Hill Book Company, Inc., New York, 1927.

3. The field meets a conducting surface normally.
4. In a uniform field, the potential varies linearly with distance.
5. A flux tube is parallel to the field,[1] and the electric flux is constant over any cross section of a flux tube.
6. A tube of flux originates on a positive charge and ends on an equal negative charge.

Graphical field mapping will be introduced with the aid of an example. Consider two charged sheet conductors 1 and 2 as shown in cross section in Fig. 2-23. The sheets extend infinitely far to the left and right and also normally to the page. This is a two-dimensional problem, all cross

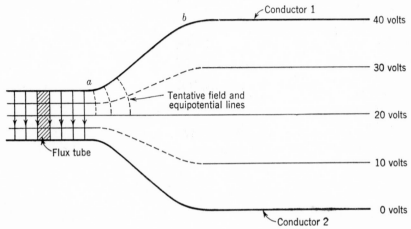

FIG. 2-23. Cross section of two sheet conductors with partially completed field map.

sections parallel to the page being the same. Therefore, the field and potential distribution everywhere between the sheets will be known if it can be found for a two-dimensional cross section such as shown in Fig. 2-23. Let the potential difference between the conductors be 40 volts, with the upper conductor positive and the lower conductor at zero potential. To the left of a and to the right of b the field is uniform so that equipotential surfaces 10 volts apart are equally spaced as indicated, the conductor surfaces being equipotentials at 0 and 40 volts. Between a and b the conductor spacing changes, and the equipotentials may be drawn tentatively as shown by the dashed lines.

The next step in the mapping procedure is to draw field lines from conductor 1 to conductor 2 in the uniform field region to the left of a with the spacing equal to that between the equipotentials. In this way the region is divided into squares. Each square is the end surface of a rectangular volume, or cell, of depth d into the page. A stack, or series,

[1] The side walls of a flux tube are field lines.

of squares bounded by the same field lines represents the side wall of a rectangular flux tube extending between the positive charge on one conductor to the negative charge on the other. The field map is next extended to the right by drawing *field lines as nearly normal to the equipotentials as possible*, with the field lines spaced so that the areas formed are as nearly square as possible. After one or two revisions of the tentative equipotentials between a and b and also of the field lines, it

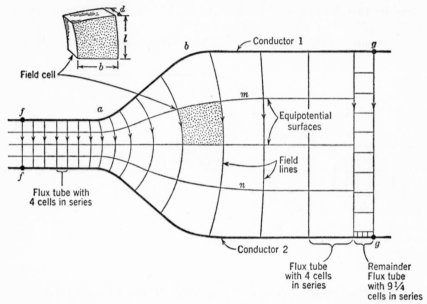

FIG. 2-24. Cross section of two sheet conductors with completed field map. A three-dimensional view of a field cell is also given.

should be possible to remap the region to the right of a so that field and equipotential lines are everywhere orthogonal and the areas between the lines are all *squares* or *curvilinear squares*.[1] The completed field map is shown in Fig. 2-24. The remainder tube at the right of the map is explained in the example on p. 86.

By a *curvilinear square* is meant *an area that tends to yield true squares as it is subdivided into smaller and smaller areas by successive halving of the equipotential interval and the flux per tube.* A partially subdivided curvilinear square is illustrated in Fig. 2-25.

A field map, such as shown in Fig. 2-24, divides the field into many squares each of which represents a side of a *field cell*. These field cells have a depth d (into the page) as suggested by the three-dimensional view

---

[1] A more accurate technique of field mapping involving circling of the squares is described in the Appendix.

of the typical field cell in Fig. 2-24.   The cell has a length l (parallel to
the field) and a width b.   The side walls of a field cell are the walls of a
flux tube (parallel to the field), while the top and bottom coincide with
equipotential surfaces.   As curvilinear cells are subdivided into smaller
cells, their end areas tend to become true squares.   The subdivided cells

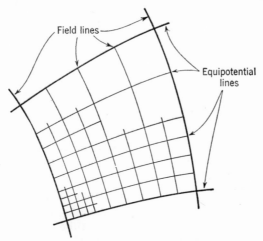

FIG. 2-25. Partially subdivided curvilinear square.

are always of depth d (into the page) the same as the larger cells.   Thus,
a *field cell*, or simply a *cell*, may be defined as a *curvilinear square volume.*
    If thin sheets of metal foil are applied to the equipotential surfaces of a
field cell, we have a *field cell capacitor.*   The capacitance C of a parallel-
plate capacitor is from (2-55)

$$C = \frac{\epsilon A}{l} \qquad (2\text{-}103)$$

where ϵ = permittivity of medium
  A = area of plates
  l = spacing of plates
Applying this relation to a field cell capacitor with a square end ($b = l$),
we have for the capacitance C_0 of the field cell

$$C_0 = \frac{\epsilon b d}{l} = \epsilon d \qquad (2\text{-}104)$$

Dividing by d, we obtain the capacitance per unit depth of a field cell as

$$\frac{C_0}{d} = \epsilon \qquad (2\text{-}105)$$

where ϵ = permittivity of medium (farads/meter).
    Thus, the significance of the value of ϵ is that it is the capacitance per

unit depth of a field cell capacitor.   For example, a field cell capacitor of unit depth in a medium of air (or vacuum) has a capacitance of 8.85 $\mu\mu$f. Such a capacitor is illustrated in Fig. 2-26.[1]

Any field cell can be subdivided into smaller square-ended cells with as many cells in parallel as in series.   Hence the capacitance† per unit depth of *any* field cell, large or small, exactly square or curvilinear is equal to ϵ.

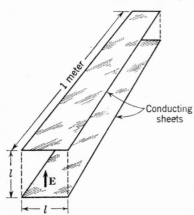

In a field map, such as in Fig. 2-24, most of the area is divided into "regular" cells with four in series for each flux tube.   These cells all have the same potential difference across them (10 volts).   Hence these cells may be defined as *cells of the same kind.*   The remaining area of the map consists of a fractional, or remainder, flux tube. This tube is also divided into cells. These cells are of two kinds, both different from those in the rest of the map.   One kind of cell in the remainder flux tube has about 4.3 volts across it and the other kind about 1 volt across it.   There are nine 4.3-volt cells and four 1-volt cells.

FIG. 2-26. Air-filled field-cell capacitor of unit depth having a capacitance of 8.85 $\mu\mu$f.   Volume between plates is $l \times l \times 1$ meter.

Any field cell has the same capacitance per unit depth.   Many additional properties are common to *field cells of the same kind.*   These cells of the same kind have the same potential difference across them.   In uniform fields the areas of the ends of those cells are the same, but in nonuniform fields the areas will not be the same.

Since the capacitance per unit depth of any cell of the same kind is the same, it follows that the electric flux through any cell of the same kind is the same $(Q/d = VC/d)$.   Thus, the 10-volt cells in Fig. 2-24 have a flux of 10ϵ coulombs per unit depth, while the 4.3- and 1-volt cells have 4.3ϵ and ϵ coulombs per unit depth, respectively.

Now the average flux density D at the equipotential surface of a field cell is given by

$$D = \frac{Q}{bd} = \rho_s \qquad \text{coulombs/meter}^2 \qquad (2\text{-}106)$$

[1] The capacitance of an isolated capacitor such as shown in Fig. 2-26 is somewhat greater than 8.85 $\mu\mu$f because of fringing of the field.   However, a field cell represents only a portion of a more extensive field, and its sides are parallel to the field (no fringing).

† It is understood that this capacitance is that which would be obtained if the *field cell* is made into a *field cell capacitor* by placing thin sheets of metal foil coincident with its equipotential surfaces (if no conductor is already present).

where Q = total charge on foil at equipotential surface of field cell (also
          equal to total flux ψ through cell) (coulombs)
    b = width of cell (meters)
    d = depth of cell (meters)
    ρ_s = average surface charge density on foil at equipotential surface
          (coulombs/meter^2)

Hence, the average flux density is inversely proportional to the field cell
or flux tube width.   Also the average surface charge density ρ_s at a conducting surface is inversely proportional to the width of the field cell or
flux tube at the surface.   For example, the spacing of conductors 1 and 2
to the right of b in Fig. 2-24 is four times that to the left of a; so in the
uniform field region to the left of a the surface charge density ρ_s is four
times the value of ρ_s in the uniform field region to the right of b.   The
surface charge density is even smaller than to the right of b in the region
of concave conductor curvature near b and somewhat larger than to the
left of a in the region of convex conductor curvature near a.

Since $E = D/\epsilon$, the field intensity is also inversely proportional to the
cell width, or length ($E = V/l$).   Furthermore, the energy $W(=\frac{1}{2}QV)$
stored in any cell of the same kind is the same.   It follows that the
average energy density w is inversely proportional to the area of the end
of the cell ($= bl$ for a square-ended cell).   For example, the energy
density in the uniform field region to the left of a in Fig. 2-24 is 16 times
the energy density in the uniform field region to the right of b.

To summarize, *the properties of an accurate electric field map*[1] *are as
follows:*

1. The capacitance of *any* field cell is the same.
2. The capacitance C_0 per unit depth of *any* field cell is equal to the
   permittivity ϵ of the medium.
3. The potential difference across any field cell of the same kind is the
   same.
4. The flux ψ through any field cell of the same kind is the same.
5. The flux ψ over any cross section of a flux tube is the same.
6. The average flux density D in any cell of the same kind is inversely
   proportional to the width of the cell or flux tube.
7. The average charge density ρ_s at the conducting boundary of any
   cell of the same kind is inversely proportional to the width of the
   cell or flux tube at the surface.
8. The average field intensity E in any cell of the same kind is
   inversely proportional to the cell width.
9. The energy stored in any cell of the same kind is the same.
10. The average energy density w in any cell of the same kind is

---

[1] In a single medium of uniform permittivity.

inversely proportional to the area of the end of the cell. (This is the area that appears in the field map.)

In order to test the accuracy of a field map, and hence the accuracy with which the above properties hold for a particular map, the curvilinear squares of the map can be further subdivided by halving the equipotential interval and halving the flux per tube as in Fig. 2-25. If the smaller regions so produced tend to become more nearly true squares, the field is accurately mapped. However, if the regions tend to become rectangles, the map is inaccurate and another attempt should be made. Often it is preferable to erase and begin again than to attempt to revise an inaccurate map. In field mapping an eraser is as important as a pencil.

Field and equipotential lines should intersect orthogonally. It is especially important that this rule be observed at all stages of making a field map. If this is done it is possible to determine what modifications are necessary to make all areas squares or curvilinear squares. However, if the intersections are not right angles, it may be very difficult to determine how to proceed in correcting the map. Additional details on field mapping techniques are given in the Appendix.

To illustrate the utility of graphical field mapping in solving a practical problem, consider the following example.

Example. Referring to Fig. 2-24, let the conductor separation at ff be 1 cm and at gg be 4 cm, and let the conductors have a depth (into the page) of 20 cm. If the conductors end at ff and gg and if fringing of the field is neglected, find the capacitance C of the resulting capacitor. The medium in the capacitor is air.

Solution. The method of solution will be to evaluate the series-parallel combination of capacitors formed by the individual cells.

Each cell has a capacitance

$$C_0 = \epsilon_0 d = 8.85 \times 0.2 = 1.77 \ \mu\mu f$$

The capacitance between the ends of each flux tube with 4 cells in series is then

$$\frac{1.77}{4} = 0.442 \mu\mu f$$

The capacitance between the ends of the remainder flux tube with 9.25 cells in series is

$$\frac{1.77}{9.25} = 0.191 \ \mu\mu f$$

There are fifteen 4-cell tubes and one remainder (9.25-cell) tube. Hence the total capacitance C between ff and gg is the sum of the capacitances of all the flux tubes, or

$$C = 15 \times 0.442 + 0.191 = 6.82 \ \mu\mu f$$

The above calculation is somewhat simplified if each cell is arbitrarily assigned a capacitance of unity. On this basis the total capacitance in arbitrary units is given by

$$\frac{15}{4} + \frac{1}{9.25} = 3.86 \text{ units}$$

and the total actual capacitance C is the product of this result and the actual capacitance of a cell, or

$$C = 3.86 \times (8.85 \times 0.2) = 6.82 \; \mu\mu\text{f}$$

Yet another method of calculation is to use the relation that the total capacitance C is given by

$$C = \frac{N}{n} C_0 \qquad (2\text{-}106a)$$

where N = number of cells (or flux tubes) in parallel
   n = number of cells in series
   C_0 = capacitance of one cell
and where all cells are of the same kind.   Thus in the above example, counting in terms of the 10-volt cells, we have

$$C = \frac{15.43}{4} \times 8.85 \times 0.2 = 6.82 \; \mu\mu\text{f}$$

Note that if the capacitance had been desired of a capacitor with conductors coinciding with the equipotentials m and n (Fig. 2-24) and of 20 cm depth, the cells in series would be reduced to two and the capacitance doubled.   In this way the capacitance of any conductor configuration conforming to the equipotential surfaces of a field map can be easily calculated.

2-28. 90° and 270° Corners.   As a further illustration of field mapping consider a long trough of two conducting sheets intersecting so as to form a 90° corner as shown in cross section in Fig. 2-27a.   The flux tubes (solid lines) and equipotential surfaces (dashed lines) are shown in the

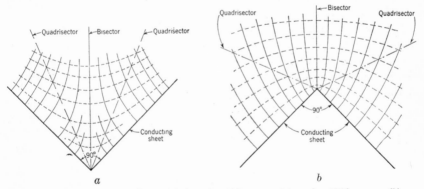

FIG. 2-27. Field maps in the vicinity of a 90° corner (a) and a 270° corner (b).

vicinity of the corner of the trough as produced by a region of positive charge at a large distance above.   The opposite situation of a long prism, or 270° corner, is illustrated in cross section by Fig. 2-27b.   If the corners are perfectly sharp, the flux density and field in the corner of Fig. 2-27a will be zero, while at the apex in Fig. 2-27b they will be infinite.   The large field or high-potential gradient near a sharp point will result in an electrical discharge to the point rather than to nearby conducting regions when the field is increased above the dielectric strength of the medium. This is the principle of the lightning rod.[1] Conversely, in a corner as in Fig. 2-27a the field is weak, and it is said that the region near the corner is shielded, at least partially, from the field above.

In mapping near corners, as in Fig. 2-27a, one can take advantage of the symmetry by drawing, as the first field line, the bisector of the corner. The field is symmetrical around this line so that it is necessary to construct a field map for only one octant, the other octant being a mirror image of the first in the bisector line. The lines that bisect the octants (or quadrisect the corner) are also lines of symmetry but with the difference that the equipotentials in one-half of the octant are mirrored as field lines in the other half, and vice versa. It is helpful to construct these quadrisectors temporarily while drawing the map in order to ensure symmetry. Quadrisectors are shown in both Figs. 2-27a and b (see also Appendix, Sec. A-2).

It is to be noted that in approaching the corners along the bisector lines **E** approaches zero in Fig. 2-27a, while **E** approaches infinity in Fig. 2-27b, it being assumed that both corners are perfectly sharp.

2-29. Divergence of the Flux Density D. In Sec. 1-19 Gauss's law is applied to surfaces enclosing finite volumes, and it is shown that the normal component of the flux density **D** integrated over a closed surface equals the electric charge enclosed. By an extension of this relation to surfaces enclosing infinitesimal volumes, we are led to a useful relation called *divergence*.

Let Δv be a small but finite volume. Assuming a uniform charge density throughout the volume, the charge ΔQ enclosed is the product of the volume charge density ρ and the volume Δv. By Gauss's law the charge enclosed is also equal to the integral of the normal component D_n of the flux density over the surface of the volume Δv. Thus,

$$\oint_s D_n \, ds = \Delta Q = \rho \, \Delta v \qquad (2\text{-}107)$$

and

$$\frac{\oint_s D_n \, ds}{\Delta v} = \rho \qquad (2\text{-}108)$$

If the charge density is not uniform throughout Δv, we may take the limit of (2-108) as Δv shrinks to zero, obtaining the charge density ρ at the point around which Δv collapses. The limit of (2-108) as Δv approaches

---

[1] If the corner is rounded, **E** is reduced. In general, to increase the breakdown voltage of high-voltage electrical equipment, the conductors are made with rounded edges of relatively large radius of curvature. Sharp edges are assiduously avoided.

zero is called the divergence of $\mathbf{D}$, written div $\mathbf{D}$ or $\mathbf{\nabla} \cdot \mathbf{D}$.   Hence

$$\lim_{\Delta v \to 0} \frac{\oint_s D_n \, ds}{\Delta v} = \text{div } \mathbf{D} = \rho \text{ coulombs/meter}^3 \qquad (2\text{-}109)$$

Whereas the integral of the normal component of $\mathbf{D}$ over a finite volume yields the *charge* enclosed, the divergence of $\mathbf{D}$ gives the *charge density at a point*.   If the charge is zero at a point, it follows that the charge density is zero and also that the divergence of $\mathbf{D}$ is zero at that point.   It is important to note that the divergence of $\mathbf{D}$ is a scalar point function.

Let us now discuss divergence in a more formal way, developing it as a differential expression.   A small volume $\Delta x \, \Delta y \, \Delta z = \Delta v$ is placed in an electric field with flux density $\mathbf{D}$, having components D_x, D_y, and D_z in the three coordinate directions as shown in Fig. 2-28.   The total flux

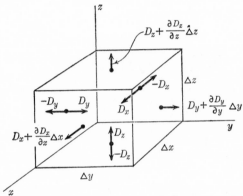

FIG. 2-28. Construction used to develop differential expression for divergence of $\mathbf{D}$.

density $\mathbf{D}$ is related to its components by

$$\mathbf{D} = \mathbf{i}D_x + \mathbf{j}D_y + \mathbf{k}D_z \qquad (2\text{-}110)$$

The normal outward component of $\mathbf{D}$ at the back face is $-D_x$ since the field is directed inward.   If the field changes between the back and front faces, the normal component of $\mathbf{D}$ at the front face can, by Taylor's theorem, be represented by an infinite series,

$$D_x + \frac{\partial D_x}{\partial x}\frac{\Delta x}{1} + \frac{\partial^2 D_x}{\partial x^2}\frac{\Delta x^2}{2!} + \frac{\partial^3 D_x}{\partial x^3}\frac{\Delta x^3}{3!} + \cdots \qquad (2\text{-}111)$$

When Δx is very small, the square and higher-order terms may be neglected, so that at the front face we have for the normal component of $\mathbf{D}$

$$D_x + \frac{\partial D_x}{\partial x}\Delta x \qquad (2\text{-}112)$$

In like manner the normal component of $\mathbf{D}$ at the left side face is $-D_y$ and at the right side face is

$$D_y + \frac{\partial D_y}{\partial y}\, \Delta y \tag{2-113}$$

Similarly at the bottom face it is $-D_z$ and at the top face is

$$D_z + \frac{\partial D_z}{\partial z}\, \Delta z \tag{2-114}$$

Now the outward flux of $\mathbf{D}$ over the back face is

$$-D_x\, \Delta y\, \Delta z \tag{2-115}$$

and over the front face is

$$\left(D_x + \frac{\partial D_x}{\partial x}\, \Delta x\right) \Delta y\, \Delta z \tag{2-116}$$

Adding up the outward flux of $\mathbf{D}$ over the entire volume, we obtain for the total flux

$$\begin{aligned}
\Delta\psi = &\left(-D_x + D_x + \frac{\partial D_x}{\partial x}\, \Delta x\right) \Delta y\, \Delta z \\
&+ \left(-D_y + D_y + \frac{\partial D_y}{\partial y}\, \Delta y\right) \Delta x\, \Delta z \\
&+ \left(-D_z + D_z + \frac{\partial D_z}{\partial z}\, \Delta z\right) \Delta x\, \Delta y \quad \text{(2-117)}
\end{aligned}$$

which simplifies to

$$\Delta\psi = \left(\frac{\partial D_x}{\partial x} + \frac{\partial D_y}{\partial y} + \frac{\partial D_z}{\partial z}\right) \Delta x\, \Delta y\, \Delta z \tag{2-118}$$

From Gauss's law we know that the total electric flux over the surface of the volume (or integral of the normal component of $\mathbf{D}$ over the surface of the volume) is equal to the charge enclosed. The charge enclosed is also equal to the integral of the charge density ρ over the volume. Therefore

$$\Delta\psi = \oint_s D_n\, ds = \left(\frac{\partial D_x}{\partial x} + \frac{\partial D_y}{\partial y} + \frac{\partial D_z}{\partial z}\right) \Delta v = \oint_v \rho\, dv \tag{2-119}$$

Dividing by Δv and taking the limit as Δv approaches zero, we obtain the divergence of $\mathbf{D}$. Thus,

$$\lim_{\Delta v \to 0} \frac{\oint_s D_n\, ds}{\Delta v} = \frac{\partial D_x}{\partial x} + \frac{\partial D_y}{\partial y} + \frac{\partial D_z}{\partial z} = \rho \tag{2-120}$$

and

$$\operatorname{div}\mathbf{D} = \frac{\partial D_x}{\partial x} + \frac{\partial D_y}{\partial y} + \frac{\partial D_z}{\partial z} = \rho \tag{2-121}$$

The center member of (2-121) is a differential relation for the divergence of **D** expressed in rectangular coordinates. The divergence of **D** can also be written as the scalar, or dot, product of the operator ∇ and **D**. That is,

$$\text{div } \mathbf{D} = \nabla \cdot \mathbf{D} \tag{2-122}$$

This may be more readily seen by expanding (2-122) into the expressions for ∇ as given in (1-42) and for **D** as given by (2-110). Then

$$\nabla \cdot \mathbf{D} = \underbrace{\left(\mathbf{i}\,\frac{\partial}{\partial x} + \mathbf{j}\,\frac{\partial}{\partial y} + \mathbf{k}\,\frac{\partial}{\partial z} \right)}_{\nabla} \cdot \underbrace{(\mathbf{i}D_x + \mathbf{j}D_y + \mathbf{k}D_z)}_{\mathbf{D}} \tag{2-123}$$

Performing the multiplication indicated in (2-123), nine dot-product terms are obtained as follows:

$$\nabla \cdot \mathbf{D} = \mathbf{i}\cdot\mathbf{i}\,\frac{\partial D_x}{\partial x} + \mathbf{j}\cdot\mathbf{i}\,\frac{\partial D_x}{\partial y} + \mathbf{k}\cdot\mathbf{i}\,\frac{\partial D_x}{\partial z} + \mathbf{i}\cdot\mathbf{j}\,\frac{\partial D_y}{\partial x} + \mathbf{j}\cdot\mathbf{j}\,\frac{\partial D_y}{\partial y}$$

$$+ \mathbf{k}\cdot\mathbf{j}\,\frac{\partial D_y}{\partial z} + \mathbf{i}\cdot\mathbf{k}\,\frac{\partial D_z}{\partial x} + \mathbf{j}\cdot\mathbf{k}\,\frac{\partial D_z}{\partial y} + \mathbf{k}\cdot\mathbf{k}\,\frac{\partial D_z}{\partial z} \tag{2-124}$$

The dot product of a unit vector on itself is unity since the angle between the vectors is zero. Hence

$$\mathbf{i}\cdot\mathbf{i} = ii\cos 0^\circ = 1$$

On the other hand, the dot product of a vector with another vector at right angles is zero since the angle between the vectors is 90°. Thus

$$\mathbf{i}\cdot\mathbf{j} = ij\cos 90^\circ = 0$$

Accordingly, six of the nine dot products in (2-124) vanish, but the three involving **i** · **i**, **j** · **j**, and **k** · **k** do not, and the product indicated by (2-123) becomes

$$\nabla \cdot \mathbf{D} = \frac{\partial D_x}{\partial x} + \frac{\partial D_y}{\partial y} + \frac{\partial D_z}{\partial z} \tag{2-125}$$

The dot product of the operator ∇ with a vector function is the divergence of the vector. The quantity ∇ · may be considered as a *divergence operator*. Thus the divergence operator applied to a vector function yields a scalar function. For example, ∇ · **D** (divergence of **D**) is given in rectangular coordinates by the right side of (2-125) and is a scalar, being equal to the charge density ρ.

If **D** is known everywhere, then taking the divergence of **D** enables us to find the sources (positive charge regions) and sinks (negative charge regions) responsible for the electric flux and, hence, for **D**. The sources or sinks of **D** are in those regions where div **D** is not zero

2-30. Maxwell's Divergence Equation. The relation of (2-120) or (2-121) that

$$\nabla \cdot \mathbf{D} = \rho \qquad (2\text{-}126)$$

was developed by an application of Gauss's law to an infinitesimal volume. It is the fundamental differential relation for static electric fields. This relation is one of a set of four differential relations known as Maxwell's equations. The other three equations are developed in later chapters.

In a region free from charge $\rho = 0$, and

$$\nabla \cdot \mathbf{D} = 0 \qquad (2\text{-}127)$$

2-31. Example of Divergence. As a simple nonelectrical example of divergence consider that a long hollow cylinder is filled with air under pressure. If the cover over one end of the cylinder is removed quickly,

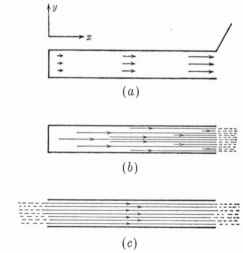

Fig. 2-29. The velocity $\mathbf{v}$ of air rushing from a tube has divergence (a and b). When air flows with uniform velocity through a tube open at both ends as at (c), the divergence of $\mathbf{v}$ is zero.

the air rushes out. It is apparent that the velocity of the air will be greatest near the open end of the cylinder as suggested by the arrows representing the velocity vector $\mathbf{v}$ in Fig. 2-29a. Suppose that the flow of air is free from turbulence so that $\mathbf{v}$ has only an x component. Let us assume that the velocity $\mathbf{v}$ in the cylinder is independent of y but is directly proportional to x as indicated by the following relation,

$$|\mathbf{v}| = v_x = Kx \qquad (2\text{-}128)$$

where K is a constant of proportionality. The question, what is the divergence of $\mathbf{v}$ in the cylinder, can be answered by applying the divergence operator to (2-128). This gives

$$\mathbf{\nabla} \cdot \mathbf{v} = \frac{\partial v_x}{\partial x} = K \qquad (2\text{-}129)$$

Hence, the divergence of $\mathbf{v}$ is equal to the constant K.

A velocity field may be represented graphically by lines showing the direction of $\mathbf{v}$ with the density of the lines indicating the magnitude of $\mathbf{v}$. The velocity field in the cylinder, when represented in this way, is illustrated in Fig. 2-29b. We note that $\mathbf{v}$ lines originate (that is, have their source) throughout the cylinder, the number increasing with x. This indicates that $\mathbf{v}$ increases as a function of x. This situation is concisely expressed by div $\mathbf{v} = K$. That is, the divergence of $\mathbf{v}$ has a constant value K throughout the cylinder, and this tells us that [assuming (2-128) to be correct] the source of the velocity field provided by the expanding air is uniformly distributed throughout the cylinder.

If, on the other hand, both ends of the cylinder were open and air passed through with the same velocity everywhere, v_x equals a constant and the divergence of $\mathbf{v}$ is zero in the cylinder.   In this case, the source of the velocity field must be somewhere external to the cylinder and the velocity field diagram would be as shown in Fig. 2-29c.

If more lines enter a small volume[1] than leave it or more leave it than enter, the field has divergence.   If the same number enter as leave the volume, the field has zero divergence.

2-32. Divergence Theorem.   From Gauss's law (1-59) we have

$$\oint_s \mathbf{D} \cdot d\mathbf{s} = \oint_v \rho \, dv \qquad (2\text{-}130)$$

where $\mathbf{D}$ is integrated over the surface s and ρ is integrated throughout the volume v enclosed by s.

From (2-126) let us introduce $\mathbf{\nabla} \cdot \mathbf{D}$ for ρ in (2-130), obtaining

$$\oint_s \mathbf{D} \cdot d\mathbf{s} = \oint_v \mathbf{\nabla} \cdot \mathbf{D} \, dv \qquad (2\text{-}131)$$

The relation stated in (2-131) is the *divergence theorem* as applied to the flux density $\mathbf{D}$, or Gauss's theorem (as distinguished from Gauss's law). This relation holds not only for $\mathbf{D}$ as in (2-131) but also for any vector function.   In words, the divergence theorem states that *the integral of the normal component of a vector function over a closed surface s equals the integral of the divergence of that vector throughout the volume v enclosed by the surface s.*

2-33. Divergence of D and P in a Capacitor.   As further illustrations of the significance of divergence let us consider the charged parallel-plate capacitor of Fig. 2-30. A slab of paraffin fills the space between the

[1] In the limit an infinitesimal volume.

plates except for the small air gaps.   True charge of surface density ρ_s is present on the surface of the plates.   Polarization charge of surface density ρ_{sp} is present on the surface of the paraffin.

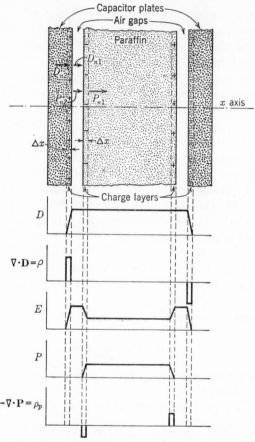

Fig. 2-30. Cross section through parallel-plate capacitor with paraffin slab showing the variation of the flux density D, charge density ρ, electric field E, polarization P, and polarization charge density ρ_p along the axis between the plates.   The thickness Δx of the charge layers is greatly exaggerated.

According to (3) of Table 2-2 the relation of **D** at a boundary is given by

$$D_{n1} - D_{n2} = \rho_s \qquad (2\text{-}132)$$

where (in this case) D_{n1} = flux density in air gap
$\qquad\qquad\qquad\quad D_{n2}$ = flux density in conducting plate = **0**
$\qquad\qquad\qquad\quad \rho_s$ = true surface charge density

Suppose that the surface charge is distributed *uniformly* throughout a thin layer of thickness Δx as suggested in Fig. 2-30.   Then the total change ΔD_n in flux density from one side of the layer to the other is given by

$$D_{n1} - D_{n2} = \Delta D_n = \Delta D_x \tag{2-133}$$

But when Δx is small,

$$\Delta D_x = \frac{dD_x}{dx} \Delta x \tag{2-134}$$

Therefore, (2-132) becomes

$$\frac{dD_x}{dx} = \frac{\rho_s}{\Delta x} = \rho \tag{2-135}$$

where ρ = volume charge density in the charge layer.
Since $\mathbf{D}$ has only an x component, dD_x/dx = div $\mathbf{D}$.   Thus,

$$\frac{dD_x}{dx} = \mathbf{\nabla} \cdot \mathbf{D} = \rho \tag{2-136}$$

Hence the change of $\mathbf{D}$ with distance (in the charge layer) equals the divergence of $\mathbf{D}$ and also the volume charge density.   It follows that if the charge layer is infinitesimally thin ($\Delta x \to 0$), then $\mathbf{\nabla} \cdot \mathbf{D}$ and ρ approach infinity.   However, it is more reasonable to consider that the charge layer is of small but finite thickness so that although $\mathbf{\nabla} \cdot \mathbf{D}$ and ρ may be large, they are not infinite.   The variation of $\mathbf{D}$ and $\mathbf{\nabla} \cdot \mathbf{D}$ along the x axis of the capacitor is shown graphically in Fig. 2-30.

At the paraffin surface $\mathbf{D}$ is constant, but both $\mathbf{E}$ and $\mathbf{P}$ change.   From (2-16)

$$\mathbf{P} = \mathbf{D} - \epsilon_0 \mathbf{E} \tag{2-137}$$

Now the change in polarization $\mathbf{P}$ is equal to the surface charge density ρ_{sp} due to polarization.   Thus

$$P_{n1} - P_{n2} = -\rho_{sp} \tag{2-138}$$

where P_{n1} = polarization in paraffin
P_{n2} = polarization in air gap $\simeq 0$
ρ_{sp} = polarization surface charge density

Assume that the polarization surface charge is uniformly distributed throughout a thin layer of thickness Δx at the paraffin surface as suggested in Fig. 2-30.   Then the total change ΔP_n in polarization from one side of the layer to the other is given by

$$P_{n1} - P_{n2} = \Delta P_n = \Delta P_x \tag{2-139}$$

But when Δx is small,

$$\Delta P_x = \frac{dP_x}{dx} \Delta x \tag{2-140}$$

Therefore, (2-138) becomes

$$\frac{dP_x}{dx} = -\frac{\rho_{sp}}{\Delta x} = -\rho_p \tag{2-141}$$

where ρ_p = volume density of polarization charge in the layer at the paraffin surface (coulombs/meter³). Polarization charge differs from true charge (ρ) in that it cannot be isolated, whereas true charge can. In this sense it is a fictitious charge. Since **P** has only an x component which is a function only of x, dP_x/dx = div **P**. Thus,

$$\frac{dP_x}{dx} = \mathbf{\nabla} \cdot \mathbf{P} = -\rho_p \tag{2-142}$$

Hence the change of **P** with distance (in the charge layer) equals the divergence of **P** and also the volume density ρ_p of polarization charge. The assumption of a polarization charge layer that is of small but finite thickness results in a value of $\mathbf{\nabla} \cdot \mathbf{P}$ that may be large but not infinite.

The divergence of **D** yields the sources of the **D** field (true charge), while the divergence of **P** yields the sources of the polarization field.

The variation of **E**, **P**, and $-\mathbf{\nabla} \cdot \mathbf{P}$ along the x axis of the capacitor is illustrated graphically in Fig. 2-30.

It may be shown (see Prob. 2-66) that the potential V_p due to a polarization distribution is given by

$$V_p = -\frac{1}{4\pi\epsilon_0} \int \frac{\mathbf{\nabla} \cdot \mathbf{P}}{r} \, dv \tag{2-143}$$

Thus, when both true charge and polarization are present and the distribution of both are fixed, the total potential V_T is

$$\begin{aligned} V_T &= \frac{1}{4\pi\epsilon_0} \int_v \frac{\rho}{r} \, dv - \frac{1}{4\pi\epsilon_0} \int_v \frac{\mathbf{\nabla} \cdot \mathbf{P}}{r} \, dv \\ &= \frac{1}{4\pi\epsilon_0} \int_v \frac{\rho - \mathbf{\nabla} \cdot \mathbf{P}}{r} \, dv \end{aligned} \tag{2-144}$$

where ρ = true charge volume density (coulombs/meter³)
  P = polarization (coulombs/meter²)
  ϵ_0 = permittivity of vacuum (8.85×10^{-12} farad/meter)
  r = distance from volume element containing charge or polarization to point at which V_T is to be calculated (meters)
The volume integration is taken over all regions containing charge or polarization.

The field intensity **E** is then

$$\mathbf{E} = -\mathbf{\nabla} V_T \tag{2-145}$$

Whereas (1-26) applies to a single homogeneous dielectric medium of permittivity ϵ, (2-144) is more general since it can be applied also to space with several different dielectric media, that is, a nonhomogeneous medium. For the case of a single homogeneous medium, (1-26) and (2-144) are equivalent.

2-34. The Laplacian Operator and Poisson's and Laplace's Equations.
As an extension of the divergence operator we are led to the Laplacian operator.   Equation (2-126) states that

$$\mathbf{\nabla} \cdot \mathbf{D} = \rho \tag{2-146}$$

Now $\mathbf{D} = \epsilon\mathbf{E}$, and also $\mathbf{E} = -\mathbf{\nabla}V$.   Thus,

$$\mathbf{D} = -\epsilon\,\mathbf{\nabla}V \tag{2-147}$$

Substituting $\mathbf{D}$ in (2-147) into (2-146), we have

$$\mathbf{\nabla} \cdot \mathbf{\nabla}V = -\frac{\rho}{\epsilon} \tag{2-148}$$

This is *Poisson's equation.*   The double operator (divergence of the gradient) is also written as $\mathbf{\nabla}^2$ (del squared) and is called the *Laplacian operator.*   Thus Poisson's equation can be written

$$\mathbf{\nabla}^2 V = -\frac{\rho}{\epsilon} \tag{2-149}[1]$$

If $\rho = 0$, (2-149) reduces to

$$\mathbf{\nabla}^2 V = 0 \tag{2-150}$$

which is known as *Laplace's equation.*
In rectangular coordinates

$$\mathbf{\nabla} = \mathbf{i}\,\frac{\partial}{\partial x} + \mathbf{j}\,\frac{\partial}{\partial y} + \mathbf{k}\,\frac{\partial}{\partial z} \tag{2-151}$$

Therefore, in rectangular coordinates

$$\mathbf{\nabla}^2 V = \mathbf{\nabla} \cdot \mathbf{\nabla}V = \left(\mathbf{i}\,\frac{\partial}{\partial x} + \mathbf{j}\,\frac{\partial}{\partial y} + \mathbf{k}\,\frac{\partial}{\partial z}\right)$$
$$\cdot \left(\mathbf{i}\,\frac{\partial V}{\partial x} + \mathbf{j}\,\frac{\partial V}{\partial y} + \mathbf{k}\,\frac{\partial V}{\partial z}\right) \tag{2-152}$$

Carrying out the dot product gives

$$\mathbf{\nabla}^2 V = \frac{\partial^2 V}{\partial x^2} + \frac{\partial^2 V}{\partial y^2} + \frac{\partial^2 V}{\partial z^2} \tag{2-153}$$

or the Laplacian operator alone in rectangular coordinates is given by

$$\mathbf{\nabla}^2 = \frac{\partial^2}{\partial x^2} + \frac{\partial^2}{\partial y^2} + \frac{\partial^2}{\partial z^2} \tag{2-154}$$

2-35. Isolated Conducting Sphere.   As mentioned earlier, the static potential distribution for any conductor configuration can be determined if a solution to Laplace's equation can be found which also satisfies the

[1] Equation (1-26) is a solution to this equation.

boundary conditions. For many conductor configurations it may be impractical to use this method. However, it is a basic method of approach of great importance in static problems. As an illustration, a very simple application of Laplace's equation will be considered in this section.

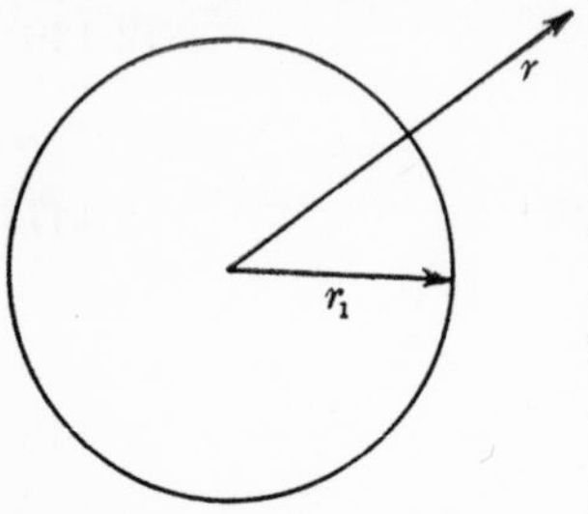

Consider an isolated metal sphere of radius r_1 with a uniformiy distributed charge Q as in Fig. 2-31. The sphere is situated in an unbounded dielectric medium of permittivity ϵ. This problem has been discussed previously but will be reconsidered here with the aid of Laplace's equation. The problem is to find a solution of Laplace's equation, $\nabla^2 V = 0$, for the space outside the sphere which gives a potential distribution satisfying the boundary conditions. These boundary conditions are that the potential V is constant over the sphere and is zero at infinity.

Fig. 2-31. Isolated conducting sphere of radius r_1.

Since the conductor has spherical symmetry, it will be advantageous to expand $\nabla^2 V$ in spherical coordinates (see Appendix). Thus

$$\nabla^2 V = \frac{1}{r^2}\frac{\partial}{\partial r}\left(r^2\frac{\partial V}{\partial r}\right) + \frac{1}{r^2\sin\theta}\frac{\partial}{\partial\theta}\left(\sin\theta\frac{\partial V}{\partial\theta}\right) + \frac{1}{r^2\sin^2\theta}\frac{\partial^2 V}{\partial\phi^2} \quad (2\text{-}155)$$

where the spherical coordinates r, θ, ϕ are as, for example, in Fig. 1-26. By virtue of the symmetry of the sphere, the potential V is independent of angle (θ and ϕ) and is a function only of r. Hence (2-155) reduces to

$$\nabla^2 V = \frac{1}{r^2}\frac{d}{dr}\left(r^2\frac{dV}{dr}\right) = \frac{d^2V}{dr^2} + \frac{2}{r}\frac{dV}{dr} = 0 \quad (2\text{-}156)$$

This is an ordinary second-order differential equation. It is the most general way of expressing the potential variation with respect to the radius r. However, to determine the particular distribution of our problem, we need to obtain a solution of the differential equation. In this case we may proceed as follows: Since $\nabla^2 V = 0$, it follows that

$$\frac{d}{dr}\left(r^2\frac{dV}{dr}\right)$$

in (2-156) must be zero, or that

$$r^2\frac{dV}{dr} = C_1 \quad (2\text{-}157)$$

where $C_1 =$ a constant. Then

$$dV = C_1 r^{-2}\, dr$$

Integrating,

$$V = C_1 \int r^{-2}\, dr = -\frac{C_1}{r} + C_2 \qquad (2\text{-}158)$$

where C_2 = another constant.   Both C_1 and C_2 must be determined from the boundary conditions.   Since $V = 0$ at infinity, $C_2 = 0$ and (2-158) therefore reduces to

$$V = -\frac{C_1}{r} \qquad (2\text{-}159)$$

By comparison with (1-11) the constant must have the value

$$C_1 = -\frac{Q}{4\pi\epsilon} \qquad (2\text{-}160)$$

so that the solution for V becomes

$$V = \frac{Q}{4\pi\epsilon r} \qquad (2\text{-}161)$$

where $r \geq r_1$.

It is to be noted that this is a three-dimensional problem so that the graphical approach of Sec. 2-27 is not applicable.

Further illustrations of Laplace's equation are given in Probs. 2-61 and 2-67.   Problem 2-61 illustrates the principles involved in applying Laplace's equation with a minimum of mathematics and is recommended as an exercise for the reader.

2-36. Dependence of Gauss's Law on the Inverse-square Law. Gauss's law as in (1-59) or (2-130) states that the surface integral of the normal component of the flux density **D** over a closed surface equals the charge enclosed.   If the enclosed charge is zero, the surface integral is zero.   This conclusion depends on the fact that **D** varies inversely as the *square* of the distance from a point charge (Coulomb's law).

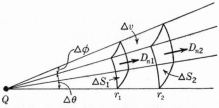

FIG. 2-32. The integral of the normal component of **D** over the surface of the volume Δv is zero because **D** varies inversely as the square of the distance r from the charge Q.

As an illustration consider a small volume Δv in the field of a point charge Q as in Fig. 2-32.   By Gauss's law the flux of **D** over the surface of the volume equals the charge enclosed.   This we should expect to be zero since all of the charge is at Q and none is in the volume.   However, let us carry through the calculation to verify this result.

The flux over the surface of the volume will be given entirely by the flux over the two curved surfaces ΔS_1 and ΔS_2.   The flux over the four flat faces of the volume is zero since D is parallel to them, and hence has no normal component.

The area of the surface ΔS_1 at a distance r_1 is given by

$$\Delta S_1 = r_1{}^2 \sin \theta \, \Delta\theta \, \Delta\phi \tag{2-162}$$

and the area of ΔS_2 at a distance r_2 by

$$\Delta S_2 = r_2{}^2 \sin \theta \, \Delta\theta \, \Delta\phi \tag{2-163}$$

The total flux $\Delta\psi$ over the surface of the volume is

$$\Delta\psi = -D_{n1} \, \Delta S_1 + D_{n2} \, \Delta S_2 \tag{2-164}$$

where D_{n1} = magnitude of normal component of D at r_1
$\qquad D_{n2}$ = same at r_2
Substituting (2-162) and (2-163) into (2-164) yields

$$\Delta\psi = (-D_{n1}r_1{}^2 + \dot{D}_{n2}r_2{}^2) \sin \theta \, \Delta\theta \, \Delta\phi \tag{2-165}$$

From (1-50) $D = Q/4\pi r^2$ so that

$$D_{n1} = \frac{Q}{4\pi r_1{}^2} \tag{2-166}$$

$$D_{n2} = \frac{Q}{4\pi r_2{}^2} \tag{2-167}$$

Substituting (2-166) and (2-167) into (2-165) gives

$$\Delta\psi = \left(-\frac{1}{r_1{}^2} r_1{}^2 + \frac{1}{r_2{}^2} r_2{}^2 \right) \frac{Q}{4\pi} \sin \theta \, \Delta\theta \, \Delta\phi \tag{2-168}$$

The expression in the parentheses of (2-168) is zero, so that $\Delta\psi = 0$ as anticipated.   However, if, instead of (1-50),

$$D = \frac{Q}{4\pi r^n} \tag{2-169}$$

where n is not equal to 2, then $\Delta\psi$ would not be zero.

This result is also readily deduced from the fact that the surfaces ΔS_1 and ΔS_2 subtend the same solid angle.   The flux over the two cross-sectional areas is equal in magnitude but opposite in sign only if D varies as $1/r^2$.

Since the net electric flux over any volume not enclosing electric charge is zero, it follows that the divergence of **D** is zero in all space free from charge.

Gravitational forces vary inversely as the square of the distance between masses, and Gauss's law also applies to these fields (see Prob. 1-23).

PROBLEMS

2-1. If two point charges $+Q$ and $-Q$ are attached to the ends of an axis 10 cm long, what is the dipole moment of the combination? $Q = 10^{-10}$ coulomb.

Ans.: 10^{-11} coulomb-meter.

2-2. Repeat Prob. 2-1 for the case where the axis is 1 cm long and $Q = 10^{-6}$ coulomb.

2-3. Confirm Eq. (2-7).

2-4. Four equal charges of magnitude Q and of sign indicated are arranged in air as shown in Fig. 2-33, forming a quadripole (double dipole). Show that at a large distance r (that is, $r \gg l$ and $r \gg s$) the potential due to this quadripole is

$$ V = \frac{Qls \sin \theta \cos \theta}{2\pi\epsilon_0 r^3} $$

where r = radial distance and θ = angle from axis to radial line (see Fig. 2-33).

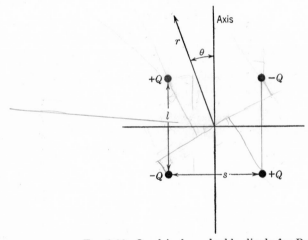

Fig. 2-33. Quadripole or double dipole for Prob. 2-4.

2-5. A dipole in a *uniform* field experiences no translational force. However, it does experience a torque tending to align the dipole axis with the field. Show that for a dipole of moment ql in a uniform field **E** this torque is $qlE \sin \theta$, where θ is the angle between the dipole axis and the field.

2-6. Show that $\mathbf{P} = \mathbf{D}(1 - 1/\epsilon_r)$.

2-7. A flat slab of dielectric ($\epsilon_r = 5$) is placed normal to a uniform field with a flux density $D = 1$ coulomb/meter^2. If the slab occupies a volume of 0.1 meter^3 and is uniformly polarized, what are (a) polarization in the slab; (b) total dipole moment of slab?   *Ans.:* (a) $P = 0.8$ coulomb/meter^2; (b) moment = 0.08 coulomb-meter.

2-8. A flat slab of sulfur ($\epsilon_r = 4$) is placed normal to a uniform field. If the polarization charge surface density ρ_{sp} on the slab surfaces is 0.5 coulomb/meter^2, what are:

a. Polarization in the slab
b. Flux density in the slab
c. Flux density outside of slab (in air)
d. Field intensity in slab
e. Field intensity outside slab (in air)

2-9. Two cavities are cut in a dielectric medium ($\epsilon_r = 5$) of large extent.   Cavity 1 (see Fig. 2-34) is a thin disc-shaped cavity with flat faces perpendicular to the direction

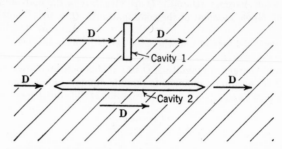

FIG. 2-34. Disc-shaped and needle-shaped cavities in dielectric for Prob. 2-9.

of **D** in the dielectric.   Cavity 2 is a long needle-shaped cavity with its axis parallel to **D**.   The cavities are filled with air.   Given that $D = 10^{-6}$ coulomb/meter^2.   What is the magnitude of the electric field intensity **E** (a) at the center of cavity 1; (b) at the center of cavity 2?

2-10. The electric field **E** in air above a block of paraffin ($\epsilon_r = 2.1$) is at an angle of 45° with respect to the plane surface of the block.   Find the angle between **E** and the surface in the paraffin.

2-11. An isolated positive point charge has a value of 10^{-10} coulomb.   What is the magnitude of **E** and **D** at a distance of 20 cm when the charge is located (a) in air; (b) in a large tank of glycerin ($\epsilon_r = 50$)?

Ans.: (a) $E = 22.5$ volts/meter, $D = 2 \times 10^{-10}$ coulomb/meter^2;
   (b) $E = 0.45$ volt/meter, $D = 2 \times 10^{-10}$ coulomb/meter^2.

2-12. What is the force on a positive point charge of 10^{-10} coulomb at a distance of 30 cm from a positive point charge of 10^{-10} coulomb when both charges are located (a) in air; (b) in glycerin ($\epsilon_r = 50$)?

2-13. What is the relative permittivity of an artificial dielectric consisting of a uniform cubical lattice with metal spheres 2 cm in diameter spaced uniformly 5 cm between centers in the x-, y-, and z-coordinate directions?

2-14. Show that the maximum possible relative permittivity of an artificial dielectric of metal spheres arranged in a uniform cubical lattice is 2.57.   It is assumed that there is no interaction between spheres and that they are almost touching.   The space between the spheres is air (or vacuum).

2-15. A capacitor of two large horizontal parallel plates has an internal separation d between plates.   A dielectric slab of relative permittivity ϵ_r and thickness a is placed on the lower plate of the capacitor.   Neglect edge effects.   If the potential difference between the capacitor plates is V, show that the electric field intensity E_1 in the dielectric is

$$E_1 = \frac{V}{\epsilon_r d - a(\epsilon_r - 1)}$$

and that the electric field intensity E_0 in the air space between the top of the dielectric slab and the upper capacitor plate is

$$E_0 = \epsilon_r E_1 = \frac{\epsilon_r V}{\epsilon_r d - a(\epsilon_r - 1)}$$

2-16. In Prob. 2-15 let the slab be of sulfur ($\epsilon_r = 4$), $V = 10$ volts, and $d = 10$ cm. Plot a graph of the potential as a function of the distance between plates for $a = 0, 1, 5, 9,$ and 10 cm.   Take the potential of the lower plate as zero.

2-17. What is the capacitance of a capacitor consisting of two parallel metal plates 30 by 30 cm separated by 5 mm in air?   Neglect fringing of the field.

2-18. What is the energy stored by the capacitor of Prob. 2-17 if the capacitor is charged to a potential difference of 500 volts?   What is the energy density?

2-19. What is the capacitance of the capacitor of Prob. 2-17 if a sheet of flint glass ($\epsilon_r = 10$) is introduced between the plates under the following conditions:

  a. Glass sheet 1 mm thick (remaining 4 mm between plates is air)
  b. Glass sheet 2.5 mm thick
  c. Glass sheet 4 mm thick
  d. Glass sheet 5 mm thick (glass entirely fills space between plates)

2-20. With flint glass ($\epsilon_r = 10$) completely filling the space between the plates of the capacitor of Prob. 2-17 what is the energy stored if the capacitor is charged to a potential difference of 500 volts?   What is the energy density?

2-21. What is the capacitance of the capacitor of Prob. 2-17 if a pressed sheet of powdered rutile (take $\epsilon_r = 114$) is introduced between the plates under the following conditions:

  a. Sheet 1 mm thick (remaining 4 mm between plates is air)
  b. Sheet 2.5 mm thick
  c. Sheet 4 mm thick
  d. Sheet 5 mm thick

2-22. Develop the relation for the capacitance of a parallel-plate capacitor from (2-52) by considering an area A of the double spherical-shell capacitor for the case where r_1 is very large and $r_2 - r_1 = l$ is small by comparison.

2-23. What is the maximum potential to which an isolated metal sphere can be charged if the sphere is 20 cm in diameter and situated in air?   Take the dielectric strength of air as 3×10^6 volts/meter.

2-24. What is the voltage between the plates of a parallel-plate air capacitor if it is first charged to 100 volts, the potential source disconnected, and the plates then separated to twice their original spacing?   What is the energy stored in the two cases?

2-25. A capacitor of two infinite parallel conducting plates spaced 10 cm apart is half filled with a dielectric medium ($\epsilon_r = 10$). The remaining space is air filled. The potential difference between the plates is 100 volts.   What is the magnitude of:

  a. **D** in air
  b. **D** in the dielectric
  c. **E** in air
  d. **E** in the dielectric

2-26. Develop Eq. (2-78) by applying Gauss's law to a cylindrical volume of length l and radius r concentric with the uniform line of charge.

2-27. A charge of 10^{-10} coulomb is distributed uniformly along a thin line 1 meter long.   The line is coincident with the y axis and its center is at the origin.   Calculate and plot the variation of the potential V along the x axis from the origin to a distance of 2 meters.

2-28. A thin line of charge of length $2a$ is coincident with the y axis with its center at the origin. The charge is uniformly distributed along the line and has a value of ρ_L coulombs/meter. Show that the potential V at any point (x, y) is given by

$$V = \frac{\rho_L}{4\pi\epsilon} \ln \left[\frac{\sqrt{x^2 + (y - a)^2} - (y - a)}{\sqrt{x^2 + (y + a)^2} - (y + a)} \right]$$

where ϵ is the permittivity of the medium.

2-29. What is the capacitance per kilometer of length of an air-filled coaxial line with an inner conductor diameter of 3 mm and an outer conductor with an inside diameter of 1 cm?

2-30. What is the capacitance of the coaxial line of Prob. 2-29 if the inner conductor is covered with rubber insulation ($\epsilon_r = 3$) to a diameter of 7 mm and the remainder of the space (to a diameter of 1 cm) filled with a dielectric of permittivity $\epsilon_r = 6$?

2-31. What is the energy stored per meter of length of the coaxial line of Prob. 2-29 if 500 volts is applied to the line? What is the energy stored under these conditions for the line of Prob. 2-30?

2-32. What is the capacitance per kilometer of length of a two-wire line of No. 8 gauge (B. & S.) wire (3.26 mm diameter) with a center-to-center spacing of the wires equal to $\frac{1}{2}$ meter? The wires are sufficiently high above ground that its effect may be neglected.

2-33. What is the capacitance per kilometer of length of a single-wire line of No. 8 gauge (B. & S.) wire spaced an average distance of 10 meters above the ground?

2-34. Show that the surface charge density ρ_s on a flat conducting ground plane due to an infinitely long positively charged thin wire parallel to the ground plane and at a height s above it, as in Fig. 2-22, is

$$\rho_s = \frac{-\rho_L s}{\pi(x^2 + s^2)}$$

where ρ_L is the charge per unit length along the wire and x is the distance along the plane, perpendicular to the wire direction and measured from the point on the plane nearest to the wire.

2-35. Draw a graph of the variation of ρ_s given in Prob. 2-34 as a function of x for distance of $10s$.

2-36. Show that the surface charge density ρ_s on a flat conducting ground plane due to a positive point charge Q at a distance s from the plane is

$$\rho_s = \frac{-Qs}{2\pi(x^2 + s^2)^{\frac{3}{2}}}$$

where x is the distance along the plane measured from the point on the plane nearest to the charge.

2-37. Draw a graph of the variation of ρ_s given in Prob. 2-36 as a function of x for a distance of $10s$.

2-38. The outer conductor of a coaxial line has an inner radius b and the inner conductor an outer radius a. If a voltage V is applied to the line, find the expression for the maximum field intensity $\mathbf{E}$ in the line. At what radius is $\mathbf{E}$ a maximum?

2-39. A high-voltage conductor is brought through a grounded metal panel by means of the double concentric capacitor bushing shown in Fig. 2-35. The space between the concentric metal sleeves is a dielectric ($\epsilon_r = 3$) with a working dielectric strength of 100 kv/cm. Neglect fringing. Also neglect the thickness of the sleeves.

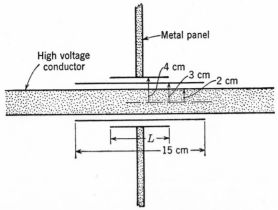

FIG. 2-35. Capacitor bushing for Prob. 2-39.

(a) What must be the length L of the outer sleeve in order to equalize the voltage across each dielectric space?   (b) What is the maximum working voltage of the bushing?

2-40. If the inner sleeve (15 cm long) of Prob. 2-39 were removed, what would be the maximum working voltage of the bushing?

2-41. If the number of concentric sleeves in the bushing of Prob. 2-39 were increased in number so that the spacing between sleeves becomes smaller, what is the ultimate working voltage of such a bushing?   Neglect the thickness of the sleeves, and assume that the sleeve lengths are adjusted so that the voltage across each dielectric space is the same.

2-42. Map the field of a coaxial line consisting of a circular inner conductor of diameter d symmetrically located inside of an outer conductor of square cross section with an inner side dimension of $3d$.   Note that because of symmetry only one octant (45° sector) needs to be mapped.

2-43. What is the capacitance per meter of length of the line of Prob. 2-42?

2-44. Map the field between two infinite parallel conductors of square cross section with adjacent sides separated by a distance equal to one side of the square.

2-45. What is the capacitance per meter of length of the two-conductor line of Prob. 2-44?

2-46. In Sec. 2-14 the energy-density relation $w = \frac{1}{2}\epsilon E^2$ is developed from the expression $\Delta W = \frac{1}{2}\Delta C \,\Delta V^2$.   Develop the same energy-density relation from the expression $\Delta W = \frac{1}{2}\Delta Q \,\Delta V$ by expressing ΔQ in terms of **D**.

2-47. A grid of parallel metal rods is introduced between the plates of a large parallel-plate air capacitor as shown in the cross section in Fig. 2-36.   Map the field in the capacitor with rods and without rods.   By what factor is the capacitance

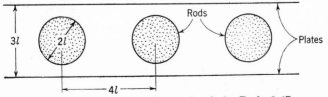

FIG. 2-36. Capacitor with metal rods for Prob. 2-47.

increased by the rods?   What is the effective permittivity of the space (with rods) between the capacitor plates?

2-48. A coaxial transmission line consists of an inner conductor of diameter d and a symmetrically situated outer conductor having the cross section of an equilateral triangle with a side length of $2.5d$.   Map the field in the line, and find the ratio of the surface charge density at the center point of a side of the outer conductor to the surface charge density at a point midway from the center to a corner.

2-49. What is the capacitance per meter for the line of Prob. 2-48 if it is filled with polystyrene?

2-50. A long, thick ribbonlike metal electrode is situated 1 cm from a large conducting ground plane as indicated in the cross section in Fig. 2-37.   If 1,000 volts is

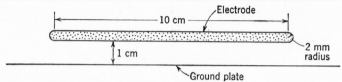

FIG. 2-37. Electrode near ground plane for Prob. 2-50.

applied between the electrode and ground plane, what is the *maximum* field intensity occurring at the electrode?

2-51. Map the field and equipotential lines for two point charges $+Q$ and $+\frac{1}{2}Q$ separated by 10 cm.   Let $Q = 10^{-10}$ coulomb.

2-52. Map the field and equipotential lines for two point charges $+Q$ and $-\frac{1}{2}Q$ separated by 10 cm.   Let $Q = 10^{-10}$ coulomb.

2-53. Map the field and equipotential lines of four equal charges of magnitude $Q = 10^{-10}$ coulomb situated at the corners of a square 10 cm on a side.   The charges at two diagonal corners are positive and at the other two diagonal corners are negative.

2-54. Construct a three-dimensional clay or plaster model of the potential distribution of the two equal positive charges of Fig. 2-17.   Make the elevation dimension of the model correspond to the potential V.   Since the potential at the charges is infinite, it is necessary to limit the maximum elevation at some arbitrary level such as 100 volts.

2-55. What is the divergence of the following vector functions:

$$\mathbf{A} = \mathbf{i}0 + \mathbf{j}\cos ax + \mathbf{k}0; \qquad \mathbf{B} = \mathbf{i}\cos ax + \mathbf{j}0 + \mathbf{k}0$$

Ans. $\nabla \cdot \mathbf{A} = 0; \nabla \cdot \mathbf{B} = -a \sin ax.$

2-56. A two-dimensional scalar distribution is expressed by the function

$$U = 1/(x^2 + y^2)$$

(*a*) What is the gradient of this function?   (*b*) What is the divergence of the gradient of this function?

2-57. What is the Laplacian of the scalar function $f = a + bx^2$?

2-58. What is the divergence of:

a. $\mathbf{A} = \mathbf{i}2x + \mathbf{j}3y^2 + \mathbf{k}4z^3$
b. $\mathbf{A} = \mathbf{i}4z^3 + \mathbf{j}2x + \mathbf{k}3y^2$
c. $\mathbf{A} = \mathbf{i}2x + \mathbf{j}4z^3 + \mathbf{k}3y^2$
d. $\mathbf{A} = \mathbf{i}2x + \mathbf{j}3y^2 + \mathbf{k}2x$

2-59. What is the divergence of the gravitational field at a point just below the surface of the ocean and at a point just above?

2-60. A parallel plate capacitor has a plate area of 1 meter^2 and a plate separation of 1 cm. The plates are maintained at a potential difference of 100 volts. Neglect fringing. Calculate the capacitance C, flux density $\mathbf{D}$, field intensity $\mathbf{E}$, polarization $\mathbf{P}$, and surface charge density ρ_s for the case where the dielectric medium between the plates is (a) air (take $\epsilon_r = 1$); (b) paraffin ($\epsilon_r = 2.1$); (c) rutile (take $\epsilon_r = 114$).

2-61. A large parallel-plate capacitor has its plates normal to the x axis. Plate 1 with a potential $V = 0$ is at the origin. Plate 2 with a potential $V = V_1$ is at $x = x_1$. Express Laplace's equation in rectangular coordinates, and solve it for this problem by the same procedure as used in Sec. 2-35, obtaining as the solution for the potential distribution, $V = (V_1/x_1)x$.

2-62. Make a field map for the case of an infinitely long positively charged cylindrical conductor of radius r and charge ρ_L per unit length. The conductor is parallel to an infinite ground plane. The center of the conductor is at a height h above the plane.

2-63. Compare the relative charge density on the ground plane as obtained from the field map of Prob. 2-62 with that calculated, using the relation given in Prob. 2-34.

2-64. Why can a solution by means of field mapping be obtained for the configuration of Prob. 2-34 but not for the configuration of Prob. 2-36?

2-65. Show that $\nabla \cdot \mathbf{P} = (\epsilon_r - 1)\epsilon_0 \nabla \cdot \mathbf{E}$.

2-66. Given that the potential V_p due to polarization is related to the polarization $\mathbf{P}$ by

$$V_p = -\frac{1}{4\pi\epsilon_0} \int \frac{\mathbf{P} \cdot \mathbf{a}_r}{r^2}\, dv$$

show that this can be reexpressed as

$$V_p = -\frac{1}{4\pi\epsilon_0} \int_v \frac{\nabla \cdot \mathbf{P}}{r}\, dv$$

2-67. Derive the expression for the electric field intensity everywhere due to a uniform spherical distribution of charge of density ρ and radius a by applying Poisson's equation or its equivalent div $\mathbf{D} = \rho$ both inside and outside the sphere. One constant is evaluated by matching solutions at the boundary of the sphere, and the other constant is evaluated by noting that $\mathbf{D}$ is zero at the center of the sphere.

2-68. A parallel-plate capacitor has a plate separation d. The capacitance with air only between the plates is C. When a slab of thickness t and relative permittivity ϵ_r is placed on one of the plates, the capacitance is C'. Show that

$$\frac{C'}{C} = \frac{\epsilon_r d}{t + \epsilon_r(d - t)}$$

Draw a graph of C'/C vs. t as based on this relation. Discuss the effect of the air gap $(d - t)$ on the capacitance.

CHAPTER 3

THE STEADY ELECTRIC CURRENT

3-1. Introduction. Electric charge in motion constitutes an *electric current*. In metallic conductors the charge is carried by electrons. One electron has a negative charge of 1.6×10^{-19} coulomb. In liquid conductors (electrolytes) the charge is carried by ions, both positive and negative.

In this chapter the important relations governing the behavior of steady electric currents in conductors are discussed. By "steady" current is meant one that is constant with time.[1] The fields associated with steady currents are also constant with time and, hence, are static fields. In Chaps. 1 and 2 the discussion is almost entirely concerned with static fields having all associated charges stationary, that is, with no currents present. In this chapter the fields are also static, but steady direct currents may be present.

3-2. Conductors and Insulators. In some metals, like silver and copper, there is but one electron in the outermost occupied shell of the atom. This electron is so loosely held that it migrates easily from atom to atom when an electric field is applied. As mentioned previously (Secs. 1-23 and 2-2) materials that permit such motion of electrons are called *conductors*. Silver and copper are examples of good conductors, their resistance to such electronic motion being relatively slight. Not all good conductors have only one electron in the outermost occupied shell. Some have two, and a few, such as aluminum, three. However, in all conductors these electrons are loosely bound and can migrate readily from atom to atom. Such electrons are often called *true* charges.

In other substances, however, the electrons may be so firmly held near their normal position that they cannot be liberated by the application of ordinary fields.[2] These materials are called *dielectrics* or *insulators*. Although a field applied to an insulator may produce no migration of charge, it can produce a polarization of the insulator, or dielectric (Sec. 2-3), that is, a displacement of the electrons with respect to their equi-

---

[1] Specifically, a *steady direct current* is meant. This should not be confused with a "steady-state" current, which may imply a time-changing current that repeats itself periodically.

[2] However, they may be torn off by mechanical means such as rubbing.

librium positions.   The charges of an insulator are often called *bound* or *polarization* charges in contrast to the free, or true, charges of a conducting material.

Certain other materials with properties intermediate between conductors and insulators are called *semiconductors*.   Under some conditions such a substance may act like an insulator but with the application of heat or sufficient field may become a fair conductor.

3-3. The Electric Current.   When an isolated conducting object is introduced into an electric field, charges migrate (currents flow) until a surface charge distribution has been built up that reduces the total field in the conductor to zero.   This was discussed in Sec. 1-23.   If, however, the conducting object is not isolated and the applied field is maintained, current will continue to flow in the conductor.

For example, consider an infinitely long conductor, such as a metal wire, in a uniform field **E** as in Fig. 3-1.   The field **E** in the conductor is not

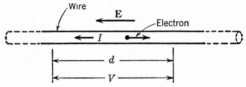

FIG. 3-1. Infinite conductor in uniform field.

zero if current is flowing.   Rather, **E** is the same inside and outside of the conductor.   This follows from the boundary relation (1) of Table 2-2 that the tangential component of the electric field is continuous across a boundary.   The field causes the electrons in the conductor to migrate parallel to the field.   Since the electrons are negatively charged, they move in a sense opposite to the field direction.   If there are n electrons per meter of length of the conductor and their average velocity is v meters per sec, then the total charge per second passing a fixed point on the wire is

$$nqv$$

where q = charge of each electron.   The electric current I in the wire is then defined as

$$I = -nqv \tag{3-1}$$

The electric current is, by definition, taken to be in the opposite direction to the electron motion.   Hence the negative sign in (3-1).   Electric current has the dimensions of charge per time, or in dimensional symbols Q/T.   The mksc unit of current is the ampere.   Thus,

$$\frac{\text{Coulombs}}{\text{Second}} = \text{amperes}$$

That is, charge flowing by a fixed point at the rate of 1 coulomb per sec constitutes a current of 1 amp.

3-4. Resistance and Ohm's Law. Referring to Fig. 3-1, it is found that at a constant temperature the potential difference V over a length d of the conductor is proportional to the current I. The constant of proportionality between V and I is called the resistance R of the length d of conductor. Thus

$$V = IR \qquad (3\text{-}2)$$

or

$$R = \frac{V}{I} \qquad (3\text{-}3)$$

or

$$I = \frac{V}{R} \qquad (3\text{-}4)$$

These relations are expressions of *Ohm's law*. In words, Ohm's law states that *the potential difference or voltage V between the ends of a conductor is equal to the product of its resistance R and the current I*.

Resistance has the dimensions

$$\frac{\text{Potential}}{\text{Current}}$$

or in dimensional symbols

$$\text{Resistance} = \frac{ML^2}{QT^2}\frac{T}{Q} = \frac{ML^2}{TQ^2}$$

The mksc unit of resistance is the ohm. Thus

$$\text{Ohms} = \frac{\text{volts}}{\text{ampere}}$$

That is, the resistance of a conductor is 1 ohm if a current of 1 amp flows when a potential difference of 1 volt is applied between the ends of the conductor.

3-5. Power Relations and Joule's Law. Referring again to Fig. 3-1, the potential difference or voltage V across the length d of the conductor is equal to the work per unit charge required to move a charge through the distance d. Multiplying by the current I (charge per unit time) yields the work per unit time or power P. Thus,

$$\frac{\text{Work}}{\text{Charge}} \times \frac{\text{charge}}{\text{time}} = \frac{\text{work}}{\text{time}} = \text{power}$$

or

$$P = VI \qquad (3\text{-}5)$$

This is the power dissipated in the length d of the conductor. The mksc unit of power is the watt.   Hence,

$$\text{Watts} = \text{volts} \times \text{amperes}$$

or in dimensional symbols

$$\text{Watts} = \frac{ML^2}{QT^2}\frac{Q}{T} = \frac{ML^2}{T^3}$$

Introducing the value of V from Ohm's law (3-2) into (3-5) yields

$$P = I^2R \tag{3-6}$$

According to (3-6) the work or energy dissipated per unit time in the conductor is given by the product of its resistance R and the square of the current I.   This energy appears as heat in the conductor.

The energy W dissipated in the conductor in a time T is then

$$W = PT = I^2RT \tag{3-7}$$

where W = energy (joules)

P = power (watts)

I = current (amp)

R = resistance (ohms)

T = time (sec)

This relation is known as *Joule's law*.   It is assumed in (3-7) that P is constant over the time T.   If it is not constant, I^2R is integrated over the time interval T.

3-6. The Electric Circuit.   The discussion in the preceding sections concerns an infinitely long conductor along which a field **E** is applied (Fig. 3-1).   Consider now a cylindrical conductor of finite length d as in Fig. 3-2a.   The conductor is in the uniform field **E** between two large conducting blocks of negligible resistance maintained at a constant potential difference V by a battery.   If the ends of the conductor were separated from the blocks by small insulating gaps, current would flow in the conductor only while a surface charge distribution was being built up that neutralizes the applied field.   However, with the conductor connected to the blocks as in Fig. 3-2a a neutralizing surface charge cannot be built up, and the total field in the conductor is equal to the applied field. This field is given by

$$E = \frac{V}{d} \tag{3-8}$$

As long as this field is maintained in the conductor, current flows that has a value

$$I = \frac{V}{R} = \frac{Ed}{R} \tag{3-9}$$

If the end blocks are removed and the battery connected as in Fig. 3-2b, the field is no longer uniform over the entire cylindrical conductor but becomes nonuniform near the ends of the conductor.   As a result the resistance R' between the terminals of the conductor is greater than the resistance R of the conductor when situated in the uniform field between the end blocks.   This effect is discussed in more detail in Sec. 3-16.   The current I' in the conductor connected as in Fig. 3-2b is then

$$I' = \frac{V}{R'} \tag{3-10}$$

Assuming that the resistance of the wires connecting the battery to the cylindrical conductor is negligible compared with R', the potential

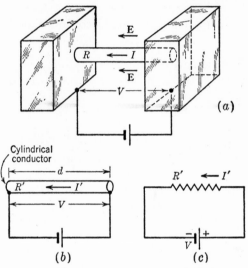

Fig. 3-2. Cylindrical conductor of length d between end blocks (a), modified arrangement (b) and schematic diagram (c).

difference V is equal to the voltage appearing across the terminals of the battery.   The arrangement of Fig. 3-2b may then be represented by the schematic diagram of Fig. 3-2c.

This is a diagram of a closed *electric circuit* of the most elementary form. It consists of a *resistor* of resistance R and a battery of voltage V.   It is to be noted that in the circuit representation no information is given explicitly concerning the field or its distribution, the circuit being described only in terms of the lumped quantities of resistance and voltage. It is, of course, true that the potential between two points is equal to the line integral of the field, but only the result of the integration is given and not the field distribution itself.

3-7. Resistivity and Conductivity.   The resistance of a conductor depends not only on the type of material of which the conductor is made

but also on its shape and size.   To facilitate comparisons between different types of substances, it is convenient to define a quantity which is
characteristic only of the substance.   The *resistivity* S is such a quantity.
The resistivity of a material is numerically equal to the resistance of a
homogeneous unit cube of the material with a uniform current distribution.   The current distribution is uniform if the field is uniform.   This
condition may be produced by clamping the cube between two heavy
blocks of negligible resistance as
in Fig. 3-3, with contact made
over the entire surface of both end
faces.   With a current I through
the cube, the resistivity S of the
material is given by $S = V/I$,
where V is the potential between
the blocks.

In mksc units, this measure-

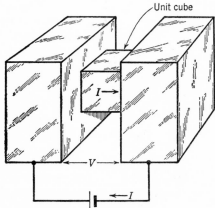

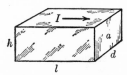

FIG. 3-3. Unit cube between end blocks.   FIG. 3-4. Block of conducting material.

ment is in ohms for a cube of material 1 meter on a side.   If two cubes
are placed in series between the blocks, the resistance measured is $2S$,
while if two cubes are placed in parallel, the resistance is $\frac{1}{2}S$.   It follows
that the resistance R of a rectangular block of length l and cross section
a, as in Fig. 3-4, is

$$R = \frac{Sl}{a} \tag{3-11}$$

where S = resistivity of block material.
Dimensionally (3-11) has the form

$$\text{Resistance} = \frac{\text{resistivity} \times \text{length}}{\text{area}}$$

from which we have

$$\text{Resistivity} = \frac{\text{resistance} \times \text{area}}{\text{length}} = \text{resistance} \times \text{length}$$

Thus, resistivity has the dimensions of resistance times length and in
mksc units is expressed in ohm-meters.   For the special case of a unit
cube (that is, a cubical block 1 meter on a side) the resistivity is numerically equal to the resistance.

The resistivity is a function of the temperature. In metallic conductors it varies nearly linearly with absolute temperature. Over a considerable temperature range from a reference or base temperature T_0 the resistivity S is given approximately by

$$S = S_0[1 + \alpha(T - T_0)] \qquad (3\text{-}12)$$

where T = temperature of material (°C)

T_0 = reference temperature (usually 20°C)

S_0 = resistivity at temperature T_0 (ohm-meters)

α = temperature coefficient of resistivity (numerical units/°C)

Example. For copper the resistivity S_0 at 20°C is 1.77×10^{-8} ohm-meter, and the corresponding coefficient $\alpha = 0.0038$ reciprocal degree. Find the resistivity at 30°C.
Solution. The resistivity S at a temperature T is

$$S = 1.77 \times 10^{-8}[1 + 0.0038(T - 20)] \qquad \text{ohm-meters}$$

At a temperature of 30°C,

$$S = 1.77 \times 10^{-8}[1 + 0.0038(10)] = 1.84 \times 10^{-8} \text{ ohm-meter}$$

This is an increase of nearly 4 per cent over the resistivity at 20°C.

The reciprocal of resistance R is *conductance* G. That is, $G = 1/R$. Since resistance is expressed in ohms, conductance is expressed in reciprocal ohms. A reciprocal ohm is called a *mho* (ohm spelled backward) so that conductance is given in mhos.

The reciprocal of resistivity S is *conductivity* σ. That is, $\sigma = 1/S$. Although the resistivity is convenient in certain applications, it is often more convenient to deal with its reciprocal, the conductivity, as, for example, where parallel circuits are involved. Since resistivity is expressed in ohm-meters, the conductivity is expressed in mhos per meter.

The resistance R of a rectangular block, as in Fig. 3-4, of material of conductivity σ is

$$R = \frac{l}{\sigma a} \qquad \text{ohms} \qquad (3\text{-}13)$$

or the conductance G of the block is

$$G = \frac{1}{R} = \frac{\sigma a}{l} \qquad \text{mhos} \qquad (3\text{-}14)$$

For the special case of a unit cube, the conductance is numerically equal to the conductivity.[1] Conversely, the conductivity of a material is numerically equal to the conductance of a homogeneous unit cube of the material with a uniform current distribution.

[1] Note that the unit cube is a special case of the square-sided block or cell ($h = l$). For such a cell, or block, of unit depth ($d = 1$ meter) the resistance R of the block is numerically equal to the resistivity S of the material, while the conductance G of the block is numerically equal to the conductivity σ of the material (see Sec. 3-16).

From (3-12) the conductivity of a metallic conductor as a function of the temperature is

$$\sigma = \frac{\sigma_0}{1 + \alpha(T - T_0)} \tag{3-15}$$

where σ_0 = conductivity at the temperature T_0 (mhos/meter)

α = same coefficient as in (3-12)

T = temperature (°C)

T_0 = reference temperature (°C)

3-8. Table of Conductivities. The conductivities σ_0 of some common materials are listed in Table 3-1 for a temperature of 20°C. By way of

TABLE 3-1
TABLE OF CONDUCTIVITIES

Substance	Type	Conductivity, mhos/meter
Quartz, fused	Insulator	10^{-17} approx
Ceresin wax	Insulator	10^{-17} approx
Sulfur	Insulator	10^{-15} approx
Mica	Insulator	10^{-15} approx
Paraffin	Insulator	10^{-15} approx
Rubber, hard	Insulator	10^{-15} approx
Glass	Insulator	10^{-12} approx
Bakelite	Insulator	10^{-9} approx
Distilled water	Insulator	10^{-4} approx
Sea water	Conductor	4 approx
Tellurium	Conductor	5×10^2 approx
Carbon	Conductor	3×10^4 approx
Graphite	Conductor	10^5 approx
Cast iron	Conductor	10^6 approx
Mercury	Conductor	10^6
Nichrome	Conductor	10^6
Constantan	Conductor	2×10^6
Silicon steel	Conductor	2×10^6
German silver	Conductor	3×10^6
Lead	Conductor	5×10^6
Tin	Conductor	9×10^6
Phosphor bronze	Conductor	10^7
Brass	Conductor	1.1×10^7
Zinc	Conductor	1.7×10^7
Tungsten	Conductor	1.8×10^7
Duralumin	Conductor	3×10^7
Aluminum, hard-drawn	Conductor	3.5×10^7
Gold	Conductor	4.1×10^7
Copper	Conductor	5.7×10^7
Silver	Conductor	6.1×10^7

contrast, both insulators and conductors are listed.[1] The materials are arranged in order of increasing conductivity.

3-9. Current Density and Ohm's Law at a Point. If the current is distributed uniformly throughout the cross section of a wire, then the *current density J* is uniform and is given by the total current I divided by the cross-sectional area of the wire. That is,

$$J = \frac{I}{a} \tag{3-16}$$

Current density has the dimensions of current per area and in mksc units is expressed in amperes per square meter.

If the current is not uniformly distributed, (3-16) gives the average current density. However, it is often of interest to consider the current density at a point. This is defined as the current ΔI through a small area Δs divided by Δs, with the limit of this ratio taken as Δs approaches zero.

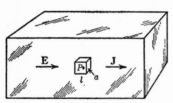

Hence, the current density at a point is given by

$$\mathbf{J} = \lim_{\Delta s \to 0} \frac{\Delta I}{\Delta s} \tag{3-17}$$

It is assumed that the surface Δs is normal to the current direction. By this definition the current density $\mathbf{J}$ is a vector point function having a magnitude equal to the current density at the point and the direction of the current at the point.

FIG. 3-5. Block of conducting material with small imaginary cell enclosing the point P.

Consider now a block of conducting material as indicated in Fig. 3-5. Let a small imaginary rectangular cell of length l and cross section a be constructed around a point P in the interior of the block with a normal to $\mathbf{J}$ as indicated. Then on applying Ohm's law (3-2) to this cell we have

$$V = IR \tag{3-18}$$

where V = potential difference between ends of cell. But $V = El$ and $I = Ja$; so

$$El = JaR \tag{3-19}$$

Solving for J, we have

$$J = \frac{l}{aR} E \tag{3-20}$$

[1] The large difference in conductivity between the insulators and conductors listed makes the distinction between the two on the basis of the conductivity alone relatively easy. The division in the table is made arbitrarily between 10^{-4} mho per meter for distilled water and 4 mhos per meter for sea water. This is for the case of a constant current or field. In the a-c or high-frequency situation, however, the conductivity alone is usually not sufficient, and it is often more useful to make a distinction as to whether a material behaves like a conductor or a dielectric, basing this arbitrarily on the ratio $\sigma/\omega\epsilon$, where $\omega = 2\pi \times$ (frequency). This is done in Chap. 11.

By making the cell enclosing P as small as we wish, this relation may be made to apply at the point P, and we may write

$$\boxed{\mathbf{J} = \sigma \mathbf{E}} \tag{3-21}$$

Equation (3-21) is *Ohm's law at a point* and relates the current density $\mathbf{J}$ at a point to the total field $\mathbf{E}$ at the point and the conductivity σ of the material. It is to be noted that $\mathbf{J}$ and $\mathbf{E}$ have the same direction (medium assumed to be isotropic).

3-10. Kirchhoff's Voltage Law and the Difference between Potential and EMF. Consider the simple electric circuit shown by the schematic diagram in Fig. 3-6. The circuit consists of a resistor R_0 and the battery. The current is I at all points in the circuit. At any point in the conducting material of the circuit we have from Ohm's law at a point (3-21) that

FIG. 3-6. Series circuit of battery and external resistance.

$$\frac{\mathbf{J}}{\sigma} = \mathbf{E} \tag{3-22}$$

where $\mathbf{E}$ = total field at the point.

In general the total field $\mathbf{E}$ may be due not only to static charges but also to other causes such as the chemical action in a battery. To indicate this explicitly, we may write

$$\mathbf{E} = \mathbf{E}_c + \mathbf{E}_e \tag{3-23}$$

where $\mathbf{E}_c$ = static electric field due to charges; the subscript c is to indicate explicitly that the field is due to *charges*

$\mathbf{E}_e$ = electric field generated by other causes as by a battery; the subscript e is to indicate explicitly that it is an *emf-producing* field (see below)

Whereas $\mathbf{E}_c$ is derivable as the gradient of a scalar potential due to charges ($\mathbf{E}_c = -\nabla V$), this is not the case for $\mathbf{E}_e$. Substituting (3-23) in (3-22), writing $\mathbf{J} = I/a$, where a is the cross-sectional area of the conductor, and noting the value of σ from (3-13),

$$\frac{\mathbf{J}}{\sigma} = I\frac{R}{l} = \mathbf{E}_c + \mathbf{E}_e \tag{3-24}$$

where R/l = resistance/unit length (ohms/meter). Equation (3-24) applies at any point in the circuit. Integrating (3-24) around the complete circuit,

$$\oint \mathbf{E}_c \cdot d\mathbf{l} + \oint \mathbf{E}_e \cdot d\mathbf{l} = I \oint \frac{R}{l}\, dl \tag{3-25}$$

From (1-19) the first term is zero, that is, the line integral of a lamellar field due to charges is zero around a closed circuit. However, the second term (in 3-25), involving the line integral of $\mathbf{E}_e$ around the circuit, is not zero but is equal to a voltage called the total *electromotive force*, or *emf*, $\mathcal{V}_T$ of the circuit.[1] The field $\mathbf{E}_e$ is produced, in the present example, by chemical action in the battery. If it were absent, no current would flow since an electric field $\mathbf{E}_c$ due to charges is not able to maintain a steady current. The right-hand side of (3-25) equals the total IR drop around the circuit. Hence (3-25) becomes

$$\mathcal{V}_T = IR_T \qquad (3\text{-}26)$$

where R_T = total resistance of circuit ($=R_0$ if internal resistance of battery is zero).

In general, for a closed circuit containing many resistors and sources of emf,

$$\sum \mathcal{V} = I \sum R \qquad (3\text{-}27)$$

This is *Kirchhoff's voltage law*. In words it states that *the algebraic sum of the emfs around a closed circuit equals the algebraic sum of the ohmic or IR drops around the circuit.*[2] As a corollary, Kirchhoff's voltage law states that the algebraic sum of all the emfs and IR drops around a closed circuit is zero. Kirchhoff's voltage law applies not only to an isolated electric circuit as in Fig. 3-6 but to any single mesh (closed path) of a network.

To distinguish emf from the scalar potential V, the symbol $\mathcal{V}$ (script V) is used for emf. Both V and $\mathcal{V}$ are expressed in volts so that either may be referred to as a voltage if one does not wish to make a distinction between potential and emf.

It is to be noted that the scalar potential V is equal to the line integral of the static field $\mathbf{E}_c$, while the emf $\mathcal{V}$ equals the line integral of $\mathbf{E}_e$. Thus, between two points a and b,[3]

$$V_{ab} = V_b - V_a = -\int_a^b \mathbf{E}_c \cdot d\mathbf{l} \qquad (3\text{-}28a)$$

and

$$\mathcal{V}_{ab} = \mathcal{V}_b - \mathcal{V}_a = \int_a^b \mathbf{E}_e \cdot d\mathbf{l} \qquad (3\text{-}28b)$$

In (3-28a) V_{ab} is independent of the path of integration between a and b, but $\mathcal{V}_{ab}$, in (3-28b), is not.

[1] Emf is also called *electromotance*.

[2] In time-varying situations, where the circuit dimensions are small compared with the wavelength, Kirchhoff's law is modified to: The algebraic sum of the *instantaneous* emfs around a closed circuit equals the algebraic sum of the *instantaneous* ohmic drops around the circuit.

[3] An open-circuited battery (no current flowing) has a terminal potential difference V equal to its emf $\mathcal{V}$. The potential V is as given by (3-28a). As explained in the examples that follow, $\mathbf{E}_c$ and $\mathbf{E}_e$ have opposite directions in the battery. Therefore, in order that $V_{ab} = \mathcal{V}_{ab}$ for an open-circuited battery, (3-28b) has no negative sign.

For closed paths

$$\oint \mathbf{E}_c \cdot d\mathbf{l} = 0 \tag{3-28c}$$

and

$$\oint \mathbf{E}_e \cdot d\mathbf{l} = \mho_T \tag{3-28d}$$

where $\mho_T = $ total emf around the circuit.

Referring again to (3-23) and (3-25), it is to be noted further that since $\oint \mathbf{E}_c \cdot d\mathbf{l} = 0$ the line integral of the total field $\mathbf{E}$ around a *closed circuit* equals the line integral of $\mathbf{E}_e$ around the same closed circuit. This, in turn, equals the total emf of the circuit. That is,

$$\oint \mathbf{E} \cdot d\mathbf{l} = \oint \mathbf{E}_e \cdot d\mathbf{l} = \mho_T \tag{3-29}$$

The difference between potential and emf is explained further in the following examples illustrating applications of Kirchhoff's voltage law.

Example 1. Let the circuit of Fig. 3-6 be redrawn as in Fig. 3-7a. The battery has an internal resistance R_1, and it will be convenient, in this example, to assume that the field $\mathbf{E}_e$ in the battery is uniform between the terminals (c and d). The point

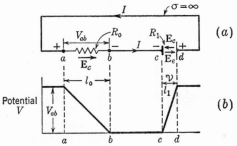

Fig. 3-7. Series circuit of battery and external resistance (a) with graph showing variation of potential around circuit (b).

b (or c) is taken arbitrarily to be at zero potential. The resistor has a uniform resistance R_0, and the wires connecting the resistor and the battery are assumed to have infinite conductivity ($\sigma = \infty$). Hence, in the wire, $\mathbf{E}_c = 0$. The field $\mathbf{E}_e$ has a value only in the battery, being zero elsewhere. Let the problem be to find the variation of the potential V around the circuit.

Solution. By Kirchhoff's voltage law the sum of the emfs around the circuit equals the sum of the IR drops. Thus

$$\mho = IR_0 + IR_1 \tag{3-30}$$

or

$$I = \frac{\mho}{R_0 + R_1} \tag{3-31}$$

In the resistor $\mathbf{E}_e = 0$, but $\mathbf{E}_c$ has a value (as discussed in connection with Fig. 3-2). Applying Ohm's law (3-21) in the resistor (between a and b), we have

$$\mathbf{E}_c = \frac{\mathbf{J}}{\sigma_0} = \mathbf{I}\frac{R_0}{l_0} \tag{3-32}$$

where $\sigma_0 = $ conductivity of resistor material (assumed uniform)
$l_0 = $ distance from a to b

Integrating (3-32) from a to b yields

$$\int_a^b \mathbf{E}_c \cdot d\mathbf{l} = I \frac{R_0}{l_0} \int_a^b dl \qquad (3\text{-}33)$$

or

$$V_{ab} = -IR_0 \qquad (3\text{-}34)$$

where V_{ab} = potential difference between a and b. Since point a is connected to d and b to c with infinitely conducting wires, $V_{cd} = -V_{ab}$, where V_{cd} is the potential difference appearing across the terminals of the battery. Therefore, from (3-34) and (3-30) we have

$$\mathcal{V} = V_{cd} + IR_1 \qquad (3\text{-}35)$$

or

$$V_{cd} = \mathcal{V} - IR_1 \qquad (3\text{-}36)$$

According to (3-36) the potential difference appearing between the terminals of the battery is equal to the emf $\mathcal{V}$ of the battery minus the drop IR_1 due to the internal resistance of the battery. Assuming that $\mathbf{E}_c$ is uniform in the battery, the variation of the potential V around the circuit is as indicated in Fig. 3-7b.

To recapitulate, there is a static electric field $\mathbf{E}_c$ in the resistor such as is discussed in connection with Fig. 3-2. Integrating $\mathbf{E}_c$ across the resistor yields the potential difference V_{ab}. Likewise in the battery there is a static field $\mathbf{E}_c$ due to the charges on the electrodes. Assuming that $\mathbf{E}_c$ is uniform inside the battery, we have on integrating $\mathbf{E}_c$ between c and d

$$\int_c^d \mathbf{E}_c \cdot d\mathbf{l} = E_c l_1 = V_{cd} \qquad (3\text{-}37)$$

There is also the field $\mathbf{E}_e$ in the battery, which has the opposite direction to $\mathbf{E}_c$. Assuming that $\mathbf{E}_e$ is uniform, we have on integrating $\mathbf{E}_e$ from c to d the emf $\mathcal{V}$. That is,

$$\int_c^d \mathbf{E}_e \cdot d\mathbf{l} = E_e l_1 = \mathcal{V} \qquad (3\text{-}38)$$

Introducing (3-37) and (3-38) into (3-36), we find that

$$E_e = E_c + I \frac{R_1}{l_1} \qquad (3\text{-}39)$$

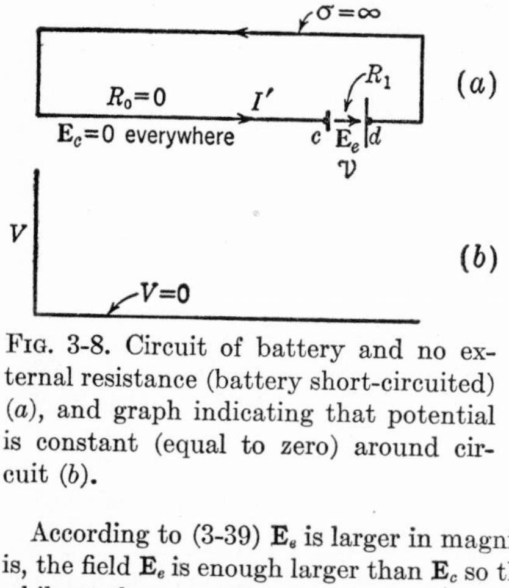

Fig. 3-8. Circuit of battery and no external resistance (battery short-circuited) (a), and graph indicating that potential is constant (equal to zero) around circuit (b).

According to (3-39) $\mathbf{E}_e$ is larger in magnitude than $\mathbf{E}_c$ by an amount IR_1/l_1. That is, the field $\mathbf{E}_e$ is enough larger than $\mathbf{E}_c$ so that it can move a positive charge *against* $\mathbf{E}_c$ while at the same time overcoming the internal resistance of the battery. In overcoming $\mathbf{E}_c$ the battery does work on the charge and hence delivers energy into the circuit. In the resistor (R_0) the charge moves with $\mathbf{E}_c$ and gives up energy which appears as heat in the resistor.

Example 2. Let the external resistor R_0 of Fig. 3-7a be removed and the battery short-circuited as in Fig. 3-8a. Find the variation of the potential V around the circuit. It is again assumed that $\mathbf{E}_e$ in the battery is uniform and constant.

Solution. According to Kirchhoff's voltage law we have

$$\mathcal{V} = I'R_1 \qquad (3\text{-}40)$$

where I' = current flowing in battery

R_1 = internal resistance of battery

This current is larger than the current I with R_0 connected. Since the terminals c and d of the battery are at the same potential, the field $\mathbf{E}_c$ in the battery is zero. Also, since there is no external resistor, $\mathbf{E}_c$ is zero everywhere. However, $\mathbf{E}_e$ in the battery is the same as before, and integrating it from c to d (or all the way around the circuit) yields the emf $\mathcal{V}$. Since $\mathbf{E}_c = 0$ everywhere, the potential V is constant (equal to zero) around the entire circuit as suggested by Fig. 3-8b. There is an emf in this circuit, but $V = 0$ everywhere.

It is instructive to compare the electrical circuits of the above examples with the analogous hydraulic systems. Thus, a hydraulic system analogous to the circuit of Example 1 (Fig. 3-7) is shown in Fig. 3-9a. Between

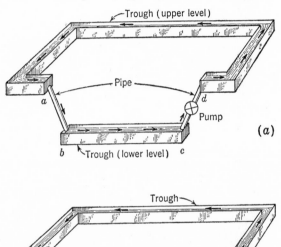

Fig. 3-9. Hydraulic analogue for electric circuit of Fig. 3-7 is shown at (a), and hydraulic analogue for electric circuit of Fig. 3-8 is shown at (b).

b and c there is an open horizontal trough at what may be called a lower level, corresponding to the ground potential in Fig. 3-7. Between c and d there is a pump which raises the water or other liquid against the gravitational field in the same manner as the battery in Fig. 3-7 raises positive charge against the static electric field $\mathbf{E}_c$. Thus, the water in the upper trough has a higher potential energy than the water in the lower trough in the same way as the charge in the wire between d and a in the electric circuit of Fig. 3-7 is at a higher potential than the charge in the wire from b to c. From d to a the water moves in a horizontal frictionless trough at an upper level corresponding to the perfectly conducting wire between these points in Fig. 3-7. From a to b the water falls through a pipe to the lower level and in so doing gives up the energy it acquired in being pumped to the upper level. The pipe offers resistance to the flow of water, and the energy given up by the water appears as heat. This energy is analogous to that appearing as heat in the resistor of Fig. 3-7 owing to charge falling in potential from a to b. In this analogy the pump does work, raising the water against the gravitational field in the same manner as the chemical action in the battery does work per unit charge (against the electrostatic field E_e and internal resistance R_i) equal to the emf of the battery.

A hydraulic analogue to the circuit of Example 2 (Fig. 3-8) is shown in Fig. 3-9b. Here the entire circuit is at the same level. The trough is assumed to be frictionless, so that the water has the same potential energy at all points of the system in the same manner that $V = 0$ in Fig. 3-8. The pump does work equal to that required to move the water from c to d against the friction of the pipe in the same manner as the battery in Fig. 3-8 does work per unit charge (against the internal resistance) equal to the emf of the battery.

In a single-cell battery with two electrodes the field E_e is largely confined to a thin layer at the surface between the electrode and the electrolyte and is zero in the electrolyte between the two electrodes. Thus, the potential variation assumed in the preceding examples is not representative of an actual two-electrode cell although it could be approached if each battery consists of a large number of cells of small emf connected in series between c and d in Figs. 3-7 and 3-8.

A picture somewhat closer to the actual situation in a two-electrode cell is portrayed in Fig. 3-10. Three conditions are shown. At (a) the battery is open-circuited ($I = 0$). At (b) the battery is connected across a large resistance (I small). At (c) the battery is short-circuited (I a maximum).[1] In each section of Fig. 3-10 the cell is shown in the upper part of the figure with the potential variation across the cell directly below it. For clarity the layers where E_e is not zero are shown with appreciable thickness, and for convenience the emf at both layers is taken to be of the same magnitude and sign. It is further assumed that the electrolyte and also the layers containing E_e have a uniform resistivity. Since, the layers containing E_e are thin, the IR drop is considered, for convenience, to be confined to the electrolyte region (see Figs. 3-10a and b).

It is to be noted that if the elements of a closed circuit containing emfs are separate from those containing resistance, the relation of (1-19)

$$\oint E_c \cdot dl = 0 \qquad (3\text{-}41)$$

gives the same result as Kirchhoff's voltage law. Thus, according to (3-41) the sum of the potential rises and potential drops around a closed circuit is zero. This version of Kirchhoff's voltage law is often convenient, but it is not always applicable. For instance, it is not applicable

[1] The emf of the cell is considered to be a constant and independent of the current.

where $E_c = 0$ (as in Example 2) unless the sources of the emfs and the resistances are separated by assuming an equivalent circuit. For example, a source of emf $\mathcal{U}$ with internal resistance R_0 may, by Thévenin's theorem, be considered equivalent to two elements in series, one of emf $\mathcal{U}$ and zero internal resistance and the other of resistance R_0 and zero emf.

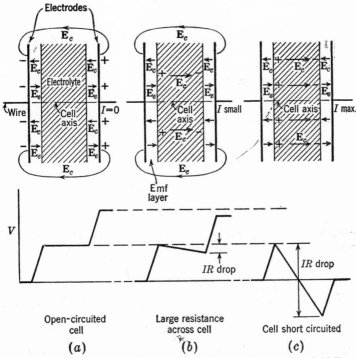

FIG. 3-10. Two electrode cell showing regions where emf-producing field E_e and field E_c due to charges are present under three conditions of cell operation. In the lower half of the figure the idealized potential variation is shown as a function of position along the cell axis for the three conditions.

Example 3. Consider the closed circuit, or mesh, shown in Fig. 3-11, which is a part of a more complex network, as suggested. Apply Kirchhoff's voltage law to this mesh.

Solution. Let us *assume* that the current in the circuit flows clockwise, the currents in each leg being as indicated. The direction assumed is arbitrary. For example, if I_1 actually flows opposite to the direction shown, it will be found to be negative. A priori the actual direction is not known so that one must be *assumed*. Starting at the point a, let us proceed toward b. Thus, traversing R_1 in the same direction as the current, we experience a potential drop equal to I_1R_1. In crossing the battery we encounter a potential rise equal to the emf $\mathcal{U}_1$. In this case the battery is assumed to have zero internal resistance, or else its resistance is combined in R_1. Applying Kirchhoff's voltage law in this way around the entire closed circuit, we obtain

$$-I_1R_1 + \mathcal{U}_1 - I_2R_2 - I_3R_3 - \mathcal{U}_3 = 0 \qquad (3\text{-}42)$$

or

$$\mathcal{V}_1 - \mathcal{V}_3 = I_1 R_1 + I_2 R_2 + I_3 R_3 \qquad (3\text{-}43)$$

If $\mathcal{V}_1$, $\mathcal{V}_3$, R_1, R_2, and R_3 are known, we need two more independent equations to find the three currents I_1, I_2, and I_3. That is, we need to know more about the adjoining circuits in order to find these currents.

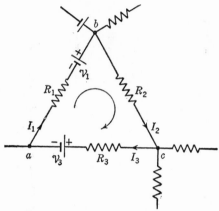

Fig. 3-11. Closed circuit, or mesh.

As a variation of the above problem, suppose that we have an isolated series circuit consisting of the circuit around the closed path $abca$ in Fig. 3-11 with all adjoining circuits disconnected. Then

$$I_1 = I_2 = I_3 \qquad (3\text{-}44)$$

Hence, if $\mathcal{V}_1$, $\mathcal{V}_3$, R_1, R_2, and R_3 are known, we can find the current from the relation

$$I_1 = \frac{\mathcal{V}_1 - \mathcal{V}_3}{R_1 + R_2 + R_3} \qquad (3\text{-}45)$$

If $\mathcal{V}_1 > \mathcal{V}_3$, the current flows clockwise as assumed. However, if $\mathcal{V}_3 > \mathcal{V}_1$, the current is negative, that is, it flows counterclockwise.

3-11. Tubes of Current. In Chap. 1 we discussed tubes of flux. Let us now consider an analogous concept, namely, that of tubes of current. A tapered section of a long conductor is shown in Fig. 3-12a. Let all the space in the conductor be filled with current tubes. Each tube is every-

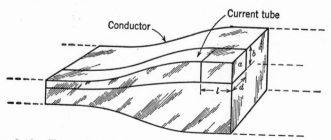

Fig. 3-12a. Tapered section of a long conductor showing current tube

where parallel to the current direction and hence, from the relation $J = \sigma E$ of (3-21), is also parallel to the electric field. Since no current passes through the wall of a current tube, the total current I_θ through any cross section of a tube is a constant. Thus

$$I_0 = \iint_a J \cdot d\mathbf{s} = \text{constant} \qquad (3\text{-}46)$$

where J = current density (amp/meter^2)
a = cross section of tube (over which J is integrated) (meters^2)
If J is constant over the cross section and normal to it, then

$$I_0 = Ja \qquad (3\text{-}47)$$

or referring to the current tube of rectangular cross section in Fig. 3-12a,

$$I_0 = Jbd \qquad (3\text{-}48)$$

where b = thickness of tube (meters)
d = depth or width of tube (meters)
If all of the conductor is divided up into current tubes, each with the same current I_0, then the total current I through the conductor is

$$I = I_0 n \qquad (3\text{-}49)$$

where n = number of current tubes.

Surfaces normal to the direction of the current (or field) are equipotential surfaces. The potential difference V between two equipotential surfaces separated by a distance l is by Ohm's law equal to the current I_0 in a current tube times the resistance R of a section of tube of length l. Thus,

$$V = I_0 R \qquad (3\text{-}50a)$$

If the current density is uniform (field uniform), the resistance R is, from (3-13), given by

$$R = \frac{l}{\sigma a} \quad \text{ohms} \qquad (3\text{-}50b)$$

where l = length of tube section (meters)
σ = conductivity of conducting medium (mhos/meter)
a = cross-sectional area of tube (meters^2)

3-12. Kirchhoff's Current Law. Whereas flux tubes in a static electric field begin and end on electric charge and hence are *discontinuous*, the tubes of a steady current form closed circuits on themselves and hence are *continuous*. To describe this continuous nature of steady currents, it is said that the current is *solenoidal*. That is, it has no sources or sinks (ending places) as do the flux tubes, which start and end on electric charges in a static electric field. As a consequence as much current must flow into a volume as leaves it. Thus, in general, the integral of the normal component of the current density **J** over a closed surface s must equal zero, or

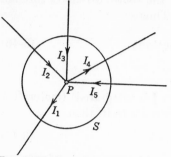

$$\oint_s \mathbf{J} \cdot d\mathbf{s} = 0 \qquad (3\text{-}51)$$

This relation is for steady currents and applies to any volume. For example, the volume may be entirely inside of a conducting medium, or it may be only partially filled with conductors. The conductors may form a network inside the volume, or they may meet at a point. As an illustration of this latter case, the surface S in Fig. 3-12b encloses a volume

Fig. 3-12b. Junction point of several conductors.

that contains five conductors meeting at a junction point P. Taking the current flowing away from the junction as positive and the current flowing toward the junction as negative, we have from (3-51) that

$$I_1 - I_2 - I_3 + I_4 - I_5 = 0 \qquad (3\text{-}52)$$

In other words, *the algebraic sum of the currents at a junction is zero*. This is *Kirchhoff's current law*, which may be expressed in general by the relation

$$\Sigma I = 0 \qquad (3\text{-}53)$$

3-13. Divergence of J and Continuity Relations for Current. Consider the small volume element Δv shown in Fig. 3-13 located inside of a conducting medium. The current density **J** is a vector having the direction

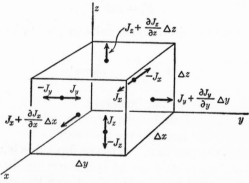

Fig. 3-13. Construction used to develop differential expression for divergence of **J**.

of the current flow. In general, it has three rectangular components that vary with position as indicated in Fig. 3-13.[1] The product of the current

[1] The development here is formally the same as in Sec. 2-29.

density and the area of a face of the volume element yields the current passing through the face. Current flowing out of the volume is taken as positive and current flowing in as negative. The integral of the normal component of $\mathbf{J}$ over the surface of the volume is equal to the sum of the outward currents for the six faces of the volume element, or

$$\oint_s \mathbf{J} \cdot d\mathbf{s} = \left(\frac{\partial J_x}{\partial x} + \frac{\partial J_y}{\partial y} + \frac{\partial J_z}{\partial z}\right) \Delta x \, \Delta y \, \Delta z = 0 \qquad (3\text{-}54)$$

Now $\Delta x \, \Delta y \, \Delta z = \Delta v$. Dividing by Δv and taking the limit as Δv approaches zero, we obtain the divergence of $\mathbf{J}$ at the point around which Δv collapses. Thus

$$\lim_{\Delta v \to 0} \frac{\oint_s \mathbf{J} \cdot d\mathbf{s}}{\Delta v} = \nabla \cdot \mathbf{J} = \frac{\partial J_x}{\partial x} + \frac{\partial J_y}{\partial y} + \frac{\partial J_z}{\partial z} = 0 \qquad (3\text{-}55)$$

or

$$\nabla \cdot \mathbf{J} = 0 \qquad (3\text{-}56)$$

This is a point relation. It applies, for example, to any point in a conductor where current is flowing. It states that steady currents have no sources or sinks. Any vector function whose divergence is zero, as in (3-56), is said to be *solenoidal*.

Let us digress briefly to consider the situation if the current is not steady as assumed above. Then (3-51) does not necessarily hold, and the difference between the total current flowing out of and into a volume must equal the rate of change of electric charge inside the volume. Specifically, a *net* flow of current *out of* the volume (positive current flow) must equal the *negative* rate of change of charge with time (rate of decrease of charge).

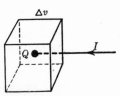

Now the total charge in the volume Δv of Fig. 3-13 is $\rho \, \Delta v$, where ρ is the average charge density. Therefore

$$\oint_s \mathbf{J} \cdot d\mathbf{s} = -\frac{\partial \rho}{\partial t} \Delta v \qquad (3\text{-}57)$$

FIG. 3-14. Construction for the continuity relation between current and charge.

Dividing by Δv and taking the limit as Δv approaches zero, we obtain

$$\nabla \cdot \mathbf{J} = -\frac{\partial \rho}{\partial t} \qquad (3\text{-}58)$$

This is the general *continuity relation* between current density $\mathbf{J}$ and the charge density ρ at a point. For steady currents as much charge enters a volume as leaves it so that $\partial \rho / \partial t = 0$ and (3-58) reduces to (3-56).

Consider now the situation shown in Fig. 3-14 where a wire carrying a current I terminates inside a small volume Δv. Applying (3-57) to this situation, the integral of $\mathbf{J}$ over the volume yields the net current entering or leaving the volume. Assuming that I is entering the volume, we have

$$\oint \mathbf{J} \cdot d\mathbf{s} = -I \qquad (3\text{-}59)$$

Now $\rho \, \Delta v$ equals the total charge Q inside the volume. Hence

$$\frac{\partial \rho}{\partial t} \, \Delta v = \frac{dQ}{dt} \qquad (3\text{-}60)$$

Substituting (3-59) and (3-60) in (3-57) yields

$$I = \frac{dQ}{dt} \qquad (3\text{-}61)$$

This is the continuity relation between the current and charge in a wire.

3-14. Current and Field at a Conductor-Insulator Boundary. The relation between the current density $\mathbf{J}$ and the electric field intensity $\mathbf{E}$ in a conductor is, from (3-21),

$$\mathbf{J} = \sigma \mathbf{E} \qquad (3\text{-}62)$$

where σ = conductivity. Thus, when current flows in a conductor, there must be a finite electric field present in the conductor (unless the conductivity is infinite[1]).

Consider now the situation at a conductor-insulator boundary as in Fig. 3-15. Assuming that the conductivity of the insulator is zero,

Fig. 3-15. Insulator-conductor boundary.

$\mathbf{J} = 0$ in the insulator. At the boundary, current in the conductor must flow tangentially to the boundary surface. Thus, on the conductor side of the boundary we have

$$E_t = \frac{J_t}{\sigma} \qquad (3\text{-}63)$$

where E_t = component of electric field tangential to boundary = $|\mathbf{E}|$
J_t = component of current density tangential to boundary = $|\mathbf{J}|$
σ = conductivity of conducting medium

By the continuity of the tangential electric field at a boundary, the tangential field on the insulator side of the boundary is also E_t.

When current flows, a conductor of finite conductivity is not an equipotential body as it is in the static case with no currents present. For

---

[1] If σ is infinite, an infinitesimal field can produce a finite current density.

example, the potential varies along a current-carrying wire with uniform current density as suggested in Fig. 3-16. The arrows indicate the field and current directions, while the transverse lines are equipotentials. Since **E** is uniform, the potential difference V of two points separated by a distance l along the wire is El. This potential difference is also equal to the IR drop, that is, $V = IR$, where I is the current in the wire and R is the resistance of a length l of the wire. The field is the same both

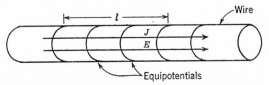

FIG. 3-16. Section of long wire.

inside and outside the wire and is entirely tangential (and parallel to the axis of the wire).

If superimposed on this situation there is a static electric charge distribution at the boundary surface due to the proximity of other conductors at a different potential, a component of the electric field E_n normal to the conductor-insulator boundary may be present on the insulator side of the boundary. The total field in the insulator is then

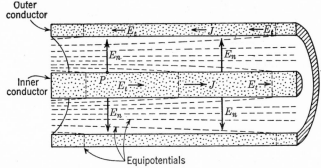

FIG. 3-17. Longitudinal cross section of coaxial transmission line. Equipotentials are shown by the dashed lines. The arrows indicate the direction of the normal and tangential field components, E_n and E_t, and the current density J.

the vector sum of the normal component E_n and the tangential component E_t. In the conductor, $E_n = 0$, and the field is entirely tangential to the boundary. For instance, consider the longitudinal cross section shown in Fig. 3-17 through a part of a long coaxial cable. Current flows to the right in the inner conductor and returns through the outer conductor. The field in the conductor is entirely tangential (and parallel to the axis of the cable) and is indicated by E_t. Since the conductivity of the conductor is large, this field is relatively weak as suggested by the short arrows for E_t. In the insulating space between the inner and outer conductors there may exist a relatively strong field due to the voltage applied at the end of the cable. This field is a static electric field (such as shown in Chap. 2 by Fig. 2-19). It originates on positive

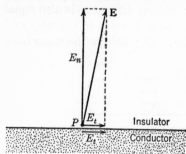

charges on the inner conductor and ends on negative charges on the inside surface of the outer conductor. It is entirely normal to the surfaces and is indicated by E_n. It is relatively strong as suggested by the long arrows for E_n. At a point P at the surface of the inner conductor (Fig. 3-17) the total field **E** is then the sum of the two components E_n and E_t added vectorially as in Fig. 3-18. If the conductivity of the metal in the cable is high,

FIG. 3-18. Total field **E** at insulator-conductor boundary resolved into normal and tangential components.

E_t may be so small that **E** is substantially normal to the surface and equal to E_n. However, the size of E_t has been exaggerated in Fig. 3-18 in order to show the slant of the total field more clearly. The shape of the total field lines across the entire insulating space between the inner and outer conductors is suggested in Fig. 3-19

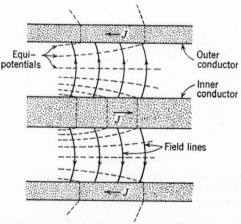

FIG. 3-19. Longitudinal cross section of coaxial transmission line showing equipotentials (dashed) and total field lines (solid).

with the slant of the field at the conductors greatly exaggerated. Equipotential surfaces are indicated by the dashed lines.

Two extreme cases of conditions at a conductor-insulator boundary have been described in the above examples. In one the total field on both sides of the boundary is entirely tangential (Figs. 3-15 and 3-16).

In the other the total field on the conductor side is entirely tangential, while the total field on the insulator side is substantially normal to the boundary (Figs. 3-17 to 3-19 inclusive).   The electric field at a conductor-insulator boundary will always be of a type similar to or somewhere between these extremes.

3-15. Current and Field at a Conductor-Conductor Boundary.   Consider the conductor-conductor boundary shown in Fig. 3-20 between two media of constants σ_1, ϵ_1 and σ_2, ϵ_2.   In general, the direction of the current changes in flowing from one medium to the other.[1]

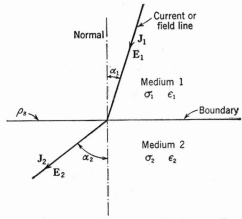

FIG. 3-20. Boundary between two different conducting media showing change in direction of current or field line.

For steady currents we have the boundary relation

$$J_{n1} = J_{n2} \tag{3-64}$$

where J_{n1} = component of current density normal to boundary in medium 1

J_{n2} = component of current density normal to boundary in medium 2

From relation (1) of Table 2-2 we also have

$$E_{t1} = E_{t2} \tag{3-65}$$

where E_{t1} = component of field tangent to the boundary in medium 1

E_{t2} = component of field tangent to the boundary in medium 2

From (3-65) it follows that

$$\frac{J_{t1}}{\sigma_1} = \frac{J_{t2}}{\sigma_2} \tag{3-66}$$

[1] Note that if $\sigma_1 = \sigma_2 = 0$, then $\mathbf{J}_1 = \mathbf{J}_2 = 0$ and the problem reduces to that considered in connection with Fig. 2-6.

where J_{t1} = component of current density tangent to boundary in medium 1

J_{t2} = component of current density tangent to boundary in medium 2

Dividing (3-66) by (3-64),

$$\frac{J_{t1}}{\sigma_1 J_{n1}} = \frac{J_{t2}}{\sigma_2 J_{n2}} \tag{3-67}$$

or

$$\frac{\tan \alpha_1}{\tan \alpha_2} = \frac{\sigma_1}{\sigma_2} \tag{3-68}$$

where α_1 and α_2 are as shown in Fig. 3-20.

According to (3) of Table 2-2 we also have the relation that

$$\epsilon_1 E_{n1} - \epsilon_2 E_{n2} = \rho_s \tag{3-69}$$

where ρ_s = surface charge density at boundary. This may be reexpressed as

$$\epsilon_1 \frac{J_{n1}}{\sigma_1} - \epsilon_2 \frac{J_{n2}}{\sigma_2} = \rho_s \tag{3-70}$$

and since $J_{n1} = J_{n2}$, we have

$$\rho_s = J_{n1} \left(\frac{\epsilon_1}{\sigma_1} - \frac{\epsilon_2}{\sigma_2} \right) \tag{3-71}$$

According to (3-71) there will, in general, be a surface charge present on the boundary between two conductors across which current is flowing. If the currents are steady, the density of this charge is a constant. If both media are solid metallic conductors, $\epsilon_1 \simeq \epsilon_0 \simeq \epsilon_2$ so that (3-71) reduces to

$$\rho_s = \epsilon_0 J_{n1} \left(\frac{1}{\sigma_1} - \frac{1}{\sigma_2} \right) \tag{3-72}$$

3-16. Current Mapping and the Resistance of Simple Geometries. Conductor Cells. If the current density is uniform throughout a conductor, its resistance is easily calculated from its dimensions and conductivity. For example, consider the homogeneous rectangular bar of conductivity σ shown in Fig. 3-21. It has a length $l' = 100$ cm, a thickness or width $b' = 40$ cm, and a width or depth $d = 40$ cm. If the end faces of the bar are clamped against heavy high-conductivity blocks, as in Fig. 3-3, the field and current density throughout the bar will be uniform. From (3-13) the resistance R of the bar is given by

$$R = \frac{l'}{\sigma d b'} = \frac{1}{0.16\sigma} \quad \text{ohms} \tag{3-73}$$

where σ = conductivity of bar (mhos/meter).

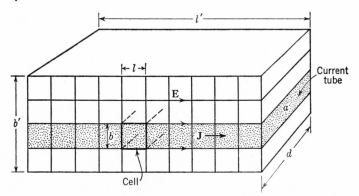

Fig. 3-21. Conductor divided into current tubes.   Vertical lines are equipotentials.

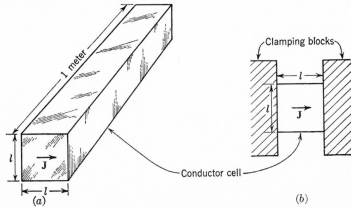

Fig. 3-22. Cell of unit depth and of conductance equal numerically to the conductivity σ of the material.   This cell also has a resistance equal numerically to the resistivity S of the material.   Method of clamping cell between large high-conductivity blocks to measure conductance or resistance is shown at (b).

The resistance of the bar can also be calculated by dividing the side of the bar into square areas each representing the end surface of a *conductor cell*. The sides of the cells are equipotentials. The top and bottom surfaces of the cell are parallel to the current direction. The resistance R_0 of such a cell is given by

$$R_0 = \frac{l}{\sigma db} = \frac{1}{\sigma d} = \frac{S}{d} \qquad (3\text{-}74a)$$

where S = resistivity of the bar material.   Hence the product of R_0 and the depth d equals the resistivity S of the bar material, or

$$R_0 d = S \qquad (3\text{-}74b)$$

For example, the resistance of a conductor cell of unit (1 meter) depth as in Fig. 3-22a is numerically equal to the value of the resistivity of the bar material. Figure 3-22b shows the method of clamping the cell to measure its resistance.

Taking the reciprocal of (3-74b) yields

$$\frac{G_0}{d} = \sigma \tag{3-74c}$$

That is, the conductance per unit depth of a conductor cell is equal to the conductivity of the medium. For instance, the conductance in mhos of a cell of unit depth, as in Fig. 3-22a, is equal numerically to the value of the conductivity σ of the medium. The above relations apply to conductor cells of any end area provided that this area is a true or a curvilinear square.

Returning to the bar of Fig. 3-21, let each cell be arbitrarily assigned a conductance of 1 mho. On this basis the total conductance of the bar equals

$$\frac{\text{Number of cells (or current tubes) in parallel}}{\text{Number of cells in series}}$$

or

$$\frac{4}{10}$$

From (3-74c) the conductance per unit depth of a conductor cell is σ so that the actual conductance G_0 of a cell of bar material is given by

$$G_0 = d\sigma = 0.4\sigma \quad \text{mhos} \tag{3-75a}$$

The actual value of the total conductance of a bar is then

$$G = \tfrac{4}{10}0.4\sigma = 0.16\sigma \quad \text{mhos} \tag{3-75b}$$

The actual value of the total resistance is the reciprocal of (3-75b), or

$$R = \frac{1}{0.16\sigma} = 6.25S \quad \text{ohms} \tag{3-75c}$$

The method of calculating the resistance or conductance of the bar by means of evaluating the series-parallel combination of conductor cells is more general than the method used in arriving at (3-73) since it can be applied not only to uniform current distributions (as here) but also to the more general situation where the current distribution is nonuniform. In a nonuniform distribution the sides of many or all of the conductor cells will be curvilinear squares. Their area and arrangement may be determined by graphical current-mapping techniques that are like the field mapping procedures discussed in Sec. 2-27 (see also Sec. 5-20 and the Appendix).

Graphical current-mapping techniques can be applied to any two-dimensional problem, that is, to a conductor whose shape can be described by a single cross section with all other cross sections parallel to this one being identical to it.   Current mapping is actually electric field mapping *in a conducting medium* since the current and the field have the same direction in isotropic media ($\mathbf{J} = \sigma\mathbf{E}$).

The following fundamental properties are useful in current mapping:

1. Current lines and equipotentials intersect at right angles.
2. Current flows tangentially to an insulating boundary.
3. The total current through any cross section of a continuous current tube is a constant.
4. In a uniform current distribution the potential varies linearly with distance.
5. Current tubes are continuous.

With these properties in mind a conductor cross section is divided into current tubes and then by equipotentials into *conductor cells* with sides that are squares or curvilinear squares, using the same trial-and-error method described in Sec. 2-27 in connection with field mapping in an insulating medium.   The tubes and equipotentials are revised until all of the cells become curvilinear squares.   By curvilinear square is meant an area that tends to yield true squares as it is subdivided into smaller and smaller areas by successive halving of the equipotential interval and the current per tube.

All cells with the same current through them may be defined as *conductor cells of the same kind.*   It follows from Ohm's law that the potential drop across all cells of the same kind is the same.

In calculating the conductance of a conductor with a nonuniform current distribution a current map is first made, as discussed above.   The conductance G is then given by

$$G = \frac{N}{n} G_0 \tag{3-76}$$

where N = number of cells (or current tubes) in parallel
  n = number of cells in series (equals number of cells per tube)
  G_0 = conductance of each cell ($= d\sigma$)
The accuracy of the conductance (or its reciprocal, the resistance) depends primarily on the accuracy with which the curvilinear squares are mapped.

In conclusion the properties of an accurate current map[1] may be stated as follows:

1. The conductance G_0 of *any* conductor cell is the same.
2. The conductance per unit depth of *any* conductor cell is equal to the conductivity σ of the medium.
3. The resistance R_0 of *any* conductor cell is the same.

[1] In a single medium of uniform conductivity.

4. The resistance-depth product for *any* conductor cell is equal to the resistivity S of the medium.

5. The current I through all conductor cells of the same kind is the same.

6. The current through any cross section of a conductor tube is the same.

7. The potential drop across all conductor cells of the same kind is the same and is equal to the IR_0 drop across the cell, where I is the current through the cell and R_0 is the resistance of the cell.

8. The average current density J in any cell of the same kind is inversely proportional to the thickness or width of the cell (or current tube).

9. The average field intensity E in any cell of the same kind is inversely proportional to the thickness or width of the cell (or current tube).[1]

10. The power dissipated as heat in all conductor cells of the same kind is the same ($= I^2 R_0$).

11. The average power density (watts per cubic meter) in all cells of the same kind is inversely proportional to the area of the end of the cell. (This is the area that appears in the map.)

Example. A homogeneous rectangular bar of conductivity σ has the dimensions shown in Fig. 3-23a. This bar is identical with the one of Fig. 3-21 except that two cuts have been made across the full width of the bar, as indicated. Find the resistance of the bar when its ends are clamped between high-conductivity blocks as in Fig. 3-3.

Solution. A longitudinal cross section of the bar is drawn to scale and a current map made with the result shown in Fig. 3-23b.[2] A portion of one quadrant has been further subdivided to test the accuracy of the curvilinear squares. From (3-74a) or (3-75a) the resistance R_0 of one conductor cell is

$$R_0 = \frac{1}{0.4\sigma} \quad \text{ohms}$$

There are 13 cells in series in a tube, and there are 4 tubes in parallel. Hence, from (3-76) the resistance R of the bar is

$$R = \frac{13R_0}{4} = \frac{13}{1.6\sigma} \doteq 8.1S \quad \text{ohms} \tag{3-77}$$

Thus, comparing this result with (3-75c) for the uniform bar, the slots in the bar produce an increase of 30 per cent in its resistance.

[1] It is also to be noted that the conductance (or the resistance) of any cell is the same for current flow in either direction across the cell. Furthermore, the conductance of any cell of unit depth is the same as the conductance of a unit cube since a cube is merely a special case of a cell.

[2] Although the entire cross section of the bar has been mapped, the symmetry is such that a map of only one quadrant would have sufficed.

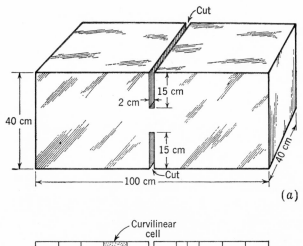

(a)

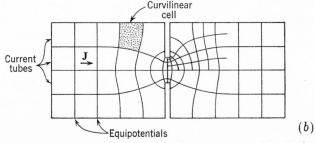

(b)

FIG. 3-23. Conducting bar with notch (a) and current map (b).   Resistance of bar
equals ratio of cells in series to cells in parallel multiplied by the resistance of each cell.

3-17. Laplace's Equation for Conducting Media.   According to (3-56)
we have the relation for steady currents that

$$\nabla \cdot \mathbf{J} = 0 \qquad (3\text{-}78)$$

From (3-21)

$$\mathbf{J} = \sigma \mathbf{E} \qquad (3\text{-}79)$$

so that (3-78) becomes

$$\sigma \nabla \cdot \mathbf{E} = 0 \qquad (3\text{-}80)$$

But from (1-33)

$$\mathbf{E} = -\nabla V \qquad (3\text{-}81)$$

Introducing this value of $\mathbf{E}$ in (3-80) yields

$$\sigma \nabla \cdot (\nabla V) = 0 \qquad (3\text{-}82)$$

or

$$\nabla^2 V = 0 \qquad (3\text{-}83)$$

This is Laplace's equation.   It was derived previously in Sec. 2-34 for
static electric fields, and since it also applies here, it follows that problems
involving distributions of steady currents in conducting media can be

handled in the same way as problems involving static field distributions in insulating media. If we have a conductor with an unknown current distribution and if a solution to Laplace's equation can be found that also satisfies the boundary conditions, we can obtain the potential and current distribution in the conductor. If this is not possible, we can nevertheless find the approximate potential and current distribution in two-dimensional problems by graphical current mapping as discussed in Sec. 3-16. From a knowledge of the current distribution, the resistance, the maximum current density, and other items of practical importance can be determined for a given conductor configuration.

In conducting media, current tubes and the conductivity σ are analogous to the flux tubes and permittivity ϵ in insulating media. Thus in conducting media we have

$$J = \sigma E \qquad \text{amp/meter}^2 \tag{3-84}$$

while in insulating media we have

$$D = \epsilon E \qquad \text{coulombs/meter}^2 \tag{3-85}$$

It is also to be noted that in a conducting medium the *conductance per unit depth* of a conductor cell equals the conductivity of the medium, or

$$\frac{G_0}{d} = \sigma \qquad \text{mhos/meter} \tag{3-86}$$

where d = depth of cell (see **Fig. 3-21**), while in an insulating medium the capacitance per unit depth of a dielectric field cell equals the permittivity ϵ of the medium, or

$$\frac{C_0}{d} = \epsilon \qquad \text{farads/meter} \tag{3-87}$$

In the case of a static electric field in a dielectric medium of permittivity ϵ there are no currents, but there is a flux density $D = \epsilon E$. In the case of a static electric field in a conducting medium of conductivity σ there is current of density $J = \sigma E$. Since both fields obey Laplace's equation, a solution in the conductor situation is also a solution for the analogous dielectric situation, and vice versa. For example, if the medium between conductors 1 and 2 in Fig. 2-24 is a conductor of conductivity σ, the conductance per unit depth between ff and gg is given by

$$\frac{G}{d} = \frac{15.43}{4} \sigma = 3.86\sigma \qquad \text{mhos/meter}$$

It is assumed that plates 1 and 2 are perfect conductors. A further discussion of fields that obey Laplace's equation is given in Chap. 14.

PROBLEMS

3-1. What is the power lost in heat in a No. 10 B. & S. gauge copper wire (2.59 mm diameter) 100 meters long if 20 volts is applied between the ends? Assume that the wire temperature is 20°C.   *Ans.: 1,205 watts.*

3-2. What will the power loss for the wire of Prob. 3-1 be if the wire temperature is 40°C?

3-3. What is the energy lost in heat in the wire of Prob. 3-1 in 1 hr?
$$Ans.: 4.34 \times 10^6 \text{ joules.}$$

3-4. What is the resistance between metal electrodes 1 meter square located at each end of a tank with nonconducting walls 1 meter square in cross section and 10 meters long when filled with a conducting liquid having a conductivity of 10 mhos/meter?

3-5. What is the current density in the tank of Prob. 3-4 if 10 volts are applied between the electrodes at the ends of the tank?

3-6. What is the current density in a No. 10 B. & S. gauge copper wire (2.59 mm diameter) carrying a constant current of 10 amp at a temperature of 20°C?

3-7. *a.* A resistance R_0 and three batteries are connected in series as shown in Fig. 3-24. For the first battery the emf $\mathcal{V}_1 = 1.5$ volts and the electrolyte or internal resistance $R_1 = 1$ ohm, for the second battery the emf $\mathcal{V}_2 = 2$ volts and the internal

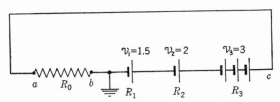

FIG. 3-24. Series circuit for Prob. 3-7.

resistance $R_2 = 0$, and for the third battery the emf $\mathcal{V}_3 = 3$ volts and the internal resistance $R_3 = 1$ ohm. The first two batteries have single cells, while the third has three cells in series, each cell of 1 volt emf and $\frac{1}{3}$ ohm internal resistance. Assume that half the total emf of a cell occurs at each electrode, and assume that all connections between cells have negligible resistance. Draw a graph such as in Fig. 3-7, showing the variation of potential with position between points *a* and *c* when $R_0 = 4.5$ ohms and also when $R_0 = 0$. Take $V = 0$ at the point *b*.

b. Referring to the circuit of Fig. 3-24, let the emfs be as indicated, and let $R_1 = 1.5$ ohms, $R_2 = 2$ ohms, and $R_3 = 3$ ohms. Draw a graph of the variation of potential with position when $R_0 = 6.5$ ohms and also when $R_0 = 0$.

3-8. What is the current magnitude in the series circuit of Fig. 3-25a? What is the current direction (clockwise or counterclockwise)? The batteries have negligible internal resistance.

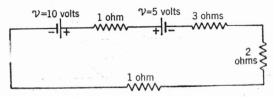

FIG. 3-25a. Series circuit for Probs. 3-8 and 3-9.

3-9. What are the current magnitude and direction in the series circuit of Fig. 3-25a if each battery has an internal resistance of 2 ohms?

3-10. Four wires meet at a common junction point. The current in wires 1 and 2 is 5 amp each and flowing away from the junction, while the current in wire 3 is 6 amp flowing toward the junction. What are the current magnitude and direction in the fourth wire?

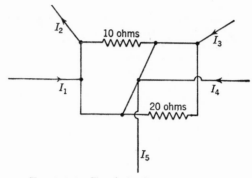

FIG. 3-25b. Circuit for Prob. 3-11.

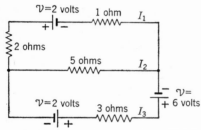

FIG. 3-26. Two mesh circuit for Prob. 3-12.

3-11. If $I_1 = I_2 = I_3 = I_4 = 1$ amp in the circuit of Fig. 3-25b, what are the magnitude and direction of I_5?

3-12. What are the magnitude and direction of the current I_2 in the circuit of Fig. 3-26? The batteries have negligible internal resistance.

3-13. A 1-cm-square copper conductor has a right-angle bend. What is the resistance of a section of the conductor including the bend that is 5 cm long each way from the bend, measuring from the outside corner? The temperature of the conductor is 20°C.

3-14. What length of straight copper conductor has the same resistance as the right-angle section of Prob. 3-13?

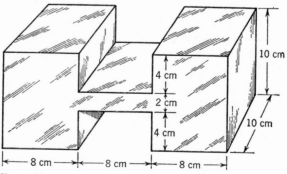

FIG. 3-27. Notched block for Probs. 3-15, 3-16, and 3-17.

3-15. How much greater is the resistance of the block of Fig. 3-27 as compared with a uniform rectangular block without the notches? The resistance to be determined is that between the left and right ends of the block. It is assumed that the block is clamped between two large high-conductivity blocks.   *Ans.:* 2.6 times.

3-16. If the conductivity of the material used for the block of Fig. 3-27 is 10^4 mhos/ meter, what is the resistance of the block?

3-17. How much greater would the resistance of the block of Fig. 3-27 be as compared with a uniform rectangular block if the height of the center section is reduced from 2 to 1 cm so that the distances from the center section to the top and bottom of the block are increased to 4.5 cm?

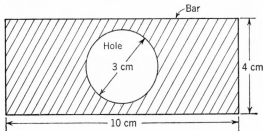

Fig. 3-28. Bar with hole for Prob. 3-18.

3-18. A rectangular nichrome bar 10 cm long by 4 cm high by 4 cm wide has a hole 3 cm in diameter located symmetrically as shown in Fig. 3-28. Find the resistance of the bar at 20°C.

3-19. A bar and strip are connected as shown in Fig. 3-29a. The bar has finite conductivity, while the strip conductivity is assumed to be infinite. If the end of the

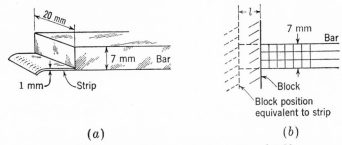

(a)   *(b)*

Fig. 3-29. Bar and strip for Probs. 3-19 and 3-20.

bar is clamped against a large, infinitely conducting block as in Fig. 3-29b instead of connected to the strip as in Fig. 3-29a, determine by what length l the bar would need to be lengthened in order that its resistance be the same as when connected to the strip?   *Ans.:* About 7 mm longer.

3-20. Why is the resistance of the bar of Fig. 3-29 larger when it is connected to the strip than when contact is made with the block?

3-21. Deduce the relation $\nabla \cdot \mathbf{J} = 0$ by applying the divergence theorem to

$$\oint_s \mathbf{J} \cdot d\mathbf{s} = 0.$$

3-22. Show that the definition of current given by Eq. (3-1) leads to the continuity relation $I = dQ/dt$, where Q = positive charge.

3-23. Demonstrate that the source of the emf energizing the coaxial line of Fig. 3-19 is at the left end by showing that if the source were at the right end the field lines would be bowed in the opposite direction.

3-24. Show that, at a conductor-conductor boundary, $\sigma_1/\sigma_2 = E_{n2}/E_{n1} = J_{t1}/J_{t2}$.

3-25. A wire 2 mm in diameter has a resistance of 1 ohm per 100 meters. A current of 20 amp is flowing in the wire. What is the field intensity in the wire?

3-26. If there is a static surface charge on the current-carrying wire of Prob. 3-25 with a uniform density of 5×10^{-12} coulomb/meter^2, what are the magnitude and direction of the field intensity just outside of the surface of the wire? The medium outside of the wire is air.

3-27. The current direction at the boundary surface between two media makes an angle of 45° with respect to the surface in medium 1; what is the angle between the current direction and the surface in medium 2? The constants for the media are as follows:

$$\text{Medium 1:} \quad \sigma_1 = 10^2 \text{ mhos/meter}$$
$$\epsilon_{r1} = 1$$
$$\text{Medium 2:} \quad \sigma_2 = 1 \text{ mho/meter}$$
$$\epsilon_{r2} = 2$$

3-28. If the total current density $\mathbf{J}$ in medium 1 is 10 amp/meter^2, what is the surface charge density at the boundary in Prob. 3-27?

3-29. Two long, parallel, zinc-plated iron pipe lines have a spacing of 4 meters between centers. The pipes are half buried in the ground as indicated in Fig. 3-30.

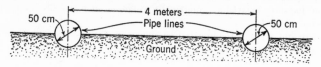

Fig. 3-30. Pipe lines for Prob. 3-29.

The diameter of the pipes is 50 cm. The conductivity of the ground (sandy soil) is 10^{-4} mhos/meter. Without drawing a field map, find the resistance between the two pipes per meter of length. *Hint:* Note the analogy between this situation and the static electric field between two parallel cylindrical conductors.

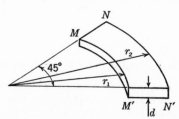

Fig. 3-31. Conducting sector for Prob. 3-30.

3-30. A conducting 45° sector of thickness d has inner and outer radii r_1 and r_2 as shown in Fig. 3-31. If the conductivity is σ mhos/meter, show that the resistance R between the curved edges MM' and NN' is given by

$$R = \frac{4}{\pi\sigma d} \ln \frac{r_2}{r_1} \quad \text{ohms}$$

Hint: Set up a 45° sector of infinitesimal radial thickness dr.

CHAPTER 4

THE STATIC MAGNETIC FIELD OF
STEADY ELECTRIC CURRENTS

4-1. Introduction. A static electric charge has an electric field, as discussed in Chaps. 1 and 2. An electric current, on the other hand, possesses a magnetic field. For instance, a wire carrying a current I has a magnetic field surrounding it, as suggested in Fig. 4-1a. If this field is

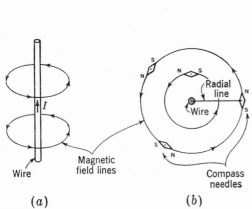

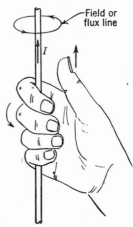

(a) (b)

Fig. 4-1. (a) Magnetic field around wire carrying a current. (b) Cross section perpendicular to the wire. The current is flowing out of the page.

Fig. 4-2. Right-hand rule relating direction of field or flux line (fingers) to direction of current I (thumb).

explored with a compass, the needle always orients itself normal to a radial line originating at the center of the wire. If one moves in the direction of the needle, it is found that the magnetic field forms *closed* circular loops around the wire.

The direction of the magnetic field is taken to be the direction indicated as "north" by the compass needle, as in Fig. 4-1b. The relation of the magnetic field direction to the current direction can be easily remembered by means of the *right-hand rule*. With the thumb pointing in the direction of the current, as in Fig. 4-2, the fingers of the right hand encircling the wire point in the direction of the magnetic field or lines of magnetic flux.

4-2. The Force between Current-carrying Wires. A current-carrying wire produces a magnetic field. If a second current-carrying wire is brought into the vicinity of the first, each wire is surrounded by two magnetic fields, its own and that due to the other wire. The result is that a force acts on the wires.

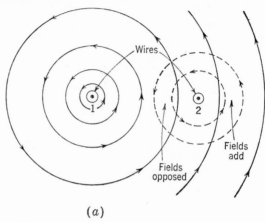

(a)

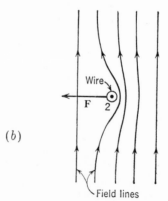

(b)

FIG. 4-3. (a) Magnetic field or flux lines around two wires carrying currents in the same direction. (b) Resulting field around wire 2 with increased magnetic flux density at the right of the wire causing a force F to the left.

This may be illustrated with the aid of Fig. 4-3a. Consider two wires 1 and 2 normal to the page with currents flowing out of the page (indicated by dot or head of an arrow in the wire). The magnetic fields of the two wires are then as shown. In order to simplify the figure, only a few of the field lines produced by wire 2 are shown.

At the right of wire 2 the two magnetic fields are in the same direction and add to give a stronger field, while at the left of wire 2 the fields are opposed and result in a weaker field.   If the field lines are considered to represent magnetic flux lines, it may be said that the magnetic flux density is greater to the right of wire 2 than to the left.   This is illustrated in Fig. 4-3b, where the magnetic flux density, designated by the symbol **B**, is seen to be greater at the right of wire 2 because the lines are more closely bunched.   There results a force **F** on wire 2 to the left as though the magnetic flux lines reacted on it like stretched rubber bands.

If the current in wire 2 is reversed, the direction of the force **F** is to the right.   This is illustrated in Fig. 4-4, where the current direction in wire 2 is into the page (indicated by an X or tail of an arrow in the wire).   Hence, *wires carrying currents in the same direction are attracted, while wires carrying currents in opposite directions are repelled.*

It is to be noted that the force **F** is perpendicular to the current direction.

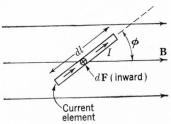

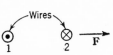

FIG. 4-4. Wires carry-ing currents in oppo-site directions.

FIG. 4-5. The force on a current element is normal to the plane containing the element and **B**.

4-3. Force on a Current Element.   Referring to Fig. 4-5, the quanti-tative relation for the magnitude of the force on a current element in a magnetic field is

$$dF = IB\,dl\,\sin\phi \qquad\qquad (4\text{-}1)$$

where dF = infinitesimal force on element dl (newtons)
$\quad I$ = current in element (amp)
$\quad B$ = magnetic flux density (newtons/amp-meter) (See Sec. 4-4)
$\quad dl$ = length of element (meters)
$\quad \phi$ = angle between direction of current and magnetic field (dimensionless)

The direction of the force dF is normal to the plane containing the element and **B**.   The magnitude of the force, as given by (4-1), is proportional to the current, to the length of the element, and to the magnetic flux density **B**.   The quantity **B** may be regarded as a measure of the strength of the magnetic field.   The force is also proportional to sin ϕ so that it is a maximum when the element is normal to **B**.

It is to be noted that (4-1) applies to a current element. To find the force on an actual circuit, it is necessary to integrate (4-1) over the length of the current-carrying conductor, which for a steady current must form a closed loop or circuit.

4-4. The Force per Current Element, or Magnetic Flux Density B. A conductor of length dl with a current I possesses a *current moment* given by $I\ dl$. That is,

$$I\ dl = \text{current} \times \text{length} = \text{current moment}$$

The dimensional relation for current moment is QL/T.

In electrostatics the electric field intensity **E** is defined as the force per unit charge. In magnetic situations the magnetic flux density **B** is defined as the *force per current moment*. Thus, if $\phi = 90°$, we have, from (4-1),

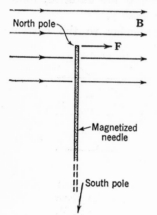

North pole

B

→ F

←Magnetized needle

South pole

Fig. 4-6. Long magnetized needle in magnetic field.

$$B = \frac{dF}{I\ dl} = \frac{\text{force}}{\text{current moment}} \quad (4\text{-}2)$$

The unit for B is the newton per ampere-meter or, as will be shown later, the weber per square meter.

Electric charge, positive and negative, can be separated. The poles of a magnet, however, cannot be separated (see Chap. 5). Although as a consequence an isolated magnetic pole is not physically realizable, its effect may be approximated by confining our attention to the region close to one pole of a very long, magnetized needle. Thus, as suggested in Fig. 4-6, the north pole of a long, magnetized needle, when introduced in a magnetic field, will be acted on by a force **F**. This force is proportional to **B** and to the strength of the pole, or

$$\mathbf{F} = \mathbf{B}Q_m \qquad \text{newtons} \qquad (4\text{-}3)$$

where Q_m = pole strength. The pole strength Q_m has the dimensions of current moment (see Chap. 5) and is expressed in ampere-meters. Dividing by Q_m,

$$\mathbf{B} = \frac{\mathbf{F}}{Q_m} = \frac{\text{force}}{\text{pole}} \qquad (4\text{-}4)$$

where **B** = force per pole (newtons/amp-meter)
  F = force (newtons)
  Q_m = pole strength (amp-meters)

Thus, **B** can be regarded either as the force per unit current moment or as the force per unit pole. The relation of (4-4) is analogous to that in Sec. 1-6 for the electric field intensity **E** or force per unit charge. That is,

$$E = \frac{F}{Q} = \frac{\text{force}}{\text{charge}} \qquad (4\text{-}5)$$

where **E** = field intensity (newtons/coulomb)

      F = force (newtons)

      Q = electric charge (coulombs)

Because of the analogy between (4-4) and (4-5), **B** might appropriately be called the *magnetic field intensity*. However, it is customary to call it the *magnetic flux density*.[1]

4-5. The Flux Density Produced by a Current Distribution. Magnetic fields are produced by electric currents (or their equivalent). The basic relation for the magnetic flux density at a point P as produced by a current-carrying element (see Fig. 4-7) is

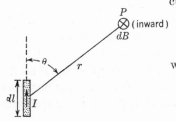

$$dB = k \frac{I \, dl \sin \theta}{r^2} \qquad (4\text{-}6)$$

where dB = infinitesimal flux density at point P

      k = constant of proportionality

      I = current in element

      dl = length of element

      θ = angle between current direction and radius vector to P

      r = distance from element to P

Fig. 4-7. The flux density at P due to a current element is given by the Biot-Savart relation (4-7).

The quantity k is a constant of proportionality given by

$$k = \frac{\mu}{4\pi}$$

where μ = permeability of the medium. By dimensional analysis of (4-6) we find that μ has the dimensions of flux per current divided by length. It will be shown in Sec. 4-15 that inductance has the dimensions of flux per current. Therefore permeability has the dimensions of inductance divided by length. The mksc unit for permeability is the henry per meter.† The permeability of vacuum is designated μ_0 and has a value of

$$4\pi \times 10^{-7} \text{ henry/meter}$$

[1] It is also sometimes called the *magnetic induction*. For a detailed discussion of magnetic units see, for example, Erik Hallén, Some Units in the Giorgi System and the C.G.S. System, *Trans. Roy. Inst. Techn. (Stockholm)*, No. 6, 1947.

† Recall that permittivity ϵ has the dimensions of *capacitance* per length and is expressed in farads per meter.

The permeability of air and also of most nonferrous materials is nearly the same as for vacuum.

It is assumed in (4-6) that the medium has a uniform permeability. In effect this restricts us to nonferrous media, for which μ is nearly equal to μ_0 (see Table 5-1).

Introducing the value for k in (4-6), we obtain

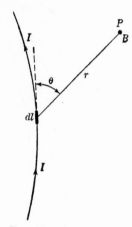

$$dB = \frac{\mu I \, dl \sin \theta}{4\pi r^2} \qquad (4\text{-}7)$$

Equation (4-7) is often referred to as the Biot-Savart law. The direction of $d\mathbf{B}$ is everywhere normal to the element of length dl, as suggested in Fig. 4-7. In fact, $d\mathbf{B}$ forms circular loops concentric with dl, as suggested in Fig. 4-1a.

In case we wish to know B at a point P, as in Fig. 4-8, due to a current I in a long, straight or curved conductor contained in the plane of the page, we assume that the conductor is made up of elements or segments of infinitesimal length dl connected in series. The total flux density B at the point P is then the sum of the contributions from all these elements, and is expressed by the integral of (4-7). Thus

FIG. 4-8. Construction for calculating flux density B at a point P due to a current I in a long conductor.

$$B = \frac{\mu I}{4\pi} \int \frac{\sin \theta}{r^2} \, dl \qquad (4\text{-}8)$$

where B = flux density at P (newtons/amp-meter)
μ = permeability of medium (henrys/meter)
I = current in conductor (amp)
dl = length of current element (meters)
r = distance from element to P (meters)
θ = angle measured clockwise from the positive direction of current along dl to direction of radius vector r extending from dl to P

The integration is carried out over the length of the conductor.

Both (4-8) and (4-1) constitute the basic magnetic field relations as stated in a simplified scalar form. These relations are restated in more general forms in later sections.

4-6. Magnetic Flux ψ_m. The magnetic flux density $\mathbf{B}$ or force per pole is also a measure of the density, or number, of magnetic flux lines passing per unit area through a surface normal to the lines. Hence the total flux or number of lines through a given area is equal to the product of the area and the component of $\mathbf{B}$ normal to it. Thus, referring to

Fig. 4-9, we have

$$\psi_m = BA \cos \alpha \qquad (4\text{-}9)$$

where ψ_m = magnetic flux through area A[1]

B = magnitude of the magnetic flux density $\mathbf{B}$

α = angle between a normal to the area A and the direction of $\mathbf{B}$

It is assumed in (4-9) that $\mathbf{B}$ is uniform over the area A.

Dimensionally we have

$$\text{Magnetic flux density} \times \text{area} = \text{magnetic flux}$$

or

$$\frac{\text{Force}}{\text{Current} \times \text{length}} \times \text{area} = \frac{\text{force} \times \text{length}}{\text{current}} = \frac{\text{mechanical moment}}{\text{current}}$$

Thus, magnetic flux has the dimensions of mechanical moment per current. The dimensional symbols for magnetic flux (ψ_m) are ML^2/QT.

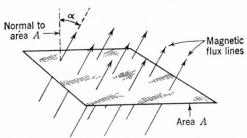

FIG. 4-9. Flux lines and area A.

The mksc unit for magnetic flux is the weber. Hence

$$\frac{\text{Newtons}}{\text{Ampere-meter}} \times \text{meters}^2 = \frac{\text{newton-meters}}{\text{ampere}} = \text{webers}$$

For the flux density $\mathbf{B}$ we have

$$\text{Flux density} = \frac{\text{flux}}{\text{area}} \text{ or } \frac{\text{webers}}{\text{meter}^2}$$

Thus, the magnetic flux density $\mathbf{B}$ can be expressed in webers per square meter as well as in newtons per ampere meter.

Instead of flux lines it is frequently more convenient to imagine that there are tubes of magnetic flux, in the same way that tubes of electric flux are often more convenient than lines of electric flux (see Sec. 1-18). A *tube of magnetic flux* is defined as an imaginary tube having walls everywhere parallel to $\mathbf{B}$ and with a constant total magnetic flux ψ_m over any cross section. The requirement that the flux over any cross section of a tube be a constant is a necessary consequence of the fact that $\mathbf{B}$ is parallel to the sides of the tube so that the flux over the side walls is zero.

[1] The subscript m is used to distinguish magnetic flux (ψ_m) from electric flux (ψ).

If **B** is not uniform over an area, the simple product (4-9) must be replaced by a surface integral so that, in general, we have

$$\psi_m = \iint B \cos \alpha \, ds \tag{4-10}$$

where ds = infinitesimal element of surface area

B = magnitude of **B**

α = angle between normal to ds and the direction of **B**

The integration is carried out over the surface through which we wish to know the total flux ψ_m.

Equation (4-10) can also be written as a scalar or dot product. Thus,

$$\psi_m = \iint \mathbf{B} \cdot d\mathbf{s} \tag{4-11}$$

where ψ_m = magnetic flux (webers)

B = magnetic flux density (webers/meter² or newtons/amp-meter)

$d\mathbf{s}$ = a vector with direction normal to the surface element ds and a magnitude equal to the area of ds (meters²)

4-7. Magnetic Flux over a Closed Surface. The flux tubes of a static electric field originate and end on electric charges. On the other hand, tubes of magnetic flux are continuous, that is, they have no sources or sinks. This is a fundamental difference between static electric and magnetic fields. To describe this continuous nature of magnetic flux tubes, it is said that the flux density **B** is solenoidal. Since it is continuous, as many magnetic flux tubes must enter a volume as leave it. Hence, when (4-11) is carried out over a *closed* surface, the result must be zero, or

$$\oint_s \mathbf{B} \cdot d\mathbf{s} = 0 \tag{4-12}[1]$$

This relation may be regarded as Gauss's law applied to magnetic fields [compare with (1-59) for electric fields].

It follows, in the same manner as shown for **J** in Sec. 3-13, that the divergence of **B** equals zero. That is,

$$\nabla \cdot \mathbf{B} = 0 \tag{4-13}$$

Both (4-12) and (4-13) are expressions of the continuous nature of **B**, (4-12) being the relation for a finite volume and (4-13) the relation at a point.

4-8. The Flux Density Produced by an Infinite Linear Conductor. The flux density **B** at a distance R from a thin linear conductor of infinite length with a constant current I can be readily obtained by an application of (4-8). This case is one of considerable interest since the flux density at a distance R from a long, straight wire is nearly the same as for an infinitely long conductor provided that R is small compared with

---

[1] The symbol $\oint_s$ indicates an integral over a closed surface.

the length of the wire. It is assumed that the conductor diameter is sufficiently small compared with R so that it can be neglected.

The geometry is shown in Fig. 4-10. With the current I as indicated, **B** at the right of the wire is into the page. This is according to the right-hand rule. Since $dl \sin \theta = r \, d\theta$ and $R = r \sin \theta$, (4-8) in this case becomes

$$B = \frac{\mu I}{4\pi} \int_0^\pi \frac{1}{r} \, d\theta = \frac{\mu I}{4\pi R} \int_0^\pi \sin \theta \, d\theta \qquad (4\text{-}14)$$

where the integration is between the angles $\theta = 0$ and $\theta = \pi$, that is, over the entire length of an infinite wire. Integrating (4-14), we have

$$B = \frac{\mu I}{4\pi R} \left[-\cos \theta \right]_0^\pi = \frac{\mu I}{4\pi R} \cdot 2 \qquad (4\text{-}15)$$

or

$$B = \frac{\mu I}{2\pi R} \qquad (4\text{-}16)$$

where B = flux density (webers/meter² or newtons/amp-meter)
μ = permeability of medium (henrys/meter)
I = current in conductor (amp)
R = radial distance (meters)

Equation (4-16) gives the flux density at a radius R from an infinite (or very long) linear conductor carrying a current I. It is assumed that the conductor is in a medium of uniform permeability μ.

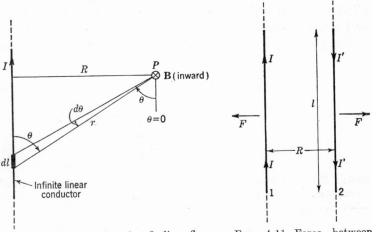

FIG. 4-10. Construction for finding flux density B near a long, straight wire.

FIG. 4-11. Force between two long parallel conductors.

4-9. The Force between Two Linear Parallel Conductors. Consider a length of two very long parallel linear conductors separated by a distance R as in Fig. 4-11. The conductors are situated in air and are in a region free from fields.   Assume now that conductor 1 carries a current I and conductor 2 a current I' in the opposite direction.   The flux lines due to conductor 1 are into the page at conductor 2.   Applying the reasoning of Sec. 4-2 (see Fig. 4-4), it follows that there is a force to the right on conductor 2 and a force to the left on conductor 1.   That is, the conductors are repelled.   If the currents were in the same direction, the forces would be reversed and the conductors would be attracted.

Let us now calculate the magnitude F of the force on a length l of conductor 2.   From (4-1) we have

$$F = I'B \int_0^l dl = I'Bl \qquad (4\text{-}17)$$

where I' = current in conductor 2
      B = flux density at conductor 2 produced by current I in conductor 1

Introducing the value of B from (4-16) gives

$$F = \frac{\mu_0 I I'}{2\pi R} l \qquad (4\text{-}18)$$

where F = force on length l of conductor 2 (newtons)
      I = current in conductor 1 (amp)
      I' = current in conductor 2 (amp)
      R = separation of conductors (meters)
      μ_0 = permeability of air = $4\pi \times 10^{-7}$ henry/meter

Since (4-18) is symmetrical in I and I', the force on a length l of conductor 1 is of the same magnitude as the force F on conductor 2.

Dividing (4-18) by l yields the *force per unit length* on either conductor as

$$\frac{F}{l} = \frac{\mu_0 I I'}{2\pi R} \qquad (4\text{-}19)$$

If $I' = I$, and introducing the value for μ_0, (4-18) becomes

$$F = 2 \times 10^{-7} \frac{I^2 l}{R} \qquad (4\text{-}20)$$

Example.   Two long parallel wires separated by 2 cm in air carry currents of 100 amp.   Find the force F on 1 meter length of a conductor.
Solution.   Evaluating (4-20) for these conditions,

$$F = 0.1 \text{ newton} \simeq \tfrac{1}{3} \text{ oz avoirdupois}$$

4-10. The Flux Density Produced by a Current Loop.   As another application of the flux density relations of Sec. 4-5, let us derive an expression for the flux density produced by a single current loop.   As a simplification the problem will be restricted to finding B at points on the loop axis.   Let the loop be in the x-y plane with its center at the origin, as in Fig. 4-12, so that the z axis coincides with the loop axis.   The loop has a radius R and current I and is situated in air.

At the point P on the loop axis the infinitesimal flux density dB produced by an infinitesimal element of length dl of the loop is, from (4-7),

$$dB = \frac{\mu I\ dl\ \sin\theta}{4\pi r^2} \qquad (4\text{-}21)$$

where θ = angle between dl and radius vector of length r.   It is assumed that the loop is in a medium of uniform permeability μ.   The direction of dB is normal to the radius vector of length r, that is, at an angle ξ with respect to the loop or z axis.

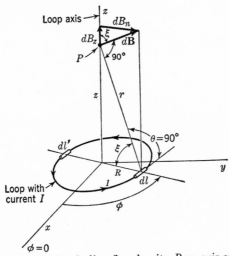

FIG. 4-12. Construction for finding flux density B on axis of current loop.

The component dB_z in the direction of the z axis is given by

$$dB_z = dB\cos\xi = dB\,\frac{R}{r} \qquad (4\text{-}22)$$

From Fig. 4-12 we note that

$$\theta = 90°$$
$$dl = R\,d\phi$$
$$r = \sqrt{R^2 + z^2}$$

Introducing these values into (4-21) and substituting this value for dB in (4-22), we have

$$dB_z = \frac{\mu I R^2}{4\pi(R^2 + z^2)^{\frac{3}{2}}}\,d\phi \qquad (4\text{-}23)$$

The total flux density B_z in the z direction is then the integral of (4-23) around the entire loop.

The element dl also produces a component of flux density dB_n normal to the axis to the loop. Integrating this component for all elements around the loop yields zero because of symmetry. This may be seen by noting that the normal component dB_n of any element of length dl is canceled by the normal component of the diametrically opposed element dl'. Hence, B_z equals the total flux density B at the point P as given by

$$B = B_z = \frac{\mu I R^2}{4\pi (R^2 + z^2)^{\frac{3}{2}}} \int_0^{2\pi} d\phi = \frac{\mu I R^2}{2(R^2 + z^2)^{\frac{3}{2}}} \qquad (4\text{-}24)$$

The point P is at an axial distance z from the center of the loop. At the center of the loop, $z = 0$, and

$$B = \frac{\mu I}{2R} \qquad (4\text{-}25)$$

where B = flux density at center of loop (webers/meter²)
  μ = permeability of medium (henrys/meter)
  I = current in loop (amp)
  R = radius of loop (meters)

4-11. The Vector, or Cross Product. A linear current-carrying conductor placed in a uniform magnetic field experiences a force F on a length l of conductor that is given, from (4-1), by

$$F = IB \sin \phi \int_0^l dl = IBl \sin \phi \qquad (4\text{-}26)$$

where F = force (newtons)
  I = current in conductor (amp)
  B = flux density of field (webers/meter²)
  l = length of conductor (meters)
  ϕ = angle between **I** and **B**

Equation (4-26) is a scalar equation and relates only the magnitudes of the quantities involved. The force **F** is perpendicular to both **I** and **B**. For example, let the conductor be normal to a uniform magnetic field of flux density **B** as in Fig. 4-13a. If the current in the conductor is flowing out of the page, it produces flux lines, as indicated, so that the flux density is increased below the wire and weakened above. The resulting force is therefore upward, as suggested in Fig. 4-13b.

Relating the directions to the coordinate axes as in Fig. 4-14a, we have **F** in the positive z direction when **I** is in the positive x direction and **B** in the positive y direction. If the direction of **I** is not perpendicular to the direction of **B** but is as shown in Fig. 4-14b, the force **F** is still in the positive z direction with a magnitude given by (4-26), where ϕ equals the .

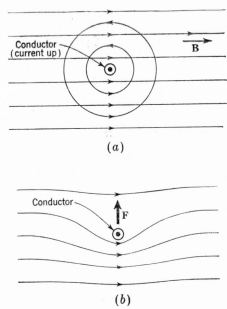

FIG. 4-13. Force **F** on current-carrying conductor in uniform magnetic field.

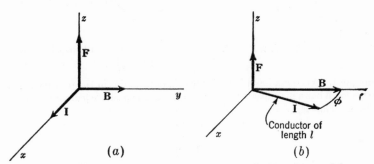

FIG. 4-14. Relation between current direction, field direction, and force.

angle measured from the positive direction of **I** to the positive direction of **B** (counterclockwise in Fig. 4-14*b*). With ϕ measured in this way, the force **F** is in the positive z direction if sin ϕ is positive.

Although with this convention concerning directions (4-26) is definite and unambiguous, a more concise and elegant method of expressing the relation is by means of the *vector*, or *cross product.*

The cross product of two vectors is defined as a third vector whose magnitude is equal to the product of the vector magnitudes and the sine of the angle between them. The direction of the third vector is perpendicular to the plane of the two vectors and in such a sense that the three vectors form a right-handed set.

For example, the cross product of **A** into **B** means that the resulting vector **C** is in the direction that a right-handed screw[1] would advance if rotated in the same direction as when **A** is turned toward **B**. The cross product of **A** into **B** is written

$$\mathbf{A} \times \mathbf{B} = \mathbf{C} \qquad (4\text{-}27)$$

If **A** is in the positive x direction and **B** in the positive y direction, then **C** is in the positive z direction as in Fig. 4-15. These three vectors form a right-handed set. (No physical significance is here attached to **A**, **B**, and **C**.)

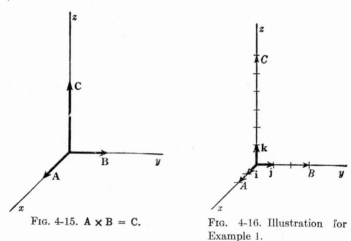

FIG. 4-15. **A** × **B** = **C**.

FIG. 4-16. Illustration for Example 1.

Example 1. Vector **A** has a magnitude of 2 units and is in the positive x direction, while vector **B** has a magnitude of 3 units and is in the positive y direction as shown in Fig. 4-16. That is,

$$\mathbf{A} = \mathbf{i}2$$

and

$$\mathbf{B} = \mathbf{j}3$$

where **i** and **j** are unit vectors in the x and y directions, respectively. What is the resultant vector **C** equal to the cross product **A** × **B**?

Solution. The magnitude of **C** is given by

$$C = AB \sin \phi = (2)(3) \sin 90° = 6$$

The angle ϕ from **A** to **B** is, in this example, equal to 90°.

The direction of **C** is at right angles to the plane containing **i** and **j** or in the z direction. Furthermore, a rotation from **i** into **j** would cause a right-handed screw to advance in the positive z direction. The direction of **C** is therefore in the positive z direction, and this is indicated by the unit vector **k**. Accordingly, the cross product of **A** and **B** is

$$\mathbf{A} \times \mathbf{B} = (\mathbf{i}A) \times (\mathbf{j}B) = \mathbf{k}AB \sin \theta = \mathbf{k}6 \sin 90° = \mathbf{k}6 = \mathbf{C}$$

[1] A right-handed screw advances in the direction of the thumb of Fig. 4-2 when the screw is turned in the direction of the fingers.

If **A** is not perpendicular to **B**, the angle ϕ is not 90° and sin ϕ is less than unity (Fig. 4-17).   In general, the cross product of **A** into **B** is therefore given by

$$\mathbf{A} \times \mathbf{B} = \mathbf{n}AB \sin \phi = \mathbf{C} \quad (4\text{-}28)$$

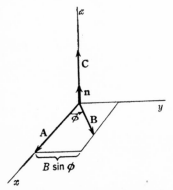

where **n** is a unit vector normal to the plane containing **A** and **B** and ϕ is the angle between **A** and **B**.   The magnitude of **C** is given by $AB \sin \phi$ and is represented by the area of the rectangle in Fig. 4-17.

In writing the scalar, or dot, product of two vectors (Sec. 1-10) the order is immaterial.   Thus,

$$\mathbf{A} \cdot \mathbf{B} = \mathbf{B} \cdot \mathbf{A}$$

FIG. 4-17. Example of cross product (**A** × **B**) where **A** and **B** are not normal to each other.

The dot product is said to obey the commutative law since the order of the operation can be reversed without affecting the result.

On the other hand, the cross product does not obey the commutative law since

$$\mathbf{A} \times \mathbf{B} = -\mathbf{B} \times \mathbf{A}$$

Therefore, if

$$\mathbf{A} \times \mathbf{B} = \mathbf{C}$$

then

$$\mathbf{B} \times \mathbf{A} = -\mathbf{C}$$

Example 2.   Work out the relations for the cross products of the unit vectors i, j, and **k** of the rectangular coordinate system.

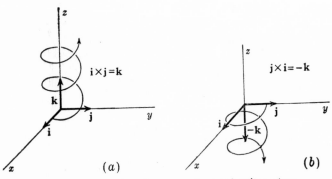

FIG. 4-18. Examples of cross products of unit vectors.

Solution. The vector products are as follows:

$$\mathbf{i} \times \mathbf{i} = (1)\,(1)\, \sin 0° = 0$$
$$\mathbf{i} \times \mathbf{j} = \mathbf{k}\,(1)\,(1)\, \sin 90° = \mathbf{k} \qquad \text{(see Fig. 4-18a)}$$
$$\mathbf{i} \times \mathbf{k} = -\mathbf{j}$$
$$\mathbf{j} \times \mathbf{i} = -\mathbf{k} \qquad \text{(see Fig. 4-18b)}$$
$$\mathbf{j} \times \mathbf{j} = 0$$
$$\mathbf{j} \times \mathbf{k} = \mathbf{i}$$
$$\mathbf{k} \times \mathbf{i} = \mathbf{j}$$
$$\mathbf{k} \times \mathbf{j} = -\mathbf{i}$$
$$\mathbf{k} \times \mathbf{k} = 0$$

$$(4\text{-}29)$$

4-12. Magnetic Field Relations in Vector Notation. Making use of the vector product, (4-1) may now be expressed[1] (see Fig. 4-19) in a more general form as

$$d\mathbf{F} = I(d\mathbf{l} \times \mathbf{B}) \qquad (4\text{-}30)$$

where $d\mathbf{F}$ = vector indicating magnitude and direction of force on element of conductor (newtons)

I = scalar magnitude of current in conductor (amp)

$d\mathbf{l}$ = vector whose magnitude ($|d\mathbf{l}|$) equals the length dl of the conductor element and whose direction is in the positive direction of the current (meters)

$\mathbf{B}$ = vector indicating magnitude and direction of the flux density (webers/meter²)

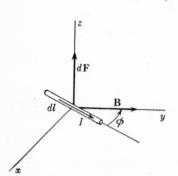

FIG. 4-19. $d\mathbf{F} = I(d\mathbf{l} \times \mathbf{B})$.

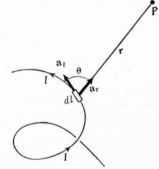

FIG. 4-20. Relation for finding $\mathbf{B}$ at a point P due to a current I in a conductor of any shape.

Equation (4-30) combines in one expression the relations between both the magnitudes and the directions of the quantities involved, whereas (4-1) related only the magnitudes.

---

[1] For a volume distribution of current we have

$$d\mathbf{F} = (\mathbf{J} \times \mathbf{B})\, dv \qquad (4\text{-}31)$$

where $d\mathbf{F}$ is the force on the volume element dv at which the current density is $\mathbf{J}$.

For a linear conductor of length 1 in a uniform field **B**, (4-30) becomes

$$\mathbf{F} = I(\mathbf{l} \times \mathbf{B}) \tag{4-32}$$

Equation (4-8) gives the magnitude of the flux density at a point as produced by a current I in a straight or curved conductor contained in a single plane. A more general relation applying to a conducting wire of any shape, as in Fig. 4-20, can be stated with the aid of the vector product as follows,

$$\mathbf{B} = \frac{\mu I}{4\pi} \int \frac{\mathbf{a}_l \times \mathbf{a}_r}{r^2} \, dl \tag{4-33}$$

where **B** = flux density at P (webers/meter^2)
  μ = permeability of medium (henrys/meter)
  I = current in conductor (amp)
  $\mathbf{a}_l$ = unit vector pointing in the positive direction of the current at element dl of conductor (dimensionless)
  $\mathbf{a}_r$ = unit vector pointing from element dl to point P (dimensionless)
  r = distance from dl to P (meters)
  dl = infinitesimal element of length of conductor[1] (meters)
The integration in (4-33) is carried out over the length of conductor under consideration.

If the current is distributed throughout a volume, the flux density **B** is given by

$$\mathbf{B} = \frac{\mu}{4\pi} \iiint \frac{\mathbf{J} \times \mathbf{a}_r}{r^2} \, dv \tag{4-34}$$

where **J** is the current density in a volume element dv at a distance r.

Equations (4-30) and (4-33) are the basic magnetic field relations. If **B** is eliminated between these equations, an equation can be obtained that expresses the force between two current elements (see Prob. 4-16).

4-13. Torque on a Loop. Magnetic Moment. When a current loop is placed parallel to a magnetic field, forces act on the loop that tend to rotate it. The tangential force times the radial distance at which it acts is called the *torque*, or mechanical moment, on the loop. Torque (or mechanical moment) has the dimensions of force × distance and is expressed in newton-meters.

---

[1] Note that $dl = |d\mathbf{l}| = |\mathbf{a}_l \, dl|$, where $d\mathbf{l}$ equals an infinitesimal vector element of length pointing in the direction of the current. Thus, another way of writing (4-33) is

$$\mathbf{B} = \frac{\mu I}{4\pi} \int \frac{d\mathbf{l} \times \mathbf{a}_r}{r^2} \tag{4-33a}$$

Consider the rectangular loop shown in Fig. 4-21a with sides of length l and d situated in a magnetic field of uniform flux density **B**. The loop has a steady current I as suggested in the figure. According to (4-30) the force of any element of the loop is

$$d\mathbf{F} = I (d\mathbf{l} \times \mathbf{B}) \qquad (4\text{-}35)$$

If the plane of the loop is at an angle β with respect to **B**, as indicated in the cross-section view of Fig. 4-21b, the tangential force is

$$F_t = |\mathbf{F}| \cos \beta = IB \cos \beta \int_0^l dl = IBl \cos \beta \qquad (4\text{-}36)$$

The total torque on the loop is then

$$T = 2F_t \frac{d}{2} = IBld \cos \beta \qquad (4\text{-}37)$$

But ld equals the area A of the loop; so

$$T = IAB \cos \beta \qquad (4\text{-}38)$$

According to (4-38) the torque is proportional to the current in the loop, to its area, and to the flux density of the field in which the loop is situated.

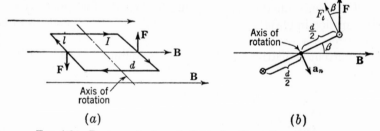

Fig. 4-21. Rectangular loop in field of uniform flux density **B**.

Now the product IA in (4-38) has the dimensions of current $\times$ area and is the *magnetic moment* of the loop. Its dimensional symbols are QL^2/T, and it is expressed in amperes $\times$ square meters. Let us designate magnetic moment by the letter m. Then[1]

$$m = IA \qquad (4\text{-}39)$$

and

$$T = mB \cos \beta \qquad (4\text{-}40)$$

or

$$T = mB \sin \gamma \qquad (4\text{-}41)$$

where γ = angle between normal to plane of loop and direction of **B** (see Fig. 4-21b). If the loop has N turns, the magnetic moment $m = NIA$.

[1] Although the loop in Fig. 4-21 has a rectangular area, the relation $m = IA$ applies regardless of the shape of the loop area.

If the magnetic moment is regarded as a vector **m** with direction $\mathbf{a}_n$, normal to the plane of the loop and with its positive sense determined by the right-hand rule (fingers in direction of current, thumb in direction of $\mathbf{a}_n$), the torque relation of (4-41) can be expressed in a more general form using the vector product. Thus

$$\mathbf{T} = \mathbf{m} \times \mathbf{B} \tag{4-42}$$

where **T** = torque on loop (newton-meters)
     m = $\mathbf{a}_n m = \mathbf{a}_n IA$ = magnetic moment of loop (amp-meters^2)
     B = flux density of field in which loop is situated (webers/meter^2)

The torque **T** is considered to be a vector coinciding with the axis of rotation of the loop as given by **m** × **B**. The direction of the torque on the loop is obtained by turning **m** into **B**.

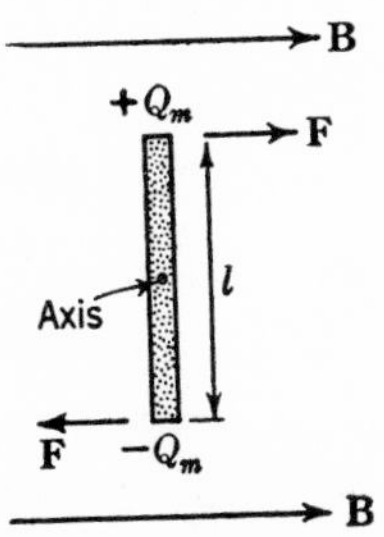

When $\gamma = 90°$, (4-41) becomes

$$m = \frac{T}{B} \tag{4-43}$$

Thus the magnetic moment of a loop is proportional to the torque, or mechanical moment, on the loop per unit of magnetic flux density. Magnetic moment, then, has the dimensions not only of current × area but also of mechanical moment per magnetic flux density. That is,

$$\text{Magnetic moment} = \frac{\text{mechanical moment}}{\text{magnetic flux density}} = \text{current} \times \text{area}$$

FIG. 4-22. A bar magnet has a magnetic moment $Q_m l$.

A current loop is equivalent in its effect to a short magnetized bar or magnetic dipole. This is discussed in more detail in Chap. 5. It may be noted here, however, that the maximum torque on a bar magnet of pole strength Q_m and length l (see Fig. 4-22) is

$$T = 2Q_m B \frac{l}{2} = Q_m l B \tag{4-44}$$

Equating this to the maximum torque on a loop from (4-38), we have

$$IA = Q_m l \tag{4-45}$$

The magnetic moment of a current loop is IA, so that for a bar magnet to be equivalent to the loop its magnetic moment $Q_m l$ must be equal to IA.

4-14. The Solenoid. A helical coil, or solenoid, is often used to produce a magnetic field. Let us calculate the flux density for such a coil.

Let the coil consist of N turns of thin wire carrying a current I. The coil has a length l and radius R (Fig. 4-23a). The spacing between turns is small compared with the radius R of the coil. A cross section through the solenoid is shown in Fig. 4-23b. If the spacing between turns is sufficiently small or if the wire is replaced by a thin conducting strip of width l/N, and with negligible spacing between turns as in Fig. 4-23c, one may consider that the current in the coil produces a current sheet with a linear current density $K = NI/l$ amp per meter.

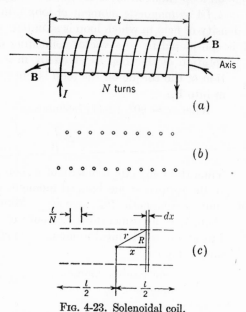

FIG. 4-23. Solenoidal coil.

To find the flux density B at the center of the solenoid, let a section of the coil of length dx, as in Fig. 4-23c, be regarded as a single turn loop with a current equal to

$$K \, dx = \frac{NI}{l} \, dx \tag{4-46}$$

From (4-24) the flux density dB at the center of the solenoid due to this loop of length dx at a distance x from the center is

$$dB = \frac{\mu NIR^2}{2l(R^2 + x^2)^{\frac{3}{2}}} \, dx \tag{4-47}$$

The total flux density B at the center of this coil is then equal to this expression integrated over the length of the coil. That is,

$$B = \frac{\mu NIR^2}{2l} \int_{-l/2}^{+l/2} \frac{dx}{(R^2 + x^2)^{\frac{3}{2}}} \tag{4-48}$$

Performing the integration,

$$B = \frac{\mu N I}{\sqrt{4R^2 + l^2}} \tag{4-49}$$

If the length of the solenoid is much greater than its radius ($l \gg R$), (4-49) reduces to

$$B = \frac{\mu N I}{l} = \mu K \tag{4-50}$$

where B = flux density (webers/meter²)
  μ = permeability of medium (henrys/meter)
  N = number of turns on solenoid (dimensionless)
  I = current through solenoid (amp)
  l = length of solenoid (meters)
  K = sheet current density (amp/meter)

Equations (4-49) and (4-50) give the flux density at the center of the solenoid. By changing the limits of integration in (4-48) to 0 and l we obtain the flux density at one end of the coil (on the axis) as

$$B = \frac{\mu N I}{2\sqrt{R^2 + l^2}} \tag{4-51}$$

For $l \gg R$ this reduces to

$$B = \frac{\mu N I}{2l} = \frac{1}{2}\mu K \tag{4-52}$$

which is one-half the value at the center of the coil as given by (4-50).

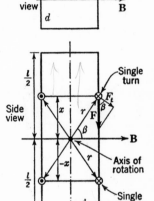

Fig. 4-24. Solenoid in field of uniform flux density **B**.

Let us now calculate the maximum torque tending to rotate a solenoid placed in a magnetic field of uniform flux density. The torque is maximum when the solenoid axis is normal to the direction of **B** as in Fig. 4-24. The axis of rotation is at the center of the solenoid. Assuming that the solenoid is of square cross section, the tangential force F_t on a single straight segment of 1 turn is given by

$$F_t = IBd \cos \beta \tag{4-53}$$

The net torque due to 2 turns, one at a distance x above the center of the solenoid and another at an equal distance below, is then

$$T = 4IBrd \cos \beta \tag{4-54}$$

But $\cos \beta = d/2r$; so

$$T = 2Id^2B = 2IAB \tag{4-55}$$

where $A = d^2$ = area of solenoid. This torque is independent of the distance of the turns from the center of the solenoid. Hence, the total torque on the solenoid is equal to (4-55) times $N/2$, where N is the number of turns. This is the maximum torque, T_m. That is,

$$T_m = NIAB = m'B \qquad (4\text{-}56)$$

where $m' = NIA$ = magnetic moment of solenoid. The magnetic moment of the solenoid is thus N times the magnetic moment of a single loop of the same area A and carrying the same current I.

For a bar magnet to be equivalent to a current solenoid its magnetic moment $Q_m l$ would need to be equal to the moment NIA for the solenoid.

4-15. Inductors and Inductance. An inductor[1] is a device for storing energy in a magnetic field. It may be regarded as the magnetic counterpart of a capacitor, which stores energy in an electric field. As examples, loops, coils, and solenoids are inductors.

The lines of magnetic flux produced by a current in a solenoidal coil form closed loops as suggested in Fig. 4-25. It is said that each flux line

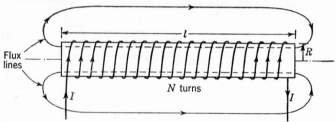

Fig. 4-25. Solenoid and flux lines.

that passes through the entire solenoid as in the figure links the current N times. If all of the flux lines link all of the turns, then the total *magnetic flux linkage* Λ (capital lambda) of the coil is equal to the total magnetic flux ψ_m through the coil times the number of turns, or

$$\text{Flux linkage} = \Lambda = N\psi_m \qquad \text{weber-turns} \qquad (4\text{-}57)$$

Since the number of turns N is dimensionless, flux linkage has the same dimensions as flux.

By definition the *inductance* L of an inductor is the ratio of its total magnetic flux linkage to the current I through the inductor, or

$$L = \frac{N\psi_m}{I} = \frac{\Lambda}{I} \qquad (4\text{-}58)$$

---

[1] An *inductor* is sometimes called an "inductance." However, it is usual practice to refer to a coil or solenoid as an inductor. This makes for uniform usage when we speak, for example, of an *inductor* of 1 henry *inductance*, a *capacitor* of 1 μf *capacitance*, or a *resistor* of 1 ohm *resistance*.

This definition is satisfactory for a medium with a constant permeability, such as air.   As discussed in Chap. 5, however, the permeability of ferrous media is not constant, and in this case the inductance is defined as the ratio of the infinitesimal change in flux linkage to the infinitesimal change in current producing it, or

$$L = \frac{d\Lambda}{dI} \qquad (4\text{-}59)$$

In linear media both (4-58) and (4-59) lead to the same result.   The inductance as given in (4-59) is discussed further in Sec. 7-16.

Inductance has the dimensions of

$$\frac{\text{Magnetic flux (linkage)}}{\text{Electric current}}$$

The unit of inductance is the *henry*.   Thus,

$$\text{Henrys} = \frac{\text{webers}}{\text{ampere}} = \frac{\text{newton-meters}}{\text{ampere}^2}$$

The dimensional symbols for inductance are ML^2/Q^2.

4-16. Inductance of Simple Geometries.   The inductance of many inductors can be readily calculated from their geometry.   As examples, expressions for the inductance of a long solenoid, a toroid, a coaxial line, and a two-wire line will be derived in this section.[1]

In Sec. 4-14 it is shown that the flux density B at the end of a long solenoid is less than at the center.   This is caused by flux leakage near the ends of the solenoid.   However, this leakage is mostly confined to a short distance at the ends of the solenoid (see Prob. 4-10) so that if the solenoid is very long, one may, to a good approximation, take B constant over the entire interior of the solenoid and equal to its value at the center (4-50).   The total flux linkage of a long solenoid is then

$$\Lambda = N\psi_m = NBA = \frac{\mu N^2 I A}{l} \qquad (4\text{-}60)$$

Thus, the inductance of a long solenoid (see Fig. 4-25) is

$$L = \frac{\Lambda}{I} = \frac{\mu N^2 A}{l} \qquad (4\text{-}61)$$

[1] For the inductance of other geometrical configurations see, for example, F. E. Terman, "Radio Engineers' Handbook," McGraw-Hill Book Company, Inc., New York, 1943, pp. 47–64; E. B. Rosa and F. W. Grover, "Formulas and Tables for the Calculation of Mutual and Self-inductance," *Natl. Bur. Standards (U.S.) Bull.*, Jan. 1, 1912, pp. 1–237; and "Radio Instruments and Measurements," *Natl. Bur. Standards (U.S.) Circ.* 74, pp. 242–296.

where L = inductance of solenoid (henrys)

Λ = flux linkage (weber-turns)

I = current through solenoid (amp)

μ = permeability of medium[1] (henrys/meter)

N = number of turns on solenoid (dimensionless)

A = cross-sectional area of solenoid (meters²)

l = length of solenoid (meters)

Example. Calculate the inductance of a solenoid of 2,000 turns wound uniformly over a length of 50 cm on a cylindrical paper tube 4 cm in diameter. The medium is air.

Solution. From (4-61) the inductance of the solenoid is

$$L = \frac{4\pi \times 10^{-7} \times 4 \times 10^6 \times \pi \times 4 \times 10^{-4}}{0.5} = 12.6 \text{ millihenrys (mh)}$$

If a long solenoid is bent into a circle and closed on itself, a toroidal coil, or toroid, is obtained. When the toroid has a uniform winding of many turns, the magnetic lines of flux are almost entirely confined to the interior of the winding, B being substantially zero outside. If the ratio R/r (see Fig. 4-26) is large, one may calculate B as though the toroid were straightened out into a solenoid. Thus, the flux linkages

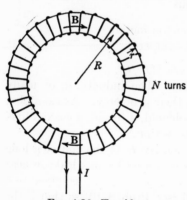

N turns

$$\Lambda = N\psi_m = NBA = \frac{\mu N^2 I \pi r^2}{2\pi R} = \frac{\mu N^2 I r^2}{2R}$$

$$(4\text{-}62)$$

Fig. 4-26. Toroid.

The inductance of the toroid is then

$$L = \frac{\Lambda}{I} = \frac{\mu N^2 r^2}{2R} \qquad (4\text{-}63)$$

where L = inductance of toroid (henrys)

μ = permeability (uniform and constant) of medium inside coil (henrys/meter)

N = number of turns of toroid (dimensionless)

r = radius of coil (see Fig. 4-26) (meters)

R = radius of toroid (meters)

Consider next a coaxial transmission line constructed of conducting

---

[1] It is to be noted that this relation applies only for the case where the medium has a uniform, constant permeability as is the case for air or vacuum (for which $\mu = \mu_0 = 4\pi \times 10^{-7}$ henry/meter).

cylinders of radius a and b as in Fig. 4-27. The current on the inner conductor is I. The return current on the outer conductor is of the same

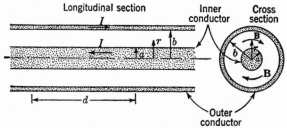

Fig. 4-27. Coaxial transmission line.

magnitude. The flux density B at any radius r is the same as at this radius from a long straight conductor with the same current, or

$$B \text{ (at } r) = \frac{\mu I}{2\pi r} \tag{4-64}$$

The total flux linkage for a length d of line is then d times the integral of (4-64) from the inner to the outer conductor, or

$$\Lambda = d \int_a^b B \, dr = \frac{d\mu I}{2\pi} \int_a^b \frac{dr}{r} = \frac{d\mu I}{2\pi} \ln \frac{b}{a} \tag{4-65}$$

Hence, the inductance of a length d of the coaxial line is

$$L = \frac{\Lambda}{I} = \frac{\mu d}{2\pi} \ln \frac{b}{a} \qquad \text{henrys} \tag{4-66}$$

or the inductance per unit length (L/d) for the coaxial line is given by

$$\frac{L}{d} = \frac{\mu}{2\pi} \ln \frac{b}{a} \qquad \text{henrys/meter} \tag{4-67}$$

where μ = permeability (uniform and constant) of medium inside coaxial
line (henrys/meter)

b = inside radius of outer conductor

a = outside radius of inner conductor (in same units as b)

It is assumed that the currents are confined to the radii a and b. This is effectively the case when the walls of the conductors are thin.[1]

Evaluating (4-67) for an air-filled line ($\mu = \mu_0$), we have

$$\frac{L}{d} = 0.2 \ln \frac{b}{a} = 0.46 \log \frac{b}{a} \qquad \text{microhenrys/meter } (\mu\text{h/meter}) \tag{4-68}$$

[1] At high frequencies the currents are effectively confined to these radii by the skin effect so that (4-67) is also applicable at high frequencies to a solid inner conductor and a thick outer conductor of inner radius b.

Let us consider finally a two-wire transmission line as illustrated in Fig. 4-28. The conductor radius is a, and the spacing between centers is D. At any radius r from one of the conductors the flux density B due to that conductor is given by (4-64). The total flux linkage due to

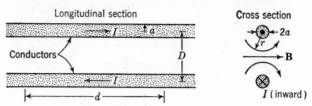

FIG. 4-28. Two-wire transmission line.

both conductors for a length d of line is then d times twice the integral of (4-64) from a to D, or

$$\Lambda = 2d \int_a^D B \, dr = \frac{\mu I d}{\pi} \int_a^D \frac{dr}{r} = \frac{\mu I d}{\pi} \ln \frac{D}{a} \qquad (4\text{-}69)$$

Hence, the inductance of a length d of the two conductor line is

$$L = \frac{\Lambda}{I} = \frac{\mu d}{\pi} \ln \frac{D}{a} \qquad (4\text{-}70)$$

or the inductance per unit length of line (L/d) is given by

$$\frac{L}{d} = \frac{\mu}{\pi} \ln \frac{D}{a} \qquad \text{henrys/meter} \qquad (4\text{-}71)$$

where μ = permeability (uniform and constant) of medium (henrys/meter)

D = spacing between centers of conductors

a = radius of conductors (in same units as D)

It is assumed that the current is confined to a radius a. This is effectively the case when the walls of the conductors are thin.[1]

Evaluating (4-71) for a medium of air ($\mu = \mu_0$), we have

$$\frac{L}{d} = 0.4 \ln \frac{D}{a} = 0.92 \log \frac{D}{a} \qquad \mu\text{h/meter} \qquad (4\text{-}72)$$

4-17. Ampère's Law and H. According to (4-16) the flux density B at a distance R from a long, straight conductor (Fig. 4-29) is given by

$$B = \frac{\mu I}{2\pi R} \qquad (4\text{-}73)$$

---

[1] Equation (4-71) also applies to solid conductors at high frequencies. For the case of solid conductors and steady or low-frequency currents, see for example, E. W. Kimbark, "Electrical Transmission of Power and Signals," John Wiley & Sons, Inc. New York, 1949, Sec. 2-11.

where μ = permeability of medium

I = current in wire

If **B** is now integrated around a path of radius R enclosing the wire once, we have

$$\oint \mathbf{B} \cdot d\mathbf{l} = \frac{\mu I}{2\pi R} \oint d l = \frac{\mu I}{2\pi R} 2\pi R = \mu I \qquad (4\text{-}74)$$

or

$$\oint \mathbf{B} \cdot d\mathbf{l} = \mu I \qquad (4\text{-}75)$$

The relation (4-75) holds not only in the example considered but also in all cases where the integration is over a singly closed path. It is to be noted that the line integral of **B** in (4-75) has the dimensions of force per pole multiplied by distance or of work per pole. Hence the line integral of **B** around the closed path in Fig. 4-29 yields the work per unit pole required to move one pole of a long magnetized needle around this path.

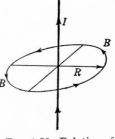

FIG. 4-29. Relation of flux density **B** to current I.

Equation (4-75) may be made independent of the medium by introducing the vector **H** defined as follows:

$$\mathbf{H} = \frac{\mathbf{B}}{\mu} \qquad (4\text{-}76)$$

According to (4-76) **H** and **B** are vectors having the same direction. This is true for all isotropic media.

The quantity **H** is called the magnetic field **H**, the vector **H**, or simply **H**.† It has the dimensions of

$$\frac{\text{Flux density}}{\text{Permeability}} = \frac{\text{current}}{\text{length}}$$

The dimensional symbols for **H** are Q/TL. In mksc units **H** is expressed in

$$\frac{\text{Webers/meter}^2}{\text{Webers/ampere-meter}} = \frac{\text{amperes}}{\text{meter}}$$

Introducing (4-76) into (4-75) yields

$$\oint \mathbf{H} \cdot d\mathbf{l} = I \qquad (4\text{-}77)$$

where **H** = **H** vector (amp/meter)

$d\mathbf{l}$ = infinitesimal element of path length (meters)

I = current enclosed (amp)

† The term "magnetic field intensity" has been used for **H**. This name, however, is not particularly appropriate since it implies that **H** is analogous to the electric field intensity **E**, which is not the case since in electric fields **E** enters in the force relations, whereas in magnetic fields it is **B** that enters the force expressions. The name "magnetizing force" is sometimes used for **H**.

This relation is known as *Ampère's law*. In words it states that *the line integral of* **H** *around a single closed path is equal to the current enclosed.*[1]

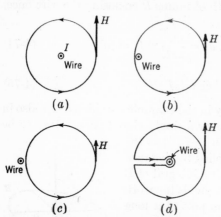

(a)   (b)

(c)   (d)

FIG. 4-30. Line integral of **H** around closed paths equals current in wire when paths enclose the wire, (a) and (b), but is zero when the paths do not enclose the wire, (c) and (d).

In the case of a single wire the integration always yields the current I in the wire regardless of the path of integration provided only that the wire is completely enclosed by the path. As illustrations, integration around the two paths at (a) and (b) in Fig. 4-30 yields I, while integration around the paths at (c) and (d) yields zero since these paths do not enclose the wire.

Example 1. The magnitude of **H** at a radius of 1 meter from a long linear conductor is 1 amp/meter. Find the current in the wire.

Solution. According to (4-77) the current in the wire is given by

$$I = \oint \mathbf{H} \cdot d\mathbf{l} = H \times 2\pi R = 2\pi \text{ amp}$$

Example 2. A solid cylindrical conductor of radius R has a uniform current density. Derive expressions for H both inside and outside of the conductor. Plot the variation of H as a function of radial distance from the center of the wire.

Solution. See Fig. 4-31a. Outside the wire ($r \geq R$)

$$H = \frac{I}{2\pi r} \qquad (4\text{-}78)$$

Inside the wire the value of H at a radius r is determined solely by the current inside the radius r. Thus, inside the wire ($r \leq R$)

$$H = \frac{I'}{2\pi r} \qquad (4\text{-}79)$$

where $I' = I(r/R)^2$ = current inside radius r. Therefore, inside the wire

$$H = \frac{I}{2\pi R^2} r \qquad (4\text{-}80)$$

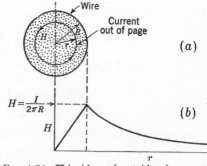

(a)

(b)

FIG. 4-31. **H** inside and outside of current-carrying wire (Example 2).

At the surface of the wire $r = R$, and (4-80) equals (4-78). A graph of the variation of H with r is presented in Fig. 4-31b.

---

[1] Equation (4-75) is another form of Ampère's law and may be stated thus: The line integral of **B** around a single closed path is equal to the permeability of the medium times the current enclosed.

4-18. Ampère's Law Applied to a Conducting Medium and Maxwell's Equation. Ampère's law as discussed in the preceding section may be applied to the more general situation of a path inside of a conducting medium. Thus, suppose that the origin of the coordinates in Fig. 4-32 is situated inside a conducting medium of large extent. Let the current density in the medium be J (amperes per square meter) in the positive y direction as shown. According to Ampère's law the line integral of H around the rectangular path enclosing the area A (Fig. 4-32) is equal to the current enclosed. In this case, the current I enclosed by the path is given by the integral of the normal component of J over the surface A, or

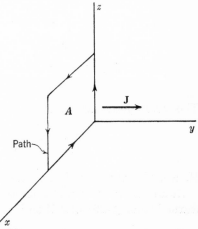

FIG. 4-32. Rectangular path in medium with current density J.

$$\oint \mathbf{H} \cdot d\mathbf{l} = \iint_A \mathbf{J} \cdot d\mathbf{s} = I \qquad (4\text{-}81)$$

This expression is a generalization of Ampère's law and constitutes one of Maxwell's equations in integral form. The corresponding equation in differential form involves the curl of H and is discussed in Sec. 4-23.

4-19. Magnetostatic Potential U and MMF F. According to (3-28c) the line integral of the static electric field E_c around a closed path is zero.[1] That is,

$$\oint \mathbf{E}_c \cdot d\mathbf{l} = 0 \qquad (4\text{-}82)$$

Fields of this type are called lamellar and can be derived from a related scalar potential function. Thus, E_c, which is due to charges, is derivable as the negative gradient of a scalar potential V, or

$$\mathbf{E}_c = -\nabla V \qquad (4\text{-}83)$$

Between any two points along a path in the field we have

$$\int_1^2 \mathbf{E}_c \cdot d\mathbf{l} = V_1 - V_2 \qquad (4\text{-}84)$$

Although the static magnetic field is not lamellar, since magnetic flux lines form closed loops, it can be treated like a lamellar field if paths of

---

[1] The symbol E_c indicates explicitly a static electric field as produced by electric charges, as distinguished from an emf-generating field E_e, as, for example, in a battery. In Chaps. 1 and 2 only E_c fields were considered, and so for simplicity no subscript was used, it being understood in those chapters that E means E_c.

integration are entirely outside of current regions and do not enclose any current. Thus, *when no current is enclosed,*

$$\oint \mathbf{H} \cdot d\mathbf{l} = 0 \qquad (4\text{-}85)$$

Under this condition, $\mathbf{H}$ can then be derived from a scalar magnetic potential function (or magnetostatic potential) U. That is,[1]

$$\mathbf{H} = -\nabla U \qquad (4\text{-}86)$$

Between any two points along a path in the field we have

$$\int_1^2 \mathbf{H} \cdot d\mathbf{l} = U_1 - U_2 \qquad (4\text{-}87)$$

The scalar potential U has the dimensions of

$$\frac{\text{Current}}{\text{Distance}} \times \text{distance} = \text{current}$$

Hence, U is expressed in amperes.

Returning now to a further consideration of electric fields, we have learned from (3-29) that if emfs exist in a path of integration,

$$\oint \mathbf{E} \cdot d\mathbf{l} = \upsilon \qquad (4\text{-}88)$$

where $\mathbf{E}$ = total field (volts/meter)
    υ = total emf around path (volts)

In a magnetic field we may write an analogous relation, based on Ampère's law, that *when current is enclosed* by a path of integration

$$\oint \mathbf{H} \cdot d\mathbf{l} = I = F \qquad \text{amp} \qquad (4\text{-}89)$$

where the quantity F, called the magnetomotance, magnetomotive force, or mmf, is equal to the current enclosed. If the path of integration in (4-89) encloses a number of turns of wire each with a current I in the same direction, (4-89) may be written

$$\oint \mathbf{H} \cdot d\mathbf{l} = NI = F \qquad \text{amp-turns} \qquad (4\text{-}90)$$

where N = number of turns of wire enclosed (dimensionless)
    I = current in each turn (amp)
The product NI is expressed in *ampere-turns*, and the mmf in this case has the same units.

The above relations for electric and magnetic fields are summarized in Table 4-1.

[1] Since $\nabla \cdot \mathbf{D} = 0$ in charge-free regions, we obtain Laplace's equation $\nabla^2 V = 0$. In a magnetic field we always have $\nabla \cdot \mathbf{B} = 0$; so if no current is enclosed, we may write Laplace's equation in the magnetostatic potential as $\nabla^2 U = 0$.

TABLE 4-1

COMPARISON OF ELECTRIC AND MAGNETIC FIELD RELATIONS

Relation	Electrostatic fields	Magnetostatic fields
Closed path	$\oint \mathbf{E}_c \cdot dl = 0$	$\oint \mathbf{H} \cdot dl = 0$. No current enclosed (Fig. 4-33)
Gradient of scalar potential	$\mathbf{E}_c = -\nabla V$ volts/meter	$\mathbf{H} = -\nabla U$ amp/meter. In current-free region
Integral between two points	$\int_1^2 \mathbf{E}_c \cdot dl = V_1 - V_2$ volts	$\int_1^2 \mathbf{H} \cdot dl = U_1 - U_2$ amp. Path avoids all currents
Closed path	$\oint \mathbf{E} \cdot dl = \mho$ volts	$\oint \mathbf{H} \cdot dl = I = F$ amp. Path encloses currents (Fig. 4-34a) or $\oint \mathbf{H} \cdot dl = NI = F$ amp-turns. Path encloses current N times (Fig. 4-34b)

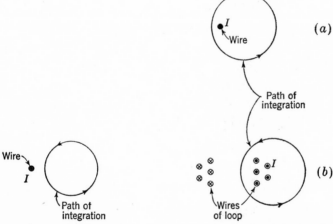

FIG. 4-33. Path of integration enclosing no current (see Table 4-1).

FIG. 4-34. (a) Path of integration enclosing current I. (b) Cross section through 5-turn loop showing path linking the 5 turns (see Table 4-1).

When the integration is restricted to current-free regions and to paths that are not closed, the potential U and mmf F are the same. The requirement that the path not link the current can be met by introducing a hypothetical barrier surface in the magnetic field through which the path is not allowed to pass. For example, imagine that a long conductor normal to the page as in Fig. 4-35 carries a current I. Let a barrier surface be constructed that extends from the wire an infinite distance to

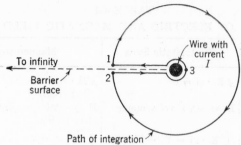

Path of integration
Fig. 4-35. Conductor and barrier surface.

the left as suggested in the figure. Now the integral of **H** from points 1 to 2 yields the current I provided 2 and 1 are separated by an infinitesimal distance. Thus

$$\int_1^2 \mathbf{H} \cdot d\mathbf{l} = U_1 - U_2 = F_1 - F_2 = I \qquad \text{amp} \qquad (4\text{-}91)$$

The requirement of (4-85) is still satisfied since the line integral of **H** around the closed path 1231 that avoids crossing the barrier is zero. That is,

$$\oint_{1231} \mathbf{H} \cdot d\mathbf{l} = 0 \qquad (4\text{-}92)$$

Both U and F are scalar functions. The potential U is independent of the path of integration, that is, U is a single-valued function of position. This follows from the fact that the path of integration never completely encloses the current and is restricted to current-free regions. If a current-carrying wire is encircled more than once by the path of integration (multiple linking), the result is called the mmf F. It is multiple-valued since its magnitude depends on the number of times the path encircles the wire. Hence F is *not*, in general, independent of the path of integration.

In Fig. 4-35 the barrier surface represents a magnetic equipotential plane. If point 1 is taken arbitrarily as zero potential, then the potential of point 2 on the other side of the barrier is I. Hence, we may construct two surfaces as in Fig. 4-36, one with $U = 0$ and the other $U = I$. Other equipotential surfaces are also drawn in Fig. 4-36 for $U = I/4$, $U = I/2$, and $U = 3I/4$.† The equipotential surfaces are everywhere normal to **H** and extend from the surface of the wire to infinity. They *do not extend into the interior of the wire*. However, if the equipotential surfaces were extended into the wire (shown dashed) and were everywhere normal to

† Potential is a measure of work per some quantity. The potential U is proportional to the work per unit magnetic pole required to move a magnetic pole from one point to another.

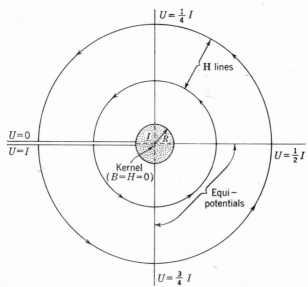

Fig. 4-36. Current-carrying wire showing magnetic equipotentials (radial) and field lines (circles).

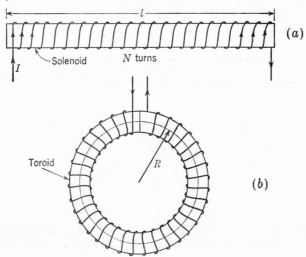

Fig. 4-37. (a) Long solenoid. (b) Solenoid bent into toroid.

H, they would meet at a point called the *kernel* where B and H are both zero.

Example. Find the value of H in a long solenoid of length l and of N turns, carrying a current I (see Fig. 4-37a), by evaluating the mmf. The diameter of the solenoid is small compared with l.

Solution. For a long solenoid the field inside is essentially uniform and will not be appreciably changed if the solenoid is bent into a circle and closed on itself, forming a toroid (as in Fig. 4-37*b*).   Then, integrating **H** once around a path entirely inside the coil (at a radius R), we link all of the turns obtaining the mmf, or

$$\oint \mathbf{H} \cdot d\mathbf{l} = F = NI \tag{4-93}$$

Let the magnitude of **H** inside be H_i.   Then (4-93) becomes

$$\oint \mathbf{H} \cdot d\mathbf{l} = H_i \oint dl = H_i 2\pi R$$
$$= H_i l = NI \tag{4-94}$$

or

$$H_i = \frac{NI}{l} = K \tag{4-95}$$

The identical result was obtained in (4-50), as may be noted by dividing (4-50) by μ.

4-20. Field Cells and Permeability.   In Sec. 4-16 the inductance was calculated for a unit length of transmission line consisting of two parallel

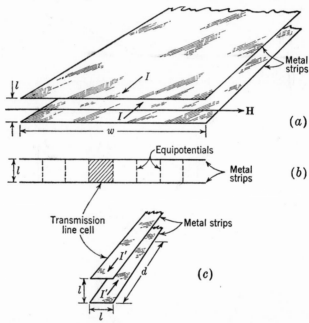

Fig. 4-38. Parallel-strip transmission line (*a*) in perspective and (*b*) in cross section. (*c*) Magnetic field cell (or transmission-line cell) with strips of width equal to spacing.

conducting wires.   Let us consider now a transmission line of two flat parallel conducting strips as in Fig. 4-38*a* and calculate its inductance per unit length.   The strips have a width w and a separation l.   Each strip carries a current I.   The transmission line is shown in cross section in Fig. 4-38*b*.   The field between the strips is uniform, except near the open sides.   If equipotentials are drawn in the uniform field region with a spacing equal to the separation l of the line, we may regard the line as being composed of a number of *field-cell transmission lines* (or *transmis-*

sion-line cells) arranged in parallel.   Each transmission-line cell has a square cross section as in Fig. 4-38c.

The current in each strip of a line cell is

$$I' = \frac{l}{w} I \tag{4-96}$$

where I = current in entire line.

Thus, across one cell

$$Hl = I' \tag{4-97}$$

Now the total flux linkage per length d of line is given by

$$\Lambda = Bld \tag{4-98}$$

The inductance of this length of line is then

$$L_0 = \frac{\Lambda}{I'} = \frac{Bld}{Hl} = \mu d \tag{4-99}$$

or the inductance per unit length is

$$\frac{L_0}{d} = \mu \tag{4-100}$$

For air $\mu = \mu_0 = 4\pi \times 10^{-7}$ henry per meter so that a field-cell transmission line with air as the medium has an inductance per unit length of $4\pi \times 10^{-7}$ henry per meter or 1.26 μh per meter.

Thus, the permeability μ of a medium may be interpreted as the inductance per unit length of a transmission-line cell filled with this medium. Another interpretation is given in Sec. 5-19.

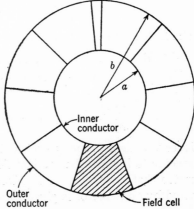

Example. Using the field-cell concept, calculate the inductance and also capacitance per unit length of the coaxial transmission line shown in cross section in Fig. 4-39. The line is air-filled.

Solution. The inductance per unit length of the coaxial line is given by

FIG. 4-39. Coaxial transmission line divided into 9.15 field-cell lines in parallel.

$$\frac{L}{d} = \frac{1}{n}\frac{L_0}{d} = \frac{\mu_0}{n} \quad \text{henrys/meter} \tag{4-101}$$

where L_0/d = inductance per unit length of transmission-line cell
n = number of line cells in parallel
μ_0 = permeability of air = $4\pi \times 10^{-7}$ henry/meter ($= 1.26$ μh/meter)

Dividing the space between the coaxial conductors into curvilinear squares, we obtain 9.15 line cells in parallel. Thus

$$\frac{L}{d} = \frac{1.26}{9.15} = 0.138 \ \mu h/meter$$

As a check, we note that the radius of the outer conductor is twice the radius of the inner so that from (4-68) we get

$$\frac{L}{d} = 0.46 \log 2 = 0.138 \ \mu h/meter$$

which is the same result as obtained above. Equation (4-68) is exact for this case. The accuracy of the cell method depends on the accuracy of construction of the curvilinear squares. However, the cell method (or field-mapping method) is applicable to conductor configurations that might be very difficult to handle mathematically. For a further discussion of the mapping of magnetic fields see Sec. 5-20.

The capacitance per unit length of the coaxial line of Fig. 4-39 is given by

$$\frac{C}{d} = n \frac{C_0}{d} = n\epsilon_0 \qquad farads/meter \tag{4-102}$$

where C_0/d = capacitance per unit length of line cell (same as capacitance per unit length of field-cell capacitor; see Sec. 2-27)

n = number of line cells in parallel

ϵ_0 = permittivity of air = 8.85 $\mu\mu f/meter$

Thus

$$\frac{C}{d} = 9.15 \times 8.85 = 81 \ \mu\mu f/meter$$

Using the exact relation of (2-82),

$$\frac{C}{d} = \frac{24.2}{\log 2} = 81 \ \mu\mu f/meter$$

which is the same as obtained by the cell method.

4-21. Energy in an Inductor. Inductance L has the dimensions of magnetic flux per current (force $\times$ distance/current²). Thus, the product LI^2 has the dimensions of energy since

$$\frac{Force \times distance}{Current^2} \times current^2 = force \times distance = energy$$

Hence we might properly expect the relation for the energy stored in an inductor to involve the product LI^2, and in Sec. 7-14 it will be demonstrated that this is the case. More specifically the magnetic energy W_m stored by an inductor is given by

$$W_m = \tfrac{1}{2}LI^2 \qquad joules \tag{4-103}$$

Now, from (4-58), $L = \Lambda/I$ so that the energy stored by an inductor can be variously expressed as

$$W_m = \frac{1}{2} LI^2 = \frac{1}{2} \Lambda I = \frac{1}{2} \frac{\Lambda^2}{L} \qquad joules \tag{4-104}$$

where W_m = energy stored (joules)

$\quad\quad L$ = inductance of inductor (henrys)

$\quad\quad I$ = current through inductor (amp)

$\quad\quad \Lambda$ = flux linkages (weber-turns)

4-22. Energy Density in a Static Magnetic Field. The energy possessed by an inductor is stored in its magnetic field. Let us find the density of this energy as a function of the flux density **B**. Consider a small unit cube of side length Δl and volume $\Delta v = \Delta l^3$ situated in a magnetic field as in Fig. 4-40a. Let thin metal sheets be placed on the top and bottom surfaces of the cube, each with a current ΔI as indicated. Also let all of the surrounding space be filled with such cubes as suggested by the cross section of Fig. 4-40b. The directions of the current flow on the sheets are indicated by the circles with dot (current out of page) and circles with cross (current into page).

Each cube can be regarded as a magnetic field-cell transmission line of length (into page) of Δl. Each cell has an inductance

$$\Delta L = \mu \, \Delta l \quad\quad (4\text{-}105)$$

The field H is related to the current ΔI by

$$H \, \Delta l = \Delta I \quad\quad (4\text{-}106)$$

The energy stored in each cell is, from (4-104),

$$\Delta W_m = \tfrac{1}{2} \, \Delta L \, \Delta I^2 \quad \text{joules} \quad (4\text{-}107)$$

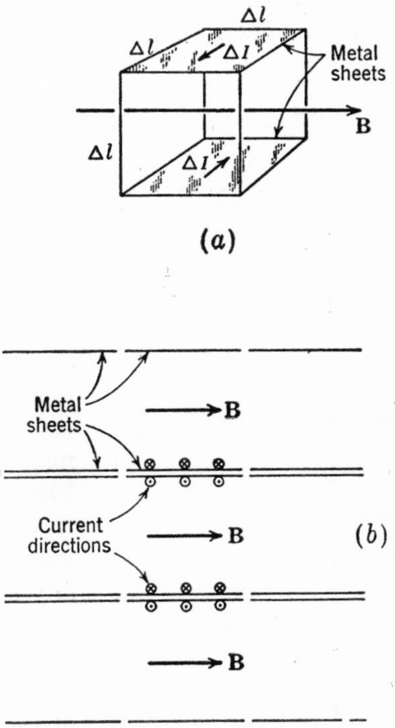

(a)

(b)

FIG. 4-40. (a) Small cubical volume in a magnetic field. (b) Cross section through region filled with many such cubes.

Introducing the value of ΔL from (4-105) and ΔI from (4-106) into (4-107) yields

$$\Delta W_m = \tfrac{1}{2}\mu H^2 \, \Delta l^3 = \tfrac{1}{2}\mu H^2 \, \Delta v \quad\quad (4\text{-}108)$$

Dividing (4-108) by Δv and taking the limit of the ratio $\Delta W_m/\Delta v$ as Δv approaches zero, we obtain the energy per volume, or *energy density*, w_m of the magnetic field at the point around which the cell of volume Δv shrinks to zero. Thus

$$w_m = \lim_{\Delta v \to 0} \frac{\Delta W}{\Delta v} = \frac{1}{2} \, \mu H^2 \quad\quad (4\text{-}109)$$

Since $H = B/\mu$, we have

$$w_m = \frac{1}{2}\mu H^2 = \frac{1}{2}\frac{B^2}{\mu} \qquad \text{joules/meter}^3 \qquad (4\text{-}110)$$

where w_m = energy density of magnetic field (joules/meter^3)
  μ = permeability of medium (henrys/meter)
  $H = H$ field (amp/meter)
  B = flux density (webers/meter^2)

The total energy W_m stored by an inductor is then the integral of (4-110) over the entire extent of its magnetic field, or

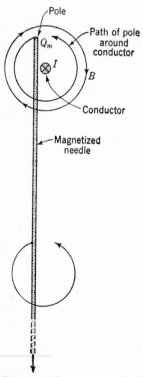

$$W_m = \int_v w_m \, dv = \frac{1}{2}\int_v \frac{B^2}{\mu}\, dv \qquad \text{joules} \tag{4-111}$$

4-23. Curl. Equation (4-75) relates the line integral of **B** around a *finite closed path*, or *loop*, to μI, where I is the *current* enclosed by the loop. The line integral of **B** may be regarded as the work per unit pole required to move a pole around the closed path. For example, the work per unit pole required to move a long magnetized needle once around a wire, as in Fig. 4-41, equals μI, where I is the current in the wire. The other pole of the needle is at a large distance and in a field that is substantially zero.

Although relations involving finite paths are useful in circuit theory, it is frequently desirable in field theory to be able to relate quantities *at a point* in space. Curl, which is discussed in this section, is such a point relation and can be regarded as an extension of Ampère's law so that it applies at a point.

Fig. 4-41. Long magnetized needle near current-carrying conductor.

Consider a small plane area Δs in a conducting medium with a current ΔI flowing through the area and normal to it. The meaning of the curl of **B** may then be expressed as follows: *The magnitude of the curl of **B** is equal to the ratio of the work per unit magnetic pole (carried around the boundary of the area) to the area Δs as Δs approaches zero. Further, the curl of **B** is a vector with a direction normal to the plane of the area.* Thus, the magnitude of the curl of **B** is given by

$$\lim_{\Delta s \to 0} \frac{\oint \mathbf{B} \cdot d\mathbf{l}}{\Delta s} = \lim_{\Delta s \to 0} \mu \frac{\Delta I}{\Delta s} = \mu J \tag{4-112}$$

where J = current density = $\Delta I/\Delta s$ as $\Delta s \to 0$

ΔI = current through area Δs

The direction of the curl of **B** is normal to the area Δs.

Equation (4-112) gives the total curl of **B** if **J** is normal to the plane of the loop. If **J** is not normal to the plane of the loop, (4-112) gives only one component of the total curl expression, which will be developed in the following paragraphs.

Suppose that the rectangular coordinate system shown in Fig. 4-42 is situated inside of a conducting medium of large extent. Let the current density in the medium be **J** and the component of the current density in

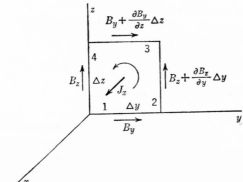

FIG. 4-42. Construction for finding x component of curl of **B**.

the x direction J_x. The permeability is uniform and equal to μ. The total current ΔI through the small area $\Delta y\,\Delta z$ (Fig. 4-42) is then

$$J_x\,\Delta y\,\Delta z = \Delta I \qquad (4\text{-}113)$$

This current produces a magnetic field. Let the flux density along edge 1 of the area at the y axis be B_y and the flux density along edge 4 at the z axis be B_z. If the field is not uniform, its value at edges 2 and 3 may be expressed to a first approximation by

$$B_z + \frac{\partial B_z}{\partial y}\,\Delta y \qquad (4\text{-}114)$$

and

$$B_y + \frac{\partial B_y}{\partial z}\,\Delta z \qquad (4\text{-}115)$$

as indicated in Fig. 4-42.

Consider now the work performed per unit magnetic pole carried around the periphery of the area. The total work is equal to the sum of the increments of work along each of the four edges. Each increment of work equals the force per unit pole (**B**) multiplied by the distance the unit pole moves. The total work will be calculated per unit magnetic pole moved around the path in a counterclockwise direction, as shown in Fig. 4-42. This is the positive direction around the path since a right-handed screw rotated in this direction will advance in the positive x direction. The work to move the unit pole along edge 1 is $B_y \, \Delta y$ and along edge 2 is

$$\left(B_z + \frac{\partial B_z}{\partial y} \, \Delta y \right) \Delta z$$

The work along edge 3 is

$$- \left(B_y + \frac{\partial B_y}{\partial z} \, \Delta z \right) \Delta y$$

the minus sign indicating that the motion is against the field. The work along edge 4 is $-B_z \, \Delta z$. The total work equals the sum of these four increments and this is equal to μ times the total current through the area as given by (4-113). Thus,

$$\oint \mathbf{B} \cdot d\mathbf{l} = B_y \, \Delta y + B_z \, \Delta z + \frac{\partial B_z}{\partial y} \, \Delta y \, \Delta z$$

$$- B_y \, \Delta y - \frac{\partial B_y}{\partial z} \, \Delta y \, \Delta z - B_z \, \Delta z = \mu J_x \, \Delta y \, \Delta z \quad (4\text{-}116)$$

The terms with $B_y \, \Delta y$ and $B_z \, \Delta z$ cancel, leaving only the differential terms. Thus

$$\oint \mathbf{B} \cdot d\mathbf{l} = \left(\frac{\partial B_z}{\partial y} - \frac{\partial B_y}{\partial z} \right) \Delta y \, \Delta z = \mu J_x \, \Delta y \, \Delta z \quad (4\text{-}117)$$

Let us now divide by the area $\Delta y \, \Delta z$ and take the limit of the ratio

$$\frac{\text{Work done around periphery of area}}{\text{Area}}$$

as the area approaches zero. By definition this is the curl of $\mathbf{B}$. In this instance it is the x component of the curl of $\mathbf{B}$, written $\mathrm{curl}_x \, \mathbf{B}$. Therefore, we have

$$\lim_{\Delta y \, \Delta z \to 0} \frac{\oint \mathbf{B} \cdot d\mathbf{l}}{\Delta y \, \Delta z} = \frac{\partial B_z}{\partial y} - \frac{\partial B_y}{\partial z} = \mu J_x = \mathrm{curl}_x \, \mathbf{B} \quad (4\text{-}118)$$

Each term in (4-118) has the dimensions of permeability times current density.

Equation (4-118) would be the complete differential expression for curl $\mathbf{B}$ if the current flows only in the x direction. However, if the current also has components flowing in the y and z directions, curl $\mathbf{B}$ also has components in these directions. Let us then derive the differential expressions for these components, considering next the component in the y direction. Assume now that the coordinate system of Fig. 4-43 is set up inside of a conducting medium of large extent as before and that the component of the current density in the y direction is J_y. The total current through the small area $\Delta x\, \Delta z$ is $J_y\, \Delta x\, \Delta z$. Let the components of the magnetic flux density along the edges of the area be as indicated in Fig. 4-43. The work accomplished per unit magnetic pole moved

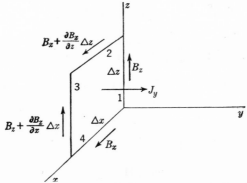

FIG. 4-43. Construction for finding y component of curl of $\mathbf{B}$.

around the periphery of the area in the positive direction is then

$$\oint \mathbf{B} \cdot d\mathbf{l} = B_z\, \Delta z + B_x\, \Delta x + \frac{\partial B_x}{\partial z}\, \Delta z\, \Delta x$$

$$- B_z\, \Delta z - \frac{\partial B_z}{\partial x}\, \Delta x\, \Delta z - B_x\, \Delta x = \mu J_x\, \Delta x\, \Delta z \quad (4\text{-}119)$$

This reduces to

$$\oint \mathbf{B} \cdot d\mathbf{l} = \left(\frac{\partial B_x}{\partial z} - \frac{\partial B_z}{\partial x}\right) \Delta x\, \Delta z = \mu J_y\, \Delta x\, \Delta z \quad (4\text{-}120)$$

Dividing by the area of the loop $\Delta x\, \Delta z$ and taking the limit of the ratio as the area approaches zero yields the component of the curl in the y direction. Thus

$$\lim_{\Delta x\, \Delta z \to 0} \frac{\oint \mathbf{B} \cdot d\mathbf{l}}{\Delta x\, \Delta z} = \operatorname{curl}_y \mathbf{B} = \frac{\partial B_x}{\partial z} - \frac{\partial B_z}{\partial x} = \mu J_y \quad (4\text{-}121)$$

In a similar way we obtain the differential expression for the component of curl $\mathbf{B}$ in the z direction[1] as

$$\operatorname{curl}_z \mathbf{B} = \frac{\partial B_y}{\partial x} - \frac{\partial B_x}{\partial y} = \mu J_z \quad (4\text{-}122)$$

Adding vectorially the three rectangular components of curl $\mathbf{B}$ as given by (4-118), (4-121), and (4-122), we have

$$\operatorname{curl} \mathbf{B} = \mathbf{i}\, \operatorname{curl}_x \mathbf{B} + \mathbf{j}\, \operatorname{curl}_y \mathbf{B} + \mathbf{k}\, \operatorname{curl}_z \mathbf{B} \quad (4\text{-}123)$$

or

$$\operatorname{curl} \mathbf{B} = \mathbf{i}\left(\frac{\partial B_z}{\partial y} - \frac{\partial B_y}{\partial z}\right) + \mathbf{j}\left(\frac{\partial B_x}{\partial z} - \frac{\partial B_z}{\partial x}\right) + \mathbf{k}\left(\frac{\partial B_y}{\partial x} - \frac{\partial B_x}{\partial y}\right) \quad (4\text{-}124)$$

[1] The student should construct the figure and confirm the result.

The curl of **B** may also be expressed in determinant form as

$$\text{curl } \mathbf{B} = \begin{vmatrix} \mathbf{i} & \mathbf{j} & \mathbf{k} \\ \dfrac{\partial}{\partial x} & \dfrac{\partial}{\partial y} & \dfrac{\partial}{\partial z} \\ B_x & B_y & B_z \end{vmatrix} \tag{4-125}$$

In these equations, curl **B** is equal to μ times the vector sum of the component current densities in the three coordinate directions so that we have

$$\text{curl } \mathbf{B} = \mu(\mathbf{i}J_x + \mathbf{j}J_y + \mathbf{k}J_z) = \mu\mathbf{J} \tag{4-126}$$

or

$$\text{curl } \mathbf{B} = \mu\mathbf{J} \tag{4-127}$$

Dividing (4-127) by μ, we have

$$\text{curl } \mathbf{H} = \mathbf{J} \tag{4-128}$$

Writing out the components for curl **H** and **J**,

$$\text{curl } \mathbf{H} = \mathbf{i}\left(\frac{\partial H_z}{\partial y} - \frac{\partial H_y}{\partial z}\right) + \mathbf{j}\left(\frac{\partial H_x}{\partial z} - \frac{\partial H_z}{\partial x}\right) + \mathbf{k}\left(\frac{\partial H_y}{\partial x} - \frac{\partial H_x}{\partial y}\right)$$
$$= \mathbf{i}J_x + \mathbf{j}J_y + \mathbf{k}J_z \tag{4-129}$$

It is to be noted that (4-129) yields three scalar equations obtained by equating the components in each of the three coordinate directions.

The curl of a quantity is a point function. Therefore, according to (4-128) the curl of **H** has a value only at points where the current density **J** is not zero. At a point inside of a wire carrying a steady current, curl **H** equals the current density **J** at the point, but at a point outside the wire curl **H** = 0.†

The curl of **H** may be indicated in different ways. Three shorthand notations for the curl of **H** are:

$$\text{curl } \mathbf{H}$$
$$\nabla \times \mathbf{H}$$
$$\text{rot } \mathbf{H}$$

All three have identical meanings. Thus

$$\text{curl } \mathbf{H} = \nabla \times \mathbf{H} = \text{rot } \mathbf{H} = \mathbf{J} \tag{4-130}$$

The notation rot **H** is often used in the European technical literature. The form $\nabla \times \mathbf{H}$ involves the cross product of the operator ∇ and the

† In the case of time-changing fields, as discussed in Chap. 7, there may be a "displacement" current at points outside the wire, and consequently curl **H** need not be zero in this situation.

vector **H**. In the next section it will be demonstrated that this cross product is equivalent to (4-129).

4-24. ∇ × H. Referring to the discussion on the cross product in Sec. 4-11, let us show that the cross product of the operator ∇ into **H**, written ∇ × **H**, is equal to the curl of **H**. To do this, we write ∇ and **H** out in terms of their three rectangular components and take the individual products. Thus

$$\nabla \times \mathbf{H} = \left(\mathbf{i}\frac{\partial}{\partial x} + \mathbf{j}\frac{\partial}{\partial y} + \mathbf{k}\frac{\partial}{\partial z} \right) \times (\mathbf{i}H_x + \mathbf{j}H_y + \mathbf{k}H_z)$$

$$= \mathbf{i} \times \mathbf{i}\frac{\partial H_x}{\partial x} + \mathbf{j} \times \mathbf{i}\frac{\partial H_x}{\partial y} + \mathbf{k} \times \mathbf{i}\frac{\partial H_x}{\partial z}$$

$$+ \mathbf{i} \times \mathbf{j}\frac{\partial H_y}{\partial x} + \mathbf{j} \times \mathbf{j}\frac{\partial H_y}{\partial y} + \mathbf{k} \times \mathbf{j}\frac{\partial H_y}{\partial z}$$

$$+ \mathbf{i} \times \mathbf{k}\frac{\partial H_z}{\partial x} + \mathbf{j} \times \mathbf{k}\frac{\partial H_z}{\partial y} + \mathbf{k} \times \mathbf{k}\frac{\partial H_z}{\partial z} \qquad (4\text{-}131)$$

Introducing the values of the cross products for the unit vectors as given in (4-29), Eq. (4-131) becomes

$$\nabla \times \mathbf{H} = -\mathbf{k}\frac{\partial H_x}{\partial y} + \mathbf{j}\frac{\partial H_x}{\partial z} + \mathbf{k}\frac{\partial H_y}{\partial x} - \mathbf{i}\frac{\partial H_y}{\partial z} - \mathbf{j}\frac{\partial H_z}{\partial x} + \mathbf{i}\frac{\partial H_z}{\partial y} \qquad (4\text{-}132)$$

Collecting terms,

$$\nabla \times \mathbf{H} = \mathbf{i}\left(\frac{\partial H_z}{\partial y} - \frac{\partial H_y}{\partial z} \right) + \mathbf{j}\left(\frac{\partial H_x}{\partial z} - \frac{\partial H_z}{\partial x} \right) + \mathbf{k}\left(\frac{\partial H_y}{\partial x} - \frac{\partial H_x}{\partial y} \right) \qquad (4\text{-}133)$$

This is identical with the expression for curl **H** in (4-129). We conclude, therefore, that the cross product of ∇ into **H** equals curl **H** or, more generally, that the operator ∇ × applied to vector function yields the curl of that vector. The operator ∇ × may, accordingly, be regarded as the *curl operator*.

4-25. Examples of Curl. In this section four examples are given to illustrate the significance of curl.

Example 1. A rectangular trough carries water in the x direction. A section of the trough is shown in Fig. 4-44a, the vertical direction coinciding with the z axis. The width of the trough is b. Find the curl of the velocity **v** of the water for two assumed conditions:

a. The velocity is everywhere uniform and equal to a constant, that is,

$$\mathbf{v} = \mathbf{i}K \qquad (4\text{-}134)$$

where **i** = unit vector in positive x direction (dimensionless)

K = a constant (meters/sec)

A top view of the trough is shown in Fig. 4-44b with the positive x direction downward. The fact that the velocity **v** is constant is suggested by the arrows of uniform length and also by the graph of v_x as a function of y in Fig. 4-44c.

b. The velocity varies from zero at the edges of the trough to a maximum at the center, the quantitative variation being given by

$$\mathbf{v} = \mathbf{i}K \sin \frac{\pi y}{b} \qquad (4\text{-}135)$$

where K = a constant (meters/sec)

b = width of trough (meters)

The sinusoidal variation of $\mathbf{v}$ is suggested by the arrows in the top view of the trough in Fig. 4-44e and also by the graph of v_x as a function of y in Fig. 4-44f.

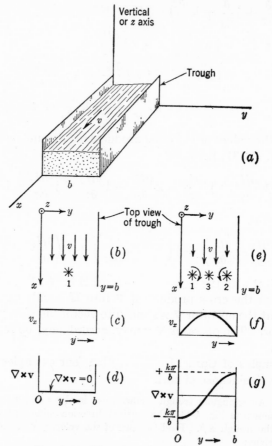

Fig. 4-44. Water trough for Example 1.

Solution.   *a.* Equation (4-134) may be reexpressed

$$\mathbf{v} = \mathbf{i}v_x \qquad (4\text{-}136)$$

where v_x = component of velocity in x direction.   Thus $v_x = K$.   Now the curl of $\mathbf{v}$ has two terms involving v_x, namely, $\partial v_x/\partial z$ and $\partial v_x/\partial y$.   Since v_x is a constant, both terms are zero and hence $\nabla \times \mathbf{v} = 0$ everywhere in the trough (see Fig. 4-44d).

b. Equation (4-135) may be reexpressed

$$\mathbf{v} = \mathbf{i}v_x$$

Thus

$$v_x = K \sin \frac{\pi y}{b} \qquad (4\text{-}137)$$

Since v_x is not a function of z, the derivative $\partial v_x/\partial z = 0$. However, v_x is a function of y so that

$$\frac{\partial v_x}{\partial y} = \frac{K\pi}{b} \cos \frac{\pi y}{b} \qquad (4\text{-}138)$$

and we have for the curl of $\mathbf{v}$

$$\nabla \times \mathbf{v} = -\mathbf{a}_z \frac{K\pi}{b} \cos \frac{\pi y}{b} \qquad (4\text{-}139)$$

where $\mathbf{a}_z$ = unit vector in positive z direction (**k** might also be used, but $\mathbf{a}_z$ is convenient here to avoid confusion with the constant K). That is, at the left of the center of the trough the curl of $\mathbf{v}$ is in the negative z direction (downward in Fig. 4-44*a*), while to the right of the center it is in the positive z direction. The variation of the curl of $\mathbf{v}$ across the trough is presented graphically in Fig. 4-44*g*.

A physical interpretation of the curl of $\mathbf{v}$ in the above example may be obtained with the aid of the curl-meter, or paddle-wheel, device[1] of Fig. 4-45. If this device is inserted with its shaft vertical into the trough with the assumed sinusoidal variation for the velocity of the water (Example 1*b*), it would spin clockwise when at the left of the center of the trough (position 1 in Fig. 4-44*e*) and would spin counterclockwise when at the right of the center of the trough (position 2 in Fig. 4-44*e*), corresponding to negative and positive values of curl. At the center of the trough (position 3 in Fig. 4-44*e*) the curl meter would not rotate since the forces on the paddles are balanced. This corresponds to the curl of $\mathbf{v}$ being zero. The rate of rotation of the paddle-wheel shaft is proportional to the curl of $\mathbf{v}$ at the point where it is inserted. Thus, it would rotate fastest near the edges of the trough. At any point the rate of rotation is also a maximum with the shaft vertical (rather than inclined to the vertical), indicating that $\nabla \times \mathbf{v}$ is in the z direction. It is assumed that the paddle wheel is small enough so that it does not appreciably affect the flow and also that it is small enough to indicate closely the conditions at a point.

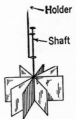

F I G . 4 - 4 5 . Paddle wheel for measuring curl.

If the curl meter with shaft vertical is inserted in water with uniform velocity, as assumed in Ex. 1*a*, it will not rotate (curl **v** equals zero).

Example 2. A rectangular trough of width b carries water in the x direction. The velocity is uniform over half the trough ($0 < y < b/2$) and equal to v_1 and also uniform over the other half ($b/2 < y < b$) but equal to a smaller velocity v_2. At the

[1] H. H. Skilling, "Fundamentals of Electric Waves," 2d ed., John Wiley & Sons, Inc., New York, 1948, p. 24.

center of the trough $(y = b/2)$ the velocity changes abruptly from v_1 to v_2. The variation of the velocity as a function of y is suggested by the arrows in the top view of the trough in Fig. 4-46a and also is indicated in the graph of Fig. 4-46b. Find the curl of **v**.

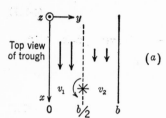

Solution. The curl of **v** is zero either side of the center of the trough since the velocity is a constant in these regions. However, at the center of the trough the velocity changes from v_1 to v_2. That is,

$$\text{For } y < \frac{b}{2}: \quad v_x = v_1$$

$$\text{For } y > \frac{b}{2}: \quad v_x = v_2$$

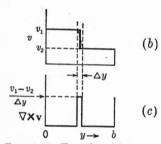

If this change is perfectly abrupt, $\partial v_x/\partial y$ is infinite at the center of the trough and hence $\nabla \times \mathbf{v}$ is infinite. It is more plausible to suppose that v_x changes at a rapid but finite rate at the center of the trough. Thus, if we assume v_x to vary at a constant rate over a small zone of width Δy at the center of the trough, as indicated by the dashed line in Fig. 4-46b, we have in this zone that

$$\frac{\partial v_x}{\partial y} = -\frac{v_1 - v_2}{\Delta y} \qquad (4\text{-}140)$$

Fig. 4-46. Trough with water of two different velocities for Example 2.

Therefore in this zone

$$\nabla \times \mathbf{v} = -\mathbf{a}_z \frac{\partial v_x}{\partial y} = \mathbf{a}_z \frac{v_1 - v_2}{\Delta y} \qquad (4\text{-}141)$$

That is, in the zone of width Δy at the center of the trough the curl of **v** has a constant magnitude of $(v_1 - v_2)/\Delta y$ and is zero either side. This variation is shown graphically in Fig. 4-46c. The curl of **v** in the center zone has the direction of the positive z axis. This may also be noted from the fact that a curl meter at the center rotates counterclockwise (see Fig. 4-46a) and a right-handed screw turned in this manner advances in the positive z direction (out of the page).

Example 3. Referring to Fig. 4-47a, a cylindrical cup of radius R is rotated around its vertical, or z, axis f rps. The cup contains water. Find the curl of the velocity v of the water for two assumed conditions:

a. No slippage, so that the water has a circumferential velocity v_θ that is proportional to the radius r. Thus,

$$v_\theta = 2\pi f r \quad \text{meters/sec} \qquad (4\text{-}142)$$

This type of variation is suggested by the arrows in the top view of the cup in Fig. 4-47b and also is shown by the graph of Fig. 4-47c.

b. Slippage is present such that the water has a circumferential velocity v_θ that is inversely proportional to the radius r. Thus,

$$v_\theta = \frac{2\pi f}{r} \quad \text{meters/sec} \qquad (4\text{-}143)$$

This type of variation is illustrated by Figs. 4-47e and f.

Solution. *a.* This problem has cylindrical symmetry, and hence it is most convenient to use curl as expressed in cylindrical coordinates (see Appendix; also Fig. 4-56

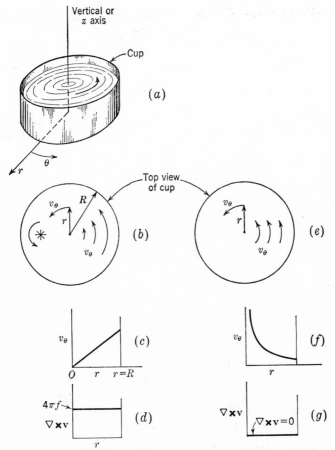

FIG. 4-47. Water rotating in a cylindrical cup (Example 3).

with Prob. 4-30). Only two terms involve the θ component of the vector. The first one $(\partial v_\theta / \partial z)$ is zero since v_θ is assumed not to vary in the z direction. The second one is

$$\mathbf{a}_z \frac{1}{r} \frac{\partial (r v_\theta)}{\partial r} \qquad (4\text{-}144)$$

where $\mathbf{a}_z$ = unit vector in positive z direction. Introducing the value of v_θ given in (4-142), we have for the curl of $\mathbf{v}$

$$\nabla \times \mathbf{v} = \mathbf{a}_z 4\pi f \qquad (4\text{-}145)$$

Hence, the curl of $\mathbf{v}$ is constant throughout the cup. This is indicated by the graph in Fig. 4-47d. The magnitude of $\nabla \times \mathbf{v}$ is $4\pi f$, and its direction is that of the positive z axis. A curl meter introduced in the cup (with axis normal to the water surface) would rotate counterclockwise and at the same rate regardless of its position in the cup.

b. Introducing (4-143) in (4-144), we obtain

$$\nabla \times \mathbf{v} = \mathbf{a}_z \frac{1}{r} \frac{\partial(2\pi f)}{\partial r} = 0 \tag{4-146}$$

Hence, the curl of $\mathbf{v}$ is zero throughout the cup as indicated in Fig. 4-47*g*. A curl meter introduced (with axis normal to the water surface) would not rotate. In general, any vector which is an inverse function of the radius (as $\mathbf{v}$ in this problem) has zero curl.

Example 4. Consider finally a current-carrying conductor of radius R as shown in cross section in Fig. 4-48*a*. The current is uniformly distributed so that the current

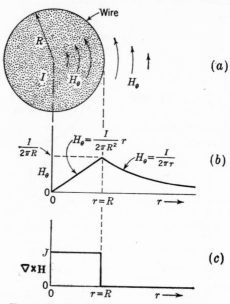

FIG. 4-48. Conducting wire (Example 4).

density $\mathbf{J}$ is a constant. Taking the axis of the wire in the z direction,

$$\mathbf{J} = \mathbf{a}_z J = \mathbf{a}_z \frac{I}{\pi R^2} \qquad \text{amp/meter}^2 \tag{4-147}$$

where I = total current in conductor (amp). Find the curl of $\mathbf{H}$ both inside and outside of the wire.

Solution. The variation of H as a function of radius was worked out for this case in Example 2 of Sec. 4-17. The variation found for H is shown in the graph of Fig. 4-48*b*. Since $\mathbf{H}$ is entirely in the θ direction, we have

$$\mathbf{H} = \mathbf{a}_\theta H_\theta \tag{4-148}$$

where $H_\theta = I/2\pi r$ outside conductor

$H_\theta = (I/2\pi R^2)\, r$ inside conductor

Using the expression for curl in cylindrical coordinates (see Appendix), we have

$$\nabla \times \mathbf{H} = 0 \qquad \text{outside conductor} \tag{4-149}$$

$$\nabla \times \mathbf{H} = \mathbf{a}_z \frac{I}{\pi R^2} = J \qquad \text{inside conductor} \tag{4-150}$$

Hence, the curl of **H** has a value only where there is current, being a constant in the conductor and zero outside (see Fig. 4-48c).

4-26. Maxwell's First Curl Equation. The relation derived from Ampère's law in Sec. 4-23 that

$$\nabla \times \mathbf{H} = \mathbf{J} \qquad (4\text{-}151)^1$$

is one of Maxwell's equations. Equation (4-151) is a differential expression and relates the field **H** to the current density **J** *at a point*. The corresponding expression in integral form, as given by (4-81), relates **H** around a *finite closed path* to the total current passing through the area enclosed.

Thus far, we have encountered three of Maxwell's four equations applying at a point. They are $\nabla \cdot \mathbf{D} = \rho$, $\nabla \cdot \mathbf{B} = 0$, and (4-151). The fourth relation, (7-60), is also an equation involving curl so that (4-151) may be referred to as Maxwell's first curl equation and (7-60) as the second.

4-27. Summary of Operations Involving ∇. We have discussed four operations involving the operator ∇ (del or nabla), namely, the gradient, divergence, Laplacian, and curl. Although the Laplacian can be resolved into the divergence of the gradient ($\nabla^2 f = \nabla \cdot \nabla f$), this operation is of such importance as to warrant listing it separately. Let us summarize these operations with their differential equivalents in rectangular coordinates. Let f represent a scalar function and **F** a vector function.

Gradient

$$\operatorname{grad} f = \nabla f = \mathbf{i} \frac{\partial f}{\partial x} + \mathbf{j} \frac{\partial f}{\partial y} + \mathbf{k} \frac{\partial f}{\partial z} \qquad (4\text{-}152)$$

Gradient operates on a scalar function to yield a vector function.

Divergence

$$\operatorname{div} \mathbf{F} = \nabla \cdot \mathbf{F} = \frac{\partial F_x}{\partial x} + \frac{\partial F_y}{\partial y} + \frac{\partial F_z}{\partial z} \qquad (4\text{-}153)$$

Divergence operates on a vector function to yield a scalar function.

Laplacian

$$\operatorname{div}(\operatorname{grad} f) = \nabla \cdot (\nabla f) = \nabla^2 f = \frac{\partial^2 f}{\partial x^2} + \frac{\partial^2 f}{\partial y^2} + \frac{\partial^2 f}{\partial z^2} \qquad (4\text{-}154)$$

---

[1] Equation (4-151) is a special form of the more general relation given in (7-127). The more general equation has an additional term involving the displacement current density. However, a displacement current is present only for time-changing fields so that for steady fields, as considered here, (7-127) reduces to (4-151).

The Laplacian operates on a scalar function to yield another scalar function.[1]

Curl

$$\text{curl } \mathbf{F} = \nabla \times \mathbf{F} = \mathbf{i}\left(\frac{\partial F_z}{\partial y} - \frac{\partial F_y}{\partial z}\right) + \mathbf{j}\left(\frac{\partial F_x}{\partial z} - \frac{\partial F_z}{\partial x}\right)$$
$$+ \mathbf{k}\left(\frac{\partial F_y}{\partial x} - \frac{\partial F_x}{\partial y}\right) \quad (4\text{-}155)$$

or

$$\nabla \times \mathbf{F} = \begin{vmatrix} \mathbf{i} & \mathbf{j} & \mathbf{k} \\ \dfrac{\partial}{\partial x} & \dfrac{\partial}{\partial y} & \dfrac{\partial}{\partial z} \\ F_x & F_y & F_z \end{vmatrix} \quad (4\text{-}156)$$

Curl operates on a vector function to yield another vector function.

4-28. A Comparison of Divergence and Curl. Whereas divergence operates on a vector function to yield a scalar function, curl operates on a vector function to yield a vector function. There is another important difference. Referring to the differential relation for the divergence in (4-153), we note that the differentiation with respect to x is on the x component of the field, the differentiation with respect to y is on the y component, etc. Therefore, to have divergence the field must vary in magnitude along a line having the same direction as the field.[2]

Referring to the relation for curl in (4-155), we note, on the other hand, that the differentiation with respect to x is on the y and z components of the field, the differentiation with respect to y is on the x and z components, etc. Therefore, to have curl the field must vary in magnitude along a line normal to the direction of the field.[3]

This comparison is illustrated in Fig. 4-49. The field at (a) is everywhere in the y direction. It has no variation in the x or z directions but varies in magnitude as a function of y. Therefore this field has diver-

---

[1] In rectangular coordinates it is also possible to interpret the Laplacian of a vector function as the vector sum of the Laplacians of the three scalar components of the vector. Thus

$$\nabla^2 \mathbf{F} = \mathbf{i} \, \nabla^2 F_x + \mathbf{j} \, \nabla^2 F_y + \mathbf{k} \, \nabla^2 F_z$$

However, in no other coordinate system is this simple interpretation possible.

[2] This is a necessary but not a sufficient condition that a vector field has divergence. For example, the $\mathbf{D}$ field due to a point charge is radial and varies as $1/r^2$ but has no divergence except at the charge. If, however, the field is *everywhere* in the y direction, as in Fig. 4-49a, and varies only as a function of y, then this field does have divergence.

[3] This is also a necessary but not a sufficient condition that a vector field has curl. For example, the $\mathbf{H}$ field outside of a long wire varies in magnitude as $1/r$ and has a direction normal to the radius vector; yet $\mathbf{H}$ has no curl in this region. If, however, the field is *everywhere* in the y direction, as in Fig. 4-49b, and varies only as a function of z, then this field does have curl.

gence but no curl.   The field at (b) is also everywhere in the y direction. It has no variation in the x and y directions but does vary in magnitude as a function of z.   Therefore, this field has curl but no divergence.

Let us now discuss the significance of operations involving ∇ two times. First consider the divergence of the curl of a vector function.   That is,

$$\nabla \cdot (\nabla \times F) \qquad (4\text{-}157)$$

where F is any vector function given in rectangular coordinates by

$$F = iF_x + jF_y + kF_z$$

If we first take the curl of F, we obtain another vector.   Next taking the divergence of this vector, the result is identically zero.   Thus

$$\nabla \cdot (\nabla \times F) \equiv 0 \qquad (4\text{-}158)$$

This may be proved by carrying out the operations indicated.   This is left as an exercise for the reader (see Prob. 4-28).   In words (4-158)

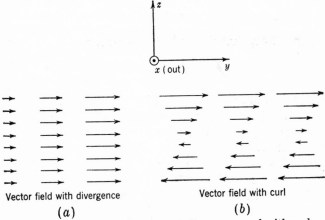

Vector field with divergence

(a)

Vector field with curl

(b)

FIG. 4-49. Examples of fields with divergence and with curl.

states that *the divergence of the curl of a vector function is zero*.   As a corollary we may say that if the divergence of a vector function is zero, then it must be the curl of some other vector function.

For example, the divergence of B is always zero everywhere.   That is,

$$\nabla \cdot B = 0 \qquad (4\text{-}159)$$

Therefore, B can be expressed as the curl of some other vector function. Let us designate this other vector function by A.   Then

$$B = \nabla \times A \qquad (4\text{-}160)$$

The function **A** in (4-160) is called the *vector potential* and is discussed in more detail in the next section.

Let us consider another operation involving ∇ twice, namely, the curl of the gradient of a scalar function f. That is,

$$\nabla \times (\nabla f) \tag{4-161}$$

Taking first the gradient of f and then the curl of the resulting vector function, the result is found to be identically zero. Thus

$$\nabla \times (\nabla f) \equiv 0 \tag{4-162}$$

The steps are left to the reader as an exercise (see Prob. 4-29). In words (4-162) states that *the curl of the gradient of a scalar function is zero.* As a corollary any vector function, which is the gradient of some scalar function, has no curl.

For example, we recall from (1-33) that the static electric field due to charges $\mathbf{E}_c$ is derivable as the gradient of a scalar potential V. Thus

$$\mathbf{E}_c = -\nabla V \tag{4-163}$$

It follows, therefore, that the curl of $\mathbf{E}_c$ is zero, or

$$\nabla \times \mathbf{E}_c = 0 \tag{4-164}$$

If a vector field has no curl, it is said that the field is *lamellar*. Thus the electric field $\mathbf{E}_c$ is lamellar. The flux tubes of such fields are discontinuous. They originate on positive charges (as sources) and terminate on negative charges (as sinks). On the other hand, if a vector field has no divergence such as $\mathbf{B}$, it is said that the field is *solenoidal*. Its flux tubes are continuous, having no sources or sinks.

Finally let us consider the relation (involving ∇ twice) of the divergence of the gradient of a scalar function f. This is the Laplacian of the scalar function. Thus

$$\nabla \cdot \nabla f = \nabla^2 f \tag{4-165}$$

The differential expression for the Laplacian in rectangular coordinates is given in (4-154). In general, the Laplacian of a scalar is not zero. For example, the Laplacian of the electric scalar potential V is

$$\nabla^2 V = -\frac{\rho}{\epsilon} \tag{4-166}$$

This is Poisson's equation (2-149). If the charge density ρ is zero, $\nabla^2 V = 0$, which is Laplace's equation.

4-29. The Vector Potential. According to (4-34) the magnetic flux density **B** at a point P produced by a current distribution, as in Fig. 4-50, is given by

$$\mathbf{B} = \frac{\mu}{4\pi} \iiint \frac{\mathbf{J} \times \mathbf{a}_r}{r^2}\, dv \quad (4\text{-}167)$$

where **B** = flux density (webers/meter²)

μ = permeability of medium (uniform) (henrys/meter)

J = current density at volume element (amp/meter²)

$\mathbf{a}_r$ = unit vector in direction of radius vector r (dimensionless)

r = radius vector from volume element to point P (meters)

dv = volume element (meters³)

By carrying out the integration over the entire volume occupied by the current-carrying conductor the total flux density **B** at P due to the current is obtained.

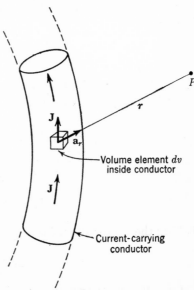

Fig. 4-50. Construction for finding flux density **B** at P.

In Sec. 4-28 we noted that since the divergence of **B** is always zero, it should be possible to express **B** as the curl of some other vector. Thus from (4-160) we can write

$$\mathbf{B} = \nabla \times \mathbf{A} \quad (4\text{-}168)$$

where **A** is called a *vector potential* since it is a potential function that is also a vector.[1] If we also make

$$\nabla \cdot \mathbf{A} = 0 \quad (4\text{-}169)$$

A is completely defined. Taking the curl of (4-168) yields

$$\nabla \times \nabla \times \mathbf{A} = \nabla \times \mathbf{B} = \mu \mathbf{J} \quad (4\text{-}170)$$

By the vector identity for the curl of the curl of a vector (see Appendix) equation (4-170) becomes

$$\nabla(\nabla \cdot \mathbf{A}) - \nabla^2 \mathbf{A} = \mu \mathbf{J} \quad (4\text{-}171)$$

Introducing the condition of (4-169), this reduces to

$$\nabla^2 \mathbf{A} = -\mu \mathbf{J} \quad (4\text{-}172)$$

[1] The potential function V from which the electric field $\mathbf{E}_c$ can be derived (by the relation $\mathbf{E}_c = -\nabla V$) is a scalar quantity, and hence V is a *scalar potential*.

or in terms of the three rectangular components of **A** and **J**

$$i \nabla^2 A_x + j \nabla^2 A_y + k \nabla^2 A_z = -\mu(iJ_x + jJ_y + kJ_z) \qquad (4\text{-}173)$$

Equation (4-173) is the vector sum of three scalar equations. Hence,

$$\left.\begin{array}{l} \nabla^2 A_x = -\mu J_x \\ \nabla^2 A_y = -\mu J_y \\ \nabla^2 A_z = -\mu J_z \end{array}\right\} \qquad (4\text{-}174)$$

Each of these relations has the same form as Poisson's equation (4-166) or (2-149).[1] Therefore solutions to the three equations of (4-174) are

$$\left.\begin{array}{l} A_x = \dfrac{\mu}{4\pi} \iiint \dfrac{J_x}{r}\, dv \\[2mm] A_y = \dfrac{\mu}{4\pi} \iiint \dfrac{J_y}{r}\, dv \\[2mm] A_z = \dfrac{\mu}{4\pi} \iiint \dfrac{J_z}{r}\, dv \end{array}\right\} \qquad (4\text{-}175)$$

Taking the vector sum of the components for **A** in (4-175) gives

$$\mathbf{A} = \frac{\mu}{4\pi} \iiint \frac{\mathbf{J}}{r}\, dv \qquad (4\text{-}176)$$

According to (4-176) the vector potential **A** at a point due to a current distribution is equal to the ratio $\mathbf{J}/r$ integrated over the volume occupied by the current distribution, where **J** is the current density at each volume element dv and r is the distance from each volume element to the point P where **A** is being evaluated (see Fig. 4-50). If the current distribution is known, **A** can be found. Knowing **A** at a point, the flux density **B** at that point is then obtained by taking the curl of **A** as in (4-168). It is left as an exercise for the student to show that taking the curl of **A** as given in (4-176) yields **B** as in (4-167) (see Prob. 4-35).

From (4-168) we note that **A** has the dimensions of

$$\text{Magnetic flux density} \times \text{distance} = \frac{\text{magnetic flux}}{\text{distance}} = \frac{\text{force}}{\text{current}}$$

From (4-176) **A** also has the equivalent dimensions of

$$\text{Permeability} \times \frac{\text{current}}{\text{area}} \times \frac{\text{volume}}{\text{distance}} = \text{permeability} \times \text{current}$$

Hence, the vector potential **A** can be expressed in webers per meter, newtons per ampere, or henry-amperes per meter. The dimensional symbols for **A** are ML/TQ.

---

[1] It follows that (4-172) may be called Poisson's equation for the vector potential **A**. In current-free regions $\mathbf{J} = 0$, and (4-172) reduces to $\nabla^2 \mathbf{A} = 0$, which is Laplace's equation for the vector potential.

As an illustration of the utility of the vector potential **A** let us consider the following example.

Example.   Consider a short copper wire of length l and a cross-sectional area a situated in air coincident with the z axis at the origin as shown in Fig. 4-51. The

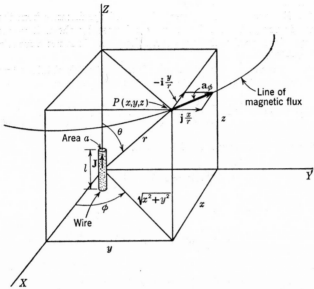

Fig. 4-51. Construction for finding the vector potential **A** and flux density **B** due to a short current-carrying wire.

current density **J** is in the positive z direction.   Assume the hypothetical situation that **J** is uniform throughout the wire and constant with respect to time.   Find the magnetic flux density **B** everywhere at a large distance from the wire, using the vector potential to obtain the solution.

Solution.   The vector potential **A** at any point P produced by the wire is given by (4-176), where the ratio $\mathbf{J}/r$ is integrated throughout the volume occupied by the wire. Since we wish to find **B** only at a large distance r from the wire, it suffices to find **A** at a large distance.   Specifically the distance r should be large compared with the length of the wire ($r \gg l$).   Then, at any point P the distance r to different parts of the wire can be considered constant and (4-176) written as

$$\mathbf{A} = \frac{\mu_0}{4\pi r} \iiint \mathbf{J} \, dv \tag{4-177}$$

Now **J** is everywhere in the z direction and also is uniform.   Thus $\mathbf{J} = \mathbf{k}J_z$, and

$$\iiint \mathbf{J} \, dv = \mathbf{k} \int_{-l/2}^{l/2} \iint_a J_z \, ds \, dl = \mathbf{k} \int_{-l/2}^{l/2} I \, dl \tag{4-178}$$

where $I = J_z a$ = current in wire.   Completing the integration in (4-178) and substituting this result in (4-177), we obtain

$$\mathbf{A} = \mathbf{k}\frac{\mu_0 I l}{4\pi r} = \mathbf{k}A_z \tag{4-179}$$

where $\mathbf{A}$ = vector potential at distance r from wire (webers/meter)
  $\mathbf{k}$ = unit vector in positive z direction (dimensionless)
  μ_0 = permeability of air ($4\pi \times 10^{-7}$ henry/meter)
  I = current in wire (amp)
  l = length of wire (meters)
  r = distance from wire (meters)

Equation (4-179) gives the vector potential $\mathbf{A}$ at a large distance from the wire. It is everywhere in the positive z direction as indicated by the unit vector $\mathbf{k}$ and is inversely proportional to the distance r from the wire. It is not a function of angle (ϕ or θ in Fig. 4-51).

Having found the vector potential $\mathbf{A}$, the flux density $\mathbf{B}$ is obtained by taking the curl of $\mathbf{A}$. In rectangular components the curl of $\mathbf{A}$ is given by

$$\nabla \times \mathbf{A} = \mathbf{i}\left(\frac{\partial A_z}{\partial y} - \frac{\partial A_y}{\partial z}\right) + \mathbf{j}\left(\frac{\partial A_x}{\partial z} - \frac{\partial A_z}{\partial x}\right) + \mathbf{k}\left(\frac{\partial A_y}{\partial x} - \frac{\partial A_x}{\partial y}\right) \quad (4\text{-}180)$$

Since $\mathbf{A}$ has only a z component, (4-180) reduces to

$$\nabla \times \mathbf{A} = \mathbf{i}\frac{\partial A_z}{\partial y} - \mathbf{j}\frac{\partial A_z}{\partial x} \quad (4\text{-}181)$$

Now $r = \sqrt{x^2 + y^2 + z^2}$. Therefore

$$\frac{\partial A_z}{\partial y} = \frac{\mu_0 Il}{4\pi}\frac{\partial}{\partial y}(x^2 + y^2 + z^2)^{-\frac{1}{2}} = -\frac{\mu_0 Il}{4\pi}\frac{y}{r^3} \quad (4\text{-}182)$$

and

$$\frac{\partial A_z}{\partial x} = \frac{\mu_0 Il}{4\pi}\frac{\partial}{\partial x}(x^2 + y^2 + z^2)^{-\frac{1}{2}} = -\frac{\mu_0 Il}{4\pi}\frac{x}{r^3} \quad (4\text{-}183)$$

Introducing these relations in (4-181) and noting the geometry in Fig. 4-51, we have

$$\nabla \times \mathbf{A} = \frac{\mu_0 Il}{4\pi r^2}\left(-\mathbf{i}\frac{y}{r} + \mathbf{j}\frac{x}{r}\right) = \mathbf{a}_\phi \frac{\mu_0 Il}{4\pi r^2}\frac{\sqrt{x^2 + y^2}}{r} \quad (4\text{-}184)$$

or

$$\mathbf{B} = \nabla \times \mathbf{A} = \mathbf{a}_\phi \frac{\mu_0 Il \sin\theta}{4\pi r^2} \quad (4\text{-}185)$$

where $\mathbf{B}$ = magnetic flux density (webers/meter²) at distance r and angle θ
  $\mathbf{a}_\phi$ = unit vector in ϕ direction (see Fig. 4-51) (dimensionless)
  θ = angle between axis of wire and radius vector r (dimensionless)
  μ_0 = permeability of air ($= 4\pi \times 10^{-7}$ henry/meter)
  I = current in wire (amp)
  l = length of wire (meters)
  r = distance from wire to point where $\mathbf{B}$ is being evaluated (meters)

According to (4-185), the flux-density $\mathbf{B}$ produced by the wire is everywhere in the ϕ direction. That is, the lines of magnetic flux form closed circles concentric with the z axis. The planes of the circles are parallel to the x-y plane. One such line of magnetic flux at a distance r from the origin is indicated in Fig. 4-51. According to (4-185), $\mathbf{B}$ is also proportional to $\sin\theta$ and inversely proportional to r^2. By way of comparison, the vector potential **A** from which **B** is obtained is everywhere in the z direction, is inversely proportional to r, and is independent of angle.   The magnitude and direction of both **B** and **A** are illustrated in Fig. 4-52a for points in the y-z plane at a fixed radius r.   The vector potential **A** is shown by dashed arrows.   It is everywhere in the z direction and of constant magnitude.   The flux density **B** is normal to the y-z plane, being in the negative x direction at points for which y is positive and in the positive x direction at points for which y is negative.   The flux density **B** is a maximum in the x-y plane and is zero at the z axis.

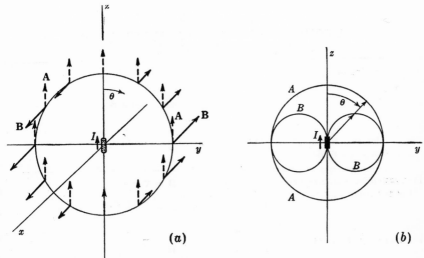

FIG. 4-52. (a) Vector potential **A** (dashed arrows) and flux density **B** (solid arrows) at a large distance in the y-z plane from a short current element.   (b) Corresponding polar patterns for A and B.

The variation of the magnitude of **B** and **A** is also effectively presented as a function of θ by a polar diagram, or pattern, as in Fig. 4-52b.   Here the radius vector from the center of the diagram to a point on the curve is proportional to the magnitude of the quantity at that angle θ from the z axis.   The B pattern is a figure of eight with a maximum at $\theta = 90°$, while the A pattern is a circle.   Both patterns are arbitrarily adjusted to the same maximum value.   It is to be noted that although the diagrams in Fig. 4-52b are shown for the y-z plane, they also apply to any plane through the origin that is parallel to the z axis or axis of the wire.

Although the result of (4-185) could have been written down almost directly from (4-167), without using the vector potential explicitly, the above example serves to illustrate the manner in which the vector potential can be applied.   Employing the vector potential in the above example is analogous to using a 10-ton steam hammer to crack a walnut.   However, on many problems of a more difficult nature the vector potential is indispensable.

4-30. A Comparison of Static Electric and Magnetic Fields. It is instructive to compare electric and magnetic fields and to note both their differences and their similarities. A partial comparison is given in this section, involving relations developed in the first four chapters for static fields. A comparison of relations for nonstatic fields is given in Sec. 7-25.

In making a comparison it is possible to see certain analogies. For example, we have noted in electric fields that **E** is involved in the force

TABLE 4-2
A COMPARISON OF STATIC ELECTRIC AND
MAGNETIC FIELD EQUATIONS

Description of equation	Electric fields	Magnetic fields
Force	$\mathbf{F} = Q\mathbf{E}$	$d\mathbf{F} = I d\mathbf{l} \times \mathbf{B}$ $\mathbf{F} = Q_m \mathbf{B}$
Basic relations for lamellar and solenoidal fields	$\nabla \times \mathbf{E}_c = 0$†	$\nabla \cdot \mathbf{B} = 0$
Derivation from scalar or vector potential	$\mathbf{E}_c = -\nabla V$ $V = \dfrac{1}{4\pi\epsilon_0} \displaystyle\int_v \dfrac{\rho}{r}\, dv$	$\mathbf{B} = \nabla \times \mathbf{A}$ $\mathbf{A} = \dfrac{\mu_0}{4\pi} \displaystyle\int_v \dfrac{\mathbf{J}}{r}\, dv$
Relations for **D** and **H**	$\mathbf{D} = \epsilon\mathbf{E}$ $D = \rho_s$ $\nabla \cdot \mathbf{D} = \rho$	$\mathbf{H} = \dfrac{\mathbf{B}}{\mu}$ $H = \dfrac{I}{2\pi R}$ $\nabla \times \mathbf{H} = \mathbf{J}$
Energy density	$w_e = \tfrac{1}{2}\epsilon E^2$	$w_m = \dfrac{1}{2}\dfrac{B^2}{\mu}$
Capacitance and inductance	$C = \dfrac{Q}{V}$	$L = \dfrac{\Lambda}{I}$
Capacitance and inductance per unit length of a cell	$\dfrac{C}{d} = \epsilon$	$\dfrac{L}{d} = \mu$
Closed path of integration	$\oint \mathbf{E} \cdot d\mathbf{l} = \mathcal{V}$ $\oint \mathbf{E}_c \cdot d\mathbf{l} = 0$	$\oint \mathbf{H} \cdot d\mathbf{l} = F = NI$ $\oint \mathbf{H} \cdot d\mathbf{l} = 0$ (no current enclosed)
Derivation from scalar potentials	$\mathbf{E}_c = -\nabla V$	$\mathbf{H} = -\nabla U$ (in current-free region)

† $\mathbf{E}_c$ is the static electric field intensity (due to charges). **E** (without subscript) implies that emf-producing fields (not due to charges) may also be present.

relations, while in magnetic fields **B** is involved in the force relations. Hence, **B** may be considered as the magnetic quantity that is analogous to the electric field intensity **E**. Furthermore, in a capacitor **D** is directly related to the electric charge on the plates ($D = \rho_s$) and is independent of the medium, while near a long current-carrying wire H is directly related to the current ($H = I/2\pi R$) and is independent of the medium. Thus, **D** and **H** may be regarded as analogous quantities.

In some other instances we may note an analogy of **H** to **E**. For example, the line integral around a closed path of the total electric field intensity **E** yields the emf ($\oint \mathbf{E} \cdot dl = \mathcal{V}$), while the line integral of **H** around a closed path yields the mmf ($\oint \mathbf{H} \cdot dl = F$). Furthermore, comparing the divergence relations $\nabla \cdot \mathbf{D} = 0$ and $\nabla \cdot \mathbf{B} = 0$ for charge-free space, we note a mathematical similarity of **B** to **D**. If this analogy of **H** to **E** and **B** to **D** is pursued, it is possible to achieve a formal, or mathematical, symmetry between many of the electric and magnetic field equations. However, electric and magnetic fields are fundamentally different, and the first analogy of **B** to **E** and **H** to **D** has more physical significance. Static electric fields are due to electric charge, a scalar quantity, while static magnetic fields are due to electric current, a vector quantity.

In Table 4-2 many of the electric and magnetic field relations developed in the first four chapters are summarized. The analogy of **B** to **E** and **H** to **D** will be noted in many of the equations, while the other analogy may be observed in a few of the relations. The first column describes the nature of the relation, the second column gives the relation for static electric fields, and the third column gives the corresponding relation or relations for static magnetic fields. The relations apply to static and slowly time-varying situations. They also apply in more rapidly time-varying situations with the exception of those relations involving the curl or the line integral (**H** $= -\nabla U$ also does not apply in rapidly time-varying cases). See Table 7-2 for the corresponding more general relations that apply in time-varying cases.

PROBLEMS

4-1. A linear conductor carries a current of 100 amp in the positive x direction. If the flux density everywhere is uniform with a magnitude $B = 2$ webers/meter^2 and has a direction parallel to the x-y plane and at an angle of 45° with respect to the x axis, find the magnitude and direction of the force on a 2-meter length of the conductor.   *Ans.:* 282.8 newtons in the positive z direction.

4-2. A thin linear conductor situated in air has a current of 10 amp. What is the flux density produced by a section of the conductor 1 cm long at a distance of 2 meters normal to the 1 cm section?

4-3. A current of 100 amp flows in the positive z direction in a long wire coincident with the z axis as shown in Fig. 4-53. A rigid square-frame loop of 1 turn carries a current of 10 amp. The loop is in the y-z plane with its center at the origin (see

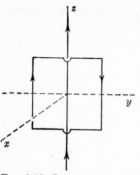

Fig. 4-53). The loop is 1 meter square. Find the magnitude and direction of the force on the loop.

Ans.: 8 × 10⁻⁴ newton in positive y-direction.

4-4. A thin linear conductor situated in air has a current of 50 amp. What is H due to a section of the conductor 2 meters long at a distance of 50 cm normal to the center of the 2-meter section?

4-5. The flux density **B** is everywhere uniform and in the positive x direction. If $B = 1$ weber/meter², find the total flux over a plane area of 2 meters² when the area is (a) parallel to the y-z plane; (b) parallel to the x-z plane; (c) parallel to the y axis and at an angle of 45° with respect to the x axis.

Fig. 4-53. Loop and wire for Prob. 4-3.

Ans.: (a) 2 webers; (b) 0; (c) 1.414 webers.

4-6. Consider a square area with corners at the origin $(0, 0)$, and at $(x_1, 0)$ $(0, y_1)$, and (x_1, y_1). If **B** normal to the area is given by

$$B = 3 \sin\left(\frac{\pi}{x_1} x\right) \sin\left(\frac{\pi}{y_1} y\right) \qquad \text{webers/meter}^2$$

find the total magnetic flux over the square area.

4-7. A thin linear conductor of length l and carrying a current I is coincident with the y axis. The medium surrounding the conductor is air. One end of the conductor is at a distance y_1 from the origin and the other end at a distance y_2. Show that the flux density due to the conductor at a point on the x axis at a distance x_1 from the origin is

$$B = \frac{\mu_0 I}{4\pi x_1}\left[\frac{y_2}{\sqrt{x_1{}^2 + y_2{}^2}} - \frac{y_1}{\sqrt{x_1{}^2 + y_1{}^2}}\right]$$

Note that if the center of the conductor coincides with the origin $(-y_1 = y_2)$ and if $x_1 \gg l$, the expression reduces to $B = \mu_0 I l / 4\pi x_1{}^2$.

4-8. Two long thin parallel wires separated by 1 cm in air carry currents of 100 amp in opposite directions. Find the magnitude and direction of the force on a 5-meter length of one wire.

4-9. A uniform cylindrical coil, or solenoid, of 1,000 turns is 50 cm long and 5 cm in diameter. If the coil carries a current of 10 ma, find the flux density (a) at the center of the coil; (b) on the axis at one end of the coil; (c) on the axis halfway between the center and end of the coil.

4-10. Calculate and plot a graph of B as function of position along the axis of the solenoid of Prob. 4-9 from the center of the solenoid to a distance of 50 cm beyond one end.

4-11. A solenoid 20 cm long and 1 cm in diameter has a uniform winding of 1,000 turns. If the solenoid is placed in a *uniform* field of 2 webers/meter² flux density and a current of 10 amp is passed through the solenoid winding, what is the maximum (a) force on the solenoid; (b) torque on the solenoid?

Ans.: (a) $F = 0$; (b) $T = \pi/2$ newton-meters.

4-12. Show that the flux density at a point P on the axis of a uniform solenoid is given by

$$B = \mu_0 \frac{NI}{l}\left(1 - \frac{\Omega_1 + \Omega_2}{4\pi}\right)$$

where Ω_1 = solid angle subtended from the point P by the left end of the solenoid (equals 2π if P is at the left end of the solenoid) and Ω_2 = solid angle subtended from the point P by the right end of the solenoid (equals 2π if P is at the right end of the solenoid).   Note that at the center of a long slender solenoid $\Omega_1 = \Omega_2 \ll 4\pi$ so that $B = \mu_0(NI/l) = \mu_0 K$.

4-13. (a) What is the maximum torque on a square loop of 100 turns in a field of uniform flux density $B = 3$ webers/meter²?   The loop is 10 cm on a side and carries a current of 6 amp.   (b) What is the magnetic moment of the loop?   (c) What is the magnetic moment of the solenoid of Prob. 4-11?

4-14. What is the maximum torque on a small coil of magnetic moment 10^{-4} amp-meter² situated near the center of a long air-filled solenoid of 1,000 turns/meter with a current of 1 amp?

4-15. What is the magnetic moment of a coil of 10 turns and area of 100 cm² carrying a current of 1 amp?

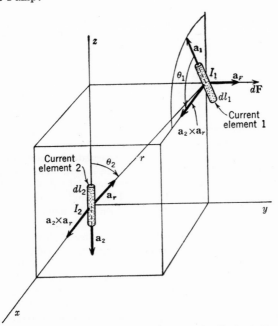

Fig. 4-54. Relation of current elements for Prob. 4-16.

4-16. Referring to Fig. 4-54, show that the force between the two current elements situated in air is given by

$$dF = \frac{\mu_0 I_2 \, dl_2 \, I_1 \, dl_1}{4\pi r^2} \, \mathbf{a}_1 \times (\mathbf{a}_2 \times \mathbf{a}_r) \qquad (1)$$

where dF = force on element 1 due to current I_2 in element 2 (newtons)

μ_0 = permeability of air (henry/meter)

dl_1 and dl_2 = lengths of current elements 1 and 2, respectively (meters)

I_1 and I_2 = currents in elements 1 and 2, respectively (amp)

r = distance between elements (meters)

$\mathbf{a}_1$ = unit vector in direction of current I_1 and in element 1 (dimensionless)

$\mathbf{a}_2$ = unit vector in direction of current I_2 in element 2 (dimensionless)

$\mathbf{a}_r$ = unit vector in direction from element 2 to 1 (dimensionless)

Show further that $d\mathbf{F} = \mathbf{a}_F dF$, where dF is given by

$$dF = |d\mathbf{F}| = \frac{\mu_0 I_2 \, dl_2 \, I_1 \, dl_1 \, \sin \theta_2 \, \sin \theta_1}{4\pi r^2}$$

where θ_2 = angle between $\mathbf{a}_2$ and $\mathbf{a}_r$ (see Fig. 4-54) and θ_1 = angle between $\mathbf{a}_1$ and $\mathbf{a}_2 \times \mathbf{a}_r$, and

$$\mathbf{a}_F = \frac{\mathbf{a}_1 \times (\mathbf{a}_2 \times \mathbf{a}_r)}{\sin \theta_2 \, \sin \theta_1}$$

where $\mathbf{a}_F$ = unit vector in direction of force $d\mathbf{F}$.

It is to be noted that these equations give the force on element 1 due to the presence of element 2, but not vice versa. That is, they are not symmetrical with respect to elements 1 and 2. However, with two closed circuits the force, as given by an integral of (1), is the same for both circuits. Thus, in the case of actual circuits Newton's third law, that to every action there is an equal (and opposite) reaction, is satisfied.

4-17. Two loops are arranged as shown in cross section in Fig. 4-55. If the separation s is large compared with the size of the loops, show that the torque T on loop 2 due to loop 1 is given by

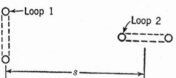

$$T = \frac{\mu_0}{2\pi} \frac{mm'}{s^3}$$

Fig. 4-55. Loops for Prob. 4-17.

where m = magnetic moment of loop 1 and m' = magnetic moment of loop 2.

4-18. Calculate the inductance of a uniform, 5,000-turn solenoidal coil 50 cm long and of 1 cm radius. The medium is air.

4-19. Calculate the inductance of an air-filled toroidal coil of 10 cm² cross-sectional area with a mean radius of 60 cm. The toroid has a uniform winding of 10,000 turns.

4-20. Find H at the center of a circular 100-turn coil 1 meter in diameter situated in air and carrying a current of 10 amp.

4-21. Two identical 100-turn circular coils 1 meter in diameter have their axes coincident and are spaced 1 meter apart, forming a "Helmholtz pair." Both carry 10 amp in the same sense. Calculate and plot the variation of H along the axis of the coils from the center of one coil to the center of the other. Also calculate and plot the variation of H, along the axis of a single 100-turn coil 1 meter in diameter, due to a current I in the coil. Let the single coil be situated halfway between the coils of the Helmholtz pair and with its axis coincident with the axis of the pair. Also let I have such a value that H at the center of the single coil is the same as H from the Helmholtz pair at this point. Assume that the coils have negligible cross-sectional area so that each may be represented by a thin single-turn loop.

4-22. A transmission line consists of two long, thin parallel conductors that carry currents of 10 amp in opposite directions. The conductors are spaced a distance $2s$ apart. Draw a field map for a plane normal to the wires. Show both H lines and lines of equal magnetic potential. Indicate the value of potential for each equipotential line. Let the line joining the wires be aribitrarily taken to have zero potential. (Compare this map with Fig. 2-21 for two parallel lines of charge spaced a distance $2s$.)

4-23. Neglecting edge effects, calculate the inductance per unit length of a d-c transmission line consisting of two parallel conducting strips 30 cm wide situated in air. The separation everywhere between the strips is 2 cm.

4-24. An air-filled coaxial d-c transmission line has an inner conductor of circular cross section (diameter = 3 cm) situated symmetrically inside of an outer conductor of square cross section (side dimension = 5 cm). Find the inductance per unit length of line.

4-25. A long, straight tubular conductor of circular cross section with an outside diameter of 5 cm and wall thickness of 0.5 cm carries a direct current of 100 amp. Find H (a) just inside the wall of the tube; (b) just outside the wall of the tube; (c) at a point in the tube wall halfway between the inner and outer surfaces.

4-26. A toroidal air-filled coil has a uniform winding of 5,000 turns. If the coil cross section is 15 cm², the mean radius 1 meter, and the current 2 amp, find (a) the inductance of the coil; (b) the energy stored by the magnetic field of the coil; (c) the magnetic energy density inside the coil.

4-27. A transmission line consists of two parallel conducting strips 30 cm wide situated in air with a uniform separation of 2 cm. The line carries a direct current of 100 amp. Neglecting edge effects, find the magnetic energy density at a point between the strips.

4-28. Prove that $\nabla \cdot (\nabla \times \mathbf{F}) = 0$, where $\mathbf{F}$ is a vector function given by

$$\mathbf{F} = \mathbf{i}F_x + \mathbf{j}F_y + \mathbf{k}F_z$$

4-29. Prove that $\nabla \times (\nabla f) = 0$, where f is a scalar function.

4-30. Develop curl $\mathbf{B}$ in cylindrical coordinates by applying the procedure of Sec. 4-23 to three sides of the volume shown in Fig. 4-56.

4-31. For steady currents $\mathbf{J} = \nabla \times \mathbf{H}$. Show that

$$\nabla \cdot \mathbf{J} = 0$$

4-32. For static fields $\mathbf{E}_c = -\nabla V$. Show that

$$\nabla \times \mathbf{E}_c = 0$$

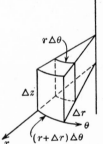

Fig. 4-56. Volume element for Prob. 4-30.

4-33. Given that $\mathbf{B} = \nabla \times \mathbf{A}$, show that $\nabla \cdot \mathbf{B} = 0$.

4-34. Derive (4-185) for the flux density due to a short linear conductor using the vector potential and spherical coordinates. *Hint:* Convert A_z into its spherical components, and then apply curl $\mathbf{A}$ in spherical coordinates (see Appendix).

4-35. Show that the curl of vector potential $\mathbf{A}$ as given in (4-176) yields the flux density $\mathbf{B}$ as in (4-167). *Hint:* Note the vector identity:

$$\nabla \times (f\mathbf{F}) = (\nabla f) \times \mathbf{F} + f(\nabla \times \mathbf{F})$$

where f is a scalar function and $\mathbf{F}$ a vector function.

4-36. Find the curl of the vector function $\mathbf{A} = \mathbf{i}x^2y^2 + \mathbf{j}z^{\frac{1}{2}}$.

4-37. A vector field is given by $\mathbf{F} = \mathbf{j}x^3$. Find the curl of the curl of $\mathbf{F}$.

Ans.: $-\mathbf{j}6x$.

4-38. If $\mathbf{H}$ has only a z component given by $H_z = 3 \cos \beta x + 6 \sin \gamma y$ amp/meter, what is the expression for the current density $\mathbf{J}$? The field is steady with respect to time.

4-39. A vector field $\mathbf{G} = \mathbf{j} (\sin x)^2$. Find (a) the curl of $\mathbf{G}$; (b) the value of the curl of $\mathbf{G}$ at $x = \pi/4$. *Ans.:* (a) $\mathbf{k} \sin 2x$; (b) $\mathbf{k}$.

4-40. A vector function $\mathbf{F} = \mathbf{i}2x + \mathbf{j}3xy^2z$. (a) Find the curl of the curl of $\mathbf{F}$. (b) Evaluate the curl of the curl of $\mathbf{F}$ at the point $x = 2$, $y = 2$, $z = 2$.

4-41. If the vector potential $\mathbf{A} = \mathbf{i}5(x^2 + y^2 + z^2)^{-1}$ weber/meter, what is the relation for the flux density $\mathbf{B}$?

4-42. Prove that $\nabla \times \mathbf{H} = 0$, where $\mathbf{H}$ is the field outside of a long, straight wire carrying a current I.

4-43. A vector function $\mathbf{F} = \mathbf{i}x + \mathbf{j}xy + \mathbf{k}xz$. Find the curl of $\mathbf{F}$.

4-44. What is the flux density at the center of a square loop of 10 turns carrying a current of 10 amp? The loop is in air and is 2 meters on a side.

CHAPTER 5

THE STATIC MAGNETIC FIELD OF
FERROMAGNETIC MATERIALS

5-1. Introduction. Magnetic fields are present around a current-carrying conductor. They also exist around a magnetized object such as an iron bar magnet. Although the field of the iron bar is not produced by current circuits of the type considered in Chap. 4, we may regard currents as the cause. However, in the bar the current circuits are of atomically small dimensions. In contrast to these *microscopic* circuits, the circuits considered in Chap. 4 are of *macroscopic* size.

An electron revolving in its orbit around the nucleus of an atom forms a tiny electric current loop. Since a current loop has a magnetic field and all atoms have revolving electrons we might suppose that all substances would exhibit magnetic effects. However, such effects are very weak in most materials. There is a group of substances, however, including iron, nickel, and cobalt, in which magnetic effects are very strong. These substances are called *ferromagnetic materials*. Both the orbital motion and the electron spin (or rotation of the electron around its own axis) contribute to the magnetic effect, the spin being particularly important. This electron, or charge, motion is equivalent in its effect to an exceedingly tiny current loop. This tiny loop is in effect a miniature magnet or magnetic dipole with magnetic moment $(Q_m l)$ equal to the moment (IA) of the current loop. Although the moment of each atomic current loop is very small, the combined effect of billions of them in an iron bar results in a strong magnetic field around the bar.

5-2. Bar Magnets and Magnetic Poles. If an iron bar magnet is freely suspended, it will turn in the earth's magnetic field so that one end points north. This end is called the "north-seeking pole" of the magnet or simply its *north pole*. The other end of the magnet has a pole of opposite polarity called a *south pole*.[1]

All magnetized bodies have both a north and a south pole. They cannot be isolated. For example, consider the long magnetized iron rod of Fig. 5-1a. This rod has a north pole at one end and a south pole at the

---

[1] It is sometimes convenient to call a *north pole* a *positive pole* and a *south pole* a *negative pole*.

other.   If the rod is cut in half, new poles appear as in Fig. 5-1b so that there are two magnets.   If each of these is cut in half, we obtain four magnets as in Fig. 5-1c, each with a north and a south pole.   The reason for this is that the ultimate source of the ferromagnetism is a moving electron or atomic current circuit which acts like a tiny magnet with a north and a south pole.   Therefore, even if the cutting process could be continued to atomic dimensions and a single iron atom isolated, it would still have a north and a south pole.

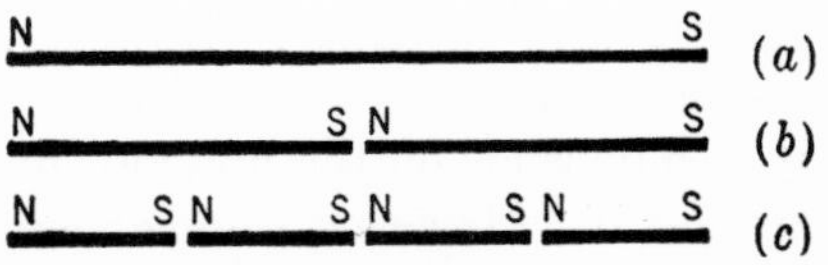

Fig. 5-1. New poles appear at each point of division of a bar magnet.

The fact that magnetic poles cannot be isolated, whereas electric charges can, is an important point of difference between electric charges and magnetic poles.

5-3. Magnetic Materials.   All materials show some magnetic effects. With the exception of the ferromagnetic group these effects are weak.

Depending on their magnetic behavior, substances can be classified as *diamagnetic, paramagnetic,* and *ferromagnetic.*   In diamagnetic materials the magnetization (see Sec. 5-7) is opposed to the applied field, while in paramagnetic materials the magnetization is in the same direction as the field.   The materials in both groups, however, show only weak magnetic effects.   Materials in the ferromagnetic group, on the other hand, show very strong magnetic effects.   The magnetization is in the same direction as the field, the same as for paramagnetic materials.[1]   Most of this chapter deals with the magnetic fields of the ferromagnetic materials.

A number of substances are classified in Table 5-1 according to their magnetic behavior.   Many substances show such weak magnetic effects that they are called "nonmagnetic."   However, vacuum is the only truly nonmagnetic medium.

5-4. Relative Permeability.   In dealing with many media, it is often convenient to speak of the relative permeability μ_r defined as

$$\mu_r = \frac{\mu}{\mu_0} \qquad (5\text{-}1)$$

where μ_r = relative permeability (dimensionless)
  μ = permeability (henrys/meter)
  μ_0 = permeability of vacuum ($4\pi \times 10^{-7}$ henry/meter)

It is to be noted that the relative permeability is a dimensionless ratio.

The relative permeability of vacuum or free space is unity by definition. The relative permeability of diamagnetic substances is slightly less than 1, while for paramagnetic substances it is slightly greater than 1.   The

---

[1] Ferromagnetic materials are sometimes classed as "strongly paramagnetic."

relative permeability of the ferromagnetic materials is generally much greater than 1 and in some special alloys may be as large as 1 million.

The relative permeability of diamagnetic and paramagnetic substances is relatively constant and independent of the applied field much as the relative permittivity of dielectric substances is independent of the applied electric field intensity. However, the relative permeability of ferromagnetic materials varies over a wide range for different applied fields. It also depends on the previous history of the specimen (see Hysteresis, Sec. 5-13). However, the *maximum* relative permeability is a relatively definite quantity for a particular ferromagnetic material although in different materials the maximum may occur at different values of the applied field. This subject is considered in more detail in Sec. 5-12.

In Table 5-1, the relative permeabilities μ_r are listed for a number of substances. The substances are arranged in order of increasing permeability, and they are also classified as to group type. The value given for the ferromagnetic materials is the maximum relative permeability.

TABLE 5-1

Substance	Group type	Relative permeability μ_r
Bismuth............................	Diamagnetic	0.99983
Silver.............................	Diamagnetic	0.99998
Lead.............................	Diamagnetic	0.999983
Copper...........................	Diamagnetic	0.999991
Water............................	Diamagnetic	0.999991
Vacuum...........................	Nonmagnetic	1 (by definition)
Air..............................	Paramagnetic	1.0000004
Aluminum.........................	Paramagnetic	1.00002
Palladium.........................	Paramagnetic	1.0008
2-81 Permalloy powder (2 Mo, 81 Ni)†...	Ferromagnetic	130
Cobalt............................	Ferromagnetic	250
Nickel............................	Ferromagnetic	600
Ferroxcube 3 (Mn-Zn-ferrite)...........	Ferromagnetic	1,500
Mild Steel (0.2 C)....................	Ferromagnetic	2,000
Iron (0.2 impurity)...................	Ferromagnetic	5,000
Silicon iron‡ (4 Si).................	Ferromagnetic	7,000
78 Permalloy (78.5 Ni)................	Ferromagnetic	100,000
Purified iron (0.05 impurity)............	Ferromagnetic	200,000
Supermalloy (5 Mo, 79 Ni).............	Ferromagnetic	1,000,000

† Percentage composition. Remainder is iron and impurities.
‡ Used in power transformers.

5-5. The Force between Bar Magnets and Coulomb's Law. Although a magnetic pole cannot be isolated, an equivalent effect may be obtained with two very long, uniformly magnetized needles as in Fig. 5-2. Here two north poles of strength Q_{m1} and Q_{m2} are separated by a distance r.

If this distance is small compared with the distance to the south poles at the other ends of the magnets, the effect of the south poles may be neglected. Under these conditions it was found by Coulomb that the force between the needles suspended in air is proportional to the product of the pole strengths and inversely proportional to their separation r. The quantitative relation is known as Coulomb's law for magnetic poles

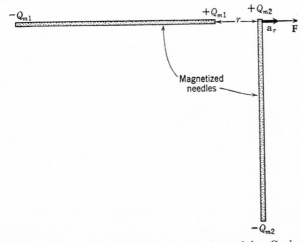

Fig. 5-2. Two long magnetized needles used in determining Coulomb's law.

and in the mksc system is expressed by

$$F = a_r \frac{\mu_0}{4\pi} \frac{Q_{m1}Q_{m2}}{r^2} \qquad (5\text{-}2)[1]$$

where F = force (newtons)

a_r = unit vector along line joining poles

μ_0 = permeability of air ($4\pi \times 10^{-7}$ henry/meter)

Q_{m1} and Q_{m2} = strength of north poles of needles (amp-meters)

r = distance between poles (meters)

As suggested in Fig. 5-2, the force is outward (repulsive) if the two poles are of the same kind, but the force is inward (attractive) if the poles are unlike.

[1] In order to achieve complete mathematical symmetry with Coulomb's law for electric changes, Coulomb's law for magnets is sometimes written

$$F = a_r \frac{1}{4\pi\mu_0} \frac{Q_{m1}^* Q_{m2}^*}{r^2}$$

where Q_{m1}^* and Q_{m2}^* are fictitious magnetic charges expressed in webers. This procedure, however, leads to inconsistencies. See Erik Hallén, Some Units in the Giorgi System and the C.G.S. System, *Trans. Roy. Inst. Techn.* (*Stockholm*), No. 6, 1947. See also J. A. Stratton, "Electromagnetic Theory," McGraw-Hill Book Company, Inc., New York, 1941, p. 242.

Dividing (5-2) by Q_{m2}, we obtain the force per unit pole as

$$\frac{\mathbf{F}}{Q_{m2}} = \mathbf{a}_r \frac{\mu_0}{4\pi} \cdot \frac{Q_{m1}}{r^2} \tag{5-3}$$

From (4-4) the force per unit pole is a measure of the flux density **B**. Thus

$$\mathbf{B} = \mathbf{a}_r \frac{\mu_0}{4\pi} \frac{Q_m}{r^2} \tag{5-4}$$

where **B** = flux density at distance r from pole of strength Q_m (newtons/amp-meter or webers/meter²).

Example. Find the flux density at a distance of 10 cm in air from a north pole with a strength of 1,000 amp meters. Also find the force on another north pole of equal strength at this distance. Assume that the south poles are at a large distance.
Solution. From (5-4) the magnitude of the flux density is

$$B = \frac{\mu_0}{4\pi} \frac{Q_m}{r^2} = \frac{4\pi \times 10^{-7}}{4\pi} \frac{10^3}{10^{-2}} = 10^{-2} \text{ newton/amp-meter}$$

Since the pole is positive, the direction of **B** is radially away from the pole. Another pole of equal strength at this point is acted on by a force of magnitude

$$\mathbf{F} = Q_m B = 10^3 \times 10^{-2} = 10 \text{ newtons}$$

The direction of the force **F** is the same as for the flux density **B**.

5-6. Magnetic Dipoles and Magnetization. According to (4-45) a loop of area A with current I has a magnetic moment of IA. The fields at a large distance from this loop are identical with those of a magnetic dipole of pole strength Q_m and length l as in Fig. 5-3 provided the magnetic moment of the bar is equal to that of the loop, that is, provided

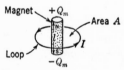

$$Q_m l = IA \tag{5-5}$$

Fig. 5-3. Bar magnet of moment $Q_m l$ and equivalent current loop of moment IA.

Although in the case of an actual magnet the value of the pole strength Q_m and pole separation l may be indefinite, their product, or *magnetic moment* $Q_m l$, is a definite quantity and is sufficient to specify the fields of a magnet at a large distance from it.

It was Ampère's theory that the pronounced magnetic effects of an iron bar occurred when large numbers of atomic-sized magnets associated with the iron atoms are oriented in the same direction so that their effects are additive. The precise nature of the tiny magnets is not important if we confine our attention to regions containing large numbers of them. Thus, they may be regarded as tiny magnets or as miniature current loops. In either case, it is sufficient to describe them by their magnetic moment, which can be expressed either as $Q_m l$ or as IA.

Consider the long iron rod shown in cross section in Fig. 5-4. Assume that all of the atomic magnets are uniformly distributed throughout the rod and are oriented in the same direction as suggested in the figure. This state of affairs may be described as one of *uniform* magnetization. The effect of the atomic magnets (or magnetic dipoles) can be con-

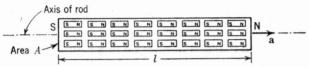

FIG. 5-4. Uniformly magnetized rod with elemental magnetic dipoles.

veniently described by a quantity called the *magnetization* **M**, which is defined as the magnetic dipole moment per unit volume.[1] Thus

$$\mathbf{M} = \frac{\mathbf{m}}{v} = \frac{Q_m\mathbf{l}}{v} \tag{5-6}$$

where $\mathbf{m} = Q_m\mathbf{l}$ = net magnetic (dipole) moment in volume v.

By regarding the separation between the poles of a magnetic dipole as a vector $\mathbf{l}$, pointing from the south or negative pole to the north pole, as in Fig. 5-5, the dipole moment $\mathbf{m}$ is a vector of magnitude $Q_m l$ with the direction of $\mathbf{l}$.

If the volume v includes the entire rod of length l and area A, we have

$$M = \frac{Q_m l}{Al} = \frac{Q_m}{A} \tag{5-7}$$

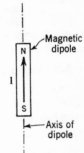

Hence, magnetization has the dimensions of both magnetic dipole moment per volume and of magnetic pole strength per area ($QL^2/TL^3 = Q/TL$). It is expressed in amperes per meter.

The magnetic pole strength per unit area may be regarded as a *pole surface density* ρ_{sm}. Thus, at the ends of the long, uniformly magnetized iron rod there is a pole surface density equal to the magnetization M. That is,

FIG. 5-5. Magnetic dipole.

$$\rho_{sm} = \frac{Q_m}{A} = M \tag{5-7a}$$

The value of **M** in (5-6) is an average for the volume v. To define **M** at a point, it is convenient to assume that the iron rod has a continuous distribution of infinitesimal magnetic dipoles, that is, a continuous magnetization, whereas the dipoles actually are of discrete, finite size. Nevertheless, the assumption of continuous magnetization leads to no

[1] The magnetization **M** is analogous to the electric polarization **P** (Sec. 2-3). The polarization $\mathbf{P} = \mathbf{p}/v = Q\mathbf{l}/v$, where $\mathbf{p} = Q\mathbf{l}$ = net dipole moment in the volume v.

appreciable error provided that we restrict our attention to volumes containing many magnetic dipoles. Then, assuming continuous magnetization, the value of $\mathbf{M}$ at a point can be defined as the net dipole moment $\mathbf{m}$ of a small volume Δv divided by the volume with the limit taken as Δv shrinks to zero around the point. Thus

$$\mathbf{M} = \lim_{\Delta v \to 0} \frac{\mathbf{m}}{\Delta v} \quad \text{amp/meter} \tag{5-8}$$

If $\mathbf{M}$ is known as a function of position in a nonuniformly magnetized rod, the total magnetic moment of the rod is given by

$$\mathbf{m} = \int_v \mathbf{M} \, dv \quad \text{amp-meters}^2 \tag{5-9}$$

where the integration is carried out over the volume of the rod.

Example. If the long, uniformly magnetized rod of Fig. 5-4 has N' elemental magnetic dipoles of moment Δm, find the magnetization of the bar.
Solution. From (5-6) the magnetization is

$$\mathbf{M} = \frac{N'}{v} \Delta\mathbf{m} = \mathbf{a}N'' \Delta m$$

where $\mathbf{M}$ = magnetization (amp/meter)
$N'' = N'/v$ = number of elemental dipoles per unit volume (meters³)
$\mathbf{a}$ = unit vector in direction of rod axis, pointing from the south to the north pole (dimensionless)
In this case the magnetization $\mathbf{M}$ is both an average value and also the value anywhere in the rod since the magnetization is assumed uniform.

5-7. Uniformly Magnetized Rod and Equivalent Solenoid. Instead of regarding that the magnetization of the rod magnet of Fig. 5-4 is caused by tiny bar magnets or magnetic dipoles, we can consider, as done by Ampère, that it is produced by miniature current loops as in Fig. 5-6.[1] That is, in place of each dipole of Fig. 5-4 there is a current loop in Fig. 5-6, their magnetic moments being equal. Thus

$$Q_m l' = I A' \tag{5-10}$$

where $Q_m l'$ = magnetic moment of elemental magnetic dipole of pole strength Q_m and length l'
$I A'$ = magnetic moment of equivalent current loop of area A' with current I

Assuming that there are n loops in a single cross section of the rod (as in end view in Fig. 5-6), we have

$$n A' = A \tag{5-11}$$

where A' = area of elemental loop
A = cross-sectional area of rod

---

[1] It is assumed that the rod is uniformly magnetized.

Further, let us assume that there are N such sets of loops in the length of the rod (see side view in Fig. 5-6).   Then

$$nN = N' \qquad (5\text{-}12)$$

where n = number of loops in a cross section of rod
  N = number of such sets of loops
  N' = total number of loops in rod
It follows that the magnetization M of the rod is given by

$$M = \frac{m}{v} = \frac{N'IA'}{lA} = \frac{NI}{l}\frac{nA'}{A} = \frac{NI}{l} = K' \qquad (5\text{-}13)$$

where K' = equivalent sheet current density on the outside surface of the rod (amp/meter).

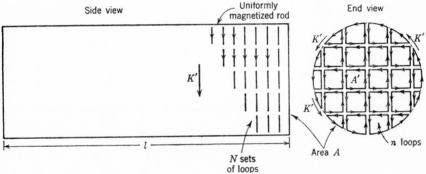

FIG. 5-6. Uniformly magnetized rod with elemental current loops.

Referring to the end view of the rod in Fig. 5-6, it is to be noted that there are equal and oppositely directed currents wherever loops are adjacent so that the currents have no net effect with the exception of the currents at the periphery of the rod. As a result there is the equivalent of a current sheet flowing around the rod as suggested in Fig. 5-6 and also Fig. 5-7a. This sheet has a linear current density K' amp per meter. Although the sets of current loops are shown for clarity in Fig. 5-6 with a large spacing, the actual spacing is of atomic dimensions so that macro-

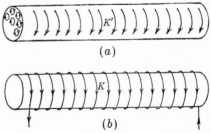

FIG. 5-7. (a) Uniformly magnetized rod and (b) equivalent solenoid.

scopically we can assume that the current sheet is continuous.

This type of a current sheet is effectively what we also have in the case of a solenoid with many turns of fine wire, as in Fig. 5-7b.   The actual sheet current density K for the solenoid is

$$K = \frac{NI}{l} \quad \text{amp/meter} \qquad (5\text{-}14)$$

where N = number of turns in solenoid (dimensionless)

$\quad I$ = current through each turn (amp)

$\quad l$ = length of solenoid (meters)

The sheet current density K may be expressed either in amperes per meter or in ampere-turns per meter.

If the solenoid of Fig. 5-7b is the same length and diameter as the rod of Fig. 5-7a, and if $K = K'$, the solenoid is the magnetic equivalent of the rod.

At the center of a long, slender solenoid the magnitude of the flux density $\mathbf{B}$ is, from (4-50),

$$B = \mu_0 \frac{NI}{l} = \mu_0 K \quad \text{webers/meter}^2 \qquad (5\text{-}14a)$$

At the center of a permanently magnetized, long, slender rod

$$B = \mu_0 K' \quad \text{webers/meter}^2 \qquad (5\text{-}14b)$$

If the rod is inside the solenoid, the magnitude of $\mathbf{B}$ at the center of the rod is

$$B = \mu_0(K + K') \quad \text{webers/meter}^2 \qquad (5\text{-}14c)$$

where K' is not, in general, the same as in (5-14b). In (5-14b) K' is due only to permanent magnetization, while in (5-14c) it also includes the induced magnetization (see Sec. 5-11).

Example. A uniformly magnetized rod 20 cm long and with a circular cross-sectional area of 10 cm^2 has a pole strength of 100 amp-meters. Find the equivalent sheet current density K'. Also find the current I required for a 1,000-turn solenoid of the same size to be magnetically equivalent.

Solution. From (5-13)

$$K' = \frac{m}{v} = \frac{Q_m l}{v} = \frac{100 \times 0.2}{10^{-3} \times 0.2} = 10^5 \text{ amp/meter}$$

For the solenoid to be equivalent we put $K = K'$, or

$$K = \frac{NI}{l} = K' = 10^5$$

from which

$$I = \frac{K'l}{N} = \frac{10^5 \times 0.2}{10^3} = 20 \text{ amp}$$

5-8. The Magnetic Vectors B, H, and M. Equation (4-76) states that, in general,

$$\mathbf{H} = \frac{\mathbf{B}}{\mu} \quad \text{or} \quad \mathbf{B} = \mu \mathbf{H} \qquad (5\text{-}15)$$

where $\mathbf{H}$ = H field, or vector $\mathbf{H}$† (amp/meter)

   $\mathbf{B}$ = flux density (webers/meter^2)

   μ = permeability of medium (henrys/meter)

In nonferromagnetic media μ is substantially the same as the permeability of vacuum μ_0. Hence, in nonferromagnetic media

$$\mathbf{H} = \frac{\mathbf{B}}{\mu_0} \qquad (5\text{-}16)$$

In ferromagnetic media μ is not equal to μ_0, and $\mathbf{H}$ is defined by a modification of (5-16) that involves the magnetization $\mathbf{M}$. That is,

$$\mathbf{H} = \frac{\mathbf{B}}{\mu_0} - \mathbf{M} \qquad (5\text{-}17)$$

where $\mathbf{M}$ = magnetization of ferromagnetic material (amp/meter).

   From (5-17)

$$\mathbf{B} = \mu_0(\mathbf{H} + \mathbf{M}) = \mu_0 \left(1 + \frac{\mathbf{M}}{\mathbf{H}}\right)\mathbf{H} \qquad (5\text{-}18)$$

By comparison of (5-18) with (5-15) it follows that, in general, the permeability is given by[1]

$$\mu = \mu_0 \left(1 + \frac{\mathbf{M}}{\mathbf{H}}\right) \qquad (5\text{-}19)$$

In isotropic media $\mathbf{M}$ and $\mathbf{H}$ are in the same direction so that their quotient is a scalar, and hence μ is a scalar. In nonisotropic media, such as crystals, $\mathbf{M}$ and $\mathbf{H}$ are, in general, not in the same direction, and μ is not a scalar but becomes a nine-component quantity, or tensor. Only when $\mathbf{H}$ is parallel to a crystal axis of a nonisotropic medium will both $\mathbf{M}$ and $\mathbf{H}$ be in the same direction and μ a scalar. Hence, (5-17) is a general relation, while (5-15) is a more concise expression, which, however, has a simple significance only for isotropic media or certain special cases in nonisotropic media, that is, wherever $\mathbf{M}$, $\mathbf{H}$, and $\mathbf{B}$ are parallel.

   A single iron crystal is nonisotropic, but most iron specimens consist of an aggregate of numerous crystals oriented at random so that macroscopically such specimens may be treated as though they were isotropic. In such cases (5-15) can also be applied as a strictly macroscopic, or large-scale, relation.

   Since $\nabla \cdot \mathbf{B} = 0$, we have, on taking the divergence of (5-17),

$$\nabla \cdot \mathbf{H} = -\nabla \cdot \mathbf{M} \qquad (5\text{-}20)$$

† $\mathbf{H}$ is sometimes called the "magnetizing force."

[1] The ratio $\mathbf{M}/\mathbf{H}$ is a dimensionless quantity and is called the *magnetic* susceptibility χ_m, that is $\mathbf{M}/\mathbf{H} = \chi_m$. Therefore, from (5-19) $\mu = \mu_0(1 + \chi_m)$. The analogous electrical quantity is the electric susceptibility. See footnote concerning Eq. (2-19), p. 51.

If the divergence of a vector field is not zero, the field has a source, or place of origin. We recall from the polarized dielectric case (Sec. 2-33) that $\nabla \cdot \mathbf{P} = \rho_p$, which indicates that the polarization field originates on the polarization charge (of apparent volume density ρ_p) at the dielectric surface. In an analogous manner, (5-20) indicates that the $\mathbf{H}$ field originates where the magnetization field $\mathbf{M}$ ends and that the $\mathbf{H}$ field ends where the $\mathbf{M}$ field originates. This occurs at the ends of the rod in Fig. 5-4.[1]

The dimensions of (5-20) are current per area (amp/meter^2) or pole strength per volume (amp-meters/meters^3). Thus, div $\mathbf{H}$ or div $\mathbf{M}$ has the dimensions of pole volume density, and we may write

$$\nabla \cdot \mathbf{H} = -\nabla \cdot \mathbf{M} = \rho_m \qquad (5\text{-}22)$$

where ρ_m = pole volume density (amp-meters/meter^3).

The locations where $\nabla \cdot \mathbf{H}$, or $\nabla \cdot \mathbf{M}$, is not zero may be regarded as the locations of the magnetic poles of a magnetized object. Thus the poles of a uniformly magnetized rod, as in Fig. 5-4, are at the end faces of the rod.[2]

The quantity ρ_m is like the polarization volume density ρ_p in that it cannot be isolated and, in this respect, is fictitious. By assuming that ρ_m exists in a layer of small but finite thickness at the ends of a magnetized rod, $\nabla \cdot \mathbf{H}$ or $\nabla \cdot \mathbf{M}$ may be large but not infinite.

For a uniformly magnetized rod, as in Fig. 5-4, we have, from (5-7), that

$$|M| = \frac{Q_m}{A} = \rho_{sm} \qquad (5\text{-}23)$$

where Q_m = pole strength of the rod (amp-meters)
A = area of rod (meters^2)
M = magnetization of rod medium (amp/meter)
ρ_{sm} = pole surface density at ends of rod (amp-meters/meter^2)

The magnetization $\mathbf{M}$ has the dimensions of current per length (amp/meter). Equivalent dimensions are magnetic moment per volume

---

[1] Since $\mathbf{H} = -\nabla U$, we have, from (5-20),

$$\nabla^2 U = \nabla \cdot \mathbf{M} \qquad (5\text{-}21)$$

This indicates that the magnetic potential U for a magnetized object is related to the source of the magnetization.

[2] In ordinary magnets with flat ends the magnetization tends to be nonuniform near the edges. Entirely uniform magnetization is possible in spherically or elliptically shaped magnetic objects. However, the assumption of uniform magnetization is a good approximation for a long homogeneous rod magnet, since the magnetization is nearly uniform over all of the rod except near the edges at the ends of the rod. In actual magnets with flat ends the effective separation between the pole centers is slightly less than the physical length of the magnet.

(amp-meters^2/meter^3) and pole surface density (amp-meters/meter^2). It follows that the pole strength of a uniformly magnetized rod is given by

$$Q_m = |M| \, A = \rho_{sm} A \qquad (5\text{-}24)$$

Taking the curl of (5-18), we have

$$\nabla \times \mathbf{B} = \mu_0 \nabla \times \mathbf{H} + \mu_0 \nabla \times \mathbf{M} \qquad (5\text{-}25)$$

or

$$\nabla \times \mathbf{B} = \mu_0 \mathbf{J} + \mu_0 \nabla \times \mathbf{M} \qquad (5\text{-}26)$$

Where there is no magnetization, (5-26) reduces to $\nabla \times \mathbf{B} = \mu_0 \mathbf{J}$ as in (4-127). The curl of $\mathbf{M}$ has the dimensions of current density (amp/meter^2) and represents the equivalent current of density $\mathbf{J}'$ (amp/meter^2) flowing, for example, in a very thin layer around the cylindrical surface of a uniformly magnetized rod. The linear current density for this sheet is K' (amp/meter) given by[1]

$$K' = J' \, \Delta x \qquad (5\text{-}27)$$

where Δx = thickness of layer of current of average density J'. Thus (5-26) becomes

$$\nabla \times \mathbf{B} = \mu_0 (\mathbf{J} + \mathbf{J}') \qquad (5\text{-}28)$$

where $\mathbf{J}$ = actual current density, as in a current-carrying wire (amp/meter^2)

$\mathbf{J}'$ = equivalent current density, as at the surface of a magnetized bar (amp/meter^2)

The flux density $\mathbf{B}$ is always the result of a current or its equivalent. For example, the magnitude of $\mathbf{B}$ at the center of a long, slender iron rod surrounded by a long solenoid is, from (5-14c),

$$B = \mu_0 (K + K') \qquad \text{webers/meter}^2 \qquad (5\text{-}29)$$

where K = sheet current density due to solenoid current (amp/meter)

K' = equivalent sheet current density due to magnetization of rod (amp/meter)

In many cases we can conveniently express $\mathbf{B}$ directly in terms of the currents producing it as in (5-29). In general, we can also express $\mathbf{B}$ in terms of the vector potential $\mathbf{A}$, which in turn is related to the currents. Thus

$$\mathbf{B} = \nabla \times \mathbf{A} \qquad (5\text{-}30)$$

If both conduction currents and magnetization are present,

$$\mathbf{A} = \frac{\mu_0}{4\pi} \int \frac{\mathbf{J} + \mathbf{J}'}{r} \, dv \qquad (5\text{-}30a)$$

---

[1] For a current sheet of infinitesimal thickness K' may be defined as in (5-27) with $\Delta x \to 0$ and $J' \to \infty$. However, we will assume that Δx is small but finite, with $\mathbf{M}$ varying continuously over this layer.

where $\mathbf{J} = \nabla \times \mathbf{H}$ (amp/meter)

$\mathbf{J'} = \nabla \times \mathbf{M}$ (amp/meter)

To illustrate further the significance of $\mathbf{B}$, $\mathbf{H}$, and $\mathbf{M}$, three situations will be analyzed in the following examples. These situations involve an air-filled toroidal coil (Fig. 5-8a), a magnetized iron ring of the same shape as the coil (Fig. 5-8b), and the iron ring with the toroidal coil wound over

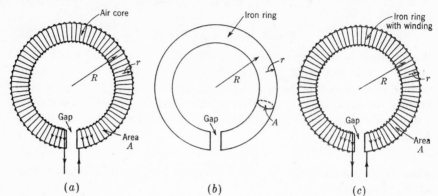

(a)   (b)   (c)

Fig. 5-8. (a) Toroidal coil with gap. (b) Permanently magnetized iron ring with gap. (c) Iron-cored toroidal coil with gap.

it (Fig. 5-8c). In all three cases there is a narrow gap as indicated in the drawings.

Example 1. Referring to Fig. 5-8a, a toroidal coil has a radius R and a cross-sectional area $A = \pi r^2$. The coil has a very narrow gap as shown in the gap detail in Fig. 5-9a. The coil is made of many turns N of fine insulated wire with a current I. Draw graphs showing the variation of $\mathbf{B}$, $\mathbf{M}$, $\mathbf{H}$, and μ along the line of radius R at the gap (center line of coil).

Solution. Neglecting the small effect of the narrow gap, $\mathbf{B}$ is substantially uniform around the inside of the entire toroid. Since $R \gg r$, its magnitude is, from (4-50), given approximately by

$$B = \frac{\mu_0 N I}{2\pi R} = \mu_0 K \qquad \text{webers/meter}^2 \qquad (5\text{-}31)$$

where K = magnitude of linear sheet current density (amp/meter). A graph of the magnitude $\mathbf{B}$ along the center line of the coil at the gap is shown in Fig. 5-9b.

No ferromagnetic material is present so that the magnetization is negligible and $M = 0$ as indicated in Fig. 5-9c. It follows that $\nabla \cdot \mathbf{M} = 0$ and also $\nabla \cdot \mathbf{H} = 0$.

Since $M = 0$, we have, from (5-17) and (5-31), that

$$H = \frac{B}{\mu_0} = \frac{\mu_0 K}{\mu_0} = K = \frac{N I}{2\pi R} \qquad \text{amp/meter} \qquad (5\text{-}32)$$

Therefore, the magnitude of $\mathbf{H}$ is constant and equal to the sheet current density K of the coil winding as indicated in Fig. 5-9d.

The permeability everywhere is μ_0 (Fig. 5-9e). This also follows from (5-19) since $M = 0$.

It is to be noted that **B** is continuous (no abrupt changes) and that in this case **H** is also continuous since there is no ferromagnetic material present. Both **B** and **H** have the same direction everywhere in this case.

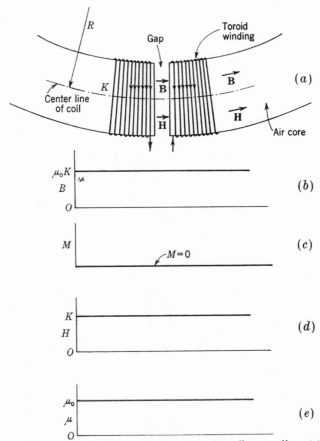

FIG. 5-9. Magnitudes of magnetic quantities along the coil center line at the gap in a toroid (see Fig. 5-8a) (Example 1).

Example 2. Consider now that the toroidal coil of Example 1 is replaced by an iron ring of the same size and also with a gap of the same dimensions, as suggested in Fig. 5-8b and Fig. 5-10a. Assume that the ring has a uniform permanent magnetization **M** that is equal in magnitude to K for the toroid in Example 1. Draw graphs showing the variation of **B**, **M**, **H**, μ, and $\nabla \cdot$ **H** along the center line of the ring at the gap.

Solution. The ring has a north pole at the left side of the gap and a south pole at the right side. Neglecting the small effect of the narrow gap, **B** is substantially uniform around the interior of the entire ring and also across the gap. It is due entirely to the equivalent sheet current density K' on the surface of the ring. From (5-13), $K' = M$. Thus

$$B = \mu_0 M = \mu_0 K' \qquad \text{webers/meter}^2 \qquad (5\text{-}32a)$$

where M and K' are, according to the stated conditions, equal to K for the solenoid in Example 1. Hence, B is the same in both examples. Its value at the gap is illustrated in Fig. 5-10b.

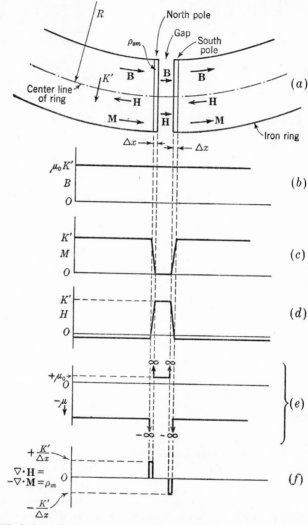

Fig. 5-10. Variation of magnetic quantities along the center line at the gap in a permanently magnetized iron ring (see Fig. 5-8b) (Example 2).

In the ring, $M = K'$, but outside the ring and in the gap $M = 0$. Suppose that the change in M from zero to K' at the gap occurs over a short distance Δx rather than as a square step function. The graph for M is then as shown in Fig. 5-10c.

Outside the ring and in the gap $M = 0$; so

$$H = \frac{B}{\mu_0} = K' \qquad \text{amp/meter} \qquad (5\text{-}33)$$

Inside the ring

$$H = \frac{B}{\mu_0} - M \qquad \text{amp/meter} \tag{5-34}$$

or approximately

$$H = K' - K' = 0 \tag{5-35}$$

The exact value of H is not zero[1] but is small and negative. The variation of H across the gap is illustrated in Fig. 5-10d.

From (5-19) the permeability in the ring is large and negative because H is small compared with M and is negative. In the air gap $\mu = \mu_0$. The variation of μ across the gap is suggested in Fig. 5-10e.

According to (5-22) the divergence of $\mathbf{H}$ equals the negative divergence of $\mathbf{M}$, and this equals the apparent pole volume density ρ_m in the ring on both sides of the gap. Thus

$$\nabla \cdot \mathbf{H} = -\nabla \cdot \mathbf{M} = \rho_m \qquad \text{(amp-meters/meter}^3) \tag{5-36}$$

This is zero everywhere except at the layers of assumed thickness Δx at the gap. Assuming that $\mathbf{M}$ changes linearly in magnitude over this thickness and assuming also that Δx is very small compared with the cross-sectional diameter $(2r)$ of the ring, we have on the center line

$$\nabla \cdot \mathbf{M} = \frac{dM_x}{dx} = \frac{\mp K'}{\Delta x} = -\rho_m \tag{5-37a}$$

or

$$\nabla \cdot \mathbf{H} = \frac{\pm K'}{\Delta x} = \rho_m \tag{5-37b}$$

where the upper sign in front of K' applies if M decreases and H increases in proceeding across Δx in a positive direction (from left to right). The variation of $\nabla \cdot \mathbf{H}$ along the center line is illustrated in Fig. 5-10f. Hence the pole volume density ρ_m has a value only in the layers of assumed thickness Δx at the sides of the gap. This locates the poles of the ring magnet at the sides of the gap, and, for this reason, the iron surfaces of the gap are called "pole faces."

From (5-7a)

$$\rho_{sm} = M = K' \tag{5-38a}$$

where ρ_{sm} is the pole surface density at the pole faces (see Fig. 5-10a). The pole surface density is expressible in ampere-meters per square meter or in amperes per meter. Assuming that ρ_m extends over a thickness Δx of the pole face, we have

$$\frac{\rho_{sm}}{\Delta x} = \rho_m \tag{5-38b}$$

where ρ_m = apparent pole volume density at a pole face (amp-meters/meter³ or amp/meter²).

Since K' in this example equals K in Example 1, B and H in the gap have identical values in both examples. In the gap, the directions of B and H are the same. In the iron ring B is the same as in the toroid of Example 1, but H is smaller and is also in the opposite direction. An H direction opposite to that of B is characteristic of condi-

---

[1] The above analysis is approximate since it neglects the effect of the gap. See Sec. 5-25.

tions *inside* of a permanent magnet. For similar reasons the direction of **E** inside of a permanent electret[1] is opposed to **D**.

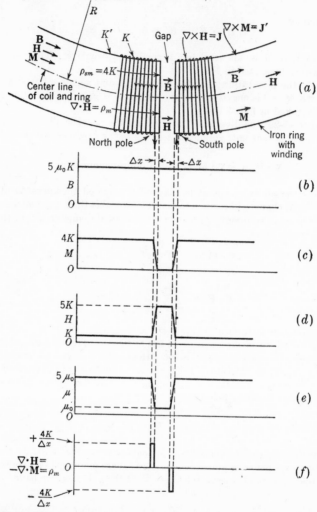

FIG. 5-11. Variation of magnetic quantities along coil center line at the gap in an iron-cored toroid (see Fig. 5-8c) (Example 3).

Example 3. Suppose now that the iron ring of the previous example has wound over it the toroidal coil of Example 1 with the gap in the toroid coinciding with the gap in the ring as shown in Fig. 5-8c and also in the gap detail of Fig. 5-11a. The combination constitutes an iron-cored toroid as contrasted with the air-cored toroid of Example 1. Let the sheet current density for the toroid winding be K as in the first

[1] A *permanent electret*, or simply an *electret*, is a dielectric body that is permanently polarized in the absence of an applied electric field. It is the electrical analogue of a permanent magnet. See footnote, p. 49.

example. Further, let the *induced* magnetization added to the *permanent* magnetization in the ring yield a *total* uniform magnetization (permanent and induced) that is equal in magnitude to $4K$. Draw graphs showing the variation of **B**, **M**, **H**, μ, and $\nabla \cdot \mathbf{H}$ along the center line of the ring at the gap.

Solution. In this case the total magnetization

$$M = K' = 4K \qquad \text{amp/meter} \tag{5-39}$$

Neglecting the small effect of the narrow gap, the flux density is substantially uniform around the inside of the ring and across the gap. From (5-14c) and (5-39) it is given by

$$B = \mu_0(K + K') = 5\mu_0 K \qquad \text{webers/meter} \tag{5-40}$$

as illustrated in Fig. 5-11b.

In the ring $M = 4K$ and in the gap $M = 0$ as shown in Fig. 5-11c. It is again assumed that M changes linearly over a short distance Δx at the pole faces.

In the gap

$$H = \frac{B}{\mu_0} = 5K \tag{5-41}$$

In the ring

$$H = \frac{B}{\mu_0} - M \tag{5-42}$$

and so we have very nearly that

$$H = 5K - 4K = K \tag{5-43}$$

The variation of H across the gap is depicted in Fig. 5-11d.

In the gap $\mu = \mu_0$. In the ring

$$\mu = \mu_0 \left(1 + \frac{M}{H} \right) = \mu_0 \left(1 + \frac{4K}{K} \right) = 5\mu_0 \tag{5-44}$$

The variation of μ is shown in Fig. 5-11e.

The divergence of **H** or pole volume density ρ_m is given by the negative of the divergence of **M**. This has a value of $\pm 4K/\Delta x$ over the assumed pole thickness Δx at the pole faces. This is illustrated in Fig. 5-11f. The fact that $\nabla \cdot \mathbf{H} = \rho_m$ at the pole faces is also indicated in Fig. 5-11a. Elsewhere $\nabla \cdot \mathbf{H} = 0$.

The pole surface density ρ_{sm} in this example is equal to $4K$.

In this example, **B** and **H** have the same direction both in the gap and in the ring. In the ring, however, **H** is weaker than in the gap.

In this example, the toroid has a sheet current density of K (amp/meter), and the ring has an equivalent sheet current density around its curved surface of

$$K' = 4K \text{ (amp/meter)}$$

Inside a wire of the toroidal coil $\nabla \times \mathbf{H} = \mathbf{J}$ (amp/meter²) as suggested in Fig. 5-11a. Elsewhere $\nabla \times \mathbf{H} = 0$. At the curved surface of the ring $\nabla \times \mathbf{M} = \mathbf{J}'$ (amp/meter²). Elsewhere $\nabla \times \mathbf{M} = 0$.

In the last two examples involving ferromagnetic material it is to be noted that the magnetization, or **M**, lines originate, or have their source, on a south (negative) pole and end on, or have as a sink, a north (positive) pole. The **H** lines, on the other hand, originate, as in Example 2, on a north pole and end on a south pole. Thus, $\nabla \cdot \mathbf{H}$ has a positive value at a north pole, while $\nabla \cdot \mathbf{M}$ has a positive value at a south pole.

As a final example let us compare the fields around a solenoid and the equivalent permanently magnetized rod.

Example 4. A long, uniform solenoid, as in Fig. 5-12a, is situated in air and has NI amp-turns and a length l. A permanently magnetized iron rod, as in Fig. 5-12e, has

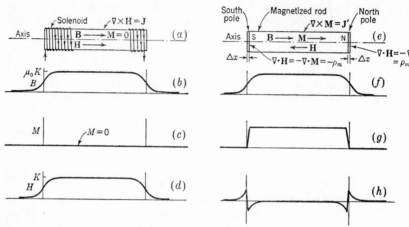

Fig. 5-12. Solenoid and equivalent permanently magnetized rod showing fields along axis (Example 4).

the same dimensions as the solenoid and has a uniform magnetization M equal to NI/l for the solenoid. Draw graphs showing the variation of $\mathbf{B}$, $\mathbf{M}$, and $\mathbf{H}$ along the axes of the solenoid and the rod. Also sketch the configuration of the fields for the two cases.

Solution. Since the rod and solenoid have the same dimensions and

$$M = K' = K = \frac{NI}{l},$$

the two are magnetically equivalent. The $\mathbf{B}$ fields for both are the same everywhere, and the $\mathbf{H}$ fields for both are the same outside the solenoid and rod. Assuming that the toroid is long compared with its diameter, the flux density at the center is nearly given by

$$B = \mu_0 \frac{NI}{l} = \mu_0 K \tag{5-45}$$

At the ends of the solenoid

$$B = \tfrac{1}{2}\mu_0 K \tag{5-46}$$

The magnitude of $\mathbf{B}$ at other locations along the solenoid axis can be obtained from (4-48) with a suitable change in limits. The variation of $\mathbf{B}$ along the solenoid axis is shown graphically in Fig. 5-12b. The variation along the rod axis is the same (Fig. 5-12f).

For the solenoid case $M = 0$ everywhere (Fig. 5-12c). In the rod the magnetization M is assumed to be uniform as in Fig. 5-12g.

For the solenoid case $\mathbf{H} = \mathbf{B}/\mu_0$ everywhere so that $H = K$ at the center and $H = \tfrac{1}{2}K$ at the ends. The variation of H along the solenoid axis is shown in Fig.

5-12*d*. Outside the rod, H is the same as for the solenoid. Inside the rod

$$H = (B/\mu_0) - M$$

so that the variation is as suggested in Fig. 5-12*h*. It is assumed that M changes from 0 to K over a short distance Δx at the ends of the rod. The direction of **H** in the rod is opposite to that for **B**.

Inside the wires of the solenoid winding $\nabla \times \mathbf{H} = \mathbf{J}$ as indicated in Fig. 5-12*a*. On the cylindrical surface of the rod $\nabla \times \mathbf{M} = \mathbf{J}'$ as suggested in Fig. 5-12*e*. In the solenoid case $\nabla \cdot \mathbf{B} = 0$ and $\nabla \cdot \mathbf{H} = 0$ everywhere. In the rod case $\nabla \cdot \mathbf{B} = 0$ everywhere, but $\nabla \cdot \mathbf{H} = -\nabla \cdot \mathbf{M} = \rho_m$ at the end faces of the rod.

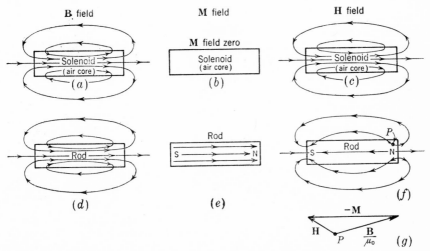

Fig. 5-13. Fields of solenoid and equivalent permanently magnetized rod. The **B** fields are the same for both solenoid and rod [see (*a*) and (*d*)]. The **M** field is zero everywhere except inside the rod [see (*b*) and (*e*)]. The **H** fields are the same outside both solenoid and rod but are different inside [see (*c*) and (*f*)].

The **B**, **M**, and **H** fields for the two cases are sketched in Fig. 5-13. It is to be noted that inside the rod **H** is directed from the north pole to the south pole. Since **M** and **B** have, in general, different directions in the rod, μ loses its simple scalar significance in this case. Here **H** can be obtained by vector addition, using (5-17). As an example, **H** at the point P in Fig. 5-13*f* is obtained by the vector addition of $\mathbf{B}/\mu_0$ and $-\mathbf{M}$ as in Fig. 5-13*g*.

Magnetic poles always appear in pairs. They cannot be isolated. In this sense, they are of an apparent, or fictitious, nature. However, they are real in the sense that they act as the centers of force near the ends of a magnet as in the above example.

Although the magnetization is based on the actual magnetization phenomenon, it is often simpler and more convenient to ignore the mechanism of the phenomenon and use the permeability μ to describe the characteristics of the magnetic medium. This is particularly true where μ can be treated as a scalar. In this case μ is determined experimentally from a sample of the material. However, since μ is not a constant for ferromagnetic materials but a function of **H**, and also the previous history of the sample, the methods for dealing with ferromagnetic materials require special consideration (see Sec. 5-11 and following sections).

5-9. Boundary Relations. In a single medium the magnetic field is continuous. That is, the field, if not constant, changes only by an infinitesimal amount in an infinitesimal distance. However, at the boundary between two different media, the magnetic field may change abruptly both in magnitude and direction. It is important in many problems to know the relations for magnetic fields at a boundary. These boundary relations are discussed in this section.

It is convenient to analyze the boundary problem in two parts, considering separately the relation of fields *normal* to the boundary and *tangent* to the boundary.

Taking up first the relation of fields normal to the boundary, consider two media of permeabilities μ_1 and μ_2 separated by the x-y plane as shown in Fig. 5-14. Suppose that an imaginary box is constructed, half in each

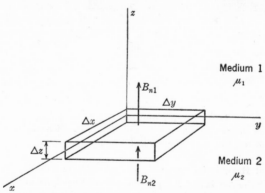

Fig. 5-14. Construction for developing continuity relation for normal component of B.

medium, of area $\Delta x\, \Delta y$ and height Δz. Let B_{n1} be the average component of **B** normal to the top of the box in medium 1 and B_{n2} the average component of **B** normal to the bottom of the box in medium 2. B_{n1} is an outward normal (positive), while B_{n2} is an inward normal (negative). By Gauss's law for magnetic fields (4-12), the total magnetic flux over a closed surface is zero. Expressed in other words, the integral of the outward normal component of **B** over a closed surface is zero. By making the height Δz of the box approach zero, the contribution of the sides of the box to the surface integral becomes zero even though there may be finite components of **B** normal to the sides. Therefore the surface integral reduces to

$$B_{n1} \, \Delta x \, \Delta y - B_{n2} \, \Delta x \, \Delta y = 0 \qquad (5\text{-}47)$$

or

$$B_{n1} = B_{n2} \qquad (5\text{-}48)$$

According to (5-48) *the normal component of the flux density* **B** *is continuous across the boundary between two media.*[1]

Turning now to the relation for magnetic fields tangent to the boundary, let two media of permeabilities μ_1 and μ_2 be separated by a plane boundary as in Fig. 5-15. Consider a rectangular path, half in each

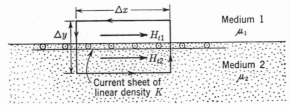

FIG. 5-15. Construction for developing continuity relation for tangential component of **H**.

medium, of length Δx parallel to the boundary and of length Δy normal to the boundary. Let the average value of **H** tangent to the boundary in medium 1 be H_{t1} and the average value of **H** tangent to the boundary in medium 2 be H_{t2}. According to (4-77) the integral of **H** around a closed path equals the current I enclosed. By making the path length Δy approach zero, the contribution of these segments of the path becomes zero even though a finite field may exist normal to the boundary. The line integral then reduces to

$$H_{t1} \, \Delta x - H_{t2} \, \Delta x = I \qquad \text{amperes} \qquad (5\text{-}49)$$

or

$$H_{t1} - H_{t2} = \frac{I}{\Delta x} = K \qquad \text{amp/meter} \qquad (5\text{-}50)$$

where K is the linear density of any current flowing in an infinitesimally thin sheet at the surface.[2]

According to (5-50) *the change in the tangential component of* **H** *across a boundary is equal in magnitude to the sheet current density K on the boundary.* It is to be noted that **K** is normal to **H**, that is, the direction of the current sheet in Fig. 5-15 is normal to the page.

---

[1] This relation applies at the boundary of *any* two media for both static and time-changing fields.

[2] If **J** is the current density in amperes per square meter in a thin sheet of thickness $\Delta y'$, then K is defined by

$$K = J \, \Delta y' \qquad \text{amp/meter} \qquad (5\text{-}50a)$$

where $J \to \infty$ as $\Delta y' \to 0$.

If $K = 0$, then (5-50) reduces to[1]

$$H_{t1} = H_{t2} \tag{5-51a}$$

According to (5-51a) *the tangential components of* **H** *are continuous across the boundary between two media provided the boundary has no current sheet of infinitesimal thickness.*

If $H_{t2} = 0$, (5-50) becomes

$$H_{t1} = K_2 \tag{5-51b}$$

where K_2 = sheet current density (amp/meter) in medium 2 at boundary.

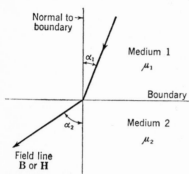

When medium 1 is air and medium 2 is a conductor, (5-51b) is approximated at high frequencies because the skin effect restricts the current in the conductor to a very thin layer at its surface (see Chap. 10).

To illustrate the application of these boundary conditions, let us consider the following examples.

Fig. 5-16. Boundary between two media of different permeability showing change in direction of magnetic field line.

Example 1. Consider a plane boundary between two media of permeability μ_1 and μ_2 as in Fig. 5-16. Find the relation between the angles α_1 and α_2. Assume that the media are isotropic with **B** and **H** in the same direction.

Solution. From the boundary relations,

$$B_{n1} = B_{n2} \qquad \text{and} \qquad H_{t1} = H_{t2} \tag{5-52}$$

From Fig. 5-16,

$$B_{n1} = B_1 \cos \alpha_1 \qquad \text{and} \qquad B_{n2} = B_2 \cos \alpha_2 \tag{5-53}$$

and

$$H_{t1} = H_1 \sin \alpha_1 \qquad \text{and} \qquad H_{t2} = H_2 \sin \alpha_2 \tag{5-54}$$

where B_1 = magnitude of **B** in medium 1
B_2 = magnitude of **B** in medium 2
H_1 = magnitude of **H** in medium 1
H_2 = magnitude of **H** in medium 2

Substituting (5-53) and (5-54) into (5-52) and dividing yields

$$\frac{\tan \alpha_1}{\tan \alpha_2} = \frac{\mu_1}{\mu_2} = \frac{\mu_{r1}}{\mu_{r2}} \tag{5-55}$$

where μ_{r1} = relative permeability of medium 1 (dimensionless)
μ_{r2} = relative permeability of medium 2 (dimensionless)

[1] Equations (5-50) and (5-51a) apply at the boundary of *any* two media (that is, two media of *any* permeabilities, permittivities, and conductivities) for both static and time-changing fields.

Equation (5-55) gives the relation between the angles α_1 and α_2 for **B** and **H** lines at the boundary between two media.[1]

Example 2. Referring to Fig. 5-17, let medium 1 be air ($\mu_r = 1$) and medium 2 be soft iron with a relative permeability of 7,000.

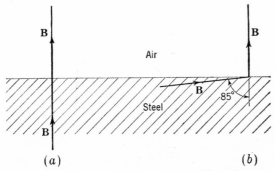

FIG. 5-17a and b. B lines at air-steel boundary.

a. If **B** in the iron is incident normally on the boundary ($\alpha_2 = 0$), find α_1.

b. If **B** in the iron is nearly tangent to the surface at an angle $\alpha_2 = 85°$, find α_1.

Solution. a. From (5-55)

$$\tan \alpha_1 = \frac{\mu_{r1}}{\mu_{r2}} \tan \alpha_2 = \frac{1}{7,000} \tan \alpha_2 \tag{5-56}$$

When $\alpha_2 = 0$, $\alpha_1 = 0$, so that the **B** line in air is also normal to the boundary (see Fig. 5-17a).

Solution. b. When $\alpha_2 = 85°$, we have, from (5-56), that $\tan \alpha_1 = 0.0016$ or $\alpha_1 = 0.1°$. Thus, the direction of **B** in air is almost normal to the boundary (within $\frac{1}{10}°$) even though its direction in the iron is nearly tangent to the boundary (within 5°) (see Fig. 5-17b). Accordingly, for many practical purposes the *direction of* **B** *or* **H** *in air or other medium of low relative permeability may be taken as normal to the boundary of a medium having a high relative permeability.* This property is reminiscent of the one for **E** or **D** at the boundary of a conductor.

The property that **B** or **H** in air is substantially normal to the boundary of a highly permeable medium has important applications in mapping magnetic fields. For example, this property permits one to predict that

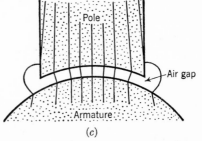

FIG. 5-17c. Field lines at air gap of d-c machine.

the magnetic field lines at the air gap between the iron pole and armature core of a simple two-pole d-c machine may be as suggested in Fig. 5-17c. The mapping of magnetic fields is discussed further in Sec. 5-19.

[1] This relation applies only if **B** and **H** have the same direction (μ a scalar). In the absence of magnetization, as in air, **B** and **H** have the same direction. When magnetization is present, as in a soft iron electromagnet, **B** and **H** also tend to have the same direction. However, this is *not* the situation in a permanent magnet.

5-10. Table of Boundary Relations for Magnetic Fields. Table 5-2 summarizes the boundary relations for magnetic fields developed in Sec. 5-9.

TABLE 5-2
BOUNDARY RELATIONS FOR MAGNETIC FIELDS†

Field component	Boundary relation	Condition
Normal.......	$B_{n1} = B_{n2}$ (1)	Any two media
Normal.......	$\mu_{r1}H_{n1} = \mu_{r2}H_{n2}$ (2)	Any two media
Tangential....	$H_{t1} - H_{t2} = K$ (3)‡	Any two media with current sheet of infinitesimal thickness at boundary
Tangential....	$H_{t1} = H_{t2}$ (4)	Any two media with no current sheet at boundary
Tangential....	$H_{t1} = K_2$ (5)‡	$H_{t2} = 0$. Also medium 2 has a current sheet of infinitesimal thickness at boundary. H_{t1} and K_2 are normal to each other

† These relations apply for both static and time-varying fields (see Chap. 7).
‡ Note that although **K** and the components of **H** are measured parallel to the boundary, they are normal to each other. Thus, in vector notation (5) is expressed by **K** = **n** × **H**, where **n** = unit vector normal to the boundary.

5-11. Ferromagnetism. Magnetic effects in most substances are weak. However, a group of substances known as ferromagnetic materials exhibits strong magnetic effects (see Sec. 5-4). The permeability of these materials is not a constant but is a function both of the applied field and of the previous magnetic history of the specimen. In view of the variable nature of the permeability of ferromagnetic materials, special consideration of their properties is needed. This is given in the following sections.

In ferromagnetic substances the magnetic effects are produced by the motion of the electrons of the individual atoms. The net effect is to make an atom of a ferromagnetic substance act like a miniature bar magnet. In a ferromagnetic substance such as iron these atomic magnets over a region of many atoms tend to orient themselves parallel to each other, with north poles pointing one way. This region is called a magnetic *domain* and is spontaneously magnetized. The size of a domain depends on conditions but usually contains millions of atoms. In some substances the shape appears to be like a long, slender rod with a transverse dimension of microscopic size but lengths of the order of a millimeter or so. Thus, a domain acts like a small, but not atomically small, bar magnet.

In an unmagnetized iron crystal the domains are parallel to the direction of easy magnetization, but as many have north poles pointing one way as the other so that the external field of the crystal is zero.   In an iron crystal there are six directions of easy magnetization.   That is, there is a positive and negative direction along each of the three mutually perpendicular crystal axes (Fig. 5-18).

Therefore the polarity of the domains in an unmagnetized iron crystal may be as suggested by the highly schematic diagram of Fig. 5-19a.   A single N represents a domain with a north pole pointing out of the page and a single S a domain with a south pole pointing out of the page. If the crystal is placed in a magnetic field parallel to one of the directions of easy magnetization, the domains with polarity opposing or perpendicular to the field

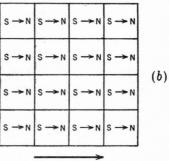

(a)

(b)

Applied magnetic field

become unstable and a few of these may rotate so that they have the same

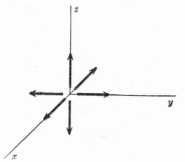

Fig. 5-18. Six directions of easy magnetization in an iron crystal.

Fig. 5-19. (a) Domain polarity in an unmagnetized iron crystal. (b) Condition after crystal is saturated by a magnetic field directed to the right.

direction as the field.   With further increase of the field more domains change over, each as an individual unit, until when all of the domains are in the same direction, *magnetic saturation* is reached as suggested by Fig. 5-19b.   The crystal is then magnetized to a maximum extent.   If the majority of the domains retain their directions after the applied field is removed, the specimen is said to be *permanently magnetized*.   Heat and mechanical shock tend to return the crystal to the original unmagnetized state.   In fact, if the temperature is raised sufficiently high, the domains themselves are demagnetized and the ferromagnetism disappears.   This is called the Curie point (about 770°C for iron).

The magnetization which appears only in the presence of an applied field may be spoken of as the *induced magnetization* as distinguished from the *permanent magnetization*, which is present in the absence of an applied field.

5-12. Magnetization Curves. The permeability μ of a substance is given by

$$\mu = \frac{B}{H} = \mu_0\mu_r \qquad (5\text{-}56a)$$

where B = magnitude of flux density (webers/meter²)

H = magnitude of field **H** (amp/meter)

μ_0 = permeability of vacuum ($4\pi \times 10^{-7}$ amp/meter)

μ_r = relative permeability of substance (dimensionless)

The permeability μ or the ratio B/H is not a constant for ferromagnetic materials. Therefore, to illustrate the relation of B to H, a graph showing B (ordinate) as a function of H (abscissa) is used. The line or curve showing B as a function of H on such a B-H chart is called a *magnetization curve* (see Fig. 5-21a). It is to be noted that μ is not the slope of the curve, which is given by dB/dH, but is equal to the ratio B/H.

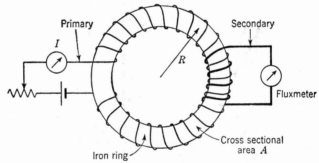

FIG. 5-20. Rowland-ring method of obtaining magnetization curve.

To measure a magnetization curve for an iron sample, a thin, closed ring may be cut from the sample. A uniform primary winding is placed over the ring, forming an iron-cored toroid as in Fig. 5-20. If the number of ampere turns in the toroid is NI, the value of H applied to the ring is

$$H = \frac{NI}{l} \qquad \text{amp-turns/meter} \qquad (5\text{-}57)$$

where $l = 2\pi R$ and R equals the mean radius of the ring or toroid. This value of H applied to the ring may be called the "magnetizing force." Hence, in general, H is sometimes called by this name. The flux density B in the ring may be regarded as the result of the applied field H and is measured by placing another (secondary) coil over the ring, as in Fig.

5-20, and connecting it to a fluxmeter.[1]   For a given change in H, produced by changing the toroid current I, there is a change in magnetic flux ψ_m through the ring.   Both H and B are substantially uniform in the ring and negligible outside.   Therefore the change in flux $\psi_m = BA$, where A is the cross-sectional area of the ring, and the resulting change in the flux density B in the ring is given by

$$B = \frac{\psi_m}{A} \quad \text{webers/meter}^2 \tag{5-58}$$

where ψ_m is measured by the fluxmeter.   This ring method of measuring magnetization curves was used by Rowland in 1873.

A typical magnetization curve for a ferromagnetic material is shown by the solid curve in Fig. 5-21a.   The specimen in this case was initially unmagnetized, and the change was noted in B as H was increased from 0. By way of comparison, four dashed lines are also shown in Fig. 5-21a, corresponding to constant relative permeabilities (μ_r) of 1, 10, 100, and 1,000.   The relative permeability at any point on the magnetization curve is given by

$$\mu_r = \frac{B}{\mu_0 H} = 7.9 \times 10^5 \frac{B}{H} \text{ (dimensionless)} \tag{5-59}$$

where B = ordinate of the point (webers/meter^2)
H = abscissa of the point (amp/meter)
A graph of the relative permeability μ_r as a function of the applied field H, corresponding to the magnetization curve in Fig. 5-21a, is presented in Fig. 5-21b.   The maximum relative permeability, and therefore the *maximum permeability*, is at the point on the magnetization curve with the largest ratio of B to H.   This is designated "max μ"; it occurs at the point of tangency with the straight line of steepest slope that passes through the origin and also intersects the magnetization curve (dash-dot line in Fig. 5-21a).

The magnetization curve for air or vacuum would be given by the dashed line for $\mu_r = 1$ (almost coincident with the H axis) in Fig. 5-21a. The difference in the ordinate B between the magnetization curve of the ferromagnetic sample and the ordinate at the same H value on the $\mu_r = 1$ line is equal to the magnetization M of the ferromagnetic material times μ_0.

The magnetization curve shown in Fig. 5-21a is an *initial magnetization curve*.   That is, the material is completely demagnetized before the field H is applied.   As H is increased, the value of B rises rapidly at first and then more slowly.   At sufficiently high values of H the curve tends to

---

[1] The *fluxmeter* operates on the emf induced in the secondary when the magnetic flux through it changes (see Sec. 7-19).

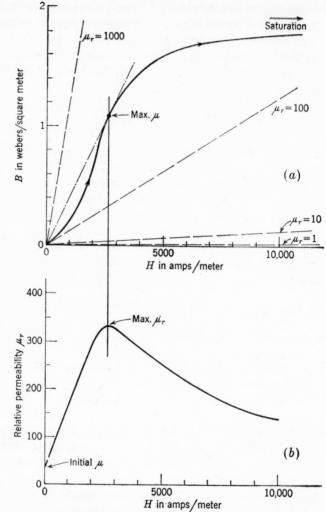

FIG. 5-21. (a) Typical magnetization curve and (b) corresponding relation of relative permeability to applied field H.

become flat as suggested by Fig. 5-21a. This condition is called *magnetic saturation*.

The magnetization curve starting at the origin has a finite slope called the *initial permeability*. Therefore the relative permeability curve in Fig. 5-21b starts with a finite permeability for infinitesimal fields.

The initial magnetization curve may be divided into two sections, (1) the steep section and (2) the flat section, the point P of division being on the upper bend of the curve (Fig. 5-22). The steep section corresponds to the condition of *easy magnetization*, while the flat section corresponds to the condition of difficult, or *hard, magnetization*.

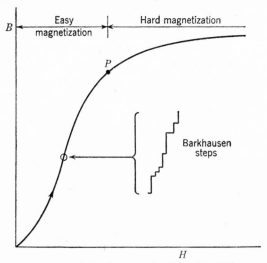

FIG. 5-22. Regions of easy and hard magnetization of initial magnetization curve.

Ordinarily a piece of iron consists not of a single crystal but of an aggregate of small crystal fragments with axes oriented at random. The situation in a small piece of iron may be represented schematically as in Fig. 5-23. Here a number of crystal fragments are shown, each with a number of magnetic domains, represented in most cases by a small square. The boundaries between crystal fragments are indicated by the heavy lines, and domain boundaries by the light lines which also indicate the direction of the crystal axes. In Fig. 5-23a, not only is the piece of iron unmagnetized, but also the individual crystal fragments are unmagnetized. The domains in each crystal are magnetized along the directions of easy magnetization, that is, along the three crystal axes.[1] However, the polarity of adjacent domains is opposite so that the total magnetization of each crystal is negligible.

With the application of a magnetic field H in the direction indicated by the arrow (Fig. 5-23) some domains with polarities opposed to or perpendicular to the applied field become unstable and rotate quickly to another direction of easy magnetization in the same direction as the field, or more nearly so. These changes take place on the steep part of the magnetization curve. The result, after all domains have changed over, is as suggested in Fig. 5-23b. This condition corresponds roughly to that at the point P on the magnetization curve (Fig. 5-22).

[1] Iron crystallizes in the cubic system with three mutually perpendicular axes.

A domain may contain millions of atoms, and since it flops from one direction of easy magnetization to another in an interval measured in

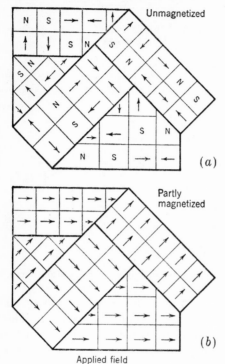

thousandths of a second, the magnetization proceeds by steps rather than in a smooth, continuous manner. These steps are called *Barkhausen steps* or *jumps*. The stepped characteristic can be observed by sensitive measurements. A much enlarged portion of the magnetization curve showing the Barkhausen steps is presented in Fig. 5-22. The Barkhausen jumps are largest on the steep part of the magnetization curve.

With further increase in the applied field, the direction of magnetization of the domains not already parallel to the field is rotated gradually toward the direction of H. This increase in magnetization is more difficult, and very high fields may be required to reach saturation, where all domains are magnetized parallel to the field, as indicated in Fig. 5-23c. This accounts for the flatness of the upper part of the magnetization curve.

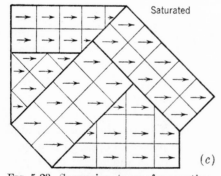

This picture of the magnetization process is an oversimplified one, but it accounts qualitatively for many of the important phenomena. Another phenomenon, which was not mentioned, is the change in size of domains during the magnetization process. Not only do domains change in size, but the entire specimen changes in length during magnetization.

Fig. 5-23. Successive stages of magnetization of a polycrystalline specimen with increasing field.

This effect is called *magnetostriction*.

5-13. Hysteresis. If the field applied to a specimen is increased to saturation and is then decreased, the flux density B decreases, but not as rapidly as it increased along the initial magnetization curve. Thus, when H reaches zero, there is a *residual flux density*, or *remanence, B_r* (Fig. 5-24).

In order to reduce B to zero, a negative field $-H_c$ must be applied (Fig. 5-24).[1] This is called the *coercive force*. As H is further increased in the negative direction, the specimen becomes magnetized with the opposite polarity, the magnetization at first being easy and then hard as saturation is approached. Bringing the field to zero again leaves a

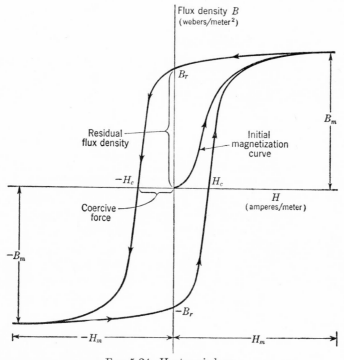

Fig. 5-24. Hysteresis loop.

residual magnetization or flux density $-B_r$, and to reduce B to zero, a coercive force $+H_c$ must be applied. With further increase in field, the specimen again becomes saturated with the original polarity.

The phenomenon which causes B to lag behind H, so that the magnetization curve for increasing and decreasing fields is not the same, is called *hysteresis*, and the loop traced out by the magnetization curve is called a *hysteresis loop* (Fig. 5-24). If the substance is carried to saturation at both ends of the magnetization curve, the loop is called the *saturation*, or *major, hysteresis loop*. The residual flux density B_r on the

[1] By reversing the battery polarity (Fig. 5-20).

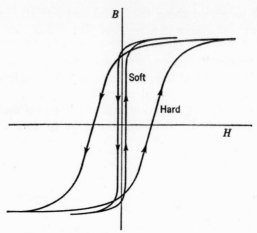

Fig. 5-25. Hysteresis loops for soft and hard magnetic materials.

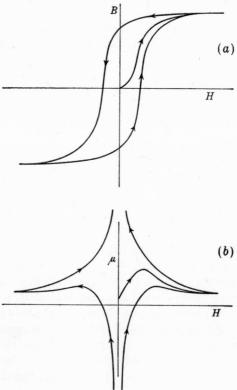

Fig. 5-26. (a) Hysteresis loop. (b) Corresponding permeability curve.

saturation loop is called the *retentivity*,[1] and the coercive force H_c on this loop is called the *coercivity*. Thus, the retentivity of a substance is the maximum value which the residual flux density can attain and the coercivity the maximum value which the coercive force can attain. For a given specimen no points can be reached on the B-H diagram outside of the saturation hysteresis loop, but any point inside can.

In "soft," or easily magnetized, materials the hysteresis loop is thin as suggested in Fig. 5-25, with a small area enclosed. By way of comparison, the hysteresis loop of a hard magnetic material is also shown, the area enclosed in this case being greater.

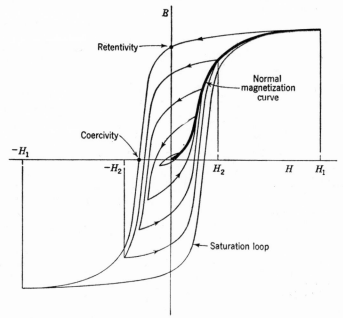

FIG. 5-27. Normal magnetization curve with relation to hysteresis loops.

Turning our attention to the permeability μ, consider the hysteresis loop of Fig. 5-26a. The corresponding graph of μ as a function of H is as shown in Fig. 5-26b. At $H = 0$, it is apparent that μ becomes infinite. On the other hand, when $B = 0$, $\mu = 0$. Under such conditions, the permeability μ becomes meaningless. Therefore the use of μ must be confined to situations where it has significance, as, for example, to the initial magnetization curve. It is to be noted that the term "maximum permeability" signifies specifically the maximum permeability for an initial magnetization curve and not for a hysteresis loop or other type of magnetization curve.

[1] The term "retentivity" is also sometimes used to mean the ratio of the residual flux density B_r to the maximum flux density B_m.

Another type of magnetization curve for which μ has a definite meaning is the *normal magnetization curve*. This curve is the locus of the tips of a series of hysteresis loops, obtained by cycling the field H over successively smaller ranges. Thus, as shown in Fig. 5-27, the field is changed slowly over the range $\pm H_1$, obtaining the saturation hysteresis loop. The field is next cycled slowly several times over a range $\pm H_2$, obtaining after a few reversals a repeatable hysteresis loop of smaller size. This process is repeated for successively smaller ranges in H, obtaining a series of loops of decreasing size. The curve passing through the tips of these loops is the *normal magnetization curve* (Fig. 5-27). This curve is useful since it is reproducible and is characteristic of the particular type of ferromagnetic material. The normal magnetization curve is actually very similar in shape to the initial magnetization curve.

5-14. Energy in a Magnet. A specimen of iron with residual magnetization contains energy since work has been performed in magnetizing it. The magnetic energy w_m per unit volume of a specimen brought to saturation from an originally unmagnetized condition is given by the integral of the initial magnetization curve expressed by

$$w_m = \int_0^{B_r} H\, dB \qquad \text{joules/meter}^3 \tag{5-60}$$

The dimensional relation for (5-60) is

$$\frac{Q}{TL} \cdot \frac{M}{TQ} = \frac{M}{LT^2}$$

where M/LT^2 has the dimensions of energy density which is expressed in the mksc system in joules per cubic meter. Thus, the area between the curve and the B axis is a measure of the energy density. This is indicated in Fig. 5-28a for an easily magnetized, (magnetically soft) substance which has been carried to the point P in the magnetization process. A magnetically hard substance takes more work to magnetize, as indicated by the larger shaded area in Fig. 5-28b. On bringing H to zero some energy is released, as indicated by the crosshatched areas in Fig. 5-28.

If H is increased and decreased so that the magnetization of a specimen repeatedly traces out a hysteresis loop as in Fig. 5-29a, the area enclosed by this loop represents the energy per unit volume expended in the magnetization-demagnetization process in one complete cycle. In general the specimen retains some energy in stored magnetic form at any point in the cycle. However, in going once around the hysteresis loop and back to this point, at which the energy will again be the same, energy proportional to the area of the loop is lost. This energy is expended in stressing the crystal fragments of the specimen and appears as heat. If no hysteresis were present and the initial magnetization curve were retraced, the area of the loop would be zero (Fig. 5-29b). The magnetization-demagnetization process could then be accomplished with no loss of energy as heat in the specimen, assuming that eddy currents (see Sec. 7-18) are negligible.

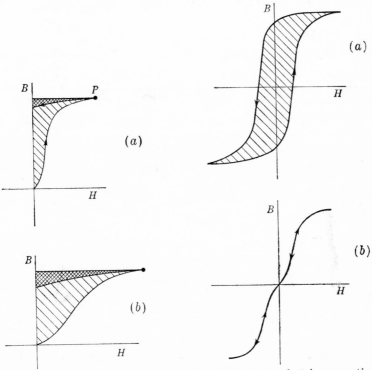

FIG. 5-28. Energy density areas for (a) soft and (b) hard magnetic materials.

FIG. 5-29. Energy lost in magnetization cycle is proportional to area enclosed by hysteresis loop.

5-15. Permanent Magnets. In many applications permanent magnets play an important part. In dealing with permanent magnets the section of the hysteresis loop in the second quadrant of the B-H diagram is of particular interest. If the loop is a saturation or major hysteresis loop, the section in the second quadrant is called the *demagnetization curve* (Fig. 5-30a). This curve is a characteristic curve for a given magnetic material. The intercept of the curve with the B axis is the maximum possible residual flux density B_r, or the retentivity, for the material, and the intercept with the H axis is the maximum coercive force, or the coercivity. It is usually desirable that permanent magnet materials have a high retentivity, but it also is important that the coercivity be large in order that the magnet will not be easily demagnetized.

In Fig. 5-30b, three demagnetization curves are shown. Curve 1 represents a material having a high retentivity but low coercivity, while curve 2 represents a material which is just the reverse, that is, it has a low retentivity and high coercivity. Curve 3 represents a material which is a compromise between the other two, having relatively high retentivity and coercivity.

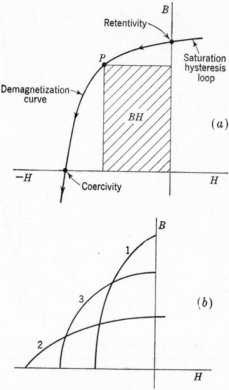

FIG. 5-30. Demagnetization curves. (B is positive and H is negative.)

The maximum BH product, abbreviated BH_{max}, is also a quantity of importance for a permanent magnet. In fact, it is probably the best single "figure of merit," or criterion, for judging the quality of a permanent magnet material. Referring to Fig. 5-30b, it is apparent that BH_{max} is greater for curve 3 than for either curves 1 or 2. The maximum BH product for a substance indicates the maximum energy density (in joules per cubic meter) in the magnet. A magnet at this point delivers a given flux with a minimum of magnetic material.

Since the product BH has the dimensions of energy density, it is sometimes called the *energy product* and its maximum value the *maximum energy product*. The product BH for any point P on the demagnetization curve is proportional to the area of the shaded rectangle, as shown in Fig. 5-30a.

Figure 5-31 shows the demagnetization curve for Alnico 5, which is one of the best permanent magnet materials.   This is an alloy containing iron, cobalt, nickel, aluminum, and copper.   A curve showing the BH product is also presented.   The maximum BH product is about 36,000 joules per meter^3 and occurs at a flux density of about 1 weber per meter^2 (see point P).

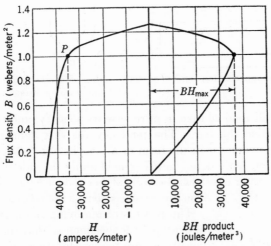

Fig. 5-31. Demagnetization and BH product curves for Alnico 5.

A discussion concerning the operating point of permanent magnets is given in Sec. 5-26.

5-16. Table of Permanent Magnetic Materials. Representative materials for permanent magnets are given in Table 5-3.   The materials are listed in the order of increasing maximum BH product, which, incidentally, is also the chronological order of their discovery.   The composition of the materials is given in per cent.

TABLE 5-3
PERMANENT MAGNETIC MATERIALS

Material	Retentivity, webers/meter^2	Coercivity, amp/meter	BH_{max} joules/meter^3
Chrome steel (98 Fe, 0.9 Cr, 0.6 C, 0.4 Mn)	1.0	4,000	1,600
Oxide (57 Fe, 28 O, 15 Co)	0.2	72,000	4,800
Alnico 2 (55 Fe, 12 Co, 17 Ni, 10 Al, 6 Cu)	0.7	44,800	13,600
Platinum cobalt (77 Pt, 23 Co)	0.4	200,000	30,400
Alnico 5 (Alcomax) (51 Fe, 24 Co, 14 Ni, 8 Al, 3 Cu)	1.25	44,000	36,000

5-17. Demagnetization. A bar of ferromagnetic material that has a residual flux density tends to become demagnetized spontaneously. The phenomenon is illustrated by Fig. 5-32, which shows a bar magnetized so that a north pole is at the left and a south pole at the right. The orientation of a single domain is indicated, and it is evident that the external field of the bar magnet opposes this domain

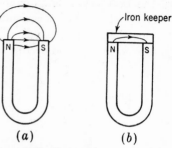

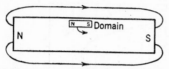

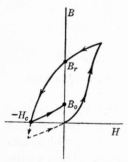

FIG. 5-32. Demagnetization effect of bar magnet field.

FIG. 5-33. U-shaped magnet with and without keeper.

and, hence, will tend to turn it, or reverse its polarity, and thereby partially demagnetize the bar. The tendency for this demagnetization is reduced if the magnet is in the form of a U as in Fig. 5-33a, since in this case there is but little demagnetizing field along the side of the magnet. The demagnetizing effect can be still further reduced by means of a soft iron *keeper* placed across the poles as in Fig. 5-33b.

The process of removing the permanent magnetization of a specimen so that the residual flux density is zero under conditions of zero **H** field is called *demagnetization* or *deperming*. It is evident that B can be reduced to zero by the application of the coercive force H_c, but on removing this field the residual flux density will rise to some value B_0 as suggested in Fig. 5-34. Although it might be possible to end up at $B = 0$ and $H = 0$ by increasing H to slightly more than the coercive force and then decreasing it to zero as suggested by the dashed lines, the process requires an accurate knowledge of B and H and the hysteresis loop.

FIG. 5-34. Partial hysteresis loop.

A longer but more simply applied method is called *demagnetization* or *deperming by reversals*. In this method, H is brought to a smaller maximum amplitude on each reversal so that eventually the specimen is left in a demagnetized state at zero field as suggested by Fig. 5-35. Although such a demagnetization procedure can be completely carried out in a matter of seconds with a small magnetic specimen such as a watch (using a-c fields), many seconds or even minutes may be required *for each reversal* for large magnetic objects because of the slow decay of the induced eddy currents and the reluctance of the domains to change polarity.   The matter of eddy currents is discussed further in Sec. 7-18.

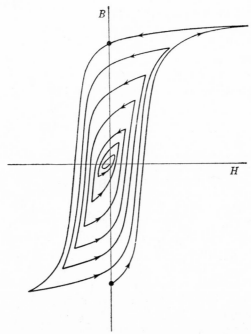

Fig. 5-35. Demagnetization by reversals.

5-18. The Magnetic Circuit.   Reluctance and Permeance.   An electric circuit forms a closed path or circuit through which the current flows. Magnetic flux tubes are continuous and form closed paths.[1]   Hence, by analogy, we may consider that a single flux tube is a *magnetic circuit*, although nothing is actually flowing.   Or all of the flux tubes of a magnetic circuit, taken in parallel, may be considered as a magnetic circuit.

Consider first an electric circuit carrying a current I.   By Kirchhoff's law the total emf in the circuit is equal to the total IR drop.   Thus

$$\mathcal{U}_T = IR_T \qquad \text{volts} \qquad (5\text{-}61)$$

where $\mathcal{U}_T$ = total emf (volts)

R_T = total resistance (ohms)

From (5-61) the total resistance is

$$R_T = \frac{\mathcal{U}_T}{I} \qquad (5\text{-}62)$$

Consider now a magnetic circuit.   Corresponding to the resistance of an electric circuit as given by (5-62), we may, by analogy, define a quan-

_____
[1] The continuous nature of steady currents in an electric circuit is expressed by $\nabla \cdot \mathbf{J} = 0$, where $\mathbf{J}$ = current density.   The analogous magnetic relation is $\nabla \cdot \mathbf{B} = 0$.

tity for the magnetic circuit called the *reluctance* $\Re$. Thus

$$\Re_T = \frac{F_T}{\psi_m} \tag{5-63}$$

where $\Re_T$ = total reluctance of magnetic circuit
F_T = total mmf of magnetic circuit (amp)
ψ_m = flux through magnetic circuit (webers)
In general, the total flux ψ_m in a magnetic circuit is given by

$$\psi_m = \iint \mathbf{B} \cdot d\mathbf{s} \qquad \text{webers} \tag{5-64}$$

where $\mathbf{B}$ = flux density (webers/meter²)
$d\mathbf{s}$ = element of surface (meters²)
The integration is carried out over the cross-sectional area of the flux tube or tubes that constitute the circuit.   If $\mathbf{B}$ is uniform over the entire cross section,

$$\psi_m = BA \qquad \text{webers} \tag{5-65}$$

where A = cross-sectional area of circuit (meters²).

Reluctance has the dimensions of current per magnetic flux, or in dimensional symbols

$$\frac{Q}{T} \frac{TQ}{ML^2} = \frac{Q^2}{ML^2}$$

The relation Q^2/ML^2 has the dimensions of the reciprocal of inductance. Thus the unit for reluctance is the *reciprocal* henry.

The reciprocal of reluctance $\Re$ is called the *permeance* $\mathcal{P}$, which is expressed in henrys.   Hence, from (5-63),

$$\mathcal{P}_T = \frac{1}{\Re_T} = \frac{\psi_m}{F_T} \tag{5-66}$$

where $\mathcal{P}_T$ = total permeance of circuit (henrys).

The total mmf of a magnetic circuit is, from (4-90), equal to the line integral of $\mathbf{H}$ around the complete circuit, and this in turn is equal to the ampere-turns enclosed.   Therefore, (5-63) becomes

$$\Re_T = \frac{1}{\mathcal{P}_T} = \frac{F_T}{\psi_m} = \frac{\oint \mathbf{H} \cdot d\mathbf{l}}{\psi_m} = \frac{NI}{\psi_m} \qquad \text{1/henrys} \tag{5-67}$$

where NI = ampere-turns.

The above discussion concerns the total reluctance of a circuit.   Let us consider next the reluctance of a portion of a magnetic circuit.   In an electric circuit, the resistance R between two points, having no emfs between them, is given by

$$R = \frac{V}{I} \qquad \text{ohms} \tag{5-68}$$

where V = potential difference between the points (volts)

I = current in circuit (amp)

In the analogous magnetic case, the reluctance $\mathcal{R}$ between two points in a magnetic circuit is given by

$$\mathcal{R} = \frac{U}{\psi_m} \qquad 1/\text{henrys} \qquad (5\text{-}69)$$

where U = magnetic potential difference between the points (amp). From (4-87) for U and (5-64) for ψ_m we have

$$\mathcal{R} = \frac{\int_1^2 \mathbf{H} \cdot d\mathbf{l}}{\int\int \mathbf{B} \cdot d\mathbf{s}} \qquad (5\text{-}70)$$

where $\mathbf{H}$ is integrated between the two points (1 and 2) between which we wish to find the magnetic potential difference U.

When the circuit has a uniform cross section of area A and the field is uniform, (5-70) reduces to

$$\mathcal{R} = \frac{Hl}{BA} = \frac{l}{\mu A} \qquad 1/\text{henrys} \qquad (5\text{-}71)$$

where $\mathcal{R}$ = reluctance between points 1 and 2 (1/henrys)

l = distance between points 1 and 2 (meters)

A = cross-sectional area of magnetic circuit (meters²)

μ = permeability of medium comprising the circuit (henrys/meter)

The permeance $\mathcal{P}$ between the points 1 and 2 is given by

$$\mathcal{P} = \frac{1}{\mathcal{R}} = \frac{\mu A}{l} \qquad \text{henrys} \qquad (5\text{-}72)$$

Reluctances in series are additive in the same way that resistances in series are additive. For reluctances in parallel the reciprocal of the total reluctance is equal to the sum of the reciprocals of the individual reluctances. For reluctances in parallel it is usually more convenient to use permeance, the total permeance being equal to the sum of the individual permeances.

Example 1. Find the reluctance and permeance between the ends of the rectangular block of iron shown in Fig. 5-36a, assuming that B is uniform throughout the block and normal to the ends. The permeability of the block is uniform and has a value $\mu_1 = 500\mu_0$, where μ_0 is the permeability of vacuum.

Solution. The reluctance of the block is from (5-69)

$$\mathcal{R} = \frac{l}{\mu A} = \frac{0.1}{500 \times 4\pi \times 10^{-7} \times 15 \times 10^{-4}} = 1.06 \times 10^5 \text{ reciprocal henrys}$$

The permeance $\mathcal{P}$ is the reciprocal of $\mathcal{R}$; so

$$\mathcal{P} = \frac{1}{1.06 \times 10^5} = 9.4 \times 10^{-6} \text{ henry}$$

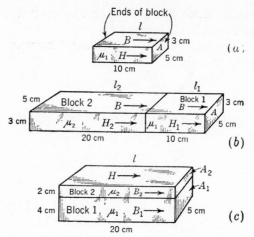

FIG. 5-36. Rectangular iron blocks.

Example 2. Find the total reluctance and permeance between the ends of the *series-connected* rectangular iron blocks shown in Fig. 5-36b, assuming that B is uniform throughout the blocks and normal to the ends. The permeability of each block is uniform, the value in block 1 being $\mu_1 = 500\mu_0$ and in block 2, $\mu_2 = 2,000\mu_0$.

Solution. The reluctance $\Re_1$ of block 1 is given in Example 1. The reluctance of block 2 is

$$\Re_2 = \frac{l_2}{\mu_2 A} = \frac{0.2}{2,000 \times 4\pi \times 10^{-7} \times 15 \times 10^{-4}} = 0.53 \times 10^5 \text{ reciprocal henrys}$$

The total reluctance $\Re_T$ equals the sum of the individual reluctances; so

$$\Re_T = \Re_1 + \Re_2 = (1.06 + 0.53) \times 10^5 = 1.59 \times 10^5 \text{ reciprocal henrys}$$

The total permeance

$$\mathcal{P}_T = \frac{1}{\Re_T} = \frac{1}{1.59 \times 10^5} = 6.3 \times 10^{-6} \text{ henry}$$

Example 3. Find the total reluctance and permeance between the ends of the *parallel-connected* rectangular iron blocks shown in Fig. 5-36c, assuming that B is uniform in each block and normal to the ends. The permeability of each block is uniform, the value in block 1 being $\mu_1 = 500\mu_0$ and in block 2 being $\mu_2 = 2,000\mu_0$.

Solution. Since the blocks are in parallel, it is more convenient to calculate the total permeance first. The permeance $\mathcal{P}_1$ of block 1 is

$$\mathcal{P}_1 = \frac{\mu_1 A_1}{l} = \frac{500 \times 4\pi \times 10^{-7} \times 20 \times 10^{-4}}{0.2} = 6.28 \times 10^{-6} \text{ henry}$$

The permeance of block 2 is

$$\mathcal{P}_2 = \frac{\mu_2 A_2}{l} = \frac{2,000 \times 4\pi \times 10^{-7} \times 10 \times 10^{-4}}{0.2} = 12.6 \times 10^{-6} \text{ henry}$$

The total permeance equals the sum of the individual permeances; so

$$\mathcal{P}_T = \mathcal{P}_1 + \mathcal{P}_2 = (6.28 + 12.6) \times 10^{-6} = 1.89 \times 10^{-5} \text{ henry}$$

The total reluctance is then given by

$$\mathcal{R}_T = \frac{1}{\mathcal{P}_T} = \frac{1}{1.89 \times 10^{-5}} = 5.3 \times 10^4 \text{ reciprocal henrys}$$

In the above examples, it is assumed that B and μ are uniform throughout *each* block. It follows that H ($= B/\mu$) is also uniform and that the end surfaces are equipotentials. For instance, if H is 1,000 amp per meter, the magnetic potential difference between the ends of the bar in Example 1 (Fig. 5-36a) is $U = Hl = 1,000 \times 0.1 = 100$ amp. The flux density $B = \mu_1 H = 500\mu_0 \times 1,000 = 6.28 \times 10^{-1}$ weber per square meter. The total flux ψ_m through the block is then equal to BA, where A is the area of the block. Thus,

$$\psi_m = BA = 6.28 \times 10^{-1} \times 15 \times 10^{-4} = 9.4 \times 10^{-4} \text{ weber}$$

In Example 2 (Fig. 5-36b) it follows from the boundary condition for the normal component of B that the flux density is the same in both blocks. Suppose that it is equal to 1 weber per square meter. Then in block 1, $H_1 = B/\mu_1 = 1/500\mu_0 = 1.59 \times 10^3$ amp per meter, and the potential difference U_1 between the end faces of block 1 is given by $U_1 = H_1 l_1 = 1.59 \times 10^3 \times 0.1 = 159$ amp. In block 2,

$$H_2 = \frac{B}{\mu_2} = \frac{1}{2,000\mu_0} = 3.97 \times 10^2 \text{ amp per meter}$$

and the potential difference U_2 between the end faces of block 2 is

$$U_2 = H_2 l_2 = 3.97 \times 10^2 \times 0.2 = 79.4 \text{ amp}$$

The total potential difference U across both blocks is then given by $U = U_1 + U_2 = 159 + 79.4 = 238.4$ amp.

In Example 3 (Fig. 5-36c) it follows from the boundary condition for the tangential components of H that H is the same in both blocks. Suppose that it is equal to 1,000 amp per meter. Then in block 1,

$$B_1 = \mu_1 H = 500\mu_0 \times 1,000 = 0.628 \text{ weber per square meter}$$

and the magnetic flux in block 1 is

$$\psi_{m1} = B_1 A_1 = 0.628 \times 20 \times 10^{-4} = 1.26 \times 10^{-3} \text{ weber}$$

In block 2, $B_2 = \mu_2 H = 2,000\mu_0 \times 1,000 = 2.52$ webers per square meter, and the flux in block 2 is $\psi_{m2} = B_2 A_2 = 2.52 \times 10^{-3}$ weber. The total flux through both blocks in parallel is then given by

$$\psi_m = \psi_{m1} + \psi_{m2} = (1.26 + 2.52) \times 10^{-3} = 3.78 \times 10^{-3} \text{ weber}$$

5-19. Magnetic Field Mapping.   Magnetic Field Cells. The examples in the preceding section illustrate how the reluctance or permeance may be found for sections of a magnetic circuit that have a uniform cross section and uniform field. In two-dimensional problems where the field and cross section are nonuniform the magnetic field configuration, and consequently the reluctance or permeance, can also be found provided the permeability may be considered constant. Graphical field-mapping techniques such as are employed in Secs. 2-27 and 3-16 are applicable to such situations.

The following basic properties are useful in magnetic field mapping:

1. The field (**H** or **B**) lines and the magnetic potential (*U*) lines intersect at right angles.
2. At the boundary between air and iron (or other high-permeability medium) the field lines on the air side of the boundary are substantially perpendicular to the boundary surface.
3. The boundary between air and iron (or other high-permeability medium) may be regarded as an equipotential with respect to the air side of the boundary but not, in general, with respect to the iron side.
4. In a uniform field the potential varies linearly with distance.
5. A magnetic flux tube is parallel to the field, and the magnetic flux over any cross section of the tube is a constant.
6. Magnetic flux tubes are continuous.

With these properties in mind a two-dimensional magnetic field may be divided into magnetic flux tubes and then by equipotentials into *mag-*

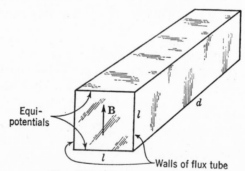

FIG. 5-37. Magnetic field cell.

netic field cells with sides that are squares or curvilinear squares, using the trial-and-error method described in Sec. 2-27 in connection with electric field mapping.

A *magnetic field cell* is bounded on two sides by equipotential surfaces and on two others by the side walls of a flux tube. For instance, the sides of the magnetic field cell in Fig. 5-37 are the walls of a flux tube, while the top and bottom surfaces are equipotentials. The field is parallel to the sides and normal to the top and bottom surfaces.   The permeance of a magnetic field cell, as measured between the equipotential surfaces, is, from (5-72),

$$\mathcal{P}_0 = \frac{\mu A}{l} = \frac{\mu l d}{l} = \mu d \qquad \text{henrys} \tag{5-73}$$

and the permeance per unit depth is

$$\frac{\mathcal{P}_0}{d} = \mu \qquad \text{henrys/meter} \tag{5-74}$$

where μ = permeability of cell medium (henrys/meter).   Thus, the value of μ for a medium is equal to the permeance per unit depth of a magnetic field cell of that medium.   For example, a magnetic field cell in air has a permeance per unit depth of $4\pi \times 10^{-7}$ henry per meter, or 1.26 μh per meter.   Thus, if d in Fig. 5-37 equals 1 meter and the medium is air, the permeance of the cell is 1.26 μh.

Any field cell can be subdivided into smaller square-ended cells with as many cells in parallel as in series.   Hence the permeance per unit depth of *any* field cell, large or small, exactly square or curvilinear, is equal to μ.

All cells with the same flux through them may be defined as *magnetic field cells of the same kind*.   It follows that the magnetic potential difference across all cells of the same kind is the same.

To illustrate some of the principles of magnetic field mapping, let us consider three examples involving three variations of a two-dimensional problem.

Example 1.   A magnetic circuit has an air gap of nonuniform separation as suggested in Fig. 5-38a.   The iron has a uniform depth d into the page of 1 meter.   The

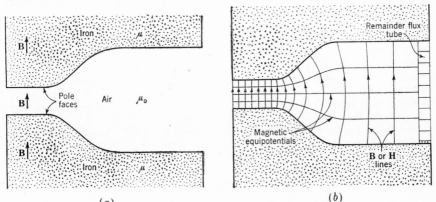

(a) (b)

FIG. 5-38. Magnetic field in air gap (Example 1).

geometry of the gap is identical with the region between ff and gg in the capacitor of Fig. 2-24.   Find the permeance of the air gap, neglecting fringing of the field.

Solution. It may be assumed that the iron permeability is much greater than μ_0 so that the field lines in the gap will be perpendicular to the air-iron boundary, and this boundary can be treated as a magnetic equipotential. Since the geometry of the gap is the same as that for the capacitor in Fig. 2-24, the field map in Fig. 2-24 may also serve in the present case, noting that the field lines here are **B** or **H** lines and the equipotentials are surfaces of equal magnetic potential U as shown in Fig. 5-38b.

With the exception of the cells in the remainder flux tube all of the field cells are of the same kind, and the permeance of the air gap is given in terms of cells of the same kind by

$$\mathcal{P} = \frac{N}{n}\,\mathcal{P}_0 \tag{5-75}$$

where N = number of field cells (or flux tubes) in parallel (dimensionless)

n = number of field cells in series (dimensionless)

$\mathcal{P}_0$ = permeance of one cell (henrys)

The remainder flux tube has $9\frac{1}{4}$ cells in series, while the other flux tubes have 4. Hence the remainder tube is

$$\frac{4}{9\frac{1}{4}} = 0.43$$

of the width of a full tube, and $N = 15 + 0.43 = 15.43$. The total permeance of the gap is then

$$\mathcal{P}_T = \frac{15.43}{4}\,\mathcal{P}_0 = 3.86\mathcal{P}_0$$

Since the depth of each cell is 1 meter, the permeance of one cell is

$$\mathcal{P}_0 = \mu_0 d = 1.26 \times 1 = 1.26\ \mu\text{h}$$

and the total permeance is

$$\mathcal{P}_T = 3.86 \times 1.26 = 4.86\ \mu\text{h}$$

It is assumed in this example that there is no fringing of the field. For an actual gap there would be fringing at the edges, and the actual permeance of the gap would be somewhat larger than given above.

Example 2. Let the problem of the above example be modified to that shown in Fig. 5-39. Here the gap of the first example is replaced by iron and the iron poles by air. The iron may be regarded as part of a magnetic circuit of iron extending further to the left and to the right as suggested by the dashed lines in Fig. 5-39. The iron extends to a depth of 1 meter normal to the page, with the cross section at any depth identical to that in Fig. 5-39. Assume that the iron has a uniform permeability μ which is much larger than μ_0. Find the permeance between the surfaces indicated by the dash-dot lines ff and gg.

Solution. The field map for this problem is the same as for Example 1 (Fig. 5-38b) except that the field and equipotential lines are interchanged as shown in Fig. 5-39. It is assumed that μ is so much greater than μ_0 that in the iron the **H** field at the air-iron boundary is substantially parallel to the boundary as indicated by the map. The total permeance between ff and gg is, from (5-75),

$$\mathcal{P} = \frac{4}{15.43}\,\mathcal{P}_0 = 0.259 \times \mu \times 1$$
$$= 0.259 \times 1.26\mu_r = 0.326\mu_r \qquad \mu\text{h}$$

where μ_r = relative permeability of iron.

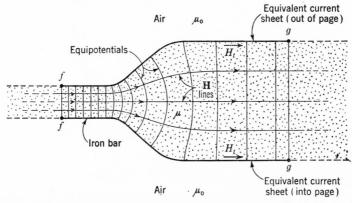

Fig. 5-39. Iron bar of nonuniform cross section with internal field (Example 2).

Example 3. Let the problem of the preceding example be modified to that of a two-strip transmission line having the same cross section as the gap of Example 1 and the iron circuit of Example 2. As shown in Fig. 5-40 the two conducting strips extend normal to the page with a sheet of steady current flowing outward on the upper strip

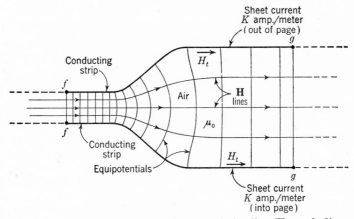

Fig. 5-40. Cross section of strip transmission line (Example 3).

and an equal current flowing inward on the lower strip. The medium in which the strips are located is air. Neglect edge effects. Find the inductance of a 1-meter length of the line.

Solution. Neglecting edge effects,[1] the field map between the strips is identical with that for the iron circuit in Fig. 5-39.

[1] If the conducting strips are extended an infinite distance to the left and right, as suggested by the dashed lines in Fig. 5-40, the field configuration is precisely as indicated. The field between the strips is produced by the currents on the strips. In Example 2 the field in the iron may be regarded as due to an equivalent current sheet at the surfaces of the iron bar normal to the page (Fig. 5-39).

If each cell in the map is regarded as a strip transmission line with sheet currents along its upper and lower surfaces, the inductance L_0 for a length d of 1 meter of the single-cell line (normal to the page in Fig. 5-40) is, from (4-100), given by

$$L_0 = \mu_0 d = 1.26 \ \mu h$$

The total inductance L_T of a meter length of the line is then

$$L_T = \frac{4}{15.43} \times 1.26 = 0.326 \ \mu h$$

At any point on either strip in Example 3 we have the boundary condition that the tangential component of **H** is equal in magnitude to the linear sheet current density K at the point, that is, $H_t = K$. Since the average H field for any cell of the same kind is inversely proportional to the cell width, it follows that the linear current density K at the left, where the strip spacing is small, is four times the density at the right, where the spacing is large, the spacing ratio being 4. The variation in K along the strips is the same as for the change density ρ_s in the capacitor problem of Fig. 2-24.

In conclusion the important properties of an accurate magnetic field map in a single medium of uniform permeability may be stated as follows:

1. The permeance $\mathcal{P}_0$ of any magnetic field cell is the same.
2. The permeance per unit depth of any magnetic field cell is the same and is equal to the permeability μ of the medium.
3. The reluctance $\mathcal{R}_0$ of any magnetic field cell is the same.
4. The reluctance-depth product for any magnetic field cell is the same and is equal to the reciprocal of the permeability μ for the medium.
5. The magnetic potential difference across any magnetic field cell of the same kind is the same and is equal to $\psi_m \mathcal{R}_0$.
6. The magnetic flux ψ_m through any magnetic field cell of the same kind is the same.
7. The magnetic flux ψ_m over any cross section of a flux tube is the same.
8. The average flux density B in any cell of the same kind is inversely proportional to the width of the cell or flux tube.
9. The average field H in any cell of the same kind is inversely proportional to the cell width.
10. The magnetic energy stored in any cell of the same kind is the same.
11. The average magnetic energy density in any cell of the same kind is inversely proportional to the area of the end of the cell. (This is the area that appears in the field map.)

5-20. Comparison of Field Maps in Electric, Magnetic, and Current Cases. Graphical field mapping was discussed in Sec. 2-27 for electric fields, in Sec. 3-16 for currents in conductors, and in Sec. 5-19 and also to some extent in Sec. 4-20 for magnetic fields. The technique is similar in all these cases. Of particular significance is the fact that a field map for a certain two-dimensional geometry may be applied to numerous problems having this geometry. An illustration of this was provided by the three examples in Sec. 5-19, in which the field map of Fig. 2-24 for a capacitor yielded the solution for the permeance of the volume with the field applied both transversely and longitudinally. The map also gave the inductance of a conducting-strip transmission line.

The same map can, in addition, supply the value of the conductance of a conducting bar with the current flowing transversely and with the current flowing longitudinally. The same map can also be applied to heat- and fluid-flow problems.

To summarize, sketches are given in Fig. 5-41, showing six different problems of the same geometry for which solutions are supplied by one field map. The actual map is shown in Fig. 5-41a, being omitted in the other sketches. The geometry of the problems is that of the capacitor of Fig. 2-24, which was also used in the problems of Figs. 5-38 to 5-40.

In Fig. 5-41a the map represents the electric field in a capacitor with the field transverse. In Fig. 5-41b the map represents the electric field in a conducting bar with current flowing transversely, while in Fig. 5-41c the current flows longitudinally. In Fig. 5-41d the map represents the magnetic field in the air gap between two iron pole faces, while in Fig. 5-41e it represents the magnetic field in an iron bar with the field applied longitudinally. In Fig. 5-41f the map represents the field between two conducting strips acting as a transmission line with current flowing normal to the page. For each case the capacitance, conductance, permeance, or inductance per unit depth (normal to the page) is given, as appropriate for the particular problem. Fringing of the field is neglected in all cases.

It is also of interest to compare the significance of the cells (square or curvilinear) of the field maps for the different problems we have considered. Thus, the capacitance per unit depth of an electric field cell equals the permittivity ϵ of the medium; the conductance per unit depth of a conductor cell equals the conductivity σ of the medium; the permeance per unit depth of a magnetic field cell equals the permeability μ of the medium; and the inductance per unit length of a transmission line cell equals the permeability μ of the medium. These relationships are summarized in the last column of Table 5-4. This table also has columns headed Flow lines, Flow tubes, and Equipotentials. By flow lines are meant the lines, such as field lines, that are analogous to the lines of flow of a fluid in the analogous fluid-flow situation.[1] Under flow lines

[1] See discussion of fluid mappers in Appendix.

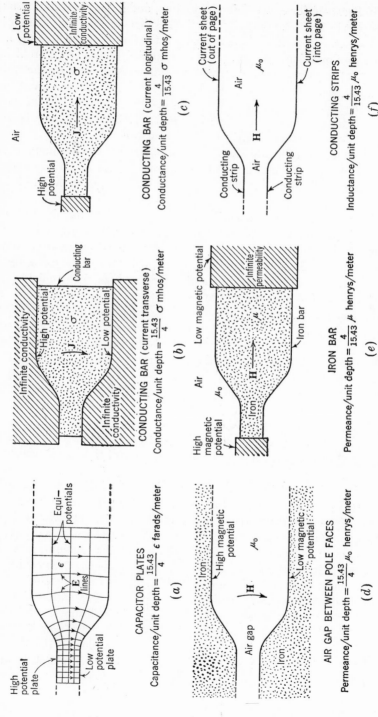

Fig. 5-41. Application of one field map to six situations.

CAPACITOR PLATES
Capacitance/unit depth = $\frac{15.43}{4}$ ϵ farads/meter
(a)

CONDUCTING BAR (current transverse)
Conductance/unit depth = $\frac{15.43}{4}$ σ mhos/meter
(b)

CONDUCTING BAR (current longitudinal)
Conductance/unit depth = $\frac{4}{15.43}$ σ mhos/meter
(c)

AIR GAP BETWEEN POLE FACES
Permeance/unit depth = $\frac{15.43}{4}$ μ_0 henrys/meter
(d)

IRON BAR
Permeance/unit depth = $\frac{4}{15.43}$ μ henrys/meter
(e)

CONDUCTING STRIPS
Inductance/unit depth = $\frac{4}{15.43}$ μ_0 henrys/meter
(f)

are listed the quantities having the direction of flow lines and under flow tubes the quantities equal to the total flux through a tube.

TABLE 5-4
IMPORTANT FIELD-MAP QUANTITIES

Field	Flow lines	Flow tubes	Equipo-tentials	Value of cell (per unit depth)
Electric.........	D or E	Electric flux ψ	V (volts)	Permittivity ϵ (farads/meter)
Current.........	J or E	Current I	V (volts)	Conductivity σ (mhos/meter)
Magnetic........	B or H	Magnetic flux ψ_m	U (amp)	Permeability μ (henrys/ meter)
Heat...........	Temperature gradient	Heat per time	Temperature	Thermal con- ductivity
Fluid flow (non-turbulent; in-compressible)	Velocity	Mass per time	Velocity po-tential	Density

Example. Apply the above analogies to find the capacitance of an air capacitor by a resistance measurement.

Solution. The capacitor plates are immersed in a large tank filled with a liquid of uniform conductivity σ, and the d-c resistance R is measured between the plates.

In general, the conductance G of a certain geometry is given by

$$G = \sigma d \frac{N}{n} \tag{5-76}$$

where N = number of cells in parallel
n = number of cells in series
d = depth of cells

An actual capacitor with the same geometry has the same field configuration (compare Figs. 5-41a and b); so the capacitance

$$C = \epsilon_0 d \frac{N}{n} \tag{5-77}$$

where N and n are the same as in (5-76). Hence, on dividing (5-77) by (5-76),

$$C = \frac{\epsilon_0}{\sigma} G = \frac{\epsilon_0}{\sigma R} \tag{5-78}$$

where C = capacitance of actual capacitor (farads)
ϵ_0 = permittivity of air (8.85×10^{-12} farad/meter)
σ = conductivity of liquid (mhos/meter)
$R = 1/G$ = measured resistance (ohms)

Thus knowing σ (which also can be measured with a rectangular volume), the capacitance of an air capacitor can be obtained from (5-78) by a resistance measurement.

5-21. Fields of Currents near an Air-Iron Boundary. Another type of problem not discussed previously is that involving a current-carrying

conductor situated near an air-iron boundary. This situation may be
treated analytically by the method of images.[1] The images are such that
boundary conditions at the air-iron surface are satisfied.

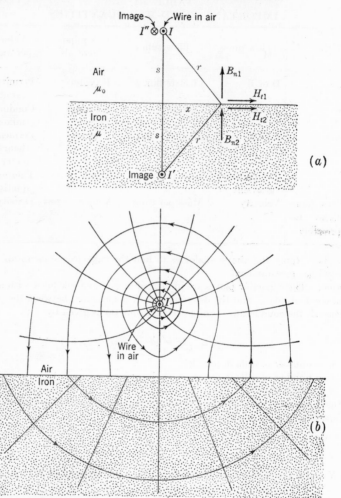

FIG. 5-42. Magnetic field lines (with arrows) and equipotentials for current-carrying
wire in air near an iron boundary.

Two cases will be considered. In the first case the conductor, or wire,
is in air at a distance s from a plane air-iron boundary as suggested in
Fig. 5-42a. In the second case the wire is in iron at a distance s from a
plane air-iron boundary as shown in Fig. 5-43a. The current in the wire
in both cases is I. The iron is assumed to have a uniform finite perme-

[1] This method was applied in the case of an electric field in Sec. 2-26.

ability μ in both cases, a somewhat dubious assumption in view of the wide range in applied field H to which it is subjected. In both cases the wire is parallel to the boundary so that the problems are two-dimensional.

Treating first the case where the wire is in air, let an image conductor with current I' be situated at a distance s below the boundary in the iron, as in Fig. 5-42a, and a second image with current I'' be situated at the wire in air. On the air side of the boundary the field is given by I and I', both assumed to be in air, and on the iron side by I and I'', both assumed to be in iron. The magnitudes and directions of the currents in the images must be such as to satisfy the boundary conditions at the air-iron surface. Assuming, a priori, that all currents are outward, we have at any point on the air side of the boundary

$$H_{t1} = \frac{s}{2\pi r^2} (I - I')$$ (5-79)

and at the same point on the iron side of the boundary

$$H_{t2} = \frac{s}{2\pi r^2} (I + I'')$$ (5-80)

Since $H_{t1} = H_{t2}$, it follows that

$$I' = -I''$$ (5-81)

On the air side we also have

$$B_{n1} = \frac{\mu_0 x}{2\pi r^2} (I + I')$$ (5-82)

and on the iron side

$$B_{n2} = \frac{\mu x}{2\pi r^2} (I + I'')$$ (5-83)

Since $B_{n1} = B_{n2}$, it follows that

$$I' = \frac{\mu - \mu_0}{\mu + \mu_0} I$$ (5-84)

and

$$I'' = -\frac{\mu - \mu_0}{\mu + \mu_0} I$$ (5-85)

Thus, if the iron has a high permeability ($\mu \gg \mu_0$), the field on the air side of the boundary is that of two parallel conductors with nearly equal currents (I and I') flowing in the same direction in air. On the iron side of the boundary the field is that of a very small current (sum of I and I'') assumed to be in iron. The field and equipotential lines for this case (μ large) are as suggested in Fig. 5-42b.

In the second case, where the wire is in the iron medium, let an image conductor with current I' be situated at a distance s above the boundary in air, as in Fig. 5-43a, and a second image with current I'' be situated at the wire in the iron. On the air side of the boundary the field is given by

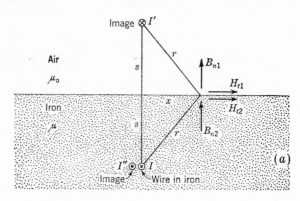

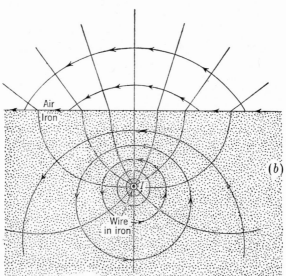

FIG. 5-43. Magnetic field (with arrows) and equipotentials for current-carrying wire in iron near an air boundary.

I and I'', both assumed to be in air, and on the iron side by I and I', both assumed to be in iron. It may be shown for this case (see Prob. 5-34) that

$$I'' = \frac{\mu - \mu_0}{\mu + \mu_0} I \qquad (5\text{-}86)$$

and

$$I' = -\frac{\mu - \mu_0}{\mu + \mu_0} I \qquad (5\text{-}87)$$

Thus, if the iron has a high permeability ($\mu \gg \mu_0$), the field on the iron side of the boundary is that of two parallel conductors with nearly equal currents (I and I') flowing in opposite directions in a medium of permeability μ. On the air side of the boundary the field is that of a current almost twice I at the wire location but assumed to be in air. Hence the presence of the iron results in a field on the air side of the boundary nearly double that which would be obtained if no iron were present. The field and equipotential lines for this case (μ large) are as suggested in Fig. 5-43b.[1]

It is to be noted in both of the above cases that close to the wire itself the field configuration is symmetrical, the same as for an isolated linear conductor.

5-22. Gapless Circuit. Consider the magnetic circuit of a closed ring of iron of uniform cross section A and mean length l. Suppose that

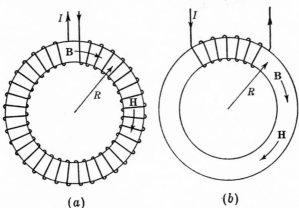

(a)   (b)

FIG. 5-44. Closed iron ring (a) with uniform winding and (b) with concentrated winding.

a coil of insulated wire is wound uniformly around the ring and that we wish to know how large the product (NI) of the number of turns and the current must be to produce a flux density B in the ring.

The coil on the ring in Fig. 5-44a forms a toroid, that is, a solenoid closed on itself. From (4-50) the flux density B in the toroid is

$$B = \frac{\mu NI}{l} = \frac{\mu NI}{2\pi R} \qquad \text{webers/meter}^2 \qquad (5\text{-}88)$$

[1] For a more detailed discussion of the magnetic fields of conductors near iron surfaces see, for example, S. S. Attwood, "Electric and Magnetic Fields," 3d ed., John Wiley & Sons, Inc., New York, 1949, Chap. 15.

where μ = permeability (assumed uniform) of medium inside of toroid
  (henrys/meter)
  N = number of turns (dimensionless)
  I = current (amp)
  l = mean length of toroid (meters)
  R = mean radius of toroid (meters)
Dividing by μ, we have

$$NI = Hl \qquad \text{amp-turns} \tag{5-89}$$

If a certain flux density B is desired in the ring, the corresponding H value
is taken from a B-H curve for the ring material and the required number
of ampere-turns calculated from (5-89).

Example 1. An iron ring has a cross-sectional area A = 10 cm² and a mean length
l = 60 cm. Find the number of ampere-turns required to produce a flux density
B = 1 weber/meter.² From a B-H curve for the iron, H = 1,000 amp/meter at
B = 1 weber/meter².
Solution. From (5-89)

$$NI = 1,000 \times 0.6 = 600 \text{ amp-turns}$$

The coil could be 100 turns with a current of 6 amp or 1,000 turns with a current
of 0.6 amp. The coil may be uniformly distributed around the ring as in Fig. 5-44a
or concentrated in a small sector as in Fig. 5-44b. With a uniformly distributed winding the magnetic field is confined to the ring. However, with the concentrated winding there is some flux density in the air outside of the ring. This flux is a leakage flux,
having escaped from the principal magnetic circuit formed by the iron ring. Owing
to the large permeability of iron compared with that of air, the effect of leakage flux in
the case of a concentrated winding may in many cases be neglected.

The required number of ampere-turns can also be found by calculating
the reluctance of the ring circuit. This is illustrated by the following
example.

Example 2. Find the number of ampere-turns required for the ring of Example 1
for B = 1 weber/meter² by first evaluating the reluctance of the ring.
Solution. From (5-70)

$$\mathcal{R} = \frac{\oint \mathbf{H} \cdot d\mathbf{l}}{BA} \tag{5-90}$$

We also have

$$\oint \mathbf{H} \cdot d\mathbf{l} = Hl = NI \tag{5-91}$$

Substituting (5-91) in (5-90) yields

$$NI = \mathcal{R}BA \tag{5-92}$$

where, from (5-71),

$$\mathcal{R} = \frac{l}{\mu A} \tag{5-93}$$

Since H = 1,000 amp/meter when B = 1 weber/meter²,

$$\mu = \frac{B}{H} = \frac{1}{1,000} = 10^{-3} \qquad \text{henry/meter} \tag{5-94}$$

It is to be noted that the relative permeability for this case is

$$\mu_r = \frac{B}{\mu_0 H} = \frac{10^{-3}}{4\pi \times 10^{-7}} = 795 \tag{5-94a}$$

Introducing (5-94) in (5-93) and also the value of l and A, the reluctance of the ring is

$$\Re = \frac{0.6}{10^{-3} \times 10^{-3}} = 6 \times 10^5 \quad 1/\text{henrys} \tag{5-95}$$

Hence, from (5-92) the required number of ampere-turns is

$$NI = \Re BA = 6 \times 10^5 \times 1 \times 10^{-3} = 600$$

as obtained in Example 1.

5-23. Magnetic Circuit with Air Gap. Let a narrow air gap of thickness g be cut in the iron ring of Sec. 5-22 as shown in Fig. 5-45a. The gap detail is presented in Fig. 5-45b. By the continuity of the normal component of B the flux density in the gap is the same as in the iron, if fringing is neglected. Neglecting the fringing involves but little error where the gap is narrow, as assumed here. The field H_g in the gap is then

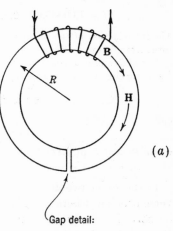

(a)

$$H_g = \frac{B}{\mu_0} \tag{5-96}$$

while the field H_i in the iron is

$$H_i = \frac{B}{\mu} = \frac{B}{\mu_r \mu_0} = \frac{H_g}{\mu_r} \tag{5-97}$$

from which

$$\frac{H_g}{H_i} = \mu_r \tag{5-98}$$

Gap detail:

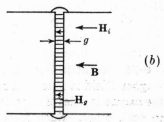

(b)

The number of ampere-turns required to produce a certain flux density B in a magnetic circuit with gap, as in Fig. 5-45a, is a problem for which the solution may be obtained directly. For instance, according to (4-90) the line integral of H once around the magnetic circuit equals the total mmf F, or ampere-turns enclosed.[1]   That is,

Fig. 5-45. Iron ring with air gap.

$$\oint \mathbf{H} \cdot d\mathbf{l} = F = NI \tag{5-99}$$

Example. Let the iron ring of Fig. 5-45 have a cross-sectional area $A = 10$ cm², an air gap of width $g = 2$ mm, and a mean length $l = 2\pi R = 60$ cm, including the

[1] This relation for a magnetic circuit is analogous to Kirchhoff's voltage law (Sec. 3-10) for an electric circuit.

air gap.   Find the number of ampere-turns required to produce a flux density

$$B = 1 \text{ weber/meter}^2$$

The iron ring is the same as considered in Sec. 5-22 except that it has an air gap.
  Solution.   From (5-99)

$$NI = \oint \mathbf{H} \cdot d\mathbf{l} = H_i(l - g) + H_g g \tag{5-100}$$

where H_i = H field in iron
  H_g = H field in gap
From a B-H curve for the iron, H_i = 1,000 amp/meter, and from (5-98) we know H_g
in terms of H_i.   Hence (5-100) becomes

$$NI = H_i[(l - g) + \mu_r g] \tag{5-101}$$

where μ_r = 795 = relative permeability of iron ring at B = 1 weber/meter² [see
(5-94a)].   Therefore,

$$NI = 1,000[(0.6 - 0.002) + 795 \times 0.002] = 2,188 \text{ amp-turns}$$

The introduction of the narrow air gap makes it necessary to increase the ampere-
turns from 600 to 2,188 to maintain the flux density at 1 weber/meter².

The above problem may also be solved by calculating the total reluctance of the
magnetic circuit.   Thus, from (5-100) we have

$$NI = \frac{\mu A}{\mu A} H_i(l - g) + \frac{\mu_0 A}{\mu_0 A} H_g g \tag{5-102}$$

and

$$NI = BA(\mathcal{R}_i + \mathcal{R}_g) \tag{5-103}$$

where R_i = $(l - g)/\mu A$ = reluctance of iron part of circuit
  R_g = $g/\mu_0 A$ = reluctance of air gap

In the above problem, B is given and the required NI found.   The converse problem where NI is given and the resulting B is to be found cannot
be solved directly since in (5-103) there are two unknowns B and μ.
However, we can assume a value of B and calculate the total NI as in the
above example.   If NI is calculated in this way for several assumed
values of B and a curve plotted of B vs. total NI, the approximate value
of B may be interpolated for any given NI.

5-24. Magnetic Gap Force.   Referring to Fig. 5-45, the effect of the
magnetic field is to exert forces which tend to close the air gap.   That is,
the magnetic poles of opposite polarity at the sides of the gap are attracted
to each other.   Such forces as are produced by magnetic fields find
application in numerous electromechanical devices.   In this section an
expression for the force between magnetic pole pieces is developed.

The density of energy stored in a magnetic field is, from (4-110),

$$w_m = \frac{1}{2} \frac{B^2}{\mu} \quad \text{joules/meter}^3 \tag{5-104}$$

If the gap is small, we may assume a uniform field in the air gap.   The
total energy W_m stored in the gap is then

$$W_m = w_m A g = \frac{B^2 A g}{2\mu_0} \quad \text{joules} \qquad (5\text{-}105)$$

where A = area of gap
  g = width of gap

Suppose now that the iron ring in Fig. 5-45 is perfectly flexible so that the gap must be held open by a force F as in Fig. 5-46.   If the force is increased so as to increase the gap by an infinitesimal amount dg, while at the same time the current through the coil is increased to maintain the flux density B constant, the energy stored in the gap is increased by the infinitesimal amount

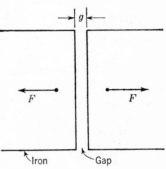

$$dW_m = \frac{B^2 A}{2\mu_0}\, dg \quad \text{joules} \quad (5\text{-}106)$$

Equation (5-106) has the dimensions of energy.   But energy may also be expressed as force times distance, which in this case is $F\,dg$, where F is the attractive force

Fig. 5-46. Forces at air gap.

between the poles.   It is equal in magnitude to the force required to hold them apart.   Thus

$$F\,dg = \frac{B^2 A}{2\mu_0}\, dg$$

or

$$F = \frac{B^2 A}{2\mu_0} \qquad (5\text{-}107)$$

where F = attractive force (newtons)
  B = flux density (webers/meter^2)
  A = area of gap (meters^2)
  μ_0 = permeability of air ($4\pi \times 10^{-7}$ henry/meter)
Dividing by the gap area A yields the pressure P.   That is,

$$P = \frac{F}{A} = \frac{B^2}{2\mu_0} \quad \text{newtons/meter}^2 \qquad (5\text{-}108)$$

5-25. Permanent Magnet with Gap.   Suppose first that a closed iron ring is magnetized to saturation with a uniform toroidal coil wound on the ring.   When the coil is removed, the flux density in the iron is equal to the retentivity (see Fig. 5-48).   If, however, the system has an air gap as in Fig. 5-47, the flux density has a smaller value as given by a point P which lies somewhere on the demagnetization curve (Fig. 5-48) (see also Sec. 5-15).   Further information is needed to locate this point.   This may be obtained as follows: From (5-99) the line integral of **H** once around a magnetic circuit is

$$\oint \mathbf{H} \cdot d\mathbf{l} = NI \tag{5-108a}$$

Since $NI = 0$,

$$\oint \mathbf{H} \cdot d\mathbf{l} = H_i(l - g) + H_g g = 0$$

or

$$H_i(l - g) = -H_g g \tag{5-109}$$

where $H_i = H$ field in the iron
   $l = 2\pi R$ = total length of magnetic circuit (including gap)
   g = width of gap
   $H_g = H$ field in gap

Thus H_i and H_g are in opposite directions as indicated in Fig. 5-47. If leakage is neglected, B is uniform around the circuit. Multiplying

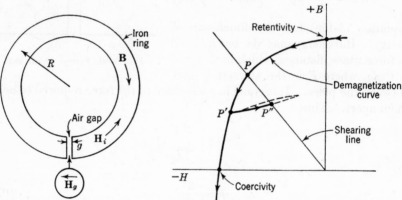

FIG. 5-47. Permanently magnetized ring with air gap.

FIG. 5-48. Demagnetization curves for permanent magnet.

(5-109) by μ_0 and solving for the ratio B/H_i, or the permeability of the iron, we obtain

$$\frac{B}{H_i} = -\mu_0 \frac{l - g}{g} \tag{5-110}$$

This ratio of the flux density B to the field H_i in the iron gives the slope of a line called the *shearing line* as shown in Fig. 5-48. The intersection of this line with the demagnetization curve determines the position of the iron on the magnetization curve (point P). This location is a function of the ratio of the iron path length $(l - g)$ to the gap length g.

In most permanent magnet applications, where it desired that B remain relatively constant, a moderate demagnetizing field is applied to the iron, moving the position of the iron to P' (Fig. 5-48). On removing the field, the iron moves to the point P'' on the shearing line. The ring magnet is now said to be *stabilized*, and when fields less than about the difference of H between points P' and P'' are applied to the ring and then removed, the iron will always return to approximately the point P''. Under these conditions the iron moves along a minor hysteresis loop as suggested by the dashed lines in Fig. 5-48.

5-26. Comparison of Electric and Magnetic Relations Involving Polarization and Magnetization. It is interesting to compare the magnetic relations where magnetization M is present with the corresponding electric relations where polarization P is present (see Chap. 2). This is done in Table 5-5.

TABLE 5-5

COMPARISON OF EQUATIONS INVOLVING POLARIZATION P AND MAGNETIZATION M

Description of equation	Electric case	Magnetic case
Dipole moment relations	$\mathbf{P} = \dfrac{\mathbf{p}}{v} = \dfrac{Ql}{v}$	$\mathbf{M} = \dfrac{\mathbf{m}}{v} = \dfrac{Q_m l}{v}$
Flux density	$\mathbf{D} = \left(\epsilon_0 + \dfrac{\mathbf{P}}{\mathbf{E}} \right) \mathbf{E}$	$\mathbf{B} = \mu_0 \left(1 + \dfrac{\mathbf{M}}{\mathbf{H}} \right) \mathbf{H}$
Permittivity and permeability	$\epsilon = \epsilon_0 + \dfrac{\mathbf{P}}{\mathbf{E}}$	$\mu = \mu_0 \left(1 + \dfrac{\mathbf{M}}{\mathbf{H}} \right)$
Relation to polarization charge density and to equivalent current density	$\nabla \cdot \mathbf{P} = \rho_p$	$\nabla \times \mathbf{M} = \mathbf{J}'$
Poisson's equations	$\nabla^2 V = -\dfrac{\rho}{\epsilon}$	$\nabla^2 U = \nabla \cdot \mathbf{M} = -\nabla \cdot \mathbf{H}$
Scalar and vector potentials	$V = \dfrac{1}{4\pi\epsilon_0} \displaystyle\int_v \dfrac{\rho - \nabla \cdot \mathbf{P}}{r}\, dv$	$\mathbf{A} = \dfrac{\mu_0}{4\pi} \displaystyle\int_v \dfrac{\mathbf{J} + \nabla \times \mathbf{M}}{r}\, dv$

PROBLEMS

5-1. A magnetized needle of 10 amp-meter^2 magnetic moment is situated in a uniform magnetic field of 2 weber/meter^2 flux density. Find the torque T on the needle.

Ans.: $T = 20$ newton-meters.

5-2. A needle of magnetic moment $Q'_m l'$ pivots freely about its center point. Assume that the center of the needle is located at the origin and that there is a magnetic field of flux density $\mathbf{B}$ in the positive y direction. What angle θ does the needle assume with respect to the y axis if a short bar magnet of moment $Q_m l$ is placed coincident with the x axis at a large distance r from the origin?

5-3. A uniformly magnetized bar with a volume of 1,000 cm^3 has a magnetic moment of 800 amp-meters^2. If the flux density $B = 0.1$ weber/meter^2 in the bar, find the value of H in the bar.

5-4. A bar magnet in a *uniform* magnetic field is acted on only by a torque, there being no translational force on the magnet. In a *nonuniform* field, however, there is a net translational force. Find the maximum value of this force on a uniformly magnetized bar magnet 1 cm long with a magnetic moment of 1 amp-meters^2 situated 20 cm from one pole of a very long magnet having a pole strength of 1,000 amp-meters.

5-5. Two ferromagnetic media are separated by a plane boundary. Medium 1 has a relative permeability of 500 and medium 2 a relative permeability of 5,000. If the magnetic field direction in medium 2 is at an angle of 80° with respect to the normal to the boundary, find the angle α_1 between the field direction and the normal to the boundary in medium 1.   *Ans.* $\alpha_1 = 29.6°$.

5-6. If the direction of the magnetic field in air near the plane surface of a large block of iron is 10° from the normal to the surface, find the angle of the field with respect to the normal in the iron. The relative permeability of the iron is 1,000.

5-7. Magnetic field lines on the air side of an air-iron boundary are usually substantially normal to the boundary. Why is this not the case in Fig. 5-43b?

5-8. A small bar magnet with a magnetic moment of 200 amp-meters² is situated parallel to a very long wire carrying a steady current of 100 amp. If the bar magnet is 1 meter from the wire, find the torque on the bar magnet.

5-9. The flux density in a ferromagnetic medium of large extent and permeability μ is B as shown in Fig. 5-49. Two cavities are cut in the medium as illustrated.

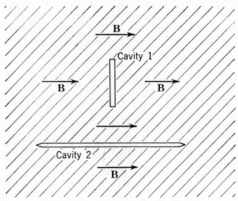

Fig. 5-49. Cavities for Prob. 5-9.

Cavity 1 is shaped like a thin disc, while cavity 2 is long and needlelike. The cavities are air filled. (*a*) What is the magnetic field H_1 at the center of cavity 1? (*b*) What is the magnetic field H_2 at the center of cavity 2? (*c*) What is the ratio of H_1 to H_2?

5-10. Show that at the center of a long, uniformly magnetized bar of uniform cross-section area A the magnitude of **H** is given closely by $2MA/\pi l^2$, where M = magnetization and l = length of bar.

5-11. Show that the permeability μ at the center of a long, permanently magnetized rod of uniform magnetization is given by $\mu_0[1 - (\pi l^2/2A)]$, where l = length and A = cross-sectional area of rod.

5-12. A copper conductor of radius 5 cm is enclosed by a concentric iron tube of inner radius 10 cm and outer radius 15 cm. If the total current in the copper conductor is 100 amp and $\mu_r = 500$ for the iron tube, find B and H at radii of 2.5, 5, 10, 12.5, 15, and 20 cm. Assume that the current density in the conductor is uniform and also that μ_r in the iron tube is uniform.

5-13. Sketch the variation of B and H as a function of radius from 0 to 25 cm for Prob. 5-12.

5-14. Show that at a large distance r from a bar magnet of dipole moment $Q_m l$ the magnetic potential $U = (Q_m l \cos \theta)/(4\pi r^2)$, where θ is the angle between the bar axis and the radius vector of length r. It is assumed that $r \gg l$.

5-15. Show that at a large distance r from a bar magnet of dipole moment $Q_m l$ the flux density **B** has an angular component

$$B_\theta = \frac{\mu_0 Q_m l \sin \theta}{4\pi r^3}$$

and a radial component

$$B_r = \frac{\mu_0 Q_m l \cos \theta}{2\pi r^3}$$

where θ is the angle between the bar axis and the radius vector of length r.   It is assumed that $r \gg l$.

5-16. Show that at a large distance from a single-turn wire loop of area A with current I the flux density **B** has an angular component

$$B_\theta = \frac{\mu_0 I A \sin \theta}{4\pi r^3}$$

and a radial component

$$B_r = \frac{\mu_0 I A \cos \theta}{2\pi r^3}$$

where θ is the angle between the axis of the loop and the radius vector of length r.   It is assumed that r is much greater than the diameter of the loop.

5-17. A magnetized rod 1 cm in diameter and 20 cm long has a uniform magnetization of 1,000 amp/meter.   Find the magnetic moment of the bar.

5-18. A uniformly magnetized rod 2 cm in diameter and 50 cm long has a magnetic moment of 10,000 amp-meters².   Find the equivalent sheet current density K' at the surface of the rod.

5-19. Assuming that the demagnetization curve of a certain ferromagnetic material is a straight line, what is the maximum BH product if the retentivity is 1 weber/meter² and the coercivity is 20,000 amp/meter?   Prove that this is the maximum value.

5-20. According to Lord Rayleigh the bottom part of the normal magnetization curve is given by $B = \mu_i H + cH^2$, where μ_i is the initial permeability (at $H = 0$, $B = 0$) and c is a constant.   Assume that this relation applies to the initial magnetization curve of an iron specimen.   What is the expression for the energy density in the iron after the field is raised from $H = 0$ to $H = H_1$?   Assume that the specimen is initially unmagnetized.

5-21. An iron ring has a uniform cross-sectional area of 1 cm² and a mean radius of 10 cm.   The ring is continuous except for a single air gap 1 mm wide.   Find the number of ampere-turns required on the ring to produce a flux density $B = 0.5$ weber/meter² in the air gap.   Neglect fringing.   When $B = 0.5$ in the iron, the relative permeability of the iron $\mu_r = 300$.

5-22. Find the total reluctance measured between the ends of two parallel iron bars, each 1 by 1 cm in cross section and 10 cm long, if one bar has a relative permeability of 500 and the other of 1,000.

5-23. Find the reluctance and permeance between the ends of an iron bar having the dimensions shown in Fig. 3-27, assuming a uniform relative permeability of 5,000.

5-24. How much greater is the reluctance of the block of Fig. 3-27 as compared with a uniform rectangular block without the notches?   The permeability is assumed to be the same in both cases.

5-25. Find the permeance per unit depth between the ends of a block of iron of uniform permeability μ having the cross-sectional dimensions shown in Fig. 3-28.

5-26. Find the permeance per unit depth between the top and bottom faces of a block of iron of uniform permeability μ having the cross-sectional dimensions shown in Fig. 3-28.

5-27. A cyclotron magnet has the dimensions shown in Fig. 5-50.   The pole pieces are cylindrical with tapered ends.   The diameter at the gap is 1 meter and the gap width 0.15 meter as indicated.   Approximately how many ampere-turns are required in each of the two windings shown to produce a flux density of 1 weber/meter² in the air gap?   Assume that the magnet is made of iron with a constant relative permeability of 3,000 and that there is no fringing at the gap.   Also neglect any leakage along the magnet structure.   As a further simplification take the effective length of sections

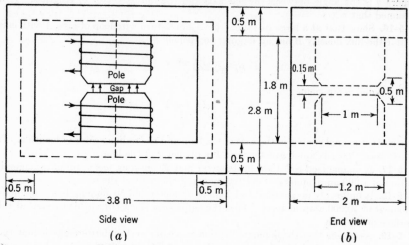

Side view   End view
(a)   (b)

FIG. 5-50. Cyclotron magnet for Prob. 5-27.

as the length measured along the center line (dashed line in Fig. 5-50a).   Take the diameter of the tapered section of the poles as the average diameter.

5-28. An electromagnet consists of a U-shaped iron yoke and iron bar as shown in Fig. 5-51.   A thin copper sheet on the top of the bar prevents an iron-to-iron contact

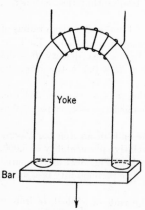

between the bar and yoke.   If the magnetic flux through the circuit is 0.01 weber and the yoke-bar contact area is 100 cm² per pole, what is the weight which the yoke will support (including the weight of the bar)?   Neglect the effect of any fringing of the field.

5-29. (a) If the contact area of the electromagnet of Prob. 5-28 is reduced to 50 cm² by means of tapered sections on the yoke, what is the weight which the yoke will support?   Assume that the total flux in the circuit is the same as before and neglect the effect of any fringing of the field.   (b) In practice what prevents the attractive force from increasing indefinitely as the contact area is reduced?

5-30. What is the contact pressure in Probs. 5-28 and 5-29a?

5-31. A ring magnet with an air gap 1 mm wide has a uniform cross section of 10 cm² and a radius of 20 cm.   If the flux density in the gap is 1 weber/ meter², find the force tending to close the gap.   Neglect fringing.

FIG.   5-51. Electromagnet for Prob. 5-28.

5-32. Show that the permeability of a permanent magnet with air gap may be expressed by $\mu = -\mu_0(\mathcal{P}_g/\mathcal{P})$, where μ_0 = permeability of air, $\mathcal{P}_g$ = permeance of air gap, and $\mathcal{P}$ = permeance of the empty space occupied by the magnet.

5-33. A long conducting tube of negligible wall thickness carries a longitudinal current of uniform sheet density $K = I/(2\pi R)$, where I = total current and R = radius of tube. Find H inside the tube $(r < R)$, at $r = R$, and outside the tube $(r > R)$. What boundary relation is obviously satisfied at $r = R$?

5-34. Referring to Fig. 5-43a, show that to satisfy the boundary conditions the image currents I' and I'' are related to the current I in the wire in the iron by (5-86) and (5-87).

5-35. A long, thin linear conductor carrying a current I extends along the plane boundary between 2 media, air and iron. Assuming that the permeability μ of the ron is uniform, show that the H field in air at a radius r from the conductor is

$$H_0 = \frac{\mu}{\mu + \mu_0} \frac{I}{\pi r}$$

while in the iron at a radius r from the conductor it is

$$H_i = \frac{\mu_0}{\mu + \mu_0} \frac{I}{\pi r}$$

CHAPTER 6

CHARGED PARTICLES IN ELECTRIC AND MAGNETIC FIELDS

6-1. Introduction. In this chapter the motion of charged particles in vacuum in the presence of electric and magnetic fields is considered. It is assumed that the velocity of the particles is small compared with the velocity of light and that the effect of the particles on each other can be neglected.

6-2. Charged Particle in a Static Electric Field. Let a particle of charge e† be placed in a uniform electric field $\mathbf{E}$. Since $\mathbf{E}$ is the force per unit charge (newtons per coulomb), the force $\mathbf{F}$ on the particle is

$$\mathbf{F} = e\mathbf{E} \qquad (6\text{-}1)$$

The force is in the same direction as the field if the charge is positive and opposite to the field if the charge is negative. If the particle is at rest and the field is applied, the particle is accelerated uniformly in the direction of the field. According to Newton's second law the force on a particle is related to its mass and acceleration by

$$\mathbf{F} = m\mathbf{a} \qquad (6\text{-}2)$$

where $\mathbf{F}$ = force (newtons)
  m = mass (kg)
  $\mathbf{a}$ = acceleration (meters/sec^2)
Therefore the acceleration of the particle is

$$\mathbf{a} = \frac{e}{m}\,\mathbf{E} \qquad (6\text{-}3)$$

The velocity $\mathbf{v}$ of the particle after a time t is then

$$\mathbf{v} = \mathbf{a}t = \frac{e}{m}\,\mathbf{E}t \qquad (6\text{-}4)$$

where $\mathbf{v}$ = velocity of particle (meters/sec)
  e = charge of particle (coulombs)
  m = mass of particle (kg)
  $\mathbf{E}$ = electric field intensity (volts/meter or newtons/coulomb)
  t = time (sec)

† The symbol e will be used to designate the charge of a particle instead of q since e is more commonly employed in dealing with the charge of a particle

272

The field imparts energy to the charged particle.   If (6-3) is reexpressed
as

$$m\mathbf{a} = e\mathbf{E} \tag{6-5}$$

it has the dimensions of force.   Integrating this force over the distance
moved yields the energy W acquired.   Thus

$$W = m \int_1^2 \mathbf{a} \cdot d\mathbf{l} = -e \int_1^2 \mathbf{E} \cdot d\mathbf{l} \tag{6-6}$$

The line integral of $\mathbf{E}$ between two points, 1 and 2, may be recognized as
the potential difference V between the points.   Substituting $\mathbf{a} = d\mathbf{v}/dt$
and $d\mathbf{l} = \mathbf{v}\,dt$, (6-6) becomes

$$W = m \int_1^2 \mathbf{v} \cdot d\mathbf{v} = eV \tag{6-7}$$

or

$$W = \tfrac{1}{2}m(v_2{}^2 - v_1{}^2) = eV \tag{6-8}$$

where W = energy acquired (joules)
v_2 = velocity at point 2, or final velocity (meters/sec)
v_1 = velocity at point 1, or initial velocity (meters/sec)
e = charge on particle (coulombs)
V = potential difference between points 1 and 2 (volts or joules/
      coulomb)
If the particle starts from rest, the initial velocity is zero so

$$W = eV = \tfrac{1}{2}mv^2. \tag{6-9}$$

where v = final velocity.   Equation (6-9) has the dimensions of energy.
The dimensional relation in mksc units is

$$\text{Joules} = \text{coulombs} \times \text{volts} = \text{kilograms}\,\frac{\text{meters}^2}{\text{seconds}^2}$$

Thus the energy acquired by a particle of charge e starting from rest and
passing through a potential drop V is given either by the product of the
charge and the potential difference or by one-half the product of the mass
of the particle and the square of the final velocity.
Solving (6-9) for the velocity,

$$v = \sqrt{\frac{2eV}{m}} \qquad \text{meters/sec} \tag{6-10}$$

The energy acquired by an electron ($e = 1.6 \times 10^{-19}$ coulomb) in
"falling" through a potential difference of 1 volt is 1.6×10^{-19} joule.
This amount of energy is a convenient unit in designating the energies of
particles and is called one *electron volt*.
In the case of an electron $e = 1.6 \times 10^{-19}$ coulomb and $m = 0.91 \times 10^{-30}$ kg so that (6-10) becomes

$$v = 5.93 \times 10^5 \sqrt{V} \qquad \text{meters/sec} \tag{6-11}$$

Thus, if $V = 1$ volt, the velocity of the electron is 5.9×10^5 meters per sec, or 590 km per sec. It is apparent that a relatively small voltage imparts a very large velocity to an electron. If $V = 2,500$ volts, the velocity is 3×10^7 meters per sec, or about one-tenth the velocity of light. As mentioned in Sec. 6-1, the above relations are based on the assumption that the particle velocity is small compared with that of light. This is because the mass of a particle approaches an infinite value as the velocity approaches that of light (relativistic effect), whereas the above relations are based on a constant mass. Actually, however, the mass increase is of negligible consequence for most applications unless the velocity is at least 10 per cent that of light. The relation between the mass m of the particle and its mass m_0 at low velocities (rest mass) is given by

$$m = \frac{m_0}{\sqrt{1 - (v^2/c^2)}} \qquad (6\text{-}12)$$

where v = velocity of particle (meters/sec)
c = velocity of light (3×10^8 meters/sec)
If the velocity is one-tenth that of light, the mass is only one-half of 1 per cent greater than the rest mass.

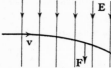

FIG. 6-1. Path of positively charged particle in electric field.

If the particle has an initial velocity which is not parallel to the field direction, as assumed above, the particle describes a parabolic path (Fig. 6-1). The deflection of an electron by a transverse electric field is discussed in a later section on the cathode-ray tube.

6-3. Charged Particle in a Static Magnetic Field.
From (4-30) the force $\mathbf{F}$ on a current element of length dl in a uniform magnetic field is

$$d\mathbf{F} = dl\,(\mathbf{I} \times \mathbf{B}) \qquad (6\text{-}13)$$

where $\mathbf{I}$ = current (a vector indicating magnitude and direction of the current)
$\mathbf{B}$ = flux density
This is the fundamental motor equation of electrical machinery. It also applies to moving charged particles in the absence of any metallic conductor.

The current $\mathbf{I}$ in a conductor or in a beam of ions or electrons can be expressed in terms of the current density $\mathbf{J}$, the charge (volume) density ρ, the beam area A, and the velocity $\mathbf{v}$ by

$$\mathbf{I} = \mathbf{J}A = \rho \mathbf{v} A \qquad (6\text{-}14)$$

Substituting (6-14) for $\mathbf{I}$ in (6-13),

$$d\mathbf{F} = \rho A\,dl\,\mathbf{v} \times \mathbf{B} \qquad (6\text{-}15)$$

But $\rho A\ dl = dq$, the charge in a length dl of the beam. Thus

$$d\mathbf{F} = dq\ \mathbf{v} \times \mathbf{B} \qquad (6\text{-}16)$$

For a single particle of charge e, we have

$$\mathbf{F} = e\mathbf{v} \times \mathbf{B} \qquad (6\text{-}17)$$

Consider now the motion of a particle of charge e in a uniform magnetic field of flux density $\mathbf{B}$. The velocity of the particle is $\mathbf{v}$. From Newton's second law the force on the particle is equal to the product of its mass m and its acceleration $\mathbf{a}(= d\mathbf{v}/dt)$. Thus

$$m\mathbf{a} = e\mathbf{v} \times \mathbf{B} \qquad (6\text{-}18)$$

or

$$\mathbf{a} = \frac{e}{m}\mathbf{v} \times \mathbf{B} \qquad (6\text{-}19)$$

According to (6-19) the acceleration is normal to the plane containing the particle path and $\mathbf{B}$. If the direction of the particle path (indicated by $\mathbf{v}$) is normal to $\mathbf{B}$, the acceleration is a maximum. If the particle is at rest, the field has no effect. Likewise, if the particle path is in the same direction as $\mathbf{B}$, there is no effect, the particle continuing with this velocity. Only when the path or the velocity $\mathbf{v}$ has a component normal to $\mathbf{B}$ does the field have an effect.

If a magnetic field of large extent is at right angles to the direction of motion of a charged particle, the particle is deflected into a circular path. Suppose that in a field-free region a positively charged particle is moving to the right as indicated in Fig. 6-2 and that when it reaches the point P a magnetic field is applied. The direction of $\mathbf{B}$ is normally outward from the page. According to the cross product of $\mathbf{v}$ into $\mathbf{B}$ in (6-19) the acceleration $\mathbf{a}$ is downward so that the particle describes a circle in the clockwise direction in the plane of the page.

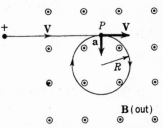

Fig. 6-2. Path of positively charged particle in magnetic field.

Let us determine the radius R of the circle. The magnitude of the force $\mathbf{F}$ (radially inward) on the particle is, by (6-19),

$$F = ma = evB \qquad (6\text{-}20)$$

This force is also given by

$$F = \frac{mv^2}{R} \qquad (6\text{-}21)$$

Equating (6-20) and (6-21) yields

$$\frac{mv^2}{R} = evB \tag{6-22}$$

or

$$R = \frac{mv}{eB} \tag{6-23}$$

where R = radius of particle (meters)

m = mass of particle (kg)

v = velocity of particle (meters/sec)

e = charge of particle (coulombs)

B = flux density (webers/meter^2)

Thus, the larger the velocity of the particle or the larger its mass, the greater the radius. On the other hand, the larger the charge or the flux density, the smaller the radius.

The number of revolutions per second of the particle in the circular path is called the frequency f of the particle. The frequency is

$$f = \frac{v}{2\pi R} = \frac{eB}{2\pi m} \qquad \text{rps} \tag{6-24}$$

Example. An electron has a velocity of 10^4 meters/sec normal to a magnetic field of 0.1 weber/meter^2 flux density. Find the radius of the electron path and also its frequency.

Solution. From (6-23) the radius

$$R = \frac{0.91 \times 10^{-30} \times 10^4}{1.6 \times 10^{-19} \times 10^{-1}} = 5.7 \times 10^{-7} \text{ meter}$$

This is a very small circle. The frequency

$$f = \frac{10^4}{2\pi \times 5.7 \times 10^{-7}} = 2.8 \times 10^9 \text{ rps}$$

If the particle in the above example had an initial velocity component parallel to **B** as well as perpendicular to **B**, the particle would move in a helical path with the axis of the helix parallel to **B**.

To illustrate applications of the relations of this and the preceding section, the operation of three electronic or ionic devices is described in the next sections. These devices are the cathode-ray tube, the cyclotron, and the mass spectrograph (Prob. 6-5).

6-4. The Cathode-ray Tube.[1] A cathode-ray tube is a device for observing rapid voltage variations. In a cathode-ray tube (Fig. 6-3) a beam of electrons is emitted from a cathode, is accelerated by an electrode A, and impinges on a fluorescent screen. By means of either a transverse electric or a transverse magnetic field the beam may be deflected so that

[1] Sometimes called a *Braun tube* after Carl F. Braun.

it strikes the screen at a distance y from the undeflected position. The spot on the screen is visible, and the particular usefulness of the cathode-ray tube is that, because of the small inertia of the electron beam, it can follow very rapid changes in the applied deflecting field. This is a somewhat oversimplified description of a cathode-ray tube but will suffice for the following brief analysis of some of its characteristics.

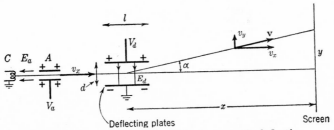

FIG. 6-3. Cathode-ray tube with electrostatic deflection.

The positive accelerating potential V_a is applied to the electrode A. This produces an accelerating field E_a that imparts a velocity v_x to the electrons.[1] From (6-10)

$$v_x = \sqrt{\frac{2eV_a}{m}} \tag{6-25}$$

After an electron leaves the accelerating electrode, it maintains this velocity v_x.

Let us consider the effect of electrostatic deflection with two plates at a potential difference V_d as in Fig. 6-3. The path of an electron in the transverse deflecting field is a parabola. Neglecting fringing of the field at the edges of the plates, the electron is subjected to the deflecting field E_d for a distance l or for a time $t = l/v_x$. The field E_d produces an acceleration a_y in the y direction which, from (6-3), is

$$a_y = \frac{eV_d}{md} \tag{6-26}$$

Thus, the electron acquires a velocity component v_y in the y direction given by

$$v_y = a_y t = \frac{eV_d l}{mdv_x} \tag{6-27}$$

---

[1] Actual cathode-ray tubes usually have several accelerating electrodes in a tandem arrangement. These serve the dual purpose of accelerating the electrons and of focusing them. The value of V_a used in (6-25), in the case of an actual tube, should be the total effective accelerating voltage. This is often called the *electron beam voltage.*

The deflection angle α (Fig. 6-3) is then

$$\alpha = \arctan \frac{v_y}{v_x} = \arctan \frac{eV_d l}{m d v_x{}^2} \tag{6-28}$$

or

$$\alpha = \arctan \frac{V_d l}{2 V_a d} \tag{6-29}$$

But from the tube geometry, assuming $x \gg l$, the angle α is also given by

$$\alpha = \arctan \frac{y}{x} \tag{6-30}$$

and so, equating the arguments in (6-29) and (6-30),

$$y = \frac{V_d l x}{2 V_a d} \qquad \text{meters} \tag{6-31}$$

where y = deflection distance at screen (meters)
  V_d = deflecting potential (volts)
  l = length of deflecting plates (meters)
  x = distance from deflecting plates to screen (meters)
  V_a = accelerating potential (volts)
  d = spacing of deflecting plates (meters)
Solving for the volts per meter of deflection (ratio V_d/y), we have

$$\frac{V_d}{y} = \frac{2 V_a d}{l x} \qquad \text{volts/meter.} \tag{6-32}$$

Example 1. A cathode-ray tube with electrostatic deflection has an accelerating voltage V_a = 1,500 volts, a deflecting-plate spacing d = 1 cm, a deflecting-plate length l = 1 cm, and a distance x = 30 cm from deflecting plates to the screen. Find the voltage V_d required to deflect the spot by 1 cm on the screen. Neglect fringing of the field.

Solution. From (6-32)

$$\frac{V_d}{y} = \frac{2 \times 1,500 \times 10^{-2}}{10^{-2} \times 30 \times 10^{-2}} = 10,000 \text{ volts/meter}$$

or

$$\frac{V_d}{y} = 100 \text{ volts/cm}$$

To increase the sensitivity, that is, to decrease the number of volts per meter of deflection, V_a or d should be decreased or an increase made in l or x.

Let us consider now the effect of a magnetic deflecting field. Suppose that the deflecting plates and electric field E_d of Fig. 6-3 are replaced by a magnetic field of flux density **B** normal to the page as in Fig. 6-4. The direction of **B** is outward from the page. In this case the acceleration due to the magnetic field is not in the y direction but is normal to the circular path of the electron. Assume, however, that l is so small that as an approximation the acceleration can be taken in the y direction. Then

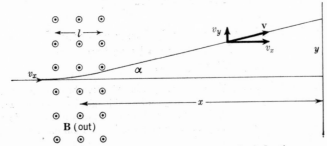

FIG. 6-4. Cathode-ray tube with magnetic deflection.

the velocity component in the y direction is

$$v_y = a_y t = a_y \frac{l}{v_x} \tag{6-33}$$

Thus from (6-20)

$$v_y = \frac{ev_x B}{m} \frac{l}{v_x} = \frac{eBl}{m} \tag{6-34}$$

The deflection angle α (Fig. 6-4) is

$$\alpha = \arctan \frac{v_y}{v_x} = \arctan \frac{eBl}{v_x m}$$

or

$$\alpha = \arctan \left(Bl \sqrt{\frac{e}{2mV_a}} \right) \tag{6-35}$$

But we have also $\alpha = \arctan y/x$, and so

$$y = xBl \sqrt{\frac{e}{2mV_a}} \qquad \text{meters} \tag{6-36}$$

where y = deflection distance at screen (meters)
  x = distance from magnetic deflecting field to screen (meters)
  B = flux density of deflecting field (webers/meter^2)
  e = charge on particle (coulombs)
  m = mass of particle (kg)
  V_a = accelerating voltage (volts)
  l = axial length of deflecting field (meters)
Solving for the flux density per meter of deflection (ratio B/y), we have

$$\frac{B}{y} = \frac{1}{xl} \sqrt{\frac{2mV_a}{e}} \tag{6-37}$$

where the ratio B/y is in webers per square meter per meter of deflection. For an electron (6-37) becomes

$$\frac{B}{y} = \frac{3.38 \times 10^{-6}}{xl} \sqrt{V_a} \tag{6-38}$$

where x = distance from deflecting field to screen (meters)
$\quad\quad l$ = axial length of deflecting field (meters)
$\quad\quad V_a$ = accelerating voltage (volts)

Example 2. A cathode-ray tube with magnetic deflection has an accelerating voltage $V_a = 1,500$ volts, a magnetic deflecting field axial length $l = 2$ cm, and a distance $x = 30$ cm from the deflecting field to the screen. Find the magnetic field flux density B required to deflect the spot of an electron beam 1 cm on the screen.

Solution. From (6-38)

$$\frac{B}{y} = \frac{3.38 \times 10^{-6} \times 1,500^{\frac{1}{2}}}{30 \times 10^{-2} \times 2 \times 10^{-2}} = 2.18 \times 10^{-2} \text{ weber/meter}^2/\text{meter}$$

or

$$\frac{B}{y} = 2.18 \times 10^{-4} \text{ weber/meter}^2/\text{cm}$$

6-5. The Cyclotron. The cyclotron is a heavy particle accelerator, invented in 1929 by Ernest O. Lawrence, for obtaining a beam of high-energy ions. Particles such as protons, deuterons, or alpha particles are given multiple accelerations in a resonance chamber. Referring to Fig. 6-5, two hollow D-shaped copper electrodes, or *dees*, are between the pole pieces of a large electromagnet. The region between the poles pieces is evacuated. In Fig. 6-5 the walls of the vacuum chamber are omitted. The two dees are connected to a high-frequency source of alternating voltage. In the case of deuteron operation, ions in heavy hydrogen gas at low pressure are produced at the center of the chamber by electrons emitted from a filament.

Starting with a deuteron at the point P, a negative potential on the right-hand dee accelerates the deuteron to the right. Entering the dee, the deuteron is in a region free of electric field but still in the magnetic field between the pole pieces. Suppose that the lower pole is a north pole so that **B** is upward. The deuteron then moves in a circle in a clockwise direction. If the timing is proper so that when the deuteron again reaches the gap between the dees the electric field has reversed, it will be accelerated to the left. Having acquired additional energy, it moves in a circle of larger radius. By repetition of this process the energy of the deuteron is increased in steps until it reaches the periphery of the dees. Here a deflecting electrode at a high negative potential pulls the deuteron through an opening in the dee so that it can impinge on a specimen placed outside the dee.

The frequency in revolutions per second of a particle moving normal to the magnetic field in a cyclotron is given by (6-24). That is,

$$f = \frac{eB}{2\pi m} \tag{6-39}$$

Provided the particle velocity is small compared with light, m is substantially constant. Since e and B are also constant, f is a constant

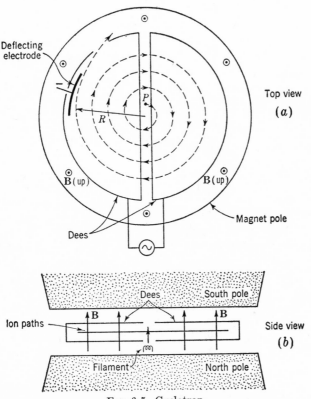

Deflecting electrode

Top view

(a)

B (up)   B (up)

Magnet pole

Dees

Dees   South pole

Ion paths

B   B

Side view

(b)

Filament   North pole

FIG. 6-5. Cyclotron.

regardless of the velocity of the particle. However, from (6-23) the radius of the circular path is proportional to the particle velocity.

Example 1. Find the frequency for a deuteron ($e = 1.6 \times 10^{-19}$ coulomb, $m = 3.34 \times 10^{-27}$ kg) in a cyclotron with a flux density $B = 1.5$ webers/meter^2.

Solution. From (6-39) the frequency

$$f = \frac{1.6 \times 10^{-19} \times 1.5}{2\pi \times 3.34 \times 10^{-27}} = 1.14 \times 10^7 \text{ rps}$$

This is the frequency that is required of the oscillator connected to the dees. Accordingly, the oscillator frequency must be 11.4 Mc/sec for accelerating deuterons.

The final energy of a particle is determined by the radius R and the flux density B. From (6-23)

$$R = \frac{mv}{eB} \quad \text{or} \quad v = \frac{ReB}{m} \tag{6-40}$$

The energy W of the particle is

$$W = \frac{1}{2} mv^2 \quad \text{or} \quad v = \sqrt{\frac{2W}{m}} \tag{6-41}$$

Equating these relations for v and solving for the energy W of the particle,

$$W = \frac{1}{2} \frac{(ReB)^2}{m} \tag{6-42}$$

Example 2. A cyclotron has a maximum working radius $R = 50$ cm, a flux density $B = 1.5$ webers/meter². Find the energy which may be imparted to deuterons. *Solution.* From (6-42) the final energy

$$W = \frac{(0.5 \times 1.6 \times 10^{-19} \times 1.5)^2}{2 \times 3.34 \times 10^{-27}} = 2.15 \times 10^{-12} \text{ joule}$$

Since

$$\text{Energy in electron volts} = \frac{\text{energy in joules}}{1.6 \times 10^{-19}}$$

this result in electron volts is

$$W_{ev} = \frac{2.15 \times 10^{-12}}{1.6 \times 10^{-19}} = 1.33 \times 10^7 \text{ electron volts}$$

or an energy of 13.3 million electron volts.

If either alpha particles or protons had been used, the energy would be doubled. In the above discussion relativistic effects have been neglected as have also interaction effects of the ions in the beam. Corrections for these effects are usually small except in the larger high-energy cyclotrons.

If the voltage V applied between the gap of the dees is small, a large number n of revolutions is required before the particle reaches the periphery. However, to reduce the dispersion of the beam it is desirable to make n small and, hence, V as large as possible. The total energy W acquired in n revolutions is

$$W = 2nVe \tag{6-43}$$

Thus, for a given energy W as determined by (6-42) and for a particular voltage V, the number of revolutions is

$$n = \frac{W}{2eV} \tag{6-44}$$

where W is in joules.   If the energy is expressed in electron volts, W_{ev},

$$n = \frac{W_{ev}}{2eV} \times 1.6 \times 10^{-19} \qquad (6\text{-}45)$$

where e = charge of particle (coulombs)
     V = dee voltage (volts)

6-6. Table of Charge and Mass for Common Particles.   The charge and mass for a number of common particles are listed in Table 6-1.   The mass given is the rest mass, or mass at zero velocity.

TABLE 6-1

Particle	Charge e, coulombs	Mass m, kg	Ratio e/m, coulombs/kg
Electron....................	-1.602×10^{-19}	9.107×10^{-31}	-1.76×10^{11}
Positron....................	$+1.602 \times 10^{-19}$	9.107×10^{-31}	$+1.76 \times 10^{11}$
Neutron....................	0	1.6747×10^{-27}	0
Proton (hydrogen nucleus).....	$+1.602 \times 10^{-19}$	1.6725×10^{-27}	$+9.6 \times 10^{7}$
Deuteron (heavy hydrogen nucleus).................	$+1.6 \times 10^{-19}$	3.34×10^{-27}	$+4.8 \times 10^{7}$
Alpha particle (helium nucleus)	$+3.2 \times 10^{-19}$	6.644×10^{-27}	$+4.81 \times 10^{7}$

PROBLEMS

6-1. A particle with a negative charge of 10^{-18} coulomb and a mass of 10^{-24} kg is at rest in a field-free space.   If a uniform electric field of intensity $E = 100$ volts/meter is applied at a time $t = 0$, what is the velocity of the particle 1 μsec later?
Ans. (a) $v = 100$ meters/sec.

6-2. An electron beam with electrons of 1,000-electron-volt energy enters the transverse static electric field of a pair of deflecting plates.   The plates are spaced 1 cm and are 2 cm long parallel to the beam direction.   If 10 volts is applied between the deflecting plates, find how far away the screen must be to obtain a deflection of 1 cm.   Assume that the field is uniform between the deflecting plates.   Neglect fringing.

6-3. If the electrostatic deflecting-plate system of Prob. 6-2 is replaced by a uniform magnetic field 2 cm long in the beam direction, find how far away the screen must be to obtain a deflection of 1 cm when the flux density $B = 10^{-4}$ weber/meter^2.

6-4. *a.* What is the maximum energy in millions of electron volts for alpha particles in a cyclotron with a maximum usable radius of 50 cm?   The flux density in the air gap is 1 weber/meter^2.

b. What is the maximum energy if protons are used?

c. What is the maximum energy for deuterons?

d. What is the resonant frequency in each case?

e. How many revolutions does each particle make if the peak potential between dees is 10,000 volts?

6-5. A *mass spectrograph* is a device for separating particles of the same charge but different mass.   Referring to Fig. 6-6, the particles are injected with a known velocity v into a uniform magnetic field of flux density B.   Particles with larger mass strike the fluorescent screen or photographic plate at a greater distance from the point of entry, as suggested. Show that two particles of the same charge e and of masses m_1 and m_2 injected with the same velocity v are separated at the screen by a distance d given by $d = (2v/Be)(m_2 - m_1)$, where $m_2 > m_1$.

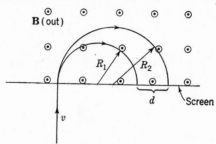

FIG. 6-6. Mass spectrograph.

6-6. In *Millikan's oil-drop experiment* a tiny charged droplet of oil of mass m is suspended in equilibrium in the gravitational field (of acceleration g) by an electric field of intensity E between two horizontal capacitor plates. If the droplet has N electron charges, show that the magnitude of the charge e on an electron is given by $e = mg/NE$. How can the polarity of the charge on the droplet be determined by this experiment?

CHAPTER 7

TIME-CHANGING ELECTRIC AND MAGNETIC FIELDS

7-1. Introduction. In the preceding chapters the principles of static electric and magnetic fields were considered. In this chapter electric and magnetic fields that change with time are discussed, and a number of new relations and concepts are introduced. Some of the more important of these are (1) *Faraday's law*, which gives the emf induced in a closed circuit due to a change of magnetic flux linking it; (2) a relation giving the emf induced in a conductor moving in a magnetic field; (3) *Maxwell's displacement current*, which represents an extension of the current concept to include charge-free space, and (4) an extension of the boundary relations developed in earlier chapters to include time-varying situations.

7-2. Faraday's Law. In Chap. 4 we observed that a current-carrying conductor produces a magnetic field. About 1831 Michael Faraday in London and Joseph Henry in Albany found independently that the reverse effect was also possible. That is, a magnetic field can produce a current in a closed circuit but with the important qualification that the magnetic flux linking the circuit must be changing.

Consider, for example, the closed wire loop in Fig. 7-1. A magnetic field with flux density **B** is normal to the plane of the loop. If **B** is directed upward and *decreasing* in magnitude, a current **I** flows in the wire in the direction indicated.[1] It is said that the current is *induced* by the magnetic field. The relation between the direction of **B** and **I** is given by the right-hand rule (Fig. 4-2).[2] This is for the case where **B** is *decreasing* in magnitude. If **B** is directed upward as before but is *increasing* in magnitude, the direction of the induced current is opposite.

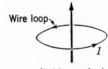

Fig. 7-1. Relation between decreasing flux density **B** and induced current *I* in loop.

---

[1] The direction is that of the conventional current, which is opposite to the direction of motion of the electron current.

[2] Here, however, it is more convenient to take **B** in the direction of the thumb and **I** in the direction of the fingers. Both this rule and that of Fig. 4-2 relate **B** and **I** in the same way.

When the applied flux density **B** is decreasing in magnitude, the current induced in the loop is in such a direction as to produce a field which tends to increase **B** (Fig. 7-2a).   On the other hand, when **B** is increasing, the current induced in the loop is in such a direction as to produce a field opposing **B** (Fig. 7-2b).   Thus *the induced current in the loop is always in such a direction as to produce flux opposing the change in* **B** (Lenz's law).

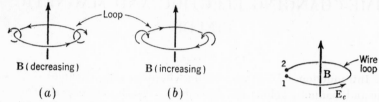

B (decreasing)   B (increasing)

(*a*)   (*b*)

Fig. 7-2. Induced currents for decreasing and increasing flux density **B**.

Fig. 7-3a. Single-turn loop.

The changing magnetic field produces an electric field $\mathbf{E}_e$.   Integrating this field around the loop yields an emf $\mathcal{v}$.   That is

$$\mathcal{v} = \oint \mathbf{E}_e \cdot d\mathbf{l} \tag{7-1}$$

When the loop is open-circuited as in Fig. 7-3a, this emf appears between the terminals.

The electric field $\mathbf{E}_e$ should be distinguished from an electric field $\mathbf{E}_c$ due to charges.   Whereas $\mathbf{E}_c$ can be described as the gradient of an electric potential V, that is,[1]

$$\mathbf{E}_c = -\boldsymbol{\nabla} V \tag{7-2}$$

the field $\mathbf{E}_e$ cannot.   The electric field $\mathbf{E}_e$ may be regarded as an *emf-producing field*.   This type of field can result from the chemical action in a battery as discussed in Sec. 3-10.   It also results, as we see here, from a changing magnetic field.

The electric potential V is a single-valued function of position.   That is, a point P in an electric field $\mathbf{E}_c$ due to charges has a single potential value V with respect to some reference point P', such as infinity or the ground.   This value of V given by

$$V = -\int_{P'}^{P} \mathbf{E}_c \cdot d\mathbf{l} \tag{7-3}$$

is independent of the path by which $\mathbf{E}_c$ is integrated from P' to P.   However, the emf $\mathcal{v}$ is not a single-valued function.   That is, the emf $\mathcal{v}$ between two points 1 and 2 as given by

$$\mathcal{v} = \int_{1}^{2} \mathbf{E}_e \cdot d\mathbf{l} \tag{7-4}$$

does depend on the path by which $\mathbf{E}_e$ is integrated from 1 to 2.   For

[1] $\mathbf{E}_c$ is a lamellar field.

example, if the terminals 1 and 2 of the wire loop in Fig. 7-3*a* are infinitesimally close together, the emf υ between them as obtained by integrating $\mathbf{E}_e$ from 1 to 2 around the loop is equal to the line integral of $\mathbf{E}_e$ around the closed loop.   But if $\mathbf{E}_e$ is integrated from 1 to 2 directly across the gap, the result is zero.

With the loop terminals open (Fig. 7-3*a*) a potential difference V equal to the emf υ appears between the terminals.   A field $\mathbf{E}_c$ is then present due to the electric charges on the terminals.   The configuration of this field is different from the field $\mathbf{E}_e$.   However, when the terminals are closed, there is no potential difference between any parts of the loop and no field $\mathbf{E}_c$.†

The quantitative relation between the emf induced in a closed loop and the magnetic field producing the emf is given by *Faraday's law*.   According to this law, *the total emf induced in a closed circuit is equal to the time rate of decrease of the total magnetic flux linking the circuit*.   Thus, in symbols,

$$\upsilon = -\frac{d\psi_m}{dt} \tag{7-5}$$

where υ = total emf (volts)

ψ_m = total flux (webers)

t = time (sec)

The negative sign indicates that the emf and current direction is positive (the right-hand rule relates positive directions) with respect to the direction of the field when the field, and hence the flux, is *decreasing* with time. This situation is indicated in Fig. 7-2*a*.

Equation (7-5) applies to a single-turn loop as in Fig. 7-1, 7-2, or 7-3*a*. For a loop of more than one turn, where all turns are linked by the same flux ψ_m, Faraday's law may be expressed

$$\upsilon = -N\frac{d\psi_m}{dt} \tag{7-6}$$

where N = number of turns.

If every turn is not linked by the same value of flux, we may write Faraday's law as follows,

$$\upsilon = -\frac{d\Lambda}{dt} \tag{7-7}$$

where Λ = total flux linkage (weber-turns).   That is, for the case of N turns,

$$\Lambda = \psi_{m1} + \psi_{m2} + \cdots + \psi_{mN} \tag{7-8}$$

where ψ_{m1} = flux linked by first turn

ψ_{m2} = flux linked by second turn

ψ_{mN} = flux linked by Nth turn

† It is assumed that the resistance per unit length of the loop conductor is uniform.

Now the total flux through a circuit is equal to the integral of the normal component of the flux density **B** over the surface bounded by the circuit. That is, the total magnetic flux ψ_m is given by

$$\psi_m = \int_s \mathbf{B} \cdot d\mathbf{s}\dagger \qquad (7\text{-}9)$$

The surface may be any continuous surface bounded by the periphery of

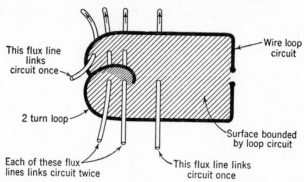

This flux line links circuit once

Wire loop circuit

2 turn loop

Surface bounded by loop circuit

Each of these flux lines links circuit twice

This flux line links circuit once

Fig. 7-3b. Circuit with 2-turn loop showing six flux-line linkages. Each passage of a flux line through the surface constitutes one linkage.

the circuit (see Fig. 7-3b). Substituting (7-9) in (7-5) yields

$$\mathcal{V} = -\frac{d}{dt} \int_s \mathbf{B} \cdot d\mathbf{s} \qquad (7\text{-}10)$$

where $\mathcal{V}$ = induced emf (volts)

$\mathbf{B}$ = flux density (webers/meter²)

$d\mathbf{s}$ = surface element (meters²)

t = time (sec)

This relation was derived by F. E. Neumann about 1845 and may be regarded as a more general form of Faraday's law. It gives the emf induced in a closed stationary circuit by a changing field. Equation (7-10) may also be applied to circuits in motion (with respect to the observer), with **B** constant or time-varying, provided that the motion of the boundary of the surface in (7-10) coincides at every instant with the motion of all parts of the physical circuit. Thus (7-10) can be applied to a loop or coil translated, rotated, or deformed in a magnetic field. How-

† The symbol $\int_s$ indicates a double or surface integral $\left(\iint\right)$ over a surface s. Although it is simplest to consider (7-9) in connection with a single-turn loop, it also applies to a closed single conductor circuit of any number of turns or loops, the boundary of the surface s coinciding with the conductor. In this case $\psi_m = \Lambda$. Thus, referring to Fig. 7-3b, the surface integral of **B** over the surface bounded by the circuit yields the total flux linkages Λ, no consideration of the number of turns being necessary.

ever, in cases where the motion of the boundary of the surface of integration is not identical with the motion of all parts of the physical circuit (see Example 4, Sec. 7-6) Eq. (7-10) may not yield the correct induced emf. For such cases, one should use the general relation of (7-18) for the induced emf.

When the loop or closed circuit is stationary or fixed, (7-10) reduces to

$$\mathcal{V} = -\int_s \frac{\partial \mathbf{B}}{\partial t} \cdot d\mathbf{s} \qquad (7\text{-}11)$$

This form of Faraday's law gives the induced emf due specifically to a time rate of change of $\mathbf{B}$ for a loop or circuit that is fixed with respect to the observer. This is sometimes called the *transformer induction* equation.

7-3. Maxwell's Equation from Faraday's Law. Integral Form.
From (7-1) and (7-11) we have

$$\mathcal{V} = \oint \mathbf{E} \cdot d\mathbf{l} = -\int_s \frac{\partial \mathbf{B}}{\partial t} \cdot d\mathbf{s} \qquad (7\text{-}12)$$

where $\mathcal{V}$ = induced emf (volts)
$\mathbf{E} = \mathbf{E}_e$ = emf-producing electric field[1] (volts/meter)
$d\mathbf{l}$ = element of path (meters)
$\mathbf{B}$ = flux density (webers/meter^2)
$d\mathbf{s}$ = element of area (meters^2)
t = time (sec)

This relation is referred to as *Maxwell's equation as derived from Faraday's law*. It appears in (7-12) in its integral form. The corresponding differential relation is given in Sec. 7-9.

According to (7-12) the line integral of the electric field around a fixed closed loop or circuit is equal to the normal component of the time rate of decrease of the flux density $\mathbf{B}$ integrated over a surface bounded by the circuit. Both are also equal to the total emf $\mathcal{V}$ induced in the circuit.

7-4. Moving Conductor in a Magnetic Field.
In the preceding sections the emf induced by a change in flux linkage is discussed. In some situations it is convenient or desirable to consider specifically the emf induced in a conductor moving in a magnetic field.

From (6-17) the force $\mathbf{F}$ on a particle of electric charge e moving with a velocity $\mathbf{v}$ in a magnetic field of flux density $\mathbf{B}$ is

$$\mathbf{F} = e\mathbf{v} \times \mathbf{B} \qquad \text{newtons} \qquad (7\text{-}13)$$

---

[1] To simplify the notation, the symbol $\mathbf{E}_e$ will be used only where it is desirable to indicate explicitly that the field is an emf-producing type. Since in (7-12) the integral of the electric field is an emf $\mathcal{V}$, it is obvious that $\mathbf{E}$ is emf-producing and to be explicit could be written $\mathbf{E}_e$.

Suppose that the charged particle is situated in a wire moving with a velocity **v** through a magnetic field of flux density **B** as suggested in Fig. 7-4. Dividing (7-13) by e, we obtain the force per charge or electric field intensity $\mathbf{E}_e$, or

$$\mathbf{E}_e = \frac{\mathbf{F}}{e} = \mathbf{v} \times \mathbf{B} \qquad \text{volts/meter} \qquad (7\text{-}14)$$

The magnitude of $\mathbf{E}_e$ is given by

$$E_e = vB \sin \theta \qquad (7\text{-}15)$$

where θ = angle between **v** and **B** (Fig. 7-5). The electric field $\mathbf{E}_e$ is of the emf-producing type and is normal to the plane containing **v** and **B**.

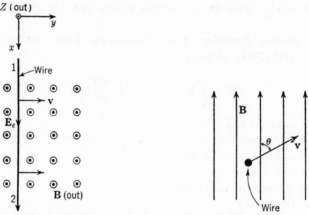

Fig. 7-4. An emf is induced in a wire moving across a magnetic field.

Fig. 7-5. Relation between direction of motion of wire and direction of **B**.

For example, in Fig. 7-4, **v** is in the positive y direction, and **B** is in the positive z direction. Hence, crossing **v** into **B** yields $\mathbf{E}_e$ in the positive x direction or along the wire. The emf $\mathcal{V}$ induced between two points 1 and 2 on the wire (Fig. 7-4) is then

$$\mathcal{V} = \int_1^2 \mathbf{E} \cdot d\mathbf{l} = \int (\mathbf{v} \times \mathbf{B}) \cdot d\mathbf{l} \qquad \text{volts} \qquad (7\text{-}16a)$$

where $\mathcal{V}$ = emf induced over a length l of wire (volts)
$\mathbf{E} = \mathbf{E}_e$ = electric field along wire (volts/meter)
$d\mathbf{l}$ = element of length of wire (meters)
$\mathbf{v}$ = velocity of wire (meters/sec)
$\mathbf{B}$ = flux density of magnetic field (webers/meter^2)

For a straight wire where **v**, **B**, and the wire are mutually perpendicular, **B** is uniform, and **v** is the same for all parts of the wire; (7-16a) reduces to

$$\mathcal{V} = El = vBl \qquad \text{volts} \qquad (7\text{-}16b)$$

where l = length of wire (meters).

Equations (7-16a) and 7-16b) are *motional induction or flux-cutting laws* giving the emf induced in a conductor moving with respect to the observer in a magnetic field.   Equation (7-16a) is the more general form, while (7-16b) applies to the special case where the directions of the wire, its motion, and the magnetic field are all mutually perpendicular.   It is also assumed in (7-16b) that all parts of the wire have the same value of **v** and that **B** is uniform.

These relations may be used to find the emf induced in any part of a circuit due to its motion through a magnetic field.   They also can be applied to find the total emf induced in a closed circuit that is moved or deformed in a magnetic field that does not change with time.   For a closed circuit (7-16a) becomes

$$\mathcal{V} = \oint \mathbf{E} \cdot d\mathbf{l} = \oint (\mathbf{v} \times \mathbf{B}) \cdot d\mathbf{l} \tag{7-17}$$

where $\mathcal{V}$ = total emf induced in circuit.

7-5. General Case of Induction.   Equation (7-12) gives the emf induced in a closed circuit due to the time rate of change of **B** (transformer induction).   Equation (7-17) gives the emf induced in a closed circuit due to its motion.   When both kinds of changes are occurring simultaneously, that is, when **B** changes with time and the circuit is also in motion, the total emf induced is equal to the sum of the emfs given by (7-12) and (7-17), or

$$\mathcal{V} = \oint (\mathbf{v} \times \mathbf{B}) \cdot d\mathbf{l} - \int_s \frac{\partial \mathbf{B}}{\partial t} \cdot d\mathbf{s} \tag{7-18}$$

The first term of the right-hand member gives the emf induced by the motion, while the second term gives the emf induced by the time change in **B**.   The line integral in the first term is taken around the entire circuit, while the surface integral in the second term is taken over the entire surface bounded by the circuit.

Equation (7-18) is a general relation and gives the correct value of total induced emf in all cases.   For the special case of motion only, $\partial B/\partial t = 0$, and (7-18) reduces to

$$\mathcal{V} = \oint (\mathbf{v} \times \mathbf{B}) \cdot d\mathbf{l} \tag{7-19}$$

For the special case of time change of flux density only, $\mathbf{v} = 0$, and (7-18) reduces to

$$\mathcal{V} = - \int_s \frac{\partial \mathbf{B}}{\partial t} \cdot d\mathbf{s} \tag{7-20}$$

In many situations the total emf induced in a closed circuit is given correctly by the flux-linking relation of (7-10).   This relation states that

$$\mathcal{V} = - \frac{d}{dt} \int_s \mathbf{B} \cdot d\mathbf{s} \tag{7-21}$$

Although (7-21) may be derived formally from (7-18), the explicit form of (7-21) is inadequate (without the introduction of relativity considerations) to problems of motion where the motion of all parts of the physical circuit is not the same as the motion of the boundary of the surface of integration in (7-21).

In the next section a number of examples are worked out to illustrate the applicability of the above four induction relations to various situations. To summarize, the four induction relations are

(I) $\mathcal{U} = \oint (\mathbf{v} \times \mathbf{B}) \cdot d\mathbf{l} - \int_s \dfrac{\partial \mathbf{B}}{\partial t} \cdot d\mathbf{s}$ general case

(II) $\mathcal{U} = \oint (\mathbf{v} \times \mathbf{B}) \cdot d\mathbf{l}$ motion only (motional induction)

(III) $\mathcal{U} = -\int_s \dfrac{\partial \mathbf{B}}{\partial t} \cdot d\mathbf{s}$ B change only (transformer induction)

(IV) $\mathcal{U} = -\dfrac{d}{dt} \int_s \mathbf{B} \cdot d\mathbf{s}$ flux linkage

7-6. Examples of Induction. In this section seven examples are given in which the total emf induced in a closed circuit (total induction) is calculated by each of the four induction relations listed at the end of the preceding section. The general relation (I) gives the correct result in all cases. The other relations lead to the correct result in some cases but not in all cases, and the reasons for this are discussed.

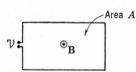

Fig. 7-6. Fixed loop of area A (for Example 1).

Example 1. Consider the fixed rectangular loop of area A shown in Fig. 7-6. The flux density $\mathbf{B}$ is normal to the plane of the loop (outward in Fig. 7-6) and is uniform over the area of the loop. However, the magnitude of $\mathbf{B}$ varies harmonically with respect to time as given by

$$B = B_0 \cos \omega t \tag{7-21a}$$

where B_0 = maximum amplitude of B (webers/meter²)
      ω = radian frequency ($= 2\pi f$, where f = frequency) (reciprocal seconds)
      t = time (sec)
Find the total emf induced in the loop.

Solution. This is a pure case of B change only, there being no motion. Hence, from (III) the total emf induced in the loop is

$$\mathcal{U} = -\int_s \dfrac{\partial \mathbf{B}}{\partial t} \cdot d\mathbf{s} = A\omega B_0 \sin \omega t \qquad \text{volts} \tag{7-22}$$

This emf appears at the terminals of the loop (Fig. 7-6). Since the velocity $\mathbf{v} = 0$, the emf calculated by (II) is zero and by (I) is identical with that in (7-22). The emf calculated by (IV) is also the same as given in (7-22).

Example 2. Consider the rectangular loop shown in Fig. 7-7. The width l of the loop is constant, but its length x is increased uniformly with time by moving the sliding conductor at a uniform velocity **v**. The flux density **B** is everywhere the same (normal to the plane of the loop) and is constant with respect to time. Find the total emf induced in the loop.

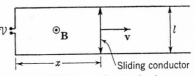

Solution. This is a pure case of motion only, the flux density **B** being constant. Hence, from (II),

$$\mathcal{U} = \oint (\mathbf{v} \times \mathbf{B}) \cdot d\mathbf{l} = vBl \qquad \text{volts} \qquad (7\text{-}23)$$

Fig. 7-7. Sliding conductor for increasing loop area (for Examples 2 and 3).

The entire emf in this case is induced in the moving conductor of length l. Since $\partial B/\partial t = 0$, the emf by (III) is zero and by (I) is identical with (7-23). The emf as calculated by (IV) is

$$\mathcal{U} = -\frac{d}{dt} \int_s \mathbf{B} \cdot d\mathbf{s} = -Bl \frac{dx}{dt} = -Blv \qquad \text{volts} \qquad (7\text{-}24)$$

This is the same as given by (7-23) except for the sign, which is arbitrary.

Example 3. Consider again the same loop with sliding conductor discussed in the preceding example (Fig. 7-7). The flux density **B** is normal to the plane of the loop and is uniform everywhere. The sliding conductor moves with a uniform velocity **v**. These conditions are the same as in the preceding example. However, in this case let the magnitude of the flux density **B** vary harmonically with time as given by

$$B = B_0 \cos \omega t \qquad (7\text{-}25a)$$

Find the total emf induced in the loop.

Solution. This is a case involving both motion and a time-changing **B**. The emf $\mathcal{U}_m$ due to the motion is given, from (II), by

$$\mathcal{U}_m = \oint (\mathbf{v} \times \mathbf{B}) \cdot d\mathbf{l} = vBl = vlB_0 \cos \omega t \qquad (7\text{-}25b)$$

The emf $\mathcal{U}_t$ due to a time-changing **B** is, from (III),

$$\mathcal{U}_t = -\int_s \frac{\partial \mathbf{B}}{\partial t} \cdot d\mathbf{s} = \omega x l B_0 \sin \omega t \qquad (7\text{-}26)$$

According to (I) the total emf $\mathcal{U}$ is the sum of the emfs of (7-25b) and (7-26), or

$$\begin{aligned}
\mathcal{U} &= \oint (\mathbf{v} \times \mathbf{B}) \cdot d\mathbf{l} - \int \frac{\partial \mathbf{B}}{\partial t} \cdot d\mathbf{s} \\
&= vB_0 l \cos \omega t + \omega x B_0 l \sin \omega t \\
&= B_0 l \sqrt{v^2 + (\omega x)^2} \sin (\omega t + \delta) \qquad (7\text{-}27)
\end{aligned}$$

where $\delta = \arctan (v/\omega x)$

x = instantaneous length of loop

The emf from (IV) is the same as given in (7-27) except that $\delta = \arctan (-v/\omega x)$.

Example 4. The circuit for a rectangular loop of width l and length x_1 is completed by sliding contacts through a thin conducting strip as suggested in Fig. 7-8. The loop is stationary, but the strip moves longitudinally with a uniform velocity **v**. The magnetic flux density **B** is normal to the strip and the plane of the loop. It is constant with respect to time and is uniform everywhere. The width of the strip is l, the same as for the loop, although for clarity the loop is shown with a slightly greater width in Fig. 7-8. Find the total emf induced in the circuit.

Solution. This is another case of motion only. Therefore from (II) the total emf is given by

$$\mho = \oint (\mathbf{v} \times \mathbf{B}) \cdot d\mathbf{l} = vBl \tag{7-28}$$

The entire emf in this case is induced in the moving strip and appears at the terminals. Since $\partial B/\partial t = 0$, the emf by (III) is zero and by (I) is identical with (7-28).

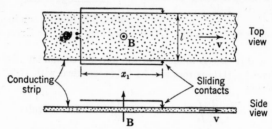

Fig. 7-8. Fixed loop with sliding strip (for Examples 4 and 5).

The emf according to (IV) is zero. This is a situation involving motion where the boundary of the surface of integration is stationary although there is physical motion, and hence (IV) is not applicable. A variation of the arrangement of Example 4 is provided by the Faraday disc generator (see Prob. 7-14).

Example 5. Consider now the same loop and strip as in the preceding example (Fig. 7-8), but let the magnitude of the flux density vary harmonically with time as given by

$$B = B_0 \cos \omega t \tag{7-29}$$

Find the total emf induced in the circuit.

Solution. This case involves both motion and a time-changing **B**. From (II) the emf $\mho_m$ due to the motion is

$$\mho_m = \oint (\mathbf{v} \times \mathbf{B}) \cdot d\mathbf{l} = vBl = vB_0 l \cos \omega t \tag{7-30}$$

From (III) the emf $\mho_t$ due to a time-changing **B** is[1]

$$\mho_t = -\int_s \frac{\partial \mathbf{B}}{\partial t} \cdot d\mathbf{s} = \omega x_1 B_0 l \sin \omega t \tag{7-31}$$

According to (I) the total emf $\mho$ is the sum of (7-30) and (7-31), or

$$\mho = \mho_m + \mho_t = vB_0 l \cos \omega t + \omega x_1 B_0 l \sin \omega t$$
$$= B_0 l \sqrt{v^2 + (\omega x_1)^2} \sin (\omega t + \delta) \tag{7-32}$$

where $\delta = \arctan (v/\omega x_1)$.

For the same reason as in Example 4 relation (IV) is not applicable in this case, an emf being obtained that is the same as given in (7-31).

Example 6. Consider next a rotating rectangular loop in a steady magnetic field as in Fig. 7-9a. The loop rotates with a uniform angular velocity ω in radians per second. This arrangement represents a simple *a-c generator*, the induced emf appear-

[1] At low frequencies the effect of eddy currents in the strip can be neglected. The effect of eddy currents will be even less if the strip is very thin and its conductivity poor.

ing at terminals connected to the slip rings.   If the radius of the loop is R and its
length l, find the total emf induced.

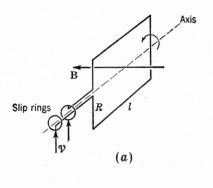

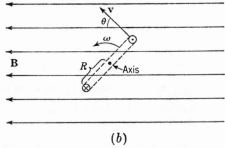

FIG. 7-9. Alternating-current generator. (a) Perspective view. (b) Cross section
perpendicular to axis.

Solution.   This is a case of motion only so that the total emf may be obtained from
(II).   Referring to Fig. 7-9b, it is given by

$$\mathcal{U} = \oint (\mathbf{v} \times \mathbf{B}) \cdot d\mathbf{l} = 2vBl \sin \theta \tag{7-33}$$

Since $\theta = \omega t$, we have

$$\mathcal{U} = 2\omega RlB \sin \omega t \tag{7-34}$$

The factor 2 is necessary because there are two conductors of length l moving through
the field, the emfs in both aiding.   Since $2Rl = A$, the area of the loop, (7-34) reduces
to

$$\mathcal{U} = \omega BA \sin \omega t \tag{7-35}$$

Since $\partial B/\partial t = 0$, the emf calculated by (III) is zero.   Hence from (I) the emf is as
given by (7-34) or (7-35).   In this case the motion of the surface of integration of (IV)
coincides with the physical motion of the loop so that (IV) also gives the same emf as
in (7-34).   Thus, from (IV),

$$\mathcal{U} = -\frac{d}{dt} \int \mathbf{B} \cdot d\mathbf{s} = -2RlB \frac{d}{dt} \cos \theta \tag{7-36}$$

$$= 2\omega RlB \sin \omega t$$

Example 7. Consider finally the same rotating loop as in the preceding example with the modification that B varies harmonically with time as given by

$$B = B_0 \sin \omega t \tag{7-37}$$

Thus, when $t = 0$, $B = 0$, and $\theta = 0$ (Fig. 7-9b). Find the total emf induced.

Solution. This case involves both motion and a time-changing B. From (II) the emf $\mathcal{U}_m$ due to the motion is

$$
\begin{aligned}
\mathcal{U}_m &= 2\omega R l B_0 \sin^2 \omega t \\
&= \omega R l B_0 - \omega R l B_0 \cos 2\omega t
\end{aligned}
\tag{7-38}
$$

From (III) the $\mathcal{U}_t$ due to a time-changing B is

$$
\begin{aligned}
\mathcal{U}_t &= -2\omega R l B_0 \cos^2 \omega t \\
&= -\omega R l B_0 - \omega R l B_0 \cos 2\omega t
\end{aligned}
\tag{7-39}
$$

From (I) the total emf $\mathcal{U}$ is given by the sum of (7-38) and (7-39), or

$$\mathcal{U} = \mathcal{U}_m + \mathcal{U}_t = -2\omega R l B_0 \cos 2\omega t \tag{7-40}$$

The total emf may also be obtained from (IV). Thus

$$
\begin{aligned}
\mathcal{U} &= -\frac{d}{dt} \int_s \mathbf{B} \cdot d\mathbf{s} = -2R l B_0 \frac{d}{dt} (\sin \omega t \cos \omega t) \\
&= -2\omega R l B_0 (\cos^2 \omega t - \sin^2 \omega t) \\
&= -2\omega R l B_0 \cos 2\omega t
\end{aligned}
\tag{7-41}
$$

The emf in this example is at twice the rotation, or magnetic field, frequency. It is to be noted that the emf calculated from either (II) or (III) alone contains a d-c component. In adding the emfs by (II) and (III) the d-c component cancels, yielding the correct total emf given by (7-40).

In the above examples we note that the general relation (I) always yields the correct total emf. The flux-linking relation (IV) gave the correct total emf in all cases except Examples 4 and 5. It is also to be noted that if the emf calculated from (II) is zero, the emf from (III) equals the total emf, or, conversely, if the emf from (III) is zero, the total emf is given by (II).

7-7. The Betatron. We have seen that a time-changing magnetic field produces an electric field. When a loop of wire is placed in the changing magnetic field, an emf is induced in the loop that is equal to the line integral of the electric field around the loop. Thus, according to (7-12),

$$\mathcal{U} = \oint \mathbf{E} \cdot d\mathbf{l} = -\int_s \frac{\partial \mathbf{B}}{\partial t} \cdot d\mathbf{s} \tag{7-42}$$

With the loop open this emf appears at the loop terminals.

It is highly significant to note that the induced electric field $\mathbf{E}$ exists

whether the wire loop is present or not.   This fact is well illustrated[1] by
an electron-accelerating device called a *betatron*.[2]

In a betatron electrons are accelerated by an electric field induced by a
time-changing magnetic field.   The magnetic field is produced by an

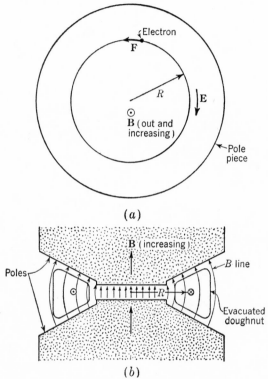

Fig. 7-10. Betatron. (*a*) Circular electron orbit. (*b*) Cross section through
betatron.

a-c electromagnet with laminated iron core.   Electrons are injected
between the pole pieces of the magnet and are accelerated during a fraction of one a-c period.

Let a magnetic field of flux density **B** be directed out of the page from a
pole piece as suggested in Fig. 7-10*a*.   The time-changing **B** induces an

---

[1] The fact that an electric field is produced in empty space by a changing magnetic
field is also illustrated by a traveling electromagnetic wave, which may be said to
propagate through space because an electric field is produced by a changing magnetic
field, with this electric field, in turn, producing another magnetic field, etc. See
Chap. 9.

[2] The betatron was developed by Donald W. Kerst about 1940, a device of this type
having been proposed earlier by Max Steenback.

electric field **E**. According to (6-1) an electron in this field experiences a force

$$F = e\mathbf{E} \qquad \text{newtons} \tag{7-43}$$

where **E** = electric field (volts/meter)

    e = charge on electron (coulombs)

Since the electron is in a magnetic field, it tends to move in a circle. Thus, if **B** in Fig. 7-10a is outward as shown and is increasing with time, the electron will rotate counterclockwise.

The energy per unit charge acquired by an electron in traveling once around a circular orbit of fixed radius R is equal to the total induced emf around the path, which, from (7-42), is

$$\mathcal{V} = 2\pi R E = -\frac{d\psi_m}{dt} \qquad \text{volts} \tag{7-44}$$

where ψ_m = total magnetic flux through the electron orbit (inside radius R). Disregarding the sign, the magnitude of the electric field is

$$E = \frac{1}{2\pi R}\frac{d\psi_m}{dt} \tag{7-45}$$

Substituting (7-45) for E in (7-43) yields a force of magnitude

$$F = eE = \frac{e}{2\pi R}\frac{d\psi_m}{dt} \tag{7-46}$$

By Newton's second law[1]

$$F = \frac{d(mv)}{dt} \tag{7-47}$$

Equating (7-46) and (7-47),

$$\frac{d(mv)}{dt} = \frac{e}{2\pi R}\frac{d\psi_m}{dt} \tag{7-48}$$

Referring to Fig. 7-11, suppose that the total flux ψ_m through the electron orbit varies harmonically as given by

$$\psi_m = \psi_{mo} \sin \omega t \tag{7-49}$$

where ψ_{mo} = maximum magnetic flux (webers)

    $\omega = 2\pi f = 2\pi/T$ = radian frequency (reciprocal seconds)

    f = frequency

    T = period

---

[1] This form of Newton's second law is used since sufficiently large electron velocities may be involved in the betatron that the mass m of the electron may become significantly greater than its rest mass [see (6-12)]. If m is a constant, (7-47) reduces to $F = m\,dv/dt = ma$.

Electrons from a hot cathode may be injected into the betatron at a radius R at a time $t = 0$ when the flux ψ_m is zero, as indicated in Fig. 7-11. Then, if an electron is removed at some later time t less than one-quarter period $(T/4)$, its momentum is, by integration of (7-48),

$$mv = \frac{e\psi_m}{2\pi R} \qquad \text{newton-sec} \qquad (7\text{-}50)$$

where ψ_m = total magnetic flux at time t through the electron orbit. Neglecting the initial momentum of the electron, (7-50) gives the

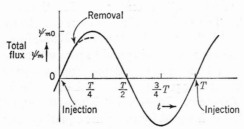

FIG. 7-11. Flux variation as a function of time in a betatron, showing times of injection and removal of electrons.

momentum mv of the electron at some time t after injection which occurs at $t = 0$ (see Fig. 7-11). The velocity of the electron is

$$v = \frac{e\psi_m}{2\pi Rm} \qquad \text{meters/sec} \qquad (7\text{-}51)$$

According to (6-40) the radius R of the electron is given by

$$R = \frac{mv}{eB} \qquad\qquad (7\text{-}52)$$

where m = mass of electron (kg)
 v = velocity of electron (meters/sec)
 e = charge of electron (coulombs)
 B = flux density at radius R (webers/meter^2)
From (7-50) and (7-52) we obtain

$$B = \frac{\psi_m}{2\pi R^2} = \frac{1}{2}\frac{\psi_m}{A} = \frac{1}{2} B_{av} \qquad (7\text{-}53)$$

where A = area of electron orbit
 B_{av} = average flux density inside electron orbit
Both B and B_{av} are instantaneous values. Hence, according to (7-53) the instantaneous flux density B at the electron orbit (radius R) must be one-half the average flux density inside the orbit at the same instant. When this condition is fulfilled, the radius R remains constant as the electrons are accelerated. To obtain the 2 to 1 ratio of B_{av} to B, the

poles of the magnet can be tapered as indicated in the cross-sectional view in Fig. 7-10b. This cross section also shows the hollow, ring-shaped glass enclosure, or "doughnut," which is pumped out to provide an evacuated space for the electron orbit.

To utilize the accelerated electrons, they may be made to impinge on a target and produce X rays. The target is placed near the orbit radius R, and a radial displacement of the orbit is caused by upsetting the 2 to 1 relation of B_{av} to B. This may be accomplished by having saturation of the poles occur sooner at one radius than at another. For example, if saturation occurs earliest at the center of poles, the electron beam tends to spiral inward. The radial displacement of the electrons so that they impinge on a target is designated as the *removal time* in Fig. 7-11. Owing to resistance of the magnet winding and to core saturation the total magnetic flux in an actual betatron may depart from a sinusoidal variation at large values of flux as suggested by the dashed line in Fig. 7-11.

7-8. Stokes' Theorem. In Sec. 7-3 Maxwell's equation from Faraday's law is stated in integral form. This equation may be transformed

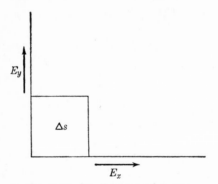

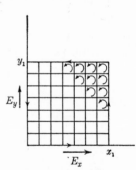

FIG. 7-12. Small rectangular area.   FIG. 7-13. Illustration for Stokes' theorem.

from an integral to a differential form by means of Stokes' theorem. This theorem is developed in this section and applied to Maxwell's equation in Sec. 7-9.

Consider a square of area Δs in the x-y plane as in Fig. 7-12. Let the electric field **E** have components E_x and E_y as shown. Now the work per coulomb required to move a charge around the perimeter of the square is given by the line integral of **E** around the perimeter. This work equals the total emf around the perimeter. That is,

$$\upsilon = \oint \mathbf{E} \cdot d\mathbf{l} \qquad (7\text{-}54)$$

Dividing by the area Δs and taking the limit of this ratio as Δs approaches zero yields the curl of **E** normal to Δs at the point around which Δs

shrinks to zero (see Sec. 4-23).   Thus

$$\lim_{\Delta s \to 0} \frac{\oint \mathbf{E} \cdot d\mathbf{l}}{\Delta s} = \mathrm{curl}_n \mathbf{E} \qquad (7\text{-}55)$$

where curl $_n$ $\mathbf{E}$ = component of the curl of $\mathbf{E}$ normal to the area Δs.

Consider now a surface of area $x_1 y_1$ as shown in Fig. 7-13. Let the area be divided into infinitesimal areas as suggested. From (7-55) the work per coulomb to carry a charge around an infinitesimal loop divided by its area is equal to the curl of $\mathbf{E}$ at the point. If the curl of $\mathbf{E}$ is integrated over the entire area $x_1 y_1$, all contributions to the total work cancel except for the work along the periphery of the area $x_1 y_1$.

The situation here is analogous to that of a single current loop with current I, Fig. 7-14a, whose effect is the same as a mesh of current loops,

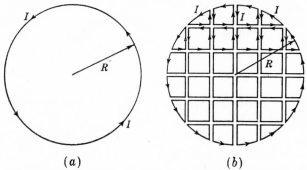

$$(a) \qquad\qquad\qquad (b)$$

Fig. 7-14. (a) Single current loop and (b) equivalent mesh of small current loops.

each with a current I, as suggested in Fig. 7-14b. It is assumed that the adjacent sides of the small loops are very close together. Since the currents in adjacent sides are oppositely directed, their fields cancel. The only currents whose effects are not canceled are those along the periphery of the area of radius R.

Returning now to the area $x_1 y_1$ in Fig. 7-13, the integral of the normal component of the curl over the area $x_1 y_1$ must equal the line integral of $\mathbf{E}$ around the periphery of the area. That is,

$$\oint \mathbf{E} \cdot d\mathbf{l} = \int_s (\mathrm{curl}\ \mathbf{E}) \cdot d\mathbf{s} \qquad (7\text{-}56)$$

Dimensionally (7-56) is of the form

$$\frac{\text{Force}}{\text{Charge}} \times \text{distance} = \frac{\text{work/charge}}{\text{area}} \times \text{area}$$

Since force $\times$ distance = work, (7-56) is balanced dimensionally. In (7-56) it is understood that if the curl of $\mathbf{E}$ is integrated over an area s, the line integral of $\mathbf{E}$ is taken around the periphery of the same area s.

That is,

$$\oint_{\substack{\text{Periphery} \\ \text{of } s}} \mathbf{E} \cdot d\mathbf{l} = \int_{\substack{\text{surface} \\ \text{of } s}} (\text{curl } \mathbf{E}) \cdot d\mathbf{s} \tag{7-57}$$

Using the notation $\nabla \times \mathbf{E}$ for the curl of $\mathbf{E}$, (7-56) becomes

$$\oint \mathbf{E} \cdot d\mathbf{l} = \int_s (\nabla \times \mathbf{E}) \cdot d\mathbf{s} \tag{7-58}$$

The relation expressed by (7-56) or (7-58) is called *Stokes' theorem* as applied to electric fields. In general, Stokes' theorem states that *the line integral of a vector function around a closed contour C is equal to the integral of the normal component of the curl of that vector function over any surface having the contour C as its bounding edge.*

7-9. Maxwell's Equation from Faraday's Law. Differential Form.
By means of Stokes' theorem (7-58), let us substitute the surface integral of the curl of $\mathbf{E}$ for the line integral of $\mathbf{E}$ in (7-12). That is,

$$\iint (\nabla \times \mathbf{E}) \cdot d\mathbf{s} = -\iint \frac{\partial \mathbf{B}}{\partial t} \cdot d\mathbf{s} \tag{7-59}$$

Since $d\mathbf{s}$ in (7-59) applies to any surface element, it is arbitrary and therefore the integrands in (7-59) are equal. Thus

$$\nabla \times \mathbf{E} = -\frac{\partial \mathbf{B}}{\partial t} \tag{7-60}$$

This is Maxwell's equation, in differential form, as derived from Faraday's law. The integral form of the equation was given in (7-12).

In words, (7-60) indicates that if $\mathbf{B}$ is changing with time at some point P, then the curl of $\mathbf{E}$ has a value different from zero at that point.

7-10. The Series Circuit.[1] Inductance Only. According to Faraday's law a change in the total flux through a coil induces an emf in the coil. Consider now that instead of an emf being induced in the coil it is situated in a field-free region and that an emf $\mathcal{V}_a$ is *applied* to the terminals of the coil. This emf causes a current I to flow, which in turn produces a counter emf $\mathcal{V}$. By Kirchhoff's voltage law the sum of the emfs around a circuit equals the total IR drop. Assuming that the resistance of the coil is zero, it follows that

$$\mathcal{V}_a + \mathcal{V} = 0 \tag{7-61}$$

From (7-7)

$$\mathcal{V} = -\frac{d\Lambda}{dt} \tag{7-62}$$

---

[1] The circuits considered in this chapter are small compared with the wavelength (see Chap. 13).

where Λ = total flux linkages of coil. According to (4-58), $\Lambda = LI$; so

$$\mathcal{V} = -\frac{d(LI)}{dt} = -L\frac{dI}{dt} \quad \text{volts} \qquad (7\text{-}63)$$

where L = inductance of coil (henrys)
     I = current through coil (amp)
It is assumed that no ferromagnetic material is present so that the inductance L is constant. From (7-61) and (7-63) we have

$$\mathcal{V}_a = L\frac{dI}{dt} \qquad (7\text{-}64)$$

or

$$\frac{dI}{dt} = \frac{\mathcal{V}_a}{L} \qquad (7\text{-}65)$$

According to (7-65) the time rate of change of the current is equal to the ratio of the applied emf to the inductance.

Example. Consider the hypothetical circuit of Fig. 7-15a containing a coil of inductance L. The emf $\mathcal{V}_a$ of a battery is applied by closing the switch S. The coil and battery are assumed to have zero resistance. It is further assumed that ferro-

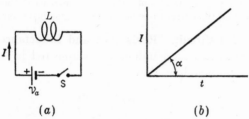

(a)   (b)

Fig. 7-15. Circuit with inductance.

magnetic materials are absent so that L is a constant. Let the switch S be closed at the time $t = 0$. Find how I varies with time.

Solution. The current at any later time t is obtained by integrating (7-65). That is,

$$I = \frac{\mathcal{V}_a}{L}t \qquad (7\text{-}66)$$

The current increases linearly with time, as indicated in Fig. 7-15b. The slope of the line is equal to $\mathcal{V}_a/L$. Thus the angle

$$\alpha = \arctan\frac{\mathcal{V}_a}{L} \qquad (7\text{-}67)$$

As time increases, the current I increases indefinitely at a constant rate.

7-11. The Series Circuit. Resistance Only. Consider a circuit containing a resistor only. By Kirchhoff's voltage law an emf $\mathcal{V}_a$ applied to the resistor is equal to the IR drop across the resistor Thus

$$\mathcal{V}_a = IR \qquad (7\text{-}68)$$

If $\mathcal{V}_a$ and R are constant, the current I is constant.

Example. The hypothetical circuit of Fig. 7-16a has a resistor of resistance R.† Let the switch S be closed at time $t = 0$, applying the emf $\mathcal{V}_a$ to the circuit. Find how I varies with time.

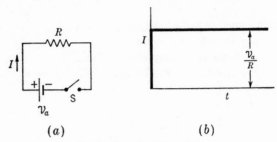

(a) (b)

Fig. 7-16. Circuit with resistance.

Solution. From (7-68)

$$I = \frac{\mathcal{V}_a}{R} \quad \text{amp} \tag{7-69}$$

That is, the current jumps instantaneously to a value $\mathcal{V}_a/R$ when the switch is closed. The current vs. time relation is indicated graphically in Fig. 7-16b. In this hypothetical circuit containing resistance only, the rate of increase of the current is infinite when $\mathcal{V}_a$ is applied and the current reaches its final value instantaneously.

7-12. The Series Circuit. Resistance and Inductance. If a circuit contains both resistance and inductance connected in series, we have, from Kirchhoff's voltage law, that

$$\mathcal{V}_a = RI + L\frac{dI}{dt} \tag{7-70}$$

where $\mathcal{V}_a$ = total applied emf (volts)
$\quad R$ = total resistance (ohms)
$\quad L$ = total inductance (henrys)
$\quad I$ = current (amp)
$\quad t$ = time (sec)

Example. Consider the series circuit containing both resistance and inductance shown in Fig. 7-17a. For convenience it is assumed that all of the resistance of the circuit is lumped in a single resistor of resistance R and that all of the inductance of the circuit is lumped in a coil of inductance L. If the switch S is closed at the time $t = 0$, applying the emf $\mathcal{V}_a$ to the circuit, find how I varies with time. In particular find the value of the current at a time $t = L/R$.

Solution. Equation (7-70) may be reexpressed as

$$\frac{dI}{dt} + \frac{R}{L}I = \frac{\mathcal{V}_a}{L} \tag{7-71}$$

† This circuit and the one in Fig. 7-15a are "hypothetical" in the sense that actual circuits are not purely resistive or inductive. Thus a coil will have some resistance, and a resistor will have some inductance.

which may be recognized as a first-order differential equation. The solution of this equation for the current I at any time t is

$$I = \frac{\mathcal{V}_a}{R} (1 - e^{-(R/L)t}) \qquad (7\text{-}72)$$

where e = base of natural logarithms ($= 2.718$). When $t = 0$, the current $I = 0$ the same as for a purely inductive circuit. As time increases, the current starts to increase at the same rate as for the pure inductance. However, this rate of increase (slope of current-time curve) approaches zero as the time increases. After a long time the current approaches a constant value of $\mathcal{V}_a/R$. This is the same value of current as would be obtained in a circuit containing only a pure resistance R. The variation of I with time is illustrated graphically by Fig. 7-17b.

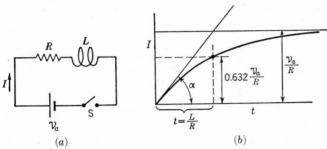

Fig. 7-17a and b. Circuit with inductance and resistance.

To demonstrate that when the switch is closed the current starts to increase at the same rate as for a pure inductance circuit, the slope of the curve may be obtained by differentiating (7-72) with respect to time. Thus, the slope at any time t is

$$\frac{dI}{dt} = \frac{\mathcal{V}_a}{L} e^{-(R/L)t} \qquad (7\text{-}73)$$

and at time $t = 0$ the slope is

$$\frac{dI}{dt} = \frac{\mathcal{V}_a}{L} \qquad (7\text{-}74)$$

which is the same as (7-65) for the pure inductance case.

Focusing attention on the term

$$e^{-(R/L)t}$$

in (7-72), its value at $t = 0$ is unity. Thus, when $t = 0$,

$$e^{-(R/L)t} = 1$$

Now when the time $t = L/R$,

$$e^{-\frac{R}{L}t} = e^{-\frac{R}{L}\frac{L}{R}} = e^{-1} = \frac{1}{e} = 0.368 \qquad (7\text{-}75)$$

Thus, when $t = L/R$, the value of the term has decreased to $1/e$ (or 36.8 per cent) of its original value. The current I in the circuit has accordingly risen to

$$100 - 36.8 = 63.2 \text{ per cent}$$

of its final value (Fig. 7-17b). Therefore, the ratio L/R determines the length of time for the current to reach 63.2 per cent of its final value. The ratio L/R is called the *time constant* of the circuit and is a convenient quantity for comparing such circuits. In mksc units the dimensional relation for the time constant L/R is

$$\frac{\text{Henrys}}{\text{Ohms}} = \text{seconds}$$

7-13. The Series Circuit. Resistance, Inductance, and Capacitance. If an emf $\mathcal{V}_a$ is applied to a capacitor of capacitance C,

$$\mathcal{V}_a = \frac{Q}{C} \tag{7-76}$$

where Q = charge on capacitor plates. For an infinitesimal change in emf $d\mathcal{V}_a$ we have an infinitesimal change in charge dQ, or

$$d\mathcal{V}_a = \frac{1}{C} dQ \tag{7-77}$$

From the continuity relation (3-61) between charge and current, (7-77) becomes

$$d\mathcal{V}_a = \frac{1}{C} I \, dt \tag{7-78}$$

where I = current to capacitor. If $\mathcal{V}_a = 0$ at $t = 0$, then at some later time t we have, on integrating (7-78), that

$$\mathcal{V}_a = \frac{1}{C} \int_0^t I \, dt \tag{7-79}$$

In a series circuit containing resistance, inductance, and capacitance it follows from Kirchhoff's voltage law and Eqs. (7-70) and (7-79) that the total applied emf is

$$\mathcal{V}_a = RI + L\frac{dI}{dt} + \frac{1}{C} \int_0^t I \, dt \qquad \text{volts} \tag{7-80}$$

where R = total resistance (ohms)
      L = total inductance (henrys)
      C = total capacitance (farads)
      I = current (amp)
      t = time (sec)

The emf $\mathcal{V}_a$ and the current I in (7-80) are instantaneous values. The solution for the current I at any time t is discussed in texts on circuit theory and will not be considered here.[1]

7-14. Energy in an Inductor. A circuit element possessing inductance stores energy in its magnetic field. This may be readily demonstrated experimentally by the circuit of Fig. 7-17c. A large inductance coil is

---

[1] See, for example, K. Y. Tang, "Alternating Current Circuits," International Textbook Co., 1940, p. 374.

connected in parallel with an incandescent lamp. With the switch S closed, current passes through both the coil and lamp. Suppose that under these conditions the lamp is dimly lighted. When the switch is opened, disconnecting the battery, the lamp, instead of going out, increases momentarily in brilliancy because the magnetic field of the coil induces a current through the circuit as the field around the coil collapses. To light the lamp requires energy, and it therefore follows that energy was stored in the magnetic field of the coil. Let us now calculate the value of this energy.

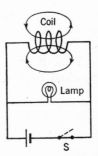

The instantaneous power P delivered to a circuit element is

$$P = VI$$

where V = voltage across the element

I = current through the element

The increase (or decrease) in the magnetic energy W_m in the element between time t_1 and time t_2 is the integral of the power P between these times. Thus

$$W_m = \int_{t_1}^{t_2} VI\, dt \qquad (7\text{-}80a)$$

Fig. 7-17c. Circuit for demonstrating energy storage in a magnetic field.

Suppose that the circuit element under consideration is a coil of inductance L. Now the voltage V across the coil is

$$V = L\frac{dI}{dt}$$

Substituting this value of V in (7-80a), changing limits, and integrating yields

$$W_m = \int_{I_1}^{I_2} LI\, dI = \tfrac{1}{2}L(I_2{}^2 - I_1{}^2) \qquad (7\text{-}80b)$$

It is assumed that L is constant. If $I_1 = 0$, (7-80b) reduces to

$$W_m = \tfrac{1}{2}LI_2{}^2 \qquad \text{joules}$$

where I_2 = final current (amp)

L = inductance (henrys)

Since $L = \Lambda/I$, this energy relation can be expressed variously as

$$W_m = \frac{1}{2}LI^2 = \frac{1}{2}\Lambda I = \frac{1}{2}\frac{\Lambda^2}{L} \qquad \text{joules} \qquad (7\text{-}80c)$$

Example. A coil has an inductance of 2 henrys. If the current through the coil is 1 amp, find the energy stored.

Solution. From (7-80c) the energy stored is

$$W_m = \tfrac{1}{2}LI^2 = 1 \text{ joule}$$

If L is not a constant as in an inductance coil with iron core, the energy must be obtained by integration of (7-80a), which may be reexpressed as

$$W_m = \int_{\Lambda_1}^{\Lambda_2} I \, d\Lambda \qquad \text{joules} \qquad (7\text{-}80d)$$

where W_m = increase (or decrease) of energy between the times t_1 and t_2 (joules)

Λ_1 = flux linkages at time t_1 (weber-turns)

Λ_2 = flux linkages at time t_2 (weber-turns)

I = current (amp)

7-15. Mutual- and Self-inductance. Consider that two uniform toroidal coils are interwound as in Fig. 7-18a. Coil 1 of N_1 turns is

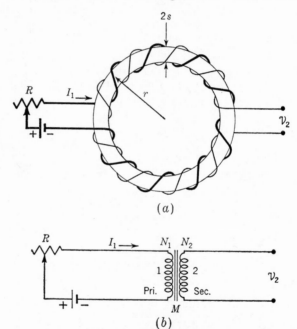

Fig. 7-18. Toroidal coil with 2 windings.

indicated by a heavy wire and coil 2 of N_2 turns by a fine wire. There is no electrical connection between the coils. The ring-shaped form on which the coils are wound is assumed to have a constant permeability μ. Coil 1 will be called the primary winding and coil 2 the secondary. A schematic diagram of the arrangement is shown in Fig. 7-18b.

If the primary current I_1 is constant in value, the emf $\mathcal{V}_2$ appearing at the terminals of the secondary coil is zero, since the flux ψ_{m1} produced by the primary coil is not changing. It is assumed that all of the magnetic field produced by I_1 is confined to the region inside the toroidal windings.

This may be realized with a uniform winding of sufficient turns. However, to simplify the drawing, only a few turns are shown in Fig. 7-18a although both windings are assumed to be uniform and consist of many turns.

Suppose now that the resistance R is decreased at a constant rate so that I_1 increases. This increases the magnetic flux ψ_{m1}. Disregarding the negative sign, we have from Faraday's law that the magnitude of the emf $\mathbb{U}_2$ induced in coil 2 and appearing at its terminals is

$$\mathbb{U}_2 = N_2 \frac{d\psi_{m1}}{dt} \tag{7-81}$$

where ψ_{m1} = magnetic flux produced by primary coil. If a long solenoid is closed on itself, we obtain a toroid. Assuming that the radius r of the toroid is large compared with the radius s of the winding (Fig. 7-18a), the flux density $\mathbf{B}$ may be considered constant over the interior of the winding. Obtaining the magnitude of $\mathbf{B}$ from (4-50), the total flux ψ_{m1} through the toroid is

$$\psi_{m1} = B\pi s^2 = \frac{\mu N_1 I_1 \pi s^2}{2\pi r} = \frac{\mu N_1 I_1 A}{l} \qquad \text{webers} \tag{7-82}$$

where A = area of winding cross section $(A = \pi s^2)$
      l = mean length of the toroidal coil $(l = 2\pi r)$

Substituting (7-82) in (7-81) gives

$$\mathbb{U}_2 = N_1 N_2 \frac{\mu A}{l} \frac{dI_1}{dt} \tag{7-83}$$

According to (7-83) the secondary emf $\mathbb{U}_2$ is proportional to the number of primary turns N_1, the number of secondary turns N_2, the permeability μ of the medium inside the winding, the cross-sectional area A of the winding, and the time rate of change of the primary current I_1 and is inversely proportional to the average length l of the winding. Putting

$$M = N_1 N_2 \frac{\mu A}{l} \tag{7-84}$$

(7-83) reduces to

$$\mathbb{U}_2 = M \frac{dI_1}{dt} \tag{7-85}$$

Dimensionally (7-85) is

$$\text{Emf} = M \frac{\text{current}}{\text{time}}$$

or

$$M = \frac{\text{emf}}{\text{current}} \times \text{time} = \text{resistance} \times \text{time}$$

In mksc units

$$M = \text{ohm-seconds} = \text{henrys}$$

Thus, M has the dimensions of inductance, and since M involves two coils, it is called the *mutual inductance* of the two coils.

The inductance L discussed in previous sections involves a single coil. Therefore, in contrast, L is called the *self-inductance*. From (7-64) the emf $\mathcal{V}_1$ applied to a coil of self-inductance L_1 is

$$\mathcal{V}_1 = L_1 \frac{dI_1}{dt} \tag{7-86}$$

where $I_1 =$ current in coil. This relation involving the self-inductance of a coil is similar in form to (7-85), which involves the mutual inductance of two coils.

From (4-63) the self-inductance of a toroid is[1]

$$L = N^2 \frac{\mu A}{l} = \frac{N^2}{l/\mu A} = \frac{N^2}{\mathcal{R}} \quad \text{henrys} \tag{7-87}$$

where $N =$ number of turns of toroid (dimensionless)
$\mathcal{R} = l/\mu A =$ reluctance of region enclosed by toroid winding (1/henrys)

From (7-84) the mutual inductance M of two coils (as in Fig. 7-18) is

$$M = N_1 N_2 \frac{\mu A}{l} = \frac{N_1 N_2}{l/\mu A} = \frac{N_1 N_2}{\mathcal{R}} \quad \text{henrys} \tag{7-88}$$

where $N_1 =$ number of primary turns (dimensionless)
$N_2 =$ number of secondary turns (dimensionless)
$\mathcal{R} =$ reluctance of magnetic circuit linking primary and secondary windings (1/henrys)

Consider next the converse of the situation described above. That is, let the battery and resistance be connected across coil 2 (Fig. 7-18), and let the terminals of coil 1 be left open. Then the emf $\mathcal{V}_1$ at the terminals of coil 1 is

$$\mathcal{V}_1 = N_1 \frac{d\psi_{m2}}{dt} \tag{7-89}$$

where $\psi_{m2} =$ magnetic flux produced by secondary coil. But

$$\psi_{m2} = \frac{\mu N_2 I_2 A}{l}$$

and so (7-89) becomes

$$\mathcal{V}_1 = N_1 N_2 \frac{\mu A}{l} \frac{dI_2}{dt} \tag{7-90}$$

or

$$\mathcal{V}_1 = M \frac{dI_2}{dt} \tag{7-91}$$

[1] See Sec. 7-17 for the significance of μ with iron-cored coils under a-c conditions.

Thus, from (7-85) and (7-91),

$$M = \frac{\mathcal{U}_1}{dI_2/dt} = \frac{\mathcal{U}_2}{dI_1/dt} \qquad (7\text{-}92)$$

Therefore, if a given time rate of change of current in the primary induces a certain voltage in the secondary, the same time rate of change of current applied to the secondary will induce the same voltage in the primary. In effect this is a statement of the *reciprocity theorem* as applied to a special case.

If the current I_1 varies harmonically with time (alternating current), we have

$$I_1 = I_0 e^{j\omega t} \qquad (7\text{-}93)$$

For harmonic variation of I_1 and I_2, (7-92) becomes

$$M = \frac{\mathcal{U}_1}{j\omega I_2} = \frac{\mathcal{U}_2}{j\omega I_1} \qquad (7\text{-}94)$$

and

$$\frac{\mathcal{U}_1}{I_2} = \frac{\mathcal{U}_2}{I_1} = j\omega M = Z_m \qquad (7\text{-}95)$$

where Z_m = *mutual impedance* (ohms).

The above relations were developed for the case where all of the flux links all of the turns. In this situation the mutual inductance can be calculated readily by (7-88). If the flux leakage can be neglected, this relation also can be applied to concentrated coils wound on an iron core as in Fig. 7-19, where the reluctance $\mathcal{R}$ is that of the iron core. If the flux leakage is appreciable, the mutual inductance is not readily calculated in this way but is nevertheless a definite quantity and can be measured with the aid of (7-92).

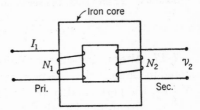

FIG. 7-19. Transformer.

7-16. The Transformer. Suppose that the two-coil arrangement of Fig. 7-19 has the secondary coil open, as shown, while the primary coil is connected to an alternating emf $\mathcal{U}_1$. The emf $\mathcal{U}_2$ appearing at the secondary terminals has a magnitude

$$\mathcal{U}_2 = N_2 \frac{d\psi_m}{dt} \qquad (7\text{-}96)$$

where N_2 = number of turns of secondary coil

ψ_m = magnetic flux through transformer core

If the primary resistance is negligible, the counter emf across the primary terminals is equal in magnitude to the applied emf υ_1, or

$$\upsilon_1 = N_1 \frac{d\psi_m}{dt} \tag{7-97}$$

where N_1 = number of turns of primary coil.   Dividing (7-96) by (7-97) yields

$$\frac{\upsilon_2}{\upsilon_1} = \frac{N_2}{N_1} \tag{7-98}$$

According to (7-98) the ratio of the secondary to the primary emf is equal to the ratio of the number of secondary turns N_2 to the number of the primary turns N_1.   The ratio is the same for effective (rms) voltages as for instantaneous.

Because the arrangement of Fig. 7-19 (or Fig. 7-18) can transform an emf or voltage from one value to another, it is called a *transformer*.   In the present discussion the transformer is an ideal one in the sense that flux leakage is assumed to be zero so that ψ_m links all primary and secondary turns.   It is further assumed that the resistance of the primary is very small and that negligible current is drawn from the secondary. This condition may be approached in practice where a transformer secondary is connected to a high-resistance circuit.

Example.   An ideal transformer has a turn ratio of 2, that is, $N_2/N_1 = 2$.   An a-c emf of 10 volts rms is applied to the primary.   Find the emf or voltage appearing at the secondary terminals.

Solution.   From (7-98) the secondary voltage is

$$\upsilon_2 = \frac{N_2}{N_1}\upsilon_1 = 2 \times 10 = 20 \text{ volts rms}$$

7-17. Alternating-current Behavior of Ferromagnetic Materials.   We noted in Chap. 5 that the permeability of iron is not a constant.   In spite of this, the permeability of the iron in an iron-cored coil carrying alternating current may be taken as a constant for certain applications, but its value, in this case, needs further explanation.

Where μ is not a constant, we have from (4-59) that the inductance L of a coil is given by

$$L = \frac{d\Lambda}{dI} \qquad \text{henrys} \tag{7-99}$$

If there is no flux leakage, $\Lambda = N\psi_m$; so

$$L = N\frac{d\psi_m}{dI} \tag{7-100}$$

For a toroidal type of coil, $d\psi_m = A\,dB$, and $dI = l\,dH/N$, where A equals the area and l equals the mean length of the coil.   Therefore

(7-100) becomes

$$L = \frac{N^2 A}{l} \frac{dB}{dH} \qquad (7\text{-}101)$$

Now dB/dH in (7-101) has the dimensions of permeability. It is equal to the slope of the hysteresis curve. At some point P, as in Fig. 7-20, this is different from the ordinary permeability, B_1/H_1, which is equal to the slope of the line from the origin to the point P. Since dB/dH involves infinitesimals, it is sometimes called the *infinitesimal* or *differential permeability*.

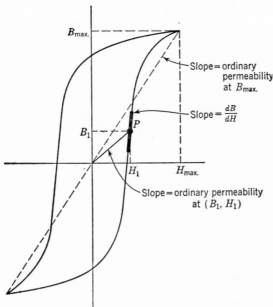

FIG. 7-20. Hysteresis loop illustrating ordinary and differential permeabilities.

If alternating current is applied to an iron-cored coil so that the condition of the iron moves around a hysteresis loop (Fig. 7-20) once per cycle, the slope dB/dH varies over a wide range and the instantaneous value of the inductance will, from (7-101), vary over a corresponding range. Under these conditions it is often convenient to consider the average inductance (over one cycle) as obtained from (7-101), using the average value of the slope dB/dH. This is equal to the ordinary permeability at the maximum value of B attained in the cycle (see Fig. 7-20). Thus

$$L_{av} = \frac{N^2 A}{l} \left(\frac{dB}{dH}\right)_{av} = \frac{N^2 A}{l} \mu \qquad (7\text{-}102)$$

where $\mu = B_{max}/H_{max} = $ ordinary permeability at B_{max}.

The above discussion is for alternating current only through the coil.

If a small alternating current is superimposed on a relatively large steady, or direct, current through the coil, the situation is as suggested in Fig. 7-21. The magnetic condition of the iron then follows a minor hysteresis loop as indicated. In this case the average value of the slope dB/dH is given by the line passing through the tips of the minor hysteresis

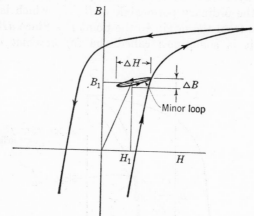

FIG. 7-21. Minor hysteresis loop illustrating incremental permeability.

loop and is called the *incremental permeability* μ_{inc}. Referring to Fig. 7-21,

$$\mu_{inc} = \left(\frac{dB}{dH}\right)_{av} = \frac{\Delta B}{\Delta H} \tag{7-103}$$

The incremental permeability is much less than the ordinary permeability B_1H_1 for a point at the center of the minor loop in Fig. 7-21.

In (7-87) the self-inductance L of a toroidal coil of N turns is given as

$$L = N^2 \frac{\mu A}{l} \qquad \text{henrys} \tag{7-104}$$

and in (7-88) the mutual inductance M of two coils mounted, for example, on a ring-shaped core is given as

$$M = N_1 N_2 \frac{\mu A}{l} \qquad \text{henrys} \tag{7-105}$$

where N_1 = number of primary turns
N_2 = number of secondary turns

For iron cores and a-c operation these relations may be used to calculate the average L or average M provided the appropriate value of μ is used. As discussed above, this value of μ is equal to the average value of dB/dH over the operating range of the iron on a B-H diagram.

Although the above discussion has concerned toroidal coils with uniform core cross section A, Eqs. (7-104) and (7-105) may be applied in the more general case, where the iron core is of nonuniform cross section and the magnetic circuit may include an air gap, by reexpressing them as follows,

$$L = \frac{N^2}{\mathcal{R}} \qquad \text{henrys} \qquad (7\text{-}106)$$

where $\mathcal{R}$ = reluctance of closed magnetic circuit through coil, and

$$M = \frac{N_1 N_2}{\mathcal{R}} \qquad \text{henrys} \qquad (7\text{-}107)$$

where $\mathcal{R}$ = reluctance of closed magnetic circuit linking the primary and secondary coils.   The above relations are applicable to both uniformly distributed coils and to concentrated coils (as in Fig. 7-19) provided that flux leakage is negligible.   The reluctance of the magnetic circuit is calculated as discussed in Secs. 5-18, 5-19, 5-22, and 5-23.

7-18. Eddy Currents.   When large conducting specimens are subjected to transformer or motional induction, currents tend to be induced in the specimen.   These currents flow in closed paths in the specimen and are called *eddy currents*.   In accordance with Lenz's law the eddy current tends to oppose the change in field inducing it.

Eddy currents result in Joule heating in the conducting specimen. The energy loss due to eddy currents in the ferromagnetic cores of a-c devices is in addition to the energy lost in the magnetization-demagnetization process (proportional to the area of the hysteresis loop), as discussed in Sec. 5-14.   In order to reduce the eddy currents in iron-cored a-c devices, the core is commonly made of thin sheets or laminations of iron insulated electrically from each other.   Thus the eddy currents are confined to individual sheets, and the power loss is reduced.   Each sheet is continuous in the direction of the magnetic flux through the core, but because of its thinness it has a relatively large reluctance.   By stacking a sufficient number of sheets in parallel the total reluctance of the magnetic circuit may be reduced to the desired value.   To reduce eddy currents to a minimum, iron wires are sometimes used in place of sheets, while at radio frequencies powdered-iron cores are commonly employed.

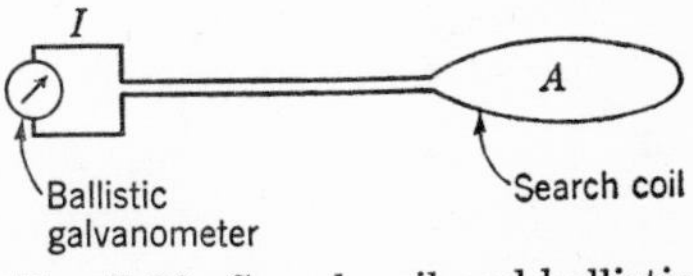

Fig. 7-22. Search coil and ballistic galvanometer.

7-19. Measurement of Magnetic Fields.   The Fluxmeter.   A steady magnetic field may be explored or measured by means of a search coil connected to a ballistic galvanometer[1] as in Fig. 7-22.   From (7-70) we have for this circuit that

[1] A *ballistic galvanometer* is a galvanometer whose deflection is proportional to the charge Q passing through it provided the time interval for the passage of the charge is sufficiently short.

$$RI + L\frac{dI}{dt} = -N\frac{d\psi_m}{dt} \tag{7-108}$$

where R = total resistance of circuit (ohms)

I = current through circuit (amp)

L = total inductance of circuit (henrys)

ψ_m = magnetic flux through search coil (webers)

N = number of turns of search coil (it is assumed that ψ_m links all turns)

This may also be expressed

$$RI + L\frac{dI}{dt} = -NA\frac{dB}{dt} \tag{7-109}$$

where A = area of search coil

B = component of flux density **B** normal to the plane of the search coil

It is assumed that the coil is small enough so that B is substantially uniform over the area of the coil. Suppose the coil is in a magnetic field of flux density **B** and that the plane of the coil is normal to the direction of **B**. Then, if the coil is quickly removed to a location of negligible magnetic field, the deflection of the ballistic galvanometer will indicate the passage of a charge Q obtained by integrating (7-109) over a time interval from $t = 0$ to $t = T$ that includes the entire action. Thus

$$\int_{t=0}^{t=T} I\,dt + \frac{L}{R}\int_{\substack{I=0 \\ (\text{at } t=0)}}^{\substack{I=0 \\ (\text{at } t=T)}} dI = -\frac{NA}{R}\int_{\substack{B=B \\ (\text{at } t=0)}}^{\substack{B=0 \\ (\text{at } t=T)}} dB \tag{7-110}$$

Since $I = 0$ at $t = 0$ and also at $t = T$, the second term yields zero and we have

$$Q = \frac{NAB}{R}$$

or

$$B = \frac{QR}{NA} \tag{7-111}$$

where B = flux density at initial location of coil (webers/meter^2) (normal to plane of coil)

Q = charge passed through ballistic galvanometer (proportional to deflection) (coulombs)

R = resistance of circuit (ohms)

N = number of turns of coil (dimensionless)

A = area of coil (meters^2)

The product BA equal to QR/N in (7-111) equals the total flux change through the coil. Hence, the search-coil and ballistic-galvanometer arrangement of Fig. 7-22 is often called a *fluxmeter*.

Another procedure for measuring the field is to keep the coil at the location where the field is to be measured and quickly to flip it over or rotate it through 180°. Under these conditions it is sometimes called a *flip coil*, and the ballistic-galvanometer deflection is doubled for the same flux density B. That is,

$$B = \frac{QR}{2NA} \qquad (7\text{-}112)$$

If the restoring torque on the galvanometer coil is removed so that its deflection is proportional to the net charge passed after some reference time t_1, then the net change in flux density between this time and some later time t_2 is given by

$$B_2 - B_1 = \frac{(Q_2 - Q_1)R}{NA} \qquad (7\text{-}112a)$$

where $B_2 - B_1$ = net change in flux density in time interval between t_1 and t_2 (webers/meter^2) (plane of search coil normal to **B**)

$Q_2 - Q_1$ = net charge through galvanometer in same interval (coulombs) (proportional to net change in deflection of galvanometer)

R = total circuit resistance (ohms)

N = number of turns of search coil (dimensionless)

A = area of search coil (meters^2)

This type of fluxmeter is often referred to as a *Grassot fluxmeter*. Thus, if a charge $2q$ passes through the galvanometer in one direction and then a charge q passes through it in the opposite direction, all in the time interval between t_1 and t_2, the net change in B in this same interval is proportional to $2q - q = q$.

In an alternating magnetic field where $B = B_0 \sin \omega t$ a peak voltmeter may be connected to the search coil. Then, if the plane of the coil is normal to the flux density **B**, we have

$$B_0 = \frac{\mathcal{V}_0}{NA\omega} \qquad (7\text{-}113)$$

where B_0 = peak flux density (webers/meter^2)

$\mathcal{V}_0$ = peak emf (volts)

N = number of turns of search coil (dimensionless)

A = area of search coil (meters^2)

ω = radian frequency (reciprocal seconds) ($=2\pi f$, where f = frequency)

7-20. Displacement Current. In this section a new concept is introduced, namely, that of *displacement current*. Consider a voltage applied to a resistor and a capacitor in parallel as in Fig. 7-23a. The nature of the current flow through the resistor is different from that through the capacitor. Thus a constant voltage across a resistor produces a continuous flow of current of constant value. On the other hand, the current through a capacitor will be constant only while the voltage is changing.

For a voltage V across a resistor of resistance R and capacitor of capacitance C in parallel as in Fig. 7-23a we have a current through the resistor given by

$$i_1 = \frac{V}{R} \qquad (7\text{-}114)$$

and a current through the capacitor given by

$$i_2 = \frac{dQ}{dt} = C\frac{dV}{dt} \qquad (7\text{-}115)$$

The instantaneous charge Q in the capacitor is given by $Q = CV$.

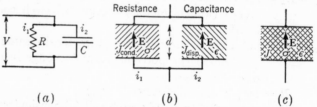

(a)   (b)   (c)

Fig. 7-23. Illustration for discussion on conduction and displacement currents.

The current through the resistor is a *conduction current*, while the current "through" the capacitor may be called a *displacement current*. Although the current does not flow through the capacitor, the external effect is as though it did, since as much current flows out of one plate as flows into the opposite one. This circuit concept may be extended to three dimensions by supposing that the resistor and capacitor elements each occupies a volume as in Fig. 7-23b. Fringing of the field is neglected. Inside of each element the electric field E equals the voltage V across the element divided by its length d. That is,

$$E = \frac{V}{d} \qquad (7\text{-}116)$$

From (3-21) the current density J_1 inside the resistor equals the product of the electric field E and the conductivity σ of the medium inside the resistor element, also i_1 divided by the cross-section area A. Or

$$J_1 = E\sigma = \frac{i_1}{A} \qquad (7\text{-}117)$$

The dimensional form of (7-117) in mksc units is

$$\frac{\text{Amperes}}{\text{Meter}^2} = \frac{\text{volts}}{\text{meter}} \times \frac{\text{mhos}}{\text{meter}}$$

From (2-55) the capacitance of a parallel-plate capacitor is $C = \epsilon A / d$, where A is the area of the plates and d is the spacing between them. Substituting this value for C, and from (7-116) for V, into (7-115) yields

$$i_2 = \frac{\epsilon A d}{d} \frac{dE}{dt} = \epsilon A \frac{dE}{dt} \qquad (7\text{-}118)$$

Dividing (7-118) by the area A gives the relation that the current density J_2 inside the capacitor equals the permittivity of the nonconducting medium filling the capacitor element multiplied by the time rate of change of the electric field. Thus

$$\frac{i_2}{A} = J_2 = \epsilon \frac{dE}{dt} \qquad (7\text{-}119)$$

The dimensions of (7-119) in mksc units are

$$\frac{\text{Amperes}}{\text{Meter}^2} = \frac{\text{farads}}{\text{meter}} \times \frac{\text{volts/meter}}{\text{second}}$$

Recalling that $D = \epsilon E$, (7-119) becomes

$$J_2 = \frac{dD}{dt} \qquad (7\text{-}120)$$

In this example J_1 is a conduction current density J_{cond}, while J_2 is a displacement current density J_{disp}. Also, since the current density $\mathbf{J}$, the electric displacement $\mathbf{D}$, and the electric field intensity $\mathbf{E}$ are actually space vectors, which all have the same direction in isotropic media, (7-117) and (7-120) may be expressed in more general form as

$$\mathbf{J}_{cond} = \sigma \mathbf{E} \qquad (7\text{-}121)$$

and

$$\mathbf{J}_{disp} = \epsilon \frac{d\mathbf{E}}{dt} = \frac{d\mathbf{D}}{dt} \qquad (7\text{-}122)$$

As a final step, suppose that instead of having two separate elements in parallel, one of which acts like a pure resistance and the other like a pure capacitance, we have only one, which has both capacitance and resistance. Thus, as in Fig. 7-23c, there is a single element filled with a conducting dielectric so that both conduction and displacement currents are present. Then the total current density $\mathbf{J}_{total}$ is

$$\mathbf{J}_{total} = \mathbf{J}_{cond} + \mathbf{J}_{disp} \qquad (7\text{-}123)$$

The concept of displacement current, or displacement current density, was introduced by James Clerk Maxwell to account for the production of magnetic fields in empty space. Here the conduction current is zero, and the magnetic fields are due entirely to displacement currents.

7-21. Maxwell's Equation from Ampère's Law. Complete Expression. According to Ampère's law the line integral of **H** around a closed contour is equal to the current enclosed. Where both conduction and displacement currents are present, this current is the *total current*. Thus (4-81), which applies only to conduction currents, may be extended as follows when both conduction and displacement currents are present,

$$\oint \mathbf{H} \cdot d\mathbf{l} = \int_s (\mathbf{J}_{cond} + \mathbf{J}_{disp}) \cdot d\mathbf{s} \qquad (7\text{-}124)$$

or

$$\oint \mathbf{H} \cdot d\mathbf{l} = \int_s \left(\sigma \mathbf{E} + \epsilon \frac{\partial \mathbf{E}}{\partial t} \right) \cdot d\mathbf{s} \qquad (7\text{-}125)$$

The line integral of **H** on the left side of (7-125) is around the boundary of the surface s over which the surface integral is taken on the right side of (7-125). Each term in (7-125) has the dimensions of current. The conduction current through the surface s is given by

$$\int_s \sigma \mathbf{E} \cdot d\mathbf{s}$$

while the displacement current through the surface s is given by

$$\int_s \epsilon \frac{\partial \mathbf{E}}{\partial t} \cdot d\mathbf{s}$$

Equation (7-125) is the complete expression in integral form of Maxwell's equation derived from Ampère's law. It is also often written

$$\oint \mathbf{H} \cdot d\mathbf{l} = \int_s \left(\mathbf{J} + \frac{\partial \mathbf{D}}{\partial t} \right) \cdot d\mathbf{s} \qquad (7\text{-}126)$$

where **J** without a subscript is understood to refer only to conduction current density.

By an application of Stokes' theorem to (7-126) or by an extension of (4-130) to include displacement currents the complete expression in *differential form of Maxwell's equation derived from Ampère's law is*

$$\nabla \times \mathbf{H} = \mathbf{J} + \frac{\partial \mathbf{D}}{\partial t} \qquad (7\text{-}127)$$

or

$$\nabla \times \mathbf{H} = \sigma \mathbf{E} + \epsilon \frac{\partial \mathbf{E}}{\partial t} \qquad (7\text{-}128)$$

It should be noted that when the electric field varies harmonically with time ($\mathbf{E} = \mathbf{E}_0 \sin \omega t$), the conduction and displacement currents are in time phase quadrature. That is,

$$\mathbf{J} = \sigma\mathbf{E} = \sigma\mathbf{E}_0 \sin \omega t \qquad (7\text{-}129)$$

and

$$\frac{\partial \mathbf{D}}{\partial t} = \epsilon\frac{\partial \mathbf{E}}{\partial t} = \omega\epsilon\mathbf{E}_0 \cos \omega t \qquad (7\text{-}130)$$

Thus, when $\omega t = 0$, the displacement current is a maximum and the conduction current is zero. On the other hand, when $\omega t = \pi/2$, the conduction current is a maximum and the displacement current is zero. Since the displacement current is a maximum one-quarter cycle ($\omega t = \pi/2$) before the conduction current, it is said that the displacement current leads the conduction current by 90°. This is similar to the situation in a circuit having a resistor and a capacitor in parallel (Fig. 7-23a) in which the current "through" the capacitor leads the current through the resistor by 90°.

This phase difference can also be readily shown by expressing the time variation of the field by[1]

$$\mathbf{E} = \mathbf{E}_0 e^{j\omega t} \qquad (7\text{-}131)$$

The displacement current is then

$$\epsilon\frac{\partial \mathbf{E}}{\partial t} = \epsilon j\omega\mathbf{E}_0 e^{j\omega t} = j\omega\epsilon\mathbf{E} \qquad (7\text{-}132)$$

Maxwell's equation (7-128) then becomes

$$\nabla \times \mathbf{H} = \sigma\mathbf{E} + j\omega\epsilon\mathbf{E} = (\sigma + j\omega\epsilon)\mathbf{E} \qquad (7\text{-}133)$$

The operator j in the displacement current term and its absence in the conduction current term signifies that the displacement current is advanced in phase by 90° with respect to the conduction current.

7-22. Dielectric Hysteresis. In dielectrics that are good insulators the d-c conduction current may be negligible. However, an appreciable a-c current in phase with the applied field may be present because of *dielectric hysteresis*. This phenomenon is analogous to magnetic hysteresis in ferromagnetic materials. Materials, such as glass, which are good insulators under static conditions may consume considerable energy in

---

[1] In using this notation it is understood that the instantaneous value of the field is given by the imaginary part of (7-131). Thus

$$\mathbf{E} \text{ (instantaneous)} = \mathbf{E}_0 \operatorname{Im} e^{j\omega t} = \mathbf{E}_0 \sin \omega t$$

One might also use the real part of $e^{j\omega t}$, which is equal to $\cos \omega t$ (that is, $\operatorname{Re} e^{j\omega t} = \cos \omega t$). However, in any given analysis one convention or the other should be adopted and used consistently. Here it is understood to be the imaginary part.

alternating fields. The heat generated in this way is sometimes applied in industrial radio-frequency heating processes.

In dealing with a-c dielectric losses, the dielectric *power factor* is a convenient quantity. Referring to the time-phase diagram of Fig. 7-24, the total current density J_{total} in a dielectric will lead the applied field E by an angle θ which is less than 90°. Thus $\theta = 90° - \delta$. The power factor (PF) is given by the cosine of θ. Thus[1]

$$\text{PF} = \cos \theta \qquad (7\text{-}134)$$

Since δ is usually not more than 2 or 3°, the power factor is small even in the case of poor high-frequency dielectrics such as glass. For example,

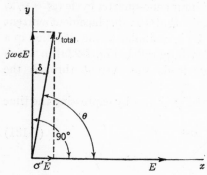

FIG. 7-24. Time-phase diagram for dielectric with losses.

the power factor for crown glass is 0.01 at 1 kc per sec. Cellulose nitrate has an even higher power factor at 1 kc per sec, being about 0.05 ($\delta = 3°$). On the other hand, the power factor for quartz at 1 kc per sec is only 0.0003 and of polystyrene 0.0002. Therefore, these materials find wide application as dielectrics at this and also much higher frequencies.

It is sometimes convenient to assume an equivalent conductivity for the dielectric which would produce the same heating as the dielectric hysteresis. Thus, although the dc conductivity of the dielectric is negligible, the equivalent conductivity σ' may be significant and is substituted in relations involving the ordinary conductivity σ. Expressing the total conduction current† J_{total} in terms of its component parts as in (7-133),

$$J_{total} = \sigma' E + j\omega\epsilon E \qquad (7\text{-}135)$$

---

[1] The dielectric behavior is also sometimes expressed in terms of tan δ. For small values of δ this is the same as cos θ.

† Sometimes the total conduction current is expressed as $J_{total} = \left(\epsilon - j\dfrac{\sigma'}{\omega} \right) j\omega E$, which is equivalent to (7-135). Then defining ϵ^* as the complex dielectric constant, $J_{total} = j\omega\epsilon^* E$, where the complex dielectric constant ϵ^* has a "real" part $\epsilon' = \epsilon$ and an "imaginary" part $\epsilon'' = \sigma'/\omega$ as given by

$$\epsilon^* = (\epsilon' - j\epsilon'') = \epsilon - j\frac{\sigma'}{\omega} \qquad (7\text{-}134a)$$

The terms *real* and *imaginary* are used in the mathematical sense. Both parts have a real physical significance, the so-called "real" part ϵ' being associated with the component of current density in phase quadrature with the field and the so-called "imaginary" part being associated with the component of current density in phase

The component parts are added like vectors to obtain J_{total}. Now, from Fig. 7-24,

$$\tan \delta = \frac{\sigma'}{\omega\epsilon} \simeq \cos \theta \qquad (7\text{-}136)$$

or

$$\sigma' \simeq \omega\epsilon \cos \theta \qquad (7\text{-}137)$$

Example. Find the average power dissipated per cubic meter in a nonconducting medium with a relative permittivity of 4 and power factor of 0.001 if $E = 1,000$ volts/meter rms and the frequency is 10 Mc/sec.

Solution. From (7-137) the equivalent conductivity is

$$\sigma' = \omega\epsilon \cos \theta = 2\pi 10^7 \times 4 \times 8.85 \times 10^{-12} \times 10^{-3}$$
$$= 2.22 \times 10^{-6} \text{ mhos/meter}$$

The power W dissipated per unit volume is then

$$W = E^2\sigma' = 10^6 \times 2.22 \times 10^{-6}$$
$$= 2.22 \text{ watts/meter}^3$$

It is to be noted that the current density and the field intensity have the same space direction in isotropic media. Although both may have the same space direction, their scalar magnitudes may have different time phase. Thus, in the above discussion the space directions are the same and are fixed, but the scalar magnitude J_{total} of the total current density leads the scalar magnitude E of the electric field intensity in time by the phase angle θ. Thus, on a time-phase diagram, such as Fig. 7-24, J_{total} and E may be *represented* by vectors separated in direction by an angle θ. Such a pseudo vector used to represent the time phase of a scalar quantity is often called a *phasor*. A dot (˙) is sometimes added when it is desired to indicate explicitly that the quantity is a complex function of time (that is, a phasor).

Thus[1]

$$\mathbf{E} = \mathbf{a}\dot{E} = \mathbf{a}E_0 e^{j\omega t} \qquad (7\text{-}138)$$

where $\mathbf{a}$ = unit (space) vector in direction of $\mathbf{E}$

$\dot{E} = E_0 e^{j\omega t}$ = vector representation of time phase (phasor)

E_0 = amplitude of $\dot{E}$

---

with the field. See for example, S. Roberts and A. von Hippel, A New Method for Measuring Dielectric Constant and Loss in the Range of Centimeter Waves, *J. Applied Phys.*, **17**, 610, July, 1946.

[1] The quantity $\mathbf{E}$ is not only a space vector but also a function of time (phasor). Thus, it may be called a vector-phasor and designated by $\dot{\mathbf{E}}(= \mathbf{a}\dot{E})$. In general, we shall use the dot over a quantity only where we wish to indicate explicitly that it is a complex function of the time (that is, a phasor). The fact that a quantity is a space vector is indicated by using boldface (heavy) type. In longhand notation a space vector may be designated by a bar placed above or below the letter.

In (7-138) the quantity $E_0 e^{j\omega t}$ is a scalar function of the time. However, it may be represented on the complex plane by a vector (or phasor) of magnitude E_0 that rotates counterclockwise one revolution per cycle. This may be made more obvious by writing $\dot{E}$ in its equivalent polar form. That is,

$$\dot{E} = E_0 \underline{/\omega t} \tag{7-139}$$

which is interpreted to mean a vector (or phasor) of magnitude E_0 at an angle ωt with respect to some reference direction (usually the real or x axis). Hence, when $t = 0$, the phasor is in the positive x direction. One-quarter of a period later ($t = T/4$ and $\omega t = \pi/2$) the phasor has rotated 90° to the positive y direction. At $t = T/2$ the phasor has rotated a total of 180° to the negative x direction, etc.

It is understood that the instantaneous magnitude of the electric field intensity $\mathbf{E}$ is given by the real (Re) part or imaginary (Im) part of $\dot{E}$. Taking it equal to the imaginary part, the instantaneous value of the electric field intensity is

$$\mathbf{E} = \mathbf{a} \operatorname{Im} \dot{E} = \mathbf{a} \operatorname{Im} E_0 e^{j\omega t} = \mathbf{a} E_0 \sin \omega t \tag{7-140}$$

Referring to (7-135), it is understood that E in this equation is a phasor as given by $E_0 e^{j\omega t}$ or $E_0 \underline{/\omega t}$. It follows that Fig. 7-24 shows the position of E and the other phasors at $t = 0$. As a function of time the entire diagram rotates counterclockwise one revolution per cycle, and the instantaneous value of any of the quantities is given by its projection on the y axis.

7-23. Boundary Relations. The boundary relations given in Tables 2-2 and 5-2 for the tangential and normal components of static electric and magnetic fields also hold for time-varying fields. This may be shown as follows: Consider first the tangential components E_t of the electric field (see Fig. 2-4). Instead of using the relation that $\oint \mathbf{E} \cdot d\mathbf{l} = 0$ for a closed path, which is true for static fields due to charges, we should, in the time-varying case, use Maxwell's equation from Faraday's law

$$\oint \mathbf{E} \cdot d\mathbf{l} = - \int_s \frac{\partial \mathbf{B}}{\partial t} \cdot d\mathbf{s} \tag{7-141}$$

If there is a flux density $\mathbf{B}$ normal to the rectangular path (half in each medium) and $\mathbf{B}$ changes with time, then $\oint \mathbf{E} \cdot d\mathbf{l}$ is not zero if the path encloses a finite area. However, it is assumed that the dimension Δy approaches zero so that E_{t1} and E_{t2} are separated by only an infinitesimal distance. Therefore the area of the rectangle approaches zero, and the surface integral of $\partial B/\partial t$ vanishes. Thus the work around the path is given by $E_{t1} \Delta x - E_{t2} \Delta x = 0$, as before, and it follows that $E_{t1} = E_{t2}$ holds for both static and time-varying situations. The two media may have any permittivities, permeabilities, and conductivities.

Consider next the tangential components of the **H** field (see Fig. 5-15). Instead of using the relation $\oint \mathbf{H} \cdot dl = \iint \mathbf{J} \cdot d\mathbf{s}$ for steady fields, we should, in the time-varying case, use Maxwell's equation from Ampère's law in its complete form,

$$\oint \mathbf{H} \cdot dl = \int_s \left(\mathbf{J} + \frac{\partial \mathbf{D}}{\partial t} \right) \cdot d\mathbf{s} \qquad (7\text{-}142)$$

If there is a time-changing **D** normal to the rectangular path (half in each medium), then there will be a contribution due to **D**. However, it is assumed that the dimension Δy approaches zero so that the surface integral of $\partial D/\partial t$ vanishes. Now in (7-142) the conduction current density **J** may also change with time. However, its surface integral also vanishes as Δy approaches zero unless the conduction current is assumed to exist in an infinitesimally thin layer at the conductor surface. Thus,

TABLE 7-1
BOUNDARY RELATIONS FOR ELECTRIC AND MAGNETIC FIELDS

Field component	Boundary relation		Condition
Tangential....	$E_{t1} = E_{t2}$	(1)	Any two media
Tangential....	$E_{t1} = 0$	(2)	Medium 2 is a perfect conductor ($\sigma_2 = \infty$)†
Tangential....	$H_{t1} = H_{t2}$	(3)	Any two media
Tangential....	$H_{t1} - H_{t2} = K$	(4)‡	Current sheet at boundary
Tangential....	$H_{t1} = K$	(5)‡	Medium 2 is a perfect conductor ($\sigma_2 = \infty$) with current sheet at surface
Tangential....	$H_{t1} = 0$	(6)	Medium 2 has infinite permeability ($\mu_2 = \infty$) (no currents)
Normal.......	$D_{n1} - D_{n2} = \rho_s$	(7)	Any two media with charge at boundary
Normal.......	$D_{n1} = D_{n2}$	(8)	Any two media with no charge at boundary
Normal.......	$D_{n1} = \rho_s$	(9)	Medium 2 is a perfect conductor with charge at surface
Normal.......	$B_{n1} = B_{n2}$	(10)	Any two media

† Under static conditions it suffices for medium 2 to be a conductor (σ_2 finite). However, for E_{t2} to be zero under time-varying conditions requires that $\sigma_2 = \infty$ (see Chap. 10).

‡ Note that although **K** and the components of **H** are measured parallel to the boundary, they are normal to each other. Thus, in vector notation (5) is expressed by $\mathbf{K} = \mathbf{n} \times \mathbf{H}$, where $\mathbf{n}$ = unit vector normal to the boundary.

for a sheet current of linear density K at the surface

$$H_{t1} - H_{t2} = K \tag{7-143}$$

as before, while in the absence of such a sheet

$$H_{t1} = H_{t2} \tag{7-144}$$

as before. Thus, the relations for the tangential **H** field of Table 5-2 hold for both static and time-changing situations. The two media may have any permeabilities, permittivities, and conductivities.

The formal approach in obtaining the continuity relations for the normal components of **D** and **B** is the same under time-varying conditions as for static conditions, and the relations given in Tables 2-2 and 5-2 apply under both conditions. The two media may have any permittivities, permeabilities, and conductivities.

Table 7-1 summarizes the boundary relations developed for electric and magnetic fields. These relations apply under all situations, except as noted.

7-24. General Field Relations. In Chap. 4 it is shown that the divergence of the curl of a vector function **F** is zero. Thus,

$$\nabla \cdot (\nabla \times \mathbf{F}) = 0$$

As a corollary, any vector function with no divergence must be the curl of some other vector function. Thus, if $\nabla \cdot \mathbf{G} = 0$, then we can write $\mathbf{G} = \nabla \times \mathbf{F}$, where **F** is some other vector function. As an example, $\nabla \cdot \mathbf{B} = 0$ so that **B** may be expressed as the curl of a vector potential ($\mathbf{B} = \nabla \times \mathbf{A}$).

It is also shown in Chap. 4 that the curl of the gradient of a scalar function f is zero. Thus $\nabla \times (\nabla f) = 0$. As a corollary, any vector function with no curl is the gradient of some scalar function. Thus, if $\nabla \times \mathbf{F} = 0$, then we can write $\mathbf{F} = \nabla g$, where g is a scalar function. As an example, the curl of the static electric field due to electric charges[1] is zero ($\nabla \times \mathbf{E} = 0$). It follows that a static electric field due to charges may be expressed as the gradient of a scalar function. That is, $\mathbf{E} = -\nabla V$, where V is the electric scalar potential.

According to Maxwell's equation derived from Faraday's law we note, however, that in time-changing situations the curl of the electric field is not zero but is equal to the time rate of decrease of **B**. Thus

$$\nabla \times \mathbf{E} = - \frac{\partial \mathbf{B}}{\partial t} \tag{7-145}$$

Since $\nabla \times \mathbf{E}$ is not zero, the relation $\mathbf{E} = -\nabla V$ is not sufficient for time-varying fields. An additional term is required. This may be found as

[1] To indicate explicitly this type of field, we have sometimes used the symbol $\mathbf{E}_c$. This type of field is said to be *lamellar* (see Sec. 4-28).

follows: Since $\mathbf{B} = \mathbf{\nabla} \times \mathbf{A}$, (7-145) becomes

$$\mathbf{\nabla} \times \mathbf{E} = -\frac{\partial (\mathbf{\nabla} \times \mathbf{A})}{\partial t} \tag{7-146}$$

from which

$$\mathbf{\nabla} \times \left(\mathbf{E} + \frac{\partial \mathbf{A}}{\partial t} \right) = 0 \tag{7-147}$$

Now since the curl of the expression in parentheses in (7-147) equals zero, it must be equal to the gradient of a scalar function. Thus we can write

$$\mathbf{E} + \frac{\partial \mathbf{A}}{\partial t} = \mathbf{\nabla} f \tag{7-148}$$

where f is a scalar function. If the electric scalar potential V is taken to be this scalar function, then a relation is obtained that satisfies the requirements for both static and time-varying situations. Thus let $f = -V$ so that from (7-148) we have

$$\mathbf{E} = -\mathbf{\nabla} V - \frac{\partial \mathbf{A}}{\partial t} \tag{7-149}$$

For static fields this reduces to $\mathbf{E} = -\mathbf{\nabla} V$, as it should. In the general case, where the field may vary with time, $\mathbf{E}$ is given by both a scalar potential V and a vector potential $\mathbf{A}$ as in (7-149). If the time variation is harmonic, (7-149) becomes

$$\mathbf{E} = -\mathbf{\nabla} V - j\omega \mathbf{A} \tag{7-150}$$

Knowing the vector potential $\mathbf{A}$ and the scalar potential V, the electric and magnetic fields may now be obtained under static or time-varying situations from the relations

$$\mathbf{E} = -\mathbf{\nabla} V - \frac{\partial \mathbf{A}}{\partial t} \quad \text{volts/meter} \tag{7-151}$$

and

$$\mathbf{B} = \mathbf{\nabla} \times \mathbf{A} \quad \text{webers/meter}^2 \tag{7-152}$$

where

$$V = \frac{1}{4\pi\epsilon_0} \int_v \frac{\rho}{r} \, dv \quad \text{volts}$$

$$\mathbf{A} = \frac{\mu}{4\pi} \int_v \frac{\mathbf{J}}{r} \, dv \quad \text{webers/meter}$$

It is assumed that the distance r in the expressions for V and $\mathbf{A}$ is small compared with a wavelength so that propagation time effects can be neglected. If this is not the case, the propagation time must be considered and the more general retarded form used for ρ and $\mathbf{J}$ as explained in Chap. 13. (See Secs. 13-3 and 13-5.)

7-25. Comparison of Electric and Magnetic Field Relations. In Table 4-2 a comparison is made of electric and magnetic field equations. All of these apply in static or slowly time-varying situations. Under rapidly time-varying conditions certain of the relations may be extended so as apply under these conditions. These relations are listed in Table 7-2. It is to be noted that under static conditions the time derivatives are zero, and these relations reduce to the corresponding special cases given in Table 4-2. These static relations (Table 4-2) are also applicable in time-changing situations provided the variations are slow enough so that the time derivatives can be neglected. In more rapidly time-varying situations where the time derivatives cannot be neglected the expressions of Table 7-2 must be employed.

TABLE 7-2

COMPARISON OF ELECTRIC AND MAGNETIC FIELD RELATIONS FOR TIME-CHANGING SITUATIONS

Description of equation	Electric field	Magnetic field
Curl equations (point relations).	$\nabla \times \mathbf{E} = -\dfrac{\partial \mathbf{B}}{\partial t}$	$\nabla \times \mathbf{H} = \mathbf{J} + \dfrac{\partial \mathbf{D}}{\partial t}$
Closed path of integration.......	$\mathcal{V} = \oint \mathbf{E} \cdot dl = -\int_s \dfrac{\partial \mathbf{B}}{\partial t} \cdot ds$	$F = \oint \mathbf{H} \cdot dl = \int_s \left(\mathbf{J} + \dfrac{\partial \mathbf{D}}{\partial t} \right) \cdot ds$
Derivation of fields from scalar and vector potentials†..	$\mathbf{E} = -\nabla V - \dfrac{\partial \mathbf{A}}{\partial t}$	$\mathbf{B} = \nabla \times \mathbf{A}$

† V and A are as indicated in connection with (7-151) and (7-152).

PROBLEMS

7-1. A 1-turn loop with an area of 1 meter² is situated in air with a uniform magnetic field normal to the plane of the loop. If the flux density is changing 2 webers/meter²/sec, what is the emf appearing at the terminals of the loop?   *Ans.:* 2 volts.

7-2. How many turns are required in a loop of 10 cm radius to develop a maximum emf of 0.1 volt rms at the loop terminals if the loop rotates 30 rps in the earth's magnetic field? Take the flux density **B** of the earth's field at 6×10^{-5} weber/meter².

7-3. A 1-turn wire loop of 0.1 meter² area is situated in air in a 10-Mc/sec radio-frequency field. If 1 volt rms is induced in the loop, what is the rms value of **H** normal to the plane of the loop?   *Ans.:* 0.126 ampere/meter.

7-4. A short bar magnet of 10 amp-meters² magnetic moment rotates around its center point at 1 rps. A 100-turn loop of 0.1 meter² area is located 2 meters from the bar magnet. What is the largest peak emf which the field of the magnet can induce in the loop? *Note:* When the circuit is fixed but the field moves, causing B at the circuit to change, Eq. (II) of Sec. 7-5 yields zero and the resultant emf is given by (III).

7-5. A toroidal coil of 1,000 turns has a mean radius of 20 cm and a radius for the winding of 2 cm. What is the average self-inductance (a) with an air core and (b) with an iron core having an average relative incremental permeability of 800?

Ans.: (a) 1.26 mh; *(b)* 1.006 henrys.

7-6. What is the mutual inductance of an ideal transformer if a 60-cps current of 1 amp rms applied to the primary induces 10 volts rms at the secondary terminals?

7-7. A fixed, square 5-turn coil with lower left corner at the origin has sides of length x_1 and y_1. If $x_1 = y_1 = 1$ meter and if the magnetic flux density **B** is normal to the plane of the coil and has a space variation of amplitude

$$B_0 = 3 \sin \frac{\pi x}{x_1} \sin \frac{\pi y}{y_1} \quad \text{webers/meter}^2$$

find the rms emf induced in the coil if B varies harmonically with time 1,000 cps.

Ans.: 27,000 volts rms.

7-8. What is the displacement current density of a magnetic field in free space given by $H_z = H_0 \sin (\omega t - \beta x)$? $H_x = H_y = 0$.

7-9. An air capacitor consisting of two flat, parallel, square plates measuring 20 by 20 cm and spaced 2 cm apart has a 1,000-ohm resistor connected between the centers of the plates. A 10-Mc/sec emf of 10 volts peak is applied to the capacitor. Neglect fringing of the field. Find (a) the rms displacement current through the capacitor, (b) the rms conduction current, and (c) the total current.

Ans. (c) 10.6 ma.

7-10. A capacitor consisting of two flat parallel plates 50 by 50 cm square and spaced 10 cm apart is completely filled with a slab of dielectric material. An emf of 2,000 volts rms at 1 Mc/sec is applied to the plates. Find the power dissipated as heat in the dielectric if the dielectric has a power factor of 0.005 and a relative dielectric constant of 8.

7-11. A 10-turn coil of 0.01 meter² area rotates 3,600 rpm (60 rps) in a uniform field of flux density $B = 0.1$ weber/meter². Find the peak induced emf. The coil axis is normal to **B**. *Ans.:* 3.77 volts.

7-12. Given that the average power dissipated per unit volume of a medium is $E(\partial D/\partial t) \cos \theta$ watts/meter³, where θ = time-phase angle between E and D. Show that the total average power dissipated in a parallel-plate capacitor is $VI \cos \theta$ watts, where V = voltage across capacitor and I = current through capacitor. The medium filling the capacitor is nonconducting. Neglect fringing. E, D, V, and I are rms values.

7-13. Show that

$$\int_s \frac{\partial \mathbf{B}}{\partial t} \cdot ds = \oint \frac{\partial \mathbf{A}}{\partial t} \cdot dl$$

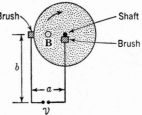

7-14. A thin brass disc 20 cm in diameter is situated with its plane normal to a magnetic field of constant flux density $B = 1$ weber/meter². The magnetic field is everywhere uniform (see Fig. 7-25). If the disc rotates 1 rps, find the emf $\mho$ developed at the terminals connected as shown to brushes, one placed against the periphery of the disc and the other against the shaft. This arrangement is called a *Faraday disc generator.*

FIG. 7-25. Faraday disc generator.

7-15. Repeat Prob. 7-14 with the modification that the magnetic field varies with time as given by $B = B_0 \sin \omega t$, where $B_0 = 1$ weber/meter² and $\omega = 2\pi \times 10$ rad/sec.

7-16. In a betatron the average flux density inside the electron orbit is given as a function of time by $B = B_0 \sin \omega t$, where $B_0 = 0.05$ weber/meter^2 and $\omega = 2\pi \times 60$ rad/sec. The radius of the electron orbit is 10 cm. Neglect relativistic effects.

a. Find the velocity v of the electrons at a time $t = 1$ millisec if $v \simeq 0$ at $t = 0$.

b. Find the energy per unit charge imparted to the electron in one revolution in its orbit.

c. Find the number of revolutions in 1 millisec.

d. Express the electron energy after 1 millisec in electron volts.

7-17. Show that a field given by $B = k/r$, where k is a constant and r is the radial distance, is a field satisfying the 1 to 2 condition at any radius in a betatron. *Note:* In practice a field $B = k/r^n$, where n is less than 1, is used. The 1 to 2 condition is still satisfied at the electron orbit $(r = R)$, but this type of field also focuses the beam in such a way as to provide radial and axial stability to the electron orbit.

7-18. A vector field is of the form $\mathbf{F} = \mathbf{i}F_x + \mathbf{j}F_y + \mathbf{k}F_z$, where $F_x = F_z = 0$ and $F_y = \sin x$. (*a*) Find curl $\mathbf{F}$. (*b*) Find div (curl $\mathbf{F}$). (*c*) Draw a diagram showing $\mathbf{F}$ and curl $\mathbf{F}$ as a function of x over a distance of at least 2π rad.

7-19. A magnetic field varying harmonically with time 10^6 cps induces a peak emf of 5 volts in a single-turn square loop of 10 meters^2 area. The plane of the loop is at an angle of 45° with respect to the direction of the field. Find the peak value of $\mathbf{B}$.

7-20. A 1-henry inductance has a resistance of 5 ohms. If a steady emf of 10 volts is applied at $t = 0$, find the length of time required for the current in the inductance to reach 80 per cent of its final value.

7-21. A small flip coil used to measure magnetic fields has 50 turns and an area of 10 cm^2. The field is normal to the plane of the coil. If a ballistic galvanometer connected to the coil indicates the passage of 10^{-4} coulomb when the coil is flipped 180°, find the flux density B. The coil-galvanometer circuit has a resistance of 500 ohms.

CHAPTER 8

THE RELATION BETWEEN FIELD AND
CIRCUIT THEORY. MAXWELL'S EQUATIONS

8-1. Introduction. In circuit theory we deal with circuit elements, the voltage V across them, and the total current I through them. In field theory we deal with the field vectors ($\mathbf{E}$, $\mathbf{D}$, $\mathbf{B}$, $\mathbf{H}$, and $\mathbf{J}$) and their values as a function of position.

Consider, for instance, a short rod of length l and cross-sectional area A in Fig. 8-1. In low-frequency-

FIG. 8-1. Conducting rod.

circuit theory it is convenient to describe the rod in terms of one quantity, its resistance R. Its length, area, and shape are of secondary importance. Thus the voltage difference between the ends of the rod is, from Ohm's law,

$$V = IR \qquad (8\text{-}1)$$

where I = current through rod.

From the field-theory point of view we consider the value of the electric field $\mathbf{E}$ at a point in the rod. From Ohm's law at a point

$$\mathbf{E} = \frac{\mathbf{J}}{\sigma} \qquad \text{volts/meter} \qquad (8\text{-}2)$$

where $\mathbf{J}$ = conduction current density (amp/meter^2)

σ = conductivity (mhos/meter)

Now, integrating (8-2) over the length of the rod, we obtain the voltage difference V between the ends. That is,

$$V = \int \mathbf{E} \cdot d\mathbf{l} = \int \frac{\mathbf{J}}{\sigma} \cdot d\mathbf{l} \qquad (8\text{-}3)$$

For a uniform rod with uniform current density this becomes

$$V = \frac{Jl}{\sigma} = JA\,\frac{l}{\sigma A} \qquad \text{volts} \qquad (8\text{-}4)$$

where $JA = I$ = current through rod (amp)

$\dfrac{l}{\sigma A} = R$ = resistance of rod (ohms)

A = cross-sectional area of rod (meters^2)

331

Thus, from (8-4) we have

$$V = IR \qquad (8\text{-}5)$$

Starting with field theory we have arrived at the circuit relation known as Ohm's law.

Historically this and other circuit relations were postulated and verified first. Then, as a generalization, they were extended so as to apply to the more general field situation. It follows, therefore, that circuit relations are simply special cases of field equations and may be deduced from them. Although field relations are more general, it is usually much simpler to use circuit equations wherever these are applicable.

Equation (8-1) is a pure circuit relation. On the other hand, (8-2) is a pure field relation. Many equations are not purely one or the other but are a combination or mixture. Such mixed relations are necessary, for example, in order to provide a connection between field and circuit theory. Two important equations that provide such connecting links are

$$V = \int \mathbf{E} \cdot d\mathbf{l} \qquad \text{volts} \qquad (8\text{-}6)$$

and

$$I = \oint \mathbf{H} \cdot d\mathbf{l} \qquad \text{amp} \qquad (8\text{-}7)$$

Equation (8-6) relates V (a circuit quantity) between two points to the line integral of $\mathbf{E}$ (a field quantity), between those points. Likewise (8-7), which is Ampère's law, relates I (a circuit quantity) to the line integral of $\mathbf{H}$ (a field quantity) around a closed path.

8-2. Applications of Circuit and Field Theory. While field relations are applicable in general, circuit relations are usually more convenient wherever V and I have a simple, well-defined significance.

Thus, in determining the capacitance of a capacitor of irregular shape with the aid of a graphical field map (see Fig. 2-24) we are in effect directing our attention to the field and its value as a function of position in the capacitor. However, once we have determined the capacitance, we may at low frequencies consider it as simply a two-terminal circuit element of capacitance C with a voltage difference V. The physical size and shape of the capacitor and the field configuration within it are then relegated to positions of secondary importance.

As another illustration let us consider the coaxial transmission line, shown in cross section in Fig. 8-2, under two conditions, one where V and I are useful quantities and one where they are not. The coaxial line has an inner conductor of radius a and an outer conductor of inside radius b. With a steady potential difference between the conductors the electric field lines are radial as shown. If a current I is flowing, the magnetic field lines $\mathbf{H}$ are circles as indicated. Now by (8-6) the potential difference between the inner and outer conductors is

$$V = \int_a^b \mathbf{E} \cdot d\mathbf{r} \qquad \text{volts} \tag{8-8}$$

Likewise from (8-7) the current I in the inner conductor is

$$I = \oint \mathbf{H} \cdot d\mathbf{l} = \int_0^{2\pi} Hr\, d\theta \qquad \text{amp} \tag{8-9}$$

In (8-8) V is independent of the path between the conductors, while in (8-9) I is independent of the radius r provided it is between a and b. Hence, V and I have a simple, definite significance in this case and are useful quantities.

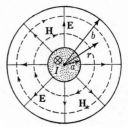

The field configuration shown in Fig. 8-2 is called a Transverse Electro Magnetic field (abbreviated TEM) because the electric and magnetic field are entirely transverse (no component in the axial direction). This type of field is the only configuration or field mode possible under steady conditions and also for time-varying situations where the wavelength is of the order of $4b$ or greater.[1] At

Fig. 8-2. Coaxial transmission line with TEM mode.

higher frequencies (shorter wavelengths) more complex field configurations known as higher-order modes become possible. These modes are characterized by having some field components in the axial direction. Although coaxial lines are seldom used under such conditions, suppose that the frequency is sufficiently high for the mode or configuration shown in Fig. 8-3 to exist. Both a cross (or transverse) section and a longitudinal (or axial) section are needed to show the field configuration. This field may be called a Transverse Magnetic (abbreviated TM) mode because the magnetic field is entirely transverse, while the electric field has a longitudinal component. Now, for this mode, the voltage V between the conductors as obtained by (8-8) may become negligible, while the current I obtained by (8-9) depends on the radius r at which $\mathbf{H}$ is integrated. Hence V and I no longer have a simple significance and are not as useful as the field quantities themselves. The breakdown of the circuit concept occurred here when the transverse dimensions became comparable with the wavelength.

[1] That is, the frequency is so high that a disturbance traveling with the velocity of light can travel only about a distance equal to the diameter ($2b$) in one-half period. In free space a wave has a wavelength λ in meters that is related to the frequency f in cycles per second by the velocity of light c as follows:

$$\lambda = c/f, \qquad \text{where } c = 3 \times 10^8 \text{ meters/sec}$$

For a further discussion of field modes in lines and guides see Chaps. 11 and 12.

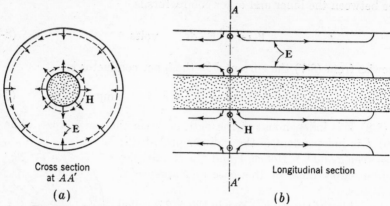

Cross section
at AA'

(a)

Longitudinal section

(b)

Fig. 8-3. Coaxial transmission line with higher-order (TM) mode.

8-3. The Series Circuit. Comparison of Field and Circuit Theory.[1]

From (7-151) the electric field $\mathbf{E}$ may be expressed in terms of a scalar potential V due to electric charges and a vector potential $\mathbf{A}$ due to currents by

$$\mathbf{E} = -\nabla V - \frac{\partial \mathbf{A}}{\partial t} \qquad (8\text{-}10)$$

At a point on or in a conductor the electric field is related to the current density $\mathbf{J}$ and the conductivity σ by Ohm's law at a point. That is,

$$\mathbf{E}_t = \frac{\mathbf{J}}{\sigma} \qquad (8\text{-}11)$$

where $\mathbf{E}_t = total$ electric field at the point. This total field is equal to $\mathbf{E}$ as given by (8-10) plus any additional applied or impressed field $\mathbf{E}_a$ due, for example, to a generator whose charges or currents are excluded from consideration in determining V and $\mathbf{A}$ in (8-10). Thus

$$\mathbf{E} + \mathbf{E}_a = \mathbf{E}_t \qquad (8\text{-}12)$$

and

$$\mathbf{E}_a = \mathbf{E}_t - \mathbf{E} \qquad \text{volts/meter} \qquad (8\text{-}13)$$

Substituting from (8-10) and (8-11) in (8-13), we obtain

$$\mathbf{E}_a = \frac{\mathbf{J}}{\sigma} + \frac{\partial \mathbf{A}}{\partial t} + \nabla V \qquad (8\text{-}14)$$

Consider now the application of this field relation to the stationary series circuit of Fig. 8-4 containing resistance, inductance, and capacitance. The total length of the circuit is assumed to be small compared

[1] See John R. Carson, Electromagnetic Theory and the Foundations of Circuit Theory, *Bell System Tech. J.*, **6**, 1–17, January, 1927.

with a wavelength so that the current I has the same value, at any instant, at all points of the circuit. A generator impresses an applied field $\mathbf{E}_a$ between terminals 1 and 2. If no capacitor is present (terminals 3 and 4 connected together) and the field relation (8-14) is integrated around a closed path that follows the conduct-ing circuit, we obtain

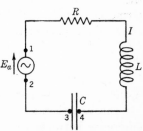

$$\oint \mathbf{E}_a \cdot d\mathbf{l} = \oint \frac{\mathbf{J}}{\sigma} \cdot d\mathbf{l} + \oint \frac{\partial \mathbf{A}}{\partial t} \cdot d\mathbf{l} \quad (8\text{-}15)$$

There is no contribution from the third term of the right-hand side of (8-14) since the line integral around a closed path of a field due to a scalar potential is zero. It is assumed that $\mathbf{E}_a$ exists only between terminals 1 and 2. Hence

$$\oint \mathbf{E}_a \cdot d\mathbf{l} = \int_1^2 \mathbf{E}_a \cdot d\mathbf{l} = \mho \quad \text{volts} \quad (8\text{-}16)$$

Fig. 8-4. Series circuit with resistance, inductance, and capacitance.

where $\mho$ = emf applied (at terminals 1 and 2) by generator. The generator is assumed to be impedanceless.

Now $\oint (\mathbf{J}/\sigma) \cdot d\mathbf{l}$ in (8-15) yields the total IR drop around the circuit. In Fig. 8-4 the total resistance R of the circuit is assumed to be lumped in a single resistor.

The last term in (8-15) may be reexpressed as[1]

$$\frac{d}{dt} \oint \mathbf{A} \cdot d\mathbf{l} = \frac{dI}{dt} \oint \frac{\mathbf{A}}{I} \cdot d\mathbf{l} = L \frac{dI}{dt} \quad (8\text{-}16a)$$

where $L = \oint \dfrac{\mathbf{A}}{I} \cdot d\mathbf{l}$ = inductance of circuit

$\mathbf{A} = \dfrac{\mu_0}{4\pi} \displaystyle\int_v \dfrac{\mathbf{J}}{r} \, dv$ = vector potential

In Fig. 8-4 the total inductance L of the circuit is shown lumped in a single inductor. Since $\mathbf{A}$ is proportional to the current, it follows that $\mathbf{A}/I$ and hence L is independent of the current. Thus, for the case of a closed circuit consisting of a generator, a resistor, and an inductance the field relation (8-15) reduces to the circuit equation

$$\mho = IR + L \frac{dI}{dt} \quad (8\text{-}17)$$

[1] The transformation of (8-16a) may be also made with the aid of Stokes' theorem, recalling that $\mathbf{B} = \nabla \times \mathbf{A}$ and $\Lambda = LI$, as follows,

$$\frac{d}{dt} \oint \mathbf{A} \cdot d\mathbf{l} = \frac{d}{dt} \int_s (\nabla \times \mathbf{A}) \cdot d\mathbf{s} = \frac{d}{dt} \int_s \mathbf{B} \cdot d\mathbf{s} = \frac{d\Lambda}{dt} = L \frac{dI}{dt}$$

where L is the inductance of the loop and I the current through it. It is simplest here, though not essential, to think of the inductor as a single-turn loop.

Let us now reintroduce the capacitor between terminals 3 and 4 (Fig. 8-4). If we integrate (8-14) for this case around a closed path that follows the conducting circuit and across the gap in the capacitor, the contribution of the term involving J/σ becomes indeterminate because in the capacitor J and σ both approach zero. Hence let us integrate all terms in (8-14) around a path that is closed except for the small gap across the capacitor (between terminals 3 and 4). This gives

$$\upsilon = IR + L\frac{dI}{dt} + V_c \qquad (8\text{-}18)$$

Assuming that the gap is very small, (8-18) is identical with (8-17) except for the additional term V_c representing the instantaneous potential difference between the plates of the capacitor. This was obtained by integrating ∇V around the conducting path from terminal 3 to 4. If we integrate ∇V from 4 to 3 across the capacitor, we obtain $-V_c$. Thus, the line integral of ∇V around a *closed path* from terminal 3 back to terminal 3 yields $V_c - V_c = 0$. Now V_c in (8-18) may be expressed in terms of the charge Q on the plates and the capacitance C by

$$V_c = \frac{Q}{C} = \frac{1}{C}\int I\,dt \qquad (8\text{-}19)$$

Thus, the field equation of (8-14) can be applied to a series RLC circuit to yield the familiar circuit equation[1]

$$\upsilon = IR + L\frac{dI}{dt} + \frac{1}{C}\int I\,dt \qquad (8\text{-}20)$$

For harmonic variation with respect to time (8-20) reduces to

$$\upsilon = IR + j\omega LI + \frac{I}{j\omega C} \qquad (8\text{-}20a)$$

or

$$\upsilon = IR + jI\left(\omega L - \frac{1}{\omega C}\right) \qquad (8\text{-}20b)$$

In deriving (8-20) from (8-14) the assumption was made that at any instant the current is the same at all parts of the circuit. This implies that a disturbance is propagated around the circuit instantaneously. If the circuit length is small compared with the wavelength, this is a satisfactory assumption. However, if the circuit length is appreciable compared with the wavelength (say at least $\frac{1}{8}$ wavelength), the variation in current and phase around the circuit may become significant. Under these circumstances the simple circuit concepts tend to become inadequate and inaccurate. It is also to be noted that the above circuit

[1] Compare with (7-80).

treatment ignores the phenomenon of radiation, which is so important at high frequencies (see Chap. 13).

There are certain exceptions to the above statement that circuit concepts become inadequate when the circuit length is comparable with the wavelength. For example, circuit concepts are successfully applied to the long transmission line. In this case, the distributed inductance and capacitance are represented by suitable lumped elements (see Chap. 11). Although the length of the line can be many wavelengths, it is significant, however, that even in this extension of circuit theory the treatment is adequate only for lines with transverse dimensions that are very small compared with the wavelength.

8-4. Maxwell's Equations as Generalizations of Circuit Equations. In the remainder of this chapter a number of relations developed in the preceding chapters are brought together and considered as a group. These relations are known as *Maxwell's equations* and consist of four expressions: one derived from Ampère's law, one from Faraday's law, and two derived from Gauss's law. These equations are of profound importance and, together with boundary, continuity, and other auxiliary relations, form the basic tools for the analysis of most electromagnetic problems.

In Chap. 4 Ampère's law relating the line integral of **H** around a closed path to the current I enclosed is given as

$$\oint \mathbf{H} \cdot d\mathbf{l} = I \qquad (8\text{-}21)$$

Replacing the current I by the surface integral of the conduction current density **J** over an area bounded by the path of integration of **H**, we have the more general relation

$$\oint \mathbf{H} \cdot d\mathbf{l} = \int_s \mathbf{J} \cdot d\mathbf{s} \qquad (8\text{-}22)$$

In Chap. 7 this relation was made even more general by adding a displacement current density to the conduction current density so that (8-22) becomes

$$\oint \mathbf{H} \cdot d\mathbf{l} = \int_s \left(\mathbf{J} + \frac{\partial \mathbf{D}}{\partial t} \right) \cdot d\mathbf{s} \qquad (8\text{-}23a)$$

This relation is called Maxwell's equation as derived from Ampère's law. In (8-23a) it is given in its integral form, the line integral of **H** being taken over a closed path bounding the surface s. In circuit parlance a closed path or loop is often called a "mesh." Hence, (8-23a) is a *mesh relation*. Applying Stokes' theorem to (8-23a), we obtain the corresponding *point relation*

$$\nabla \times \mathbf{H} = \mathbf{J} + \frac{\partial \mathbf{D}}{\partial t} \qquad (8\text{-}23b)$$

Equation (8-23b) is a differential relation and relates the field quantities at a point. It is the differential form of Maxwell's equation as derived from Ampère's law.

In Chap. 7 Faraday's law relating the emf $\mathcal{U}$ induced in a circuit to the time rate of decrease of the total magnetic flux linking the circuit is given as

$$\mathcal{U} = -\frac{d\Lambda}{dt} \qquad (8\text{-}24a)$$

Replacing the flux linkage Λ by the surface integral of $\mathbf{B}$ over the area bounded by the circuit, we have the more general equation

$$\mathcal{U} = -\frac{d}{dt}\int_s \mathbf{B} \cdot d\mathbf{s} \qquad (8\text{-}24b)$$

Replacing $\mathcal{U}$ in (8-24b) by the line integral of $\mathbf{E}$ around the circuit, we have the still more general relation (for stationary circuits) that

$$\oint \mathbf{E} \cdot d\mathbf{l} = -\int_s \frac{\partial \mathbf{B}}{\partial t} \cdot d\mathbf{s} \qquad (8\text{-}25)$$

This field relation is a generalization of Faraday's circuit law (8-24a). Equation (8-25) is called Maxwell's equation as derived from Faraday's law. It is given in (8-25) in integral form, that is to say, it is a mesh equation. The corresponding point relation may be obtained from (8-25) by an application of Stokes' theorem, yielding

$$\nabla \times \mathbf{E} = -\frac{\partial \mathbf{B}}{\partial t} \qquad (8\text{-}26)$$

Equation (8-26) is a differential relation and relates the field quantities at a point. It is the differential form of Maxwell's equation as derived from Faraday's law.

In Chap. 1 Gauss's law relating the surface integral of the electric flux density $\mathbf{D}$ to the charge Q enclosed is given as

$$\oint_s \mathbf{D} \cdot d\mathbf{s} = Q \qquad (8\text{-}27)$$

Replacing Q in (8-27) by the volume integral of the charge density ρ throughout the volume enclosed by the surface s, (8-27) may be written in a more general form as

$$\oint_s \mathbf{D} \cdot d\mathbf{s} = \int_v \rho \, dv \qquad (8\text{-}28)$$

This field relation is a generalization of Gauss's law and is called Maxwell's electric field equation as derived from Gauss's law. In (8-28) it appears in integral form and applies to a finite volume v. Applying

(8-28) to an infinitesimal volume, we can obtain the corresponding differential relation that relates the field quantities at a point as given by

$$\nabla \cdot \mathbf{D} = \rho \qquad (8\text{-}29)$$

Equation (8-29) is Maxwell's electric field equation as derived from Gauss's law in differential form.

In the case of magnetic fields the surface integral of $\mathbf{B}$ over a closed surface s yields zero. Thus the magnetic counterpart of Gauss's electric field relation (8-27) is

$$\oint_s \mathbf{B} \cdot d\mathbf{s} = 0 \qquad (8\text{-}30)$$

The corresponding differential or point relation is

$$\nabla \cdot \mathbf{B} = 0 \qquad (8\text{-}31)$$

Equations (8-30) and (8-31) may be referred to as Maxwell's magnetic field equations as derived from Gauss's law. Equation (8-30) is the integral and (8-31) is the differential form.

The development of Maxwell's equations as generalizations of circuit relations involves both inductive and physical reasoning. It is not implied that the "derivation" is rigorous. Maxwell's equations are justified by the fact that conclusions based on them have been found in innumerable cases to be in excellent agreement with experiment, in the same way as the earlier circuit relations are justified within their more restricted domain by the excellent agreement of conclusions based on them with experiment. It is perhaps worth recalling that Maxwell's equations were *not* generally accepted for many years after they were postulated (1873). His curl equations (involving $\nabla \times \mathbf{E}$ and $\nabla \times \mathbf{H}$) implied that time-varying electric and magnetic fields in empty space were interdependent, a changing electric field being able to generate a magnetic field, and vice versa. The inference from this is that a time-changing electromagnetic field would propagate energy through empty space with the velocity of light (see Chap. 9) and, further, that light is electromagnetic in nature. Radio waves were unknown at the time, and it was 15 years (1888) before Hertz demonstrated that electromagnetic (or radio) waves were possible as predicted by Maxwell.

There is no guarantee that Maxwell's equations are exact. However, in so far as the precision of experimental measurements allow, they appear to be, and therefore we may regard them as exact.

Along with Maxwell's equations certain other fundamental relations are of importance in dealing with electromagnetic problems. Among these may be mentioned Ohm's law at a point (3-21)

$$\mathbf{J} = \sigma \mathbf{E} \qquad (8\text{-}32)$$

the continuity relation (3-58)

$$\nabla \cdot \mathbf{J} = -\frac{\partial \rho}{\partial t} \tag{8-33}$$

the force relations

$$\mathbf{F} = q\mathbf{E} \tag{8-34}$$
$$d\mathbf{F} = I \, d\mathbf{l} \times \mathbf{B} \tag{8-35}$$

and the relations between $\mathbf{E}$ and $\mathbf{D}$ and between $\mathbf{B}$ and $\mathbf{H}$ as given by

$$\mathbf{D} = \epsilon\mathbf{E} = \epsilon_0\mathbf{E} + \mathbf{P} \tag{8-36}$$
$$\mathbf{B} = \mu\mathbf{H} = \mu_0(\mathbf{H} + \mathbf{M}) \tag{8-37}$$

8-5. Maxwell's Equations in Free Space. In the preceding section, Maxwell's equations are stated in their general form. For the special case of free space, where the current density $\mathbf{J}$ and the charge density ρ are zero, the equations reduce to a simpler form. In integral form the equations are

$$\oint \mathbf{H} \cdot d\mathbf{l} = \int_s \frac{\partial \mathbf{D}}{\partial t} \cdot d\mathbf{s} \tag{8-38}$$

$$\oint \mathbf{E} \cdot d\mathbf{l} = -\int_s \frac{\partial \mathbf{B}}{\partial t} \cdot d\mathbf{s} \tag{8-39}$$

$$\oint_s \mathbf{D} \cdot d\mathbf{s} = 0 \tag{8-40}$$

$$\oint_s \mathbf{B} \cdot d\mathbf{s} = 0 \tag{8-41}$$

In differential form the equations are

$$\nabla \times \mathbf{H} = \frac{\partial \mathbf{D}}{\partial t} \tag{8-42}$$

$$\nabla \times \mathbf{E} = -\frac{\partial \mathbf{B}}{\partial t} \tag{8-43}$$

$$\nabla \cdot \mathbf{D} = 0 \tag{8-44}$$
$$\nabla \cdot \mathbf{B} = 0 \tag{8-45}$$

8-6. Maxwell's Equations for Harmonically Varying Fields. If we assume that the fields vary harmonically with time, Maxwell's equations may be expressed in another special form. Thus, if $\mathbf{D}$ varies with time as given by

$$\mathbf{D} = \mathbf{D}_0 e^{j\omega t} \tag{8-46}$$

then

$$\frac{\partial \mathbf{D}}{\partial t} = j\omega\mathbf{D}_0 e^{j\omega t} = j\omega\mathbf{D} \tag{8-47}$$

Making the same assumption for $\mathbf{B}$, Maxwell's equations in integral form

TABLE 8-1
MAXWELL'S EQUATIONS IN INTEGRAL FORM

Dimensions	From Ampère	From Faraday	From Gauss	From Gauss
mksc units / Case	Mmf	Emf	Electric flux	Magnetic flux
	Amperes	Volts	Coulombs	Webers
General	$F = \oint H \cdot dl = \int_s \left(J + \frac{\partial D}{\partial t} \right) \cdot ds = I_{total}$	$\mathcal{V} = \oint E \cdot dl = - \int_s \frac{\partial B}{\partial t} \cdot ds$	$\psi = \oint_s D \cdot ds = \int_v \rho \, dv$	$\psi_m = \oint_s B \cdot ds = 0$
Free space	$F = \oint H \cdot dl = \int_s \frac{\partial D}{\partial t} \cdot ds = I_{disp}$	$\mathcal{V} = \oint E \cdot dl = - \int_s \frac{\partial B}{\partial t} \cdot ds$	$\psi = \oint_s D \cdot ds = 0$	$\psi_m = \oint_s B \cdot ds = 0$
Harmonic variation	$F = \oint H \cdot dl = (\sigma + j\omega\epsilon) \int_s E \cdot ds = I_{total}$	$\mathcal{V} = \oint E \cdot dl = -j\omega\mu \int_s H \cdot ds$	$\psi = \oint_s D \cdot ds = \int_v \rho \, dv$	$\psi_m = \oint_s B \cdot ds = 0$
Steady	$F = \oint H \cdot dl = \int_s J \cdot ds = I_{cond}$	$V = \oint E \cdot dl = 0$	$\psi = \oint_s D \cdot ds = \int_v \rho \, dv$	$\psi_m = \oint_s B \cdot ds = 0$
Static	$U = \oint H \cdot dl = 0$	$V = \oint E \cdot dl = 0$	$\psi = \oint_s D \cdot ds = \int_v \rho \, dv$	$\psi_m = \oint_s B \cdot ds = 0$

reduce to

$$\oint \mathbf{H} \cdot d\mathbf{l} = (\sigma + j\omega\epsilon) \int_s \mathbf{E} \cdot d\mathbf{s} \qquad (8\text{-}48)$$

$$\oint \mathbf{E} \cdot d\mathbf{l} = -j\omega\mu \int_s \mathbf{H} \cdot d\mathbf{s} \qquad (8\text{-}49)$$

$$\oint_s \mathbf{D} \cdot d\mathbf{s} = \int_v \rho \, dv \qquad (8\text{-}50)$$

$$\oint_s \mathbf{B} \cdot d\mathbf{s} = 0 \qquad (8\text{-}51)$$

In differential form they are

$$\nabla \times \mathbf{H} = (\sigma + j\omega\epsilon)\mathbf{E} \qquad (8\text{-}52)$$
$$\nabla \times \mathbf{E} = -j\omega\mu\mathbf{H} \qquad (8\text{-}53)$$
$$\nabla \cdot \mathbf{D} = \rho \qquad (8\text{-}54)$$
$$\nabla \cdot \mathbf{B} = 0 \qquad (8\text{-}55)$$

8-7. Tables of Maxwell's Equations. Maxwell's equations are summarized in Tables 8-1 and 8-2. Table 8-1 gives Maxwell's equations in integral form and Table 8-2 in differential form. The equations are stated for the general case, free-space case, harmonic-variation case, steady case (static fields but with steady conduction currents), and static case (static fields with no currents). In Table 8-1 the equivalence is also indicated between the various field quantities and the electric potential V, the emf υ, the magnetic potential U, the mmf F, the total current I_{total}, the displacement current I_{disp}, the conduction current I_{cond}, the electric flux ψ, and the magnetic flux ψ_m. It should be noted that Maxwell's equations as tabulated here apply specifically to stationary systems or bodies at rest.

TABLE 8-2
MAXWELL'S EQUATIONS IN DIFFERENTIAL FORM

Case \ Dimensions	From Ampère — Electric current area	From Faraday — Electric potential area	From Gauss — Electric flux volume	From Gauss — Magnetic flux volume
General	$\nabla \times \mathbf{H} = \mathbf{J} + \dfrac{\partial \mathbf{D}}{\partial t}$	$\nabla \times \mathbf{E} = -\dfrac{\partial \mathbf{B}}{\partial t}$	$\nabla \cdot \mathbf{D} = \rho$	$\nabla \cdot \mathbf{B} = 0$
Free space	$\nabla \times \mathbf{H} = \dfrac{\partial \mathbf{D}}{\partial t}$	$\nabla \times \mathbf{E} = -\dfrac{\partial \mathbf{B}}{\partial t}$	$\nabla \cdot \mathbf{D} = 0$	$\nabla \cdot \mathbf{B} = 0$
Harmonic variation	$\nabla \times \mathbf{H} = (\sigma + j\omega\epsilon)\mathbf{E}$	$\nabla \times \mathbf{E} = -j\omega\mu\mathbf{H}$	$\nabla \cdot \mathbf{D} = \rho$	$\nabla \cdot \mathbf{B} = 0$
Steady	$\nabla \times \mathbf{H} = \mathbf{J}$	$\nabla \times \mathbf{E} = 0$	$\nabla \cdot \mathbf{D} = \rho$	$\nabla \cdot \mathbf{B} = 0$
Static	$\nabla \times \mathbf{H} = 0$	$\nabla \times \mathbf{E} = 0$	$\nabla \cdot \mathbf{D} = \rho$	$\nabla \cdot \mathbf{B} = 0$

PROBLEMS

8-1. State Maxwell's equations in their general integral form. Derive their form for harmonically varying fields.

8-2. State Maxwell's equations in their general differential form. Derive their form for harmonically varying fields.

8-3. (a) Obtain the integral form of Maxwell's equation from Ampère by generalizing Ampère's law. (b) Obtain the corresponding differential or point relation by applying Stokes' theorem.

8-4. Develop Maxwell's equation involving $\nabla \times \mathbf{E}$ from fundamental considerations of a closed circuit of infinitesimal area.

8-5. Show that the expression for the low-frequency inductance as given in (8-16a) by

$$L = \oint \frac{\mathbf{A}}{I} \cdot d\mathbf{l}$$

reduces for a conducting circuit to Neumann's low-frequency inductance formula,

$$L = \frac{\mu_0}{4\pi} \oint \oint \frac{d\mathbf{l}'}{r} \cdot d\mathbf{l}$$

8-6. A transmission line consisting of two parallel conductors has a length l and a conductor separation D (center to center). The conductors are thin wall tubes of

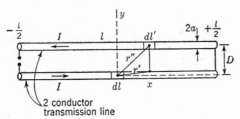

FIG. 8-5. Two-conductor transmission line.

radius a (see Fig. 8-5). Apply Neumann's low-frequency inductance formula (Prob. 8-5) to show that the inductance of the line is

$$L = \frac{\mu_0 l}{\pi} \ln \frac{D}{a} \qquad \text{henrys}$$

Compare with (4-71). Assume that $l \gg D$, and neglect end effects. *Hint:* Note that dl'/r in Neumann's formula may be expressed in this problem (see Fig. 8-5) as

$$\left(\frac{1}{r'} - \frac{1}{r''} \right) dx$$

where $r' = \sqrt{x^2 + a^2}$ and $r'' = \sqrt{x^2 + D^2}$.

CHAPTER 9

PLANE WAVES IN DIELECTRIC MEDIA

9-1. Introduction. The interdependence of electric and magnetic fields is demonstrated in a striking manner by an electromagnetic wave propagating through space. In such a wave the time-changing magnetic field may be regarded as generating a time-varying electric field, or vice versa, with the result that energy is propagated through empty space at the velocity of light.

In this chapter we begin the study of electromagnetic waves by considering the simplest case, namely, that of a plane, linearly polarized

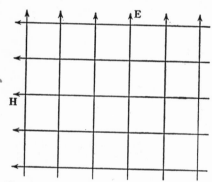

Fig. 9-1. Plane traveling wave approaching reader (out of page).

wave in a lossless dielectric medium. A plane wave may also be called a principal, zero-order, or TEM (transverse electromagnetic) wave since E and H are transverse to the direction of propagation. A study of plane waves forms an excellent introduction to wave phenomena in general and to such systems in particular as wave guides and transmission lines.

Although the following discussion deals largely with a plane wave in free space (vacuum), it is more general. It also applies for any lossless (nonconducting) dielectric medium which is isotropic, that is, one having properties that are the same in all directions.

The field lines for a wave propagating toward the reader (out of page) are indicated in Fig. 9-1. The directions of E and H are everywhere perpendicular. In a uniform plane wave E and H lie in a plane and have the same value everywhere in that plane.

9-2. Plane Waves and the Wave Equation. Referring to the right-handed coordinate system in Fig. 9-2, assume that a plane wave is traveling in the direction of the positive x axis. The electric field E has only a component E_y in the y direction and the magnetic field H only a com-

344

ponent H_z in the z direction.[1]   It is said that this wave is polarized in the y direction (vertically polarized).

Since we are dealing with a nonconducting medium, the conduction current density $\mathbf{J}$ is zero.   Thus Maxwell's equation from Ampère's law reduces to

$$\nabla \times \mathbf{H} = \frac{\partial \mathbf{D}}{\partial t} \tag{9-1}$$

or in rectangular coordinates

$$\mathbf{i}\left(\frac{\partial H_z}{\partial y} - \frac{\partial H_y}{\partial z}\right) + \mathbf{j}\left(\frac{\partial H_x}{\partial z} - \frac{\partial H_z}{\partial x}\right) + \mathbf{k}\left(\frac{\partial H_y}{\partial x} - \frac{\partial H_x}{\partial y}\right)$$
$$= \frac{\partial}{\partial t}\left(\mathbf{i}D_x + \mathbf{j}D_y + \mathbf{k}D_z\right) \tag{9-2}$$

For a plane wave traveling in the x direction the only components of (9-2) that contribute are

$$-\mathbf{j}\frac{\partial H_z}{\partial x} = \mathbf{j}\frac{\partial D_y}{\partial t} \tag{9-3}$$

Therefore

$$\frac{\partial H_z}{\partial x} = -\epsilon\frac{\partial E_y}{\partial t} \tag{9-4}$$

Maxwell's equation from Faraday's law is

$$\nabla \times \mathbf{E} = -\frac{\partial \mathbf{B}}{\partial t} \tag{9-5}$$

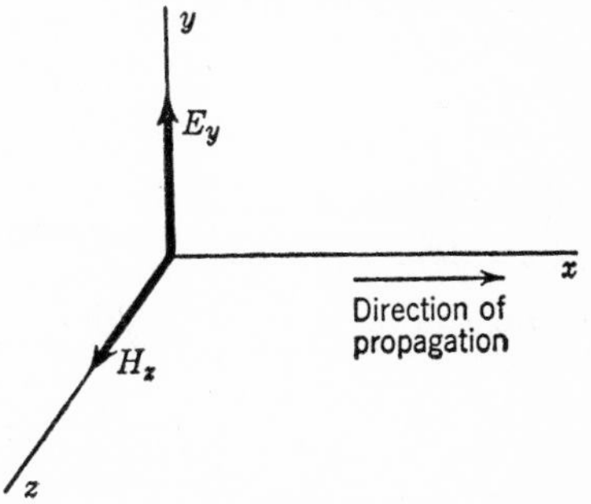

Fig. 9-2. Field components of plane wave with relation to coordinate system.

or in rectangular coordinates

$$\mathbf{i}\left(\frac{\partial E_z}{\partial y} - \frac{\partial E_y}{\partial z}\right) + \mathbf{j}\left(\frac{\partial E_x}{\partial z} - \frac{\partial E_z}{\partial x}\right) + \mathbf{k}\left(\frac{\partial E_y}{\partial x} - \frac{\partial E_x}{\partial y}\right)$$
$$= -\frac{\partial}{\partial t}\left(\mathbf{i}B_x + \mathbf{j}B_y + \mathbf{k}B_z\right) \tag{9-6}$$

For a plane wave traveling in the x direction the only components of (9-6) which contribute are[2]

$$\mathbf{k}\frac{\partial E_y}{\partial x} = -\mathbf{k}\frac{\partial B_z}{\partial t} \tag{9-7}$$

[1] The wave in Fig. 9-2 is traveling in the positive x direction since, applying the right-hand rule, $\mathbf{E}$ turned into $\mathbf{H}$ advances (as a right-handed screw) in the positive x direction.

[2] If it had been specified originally that the wave is linearly polarized with $\mathbf{E}$ in the y direction and that the wave travels in the x direction, it follows from (9-6) and also from (9-2) that $\mathbf{H}$ must be in the z direction.

Therefore

$$\frac{\partial E_y}{\partial x} = -\mu \frac{\partial H_z}{\partial t} \tag{9-8}$$

Equation (9-4) relates the space derivative of H_z to the time derivative of E_y, while (9-8) relates the space derivative of E_y to the time derivative of H_z. By differentiating (9-4) with respect to the time and (9-8) with respect to distance x, H_z can be eliminated and an expression obtained for E_y in terms of t and x. Proceeding in this way, we obtain, from (9-4),

$$\frac{\partial}{\partial t}\left(\frac{\partial H_z}{\partial x}\right) = -\epsilon \frac{\partial^2 E_y}{\partial t^2} \tag{9-9}$$

and from (9-8)

$$\frac{\partial^2 E_y}{\partial x^2} = -\mu \frac{\partial}{\partial x}\left(\frac{\partial H_z}{\partial t}\right) \tag{9-10}$$

Dividing (9-10) by $-\mu$ yields

$$-\frac{1}{\mu}\frac{\partial^2 E_y}{\partial x^2} = \frac{\partial}{\partial x}\left(\frac{\partial H_z}{\partial t}\right) \tag{9-11}$$

Since in (9-9) it does not matter whether we differentiate first with respect to x and then with respect to t, or vice versa, the left-hand side of (9-9) is equal to the right-hand side of (9-11) and it follows that

$$\frac{\partial^2 E_y}{\partial t^2} = \frac{1}{\mu\epsilon}\frac{\partial^2 E_y}{\partial x^2} \tag{9-12}$$

Equation (9-12) relates the space and time variation of the scalar magnitude E_y of the electric field intensity and is called a *wave equation* in E_y. It is, in fact, a scalar wave equation of the simplest form.

Differentiating (9-4) and (9-8) in the reverse order, that is, (9-4) with respect to x and (9-8) with respect to t, we can eliminate E_y and obtain a wave equation in H_z as

$$\frac{\partial^2 H_z}{\partial t^2} = \frac{1}{\mu\epsilon}\frac{\partial^2 H_z}{\partial x^2} \tag{9-13}$$

Both (9-12) and (9-13) are of the same form. A wave equation such as given by (9-12) and (9-13) has many important physical applications and is sometimes called *D'Alembert's equation*, having been integrated by him in 1747. If E_y in (9-12) is a transverse displacement, the equation can represent the motion of a disturbance on a stretched string. This was D'Alembert's problem. If E_y is a mechanical compression, then the equation can describe the motion of small oscillations of air in a narrow pipe. In our case E_y represents the scalar magnitude of the electric field intensity of a plane electromagnetic wave progressing in the x direction, and the equation is the most general way of describing the motion of this field as a function of time and space.

A uniform plane electromagnetic wave with both **E** and **H** transverse (perpendicular) to the direction of propagation is approximated by a small section of a free-space wave at a great distance from a source. As previously mentioned this type of wave may be called a principal or TEM wave. This kind of wave is usually the type found on two-wire or coaxial transmission lines, although on these lines the field is nonuniform, that is, **E** and **H** vary in direction and magnitude from point to point in a transverse plane. It will be noted, however, that a TEM wave cannot propagate in a hollow pipe or wave guide, since in such guides **E** and **H** are never both entirely transverse, there being always one field component in the direction of propagation. Such waves are called higher-order modes (see Chap. 12).

Let us now introduce a quantity v in (9-12) such that

$$v^2 = \frac{1}{\mu\epsilon} \qquad (9\text{-}14)$$

Equation (9-12) then becomes

$$\frac{\partial^2 E_y}{\partial t^2} = v^2 \frac{\partial^2 E_y}{\partial x^2} \qquad (9\text{-}15)$$

Dimensionally (9-15) is

$$\frac{\text{Volts}}{\text{Meter-second}^2} = v^2 \frac{\text{volts}}{\text{meter}^3}$$

so that

$$v = \frac{\text{meters}}{\text{second}}$$

Thus, it appears that v has the dimensions of velocity. This velocity is a characteristic of the medium, being dependent on the constants μ and ϵ for the medium. For free space (vacuum) v is approximately equal to 3×10^8 meters per sec.

9-3. Solutions of the Wave Equation. The wave equation (9-15) is a linear partial differential equation of the second order. To apply the equation, a solution must be found for E_y. Methods of solving this type of equation are discussed in texts on differential equations. It will suffice here to say that if we take the following trial solution

$$E_y = \sin \beta(x + mt) \qquad (9\text{-}16)$$

where $\beta = 2\pi/\lambda$
λ = wavelength
m = a constant (to be determined)
t = time
we find on substitution in (9-15) that

$$m = \pm v \qquad (9\text{-}17)$$

where v = velocity.   Hence a general solution for (9-15) is

$$E_y = \sin \beta(x + vt) + \sin \beta(x - vt) \qquad (9\text{-}18)$$

Either term alone is a solution, or the sum, as in (9-18), is a solution. This can be verified by taking the second derivatives of the solution in terms of t and x and substituting them in (9-15).   Since $v = f\lambda$, it follows that

$$\beta v = \frac{2\pi}{\lambda} f\lambda = 2\pi f = \omega \qquad (9\text{-}19)$$

Thus, (9-18) can also be expressed

$$E_y = \sin (\beta x + \omega t) + \sin (\beta x - \omega t) \qquad (9\text{-}20)$$

Suppose that the first term of (9-18) is considered by itself as a solution. That is,

$$E_y = \sin \beta(x + vt) \qquad (9\text{-}21)$$

The significance of (9-21) can be illustrated by evaluating E_y as a function of x for several values of the time t.   First let us take $t = 0$.   Then $E_y = \sin \beta x$.   The curve for this instant of time is shown by Fig. 9-3a.

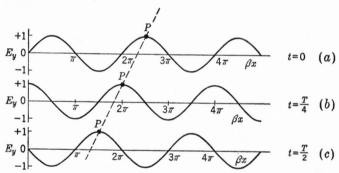

Fig. 9-3. Curves for $E_y = \sin (\beta x + \omega t)$ at three instants of time: $t = 0$, $t = T/4$, and $t = T/2$.   A constant phase point P moves to the left as time progresses.

Next consider the situation one-quarter period later, that is, when $t = T/4$, where T is the time of one period.   Then

$$\beta vt = \omega t = (2\pi f)t = \frac{2\pi}{T} t = \frac{2\pi}{T} \frac{T}{4} = \frac{\pi}{2} \qquad (9\text{-}22)$$

The curve for $t = T/4$ or $\omega t = \pi/2$ rad is shown in Fig. 9-3b.   One-half period later, $t = T/2$, and $\omega t = \pi$, yielding the curve of Fig. 9-3c.   Focusing our attention on the crest of one of the waves, as indicated by the point P, we note that as time progresses, P moves to the left.   From Fig. 9-3 we can thus interpret (9-21) as representing a wave traveling to the left, or in the negative x direction.   The maximum value of E_y for this wave is unity.

The point P is a point of constant phase and is characterized by the condition that

$$x + vt = \text{constant} \tag{9-23}$$

Taking the time derivative of (9-23) gives

$$\frac{dx}{dt} + v = 0 \tag{9-24}$$

and

$$\frac{dx}{dt} = -v \tag{9-25}$$

In (9-25), dx/dt is the rate of change of distance with respect to time, or velocity, of a constant phase point.   Hence, v is the velocity of a constant phase point and is called the *phase velocity*.   We note also that v is negative, which means that the wave is traveling in the negative x direction.

Next consider the last term of (9-18) as a solution by itself.   Then

$$E_y = \sin \beta(x - vt) = \sin (\beta x - \omega t) \tag{9-26}$$

Putting in values for $t = 0$, $T/4$, and $T/2$, we obtain from (9-26) the curves of Fig. 9-4.   Here a constant phase point P moves to the right as

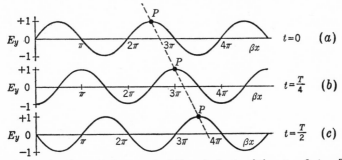

Fig. 9-4. Curves for $E_y = \sin (\beta x - \omega t)$ at three instants of time $t = 0$, $t = T/4$, and $t = T/2$.   A constant phase point P moves to the right as time progresses.

time progresses.   Hence (9-26) represents a wave traveling in the positive x direction.

If we set $x - vt$ equal to a constant and proceed in the same manner as for (9-24) and (9-25), we find in this case that

$$\frac{dx}{dt} = +v \tag{9-27}$$

Thus, the wave travels with a velocity v in the positive x direction.

To summarize, a negative sign in $x \pm vt$ or in $\beta x \pm \omega t$ is associated with a wave to the right, while a positive sign is associated with a wave to the left. Accordingly, when solutions with both positive and negative signs are given, as in (9-18), two waves are represented, one to the left and one to the right, and the complete solution is equal to the sum of both waves.

Let us now treat in somewhat more detail the wave traveling in the positive x direction as given by (9-26). A number of other forms can also be used which are equivalent except for a phase displacement. Three equivalent forms are

$$\left. \begin{array}{l} E_y = \sin{(\omega t - \beta x)} \\ E_y = \cos{(\beta x - \omega t)} \\ E_y = \cos{(\omega t - \beta x)} \end{array} \right\} \qquad (9\text{-}28)$$

These may be rewritten so that their relation to the first is more apparent. Thus, recalling that $\sin{(-u)} = -\sin{u} = \sin{(u + \pi)}$ and $\cos{(-u)} = \cos{u}$

$$\left. \begin{array}{l} E_y = \sin{(\omega t - \beta x)} = \sin{(\beta x - \omega t + \pi)} \\[2mm] E_y = \cos{(\beta x - \omega t)} = \sin{\left(\beta x - \omega t + \dfrac{\pi}{2}\right)} \\[2mm] E_y = \cos{(\omega t - \beta x)} = \sin{\left(\beta x - \omega t + \dfrac{\pi}{2}\right)} \end{array} \right\} \qquad (9\text{-}29)$$

The relation of the three forms of (9-29) to (9-26) is illustrated graphically in Fig. 9-5. Here the four forms are compared for $t = 0$. On sub-

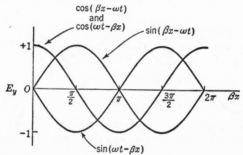

FIG. 9-5. Four forms of wave expression at $t = 0$.

stituting other values of t into the four equations, it is seen that in each case the equation represents a wave traveling to the right. The only difference between them is that in some cases there is a phase displacement of $\pi/2$ or π.

If the phase displacement is disregarded, any of the four forms given by (9-26) and (9-28) can be selected to represent a wave traveling in the positive x direction. Suppose, then, we choose the form

$$E_y = \sin(\omega t - \beta x) \tag{9-30}$$

This choice has the advantage that the term with the time t is positive for waves traveling in either the positive or the negative x direction.

Thus far, it has been assumed that the maximum amplitude of E_y is unity. If now we specify the maximum amplitude as E_0, we have

$$E_y = E_0 \sin(\omega t - \beta x) \tag{9-31}$$

Since $f = 1/T$, (9-31) can be expressed in a form in which the period T appears explicitly. For the sake of symmetry, let us also put $\beta = 2\pi/\lambda$, obtaining

$$E_y = E_0 \sin\left(2\pi \frac{t}{T} - 2\pi \frac{x}{\lambda}\right) \tag{9-32}$$

These expressions, (9-31) and (9-32), represent a wave traveling in the positive x direction. The corresponding expressions for a wave traveling in the negative x direction are

$$E_y = E_0 \sin(\omega t + \beta x) \tag{9-33}$$

and

$$E_y = E_0 \sin\left(2\pi \frac{t}{T} + 2\pi \frac{x}{\lambda}\right) \tag{9-34}$$

The solutions of the wave equation given by (9-31) and (9-33) are *trigonometric* solutions. We may also express the solution in *exponential* form. Thus

$$E_y = E_0 e^{j(\omega t \pm \beta x)} \tag{9-35}$$

where it is understood that the instantaneous value of the field is given by the imaginary (or real) part of the exponential function. Thus, taking the imaginary part (Im) we have

$$E_y = E_0 \text{ Im } e^{j(\omega t - \beta x)} = E_0 \sin(\omega t - \beta x) \tag{9-36}$$

If the real part (Re) is taken, we obtain

$$E_y = E_0 \text{ Re } e^{j(\omega t - \beta x)} = E_0 \cos(\omega t - \beta x) \tag{9-37}$$

Taking the second derivatives of (9-35) with respect to t and x, it may be verified that (9-35) is indeed a solution.

9-4. Table of Solutions of Wave Equation. In Table 9-1 both trigonometric and exponential solutions are given for a plane wave in a lossless medium. Solutions are listed for waves traveling to the left (negative x direction) and to the right (positive x direction). Solutions given by the sum of two such independent solutions are also included.

TABLE 9-1
TABLE OF SOLUTIONS OF WAVE EQUATION

	Trigonometric form	Exponential form
Wave to right..	$E_y = E_1 \sin (\omega t - \beta x)$	$E_y = E_1 e^{j(\omega t - \beta x)}$
Wave to left....	$E_y = E_0 \sin (\omega t + \beta x)$	$E_y = E_0 e^{j(\omega t + \beta x)}$
Two waves.	$E_y = E_0 \sin (\omega t + \beta x) + E_1 \sin (\omega t - \beta x)$	$E_y = E_0 e^{j(\omega t + \beta x)} + E_1 e^{j(\omega t - \beta x)}$

9-5. Phase Velocity. We have seen that $x - vt$ is a constant for a point of constant phase in a traveling wave. It follows that $\omega t - \beta x$ is a constant. That is, t and x must vary together so that

$$\omega t - \beta x = \text{constant} \tag{9-38}$$

Differentiating (9-38) with respect to time to find the velocity of the constant phase point, as done in (9-24), yields

$$\omega - \beta \frac{dx}{dt} = 0 \tag{9-39}$$

or

$$\frac{dx}{dt} = \frac{\omega}{\beta} \tag{9-40}$$

Thus, the *phase velocity*, or velocity of a constant phase point, is given by ω/β. That ω/β has the dimensions of velocity is more apparent if it is reexpressed

$$\frac{\omega}{\beta} = \frac{2\pi f}{2\pi/\lambda} = \lambda f \tag{9-41}$$

where λ = wavelength
f = frequency
The product λf has the dimensions of wavelength (distance) times frequency (reciprocal of time). Thus, λf has the dimensions of distance per time or velocity.

From (9-14) we have that the phase velocity is

$$\frac{\omega}{\beta} = v = \frac{1}{\sqrt{\mu\epsilon}} \tag{9-42}$$

Equation (9-42) gives the phase velocity of a wave in an unbounded medium of permeability μ and permittivity ϵ. For free space (vacuum) the velocity is a well-known constant (usually designated by c and usually called the *velocity* of light). Thus

$$c = \frac{1}{\sqrt{\mu_0 \epsilon_0}} = 2.998 \times 10^8 \text{ meters/sec} \qquad (9\text{-}43)$$

In the mksc system of units the permeability of vacuum is

$$\mu_0 = 4\pi \times 10^{-7} \text{ henry/meter}$$

Therefore the permittivity of vacuum is

$$\epsilon_0 = \frac{1}{\mu_0 c^2} = 8.85 \times 10^{-12} \text{ farad/meter} \qquad (9\text{-}44)$$

For other media the phase velocity relative to the velocity of light, or *relative phase velocity*, is

$$p = \frac{v}{c} = \frac{\sqrt{\mu_0 \epsilon_0}}{\sqrt{\mu \epsilon}} = \frac{1}{\sqrt{\mu_r \epsilon_r}} \text{ (dimensionless)} \qquad (9\text{-}45)$$

where μ_r = relative permeability of medium
$\quad \epsilon_r$ = relative permittivity of medium

The phase velocity of a plane wave in an unbounded lossless medium is equal to or less than the velocity of light ($p \leq 1$). In general, however, the phase velocity may have values both greater and less than the velocity of light. For example, in a hollow metal wave guide v is always equal to or greater than c (see Chap. 12).

If two waves of the same frequency travel with the same velocity in opposite directions or with different velocities in the same direction, the phase velocity of the resultant wave is not a constant but varies as a function of position. In measuring the velocity it is usually most convenient, at radio frequencies, to determine the electrical phase shift (by phase-comparison methods) between two points, one of which is taken as a reference.

For a wave traveling in the positive x direction there is an infinitesimal phase lag $d\phi$ or phase advancement $-d\phi$ in a positive distance dx. The time required for a constant phase point to move this distance is then

$$dt = -\frac{T}{2\pi} d\phi \qquad \text{sec} \qquad (9\text{-}46)$$

where T = time for one period. Therefore the phase velocity as a function of position is given by

$$v = \frac{dx}{dt} = -\frac{dx}{(T/2\pi)\, d\phi} = -\frac{\omega}{d\phi/dx} \qquad (9\text{-}47)$$

For a wave traveling in the positive x direction $d\phi/dx$ is negative, and hence v is positive.

As compared with (9-47) the phase velocity ω/β as in (9-42) is an average phase velocity as averaged over an integral number of wavelengths. Thus, dividing (9-47) by ω/β, we obtain a relative phase velocity p which is a function of position as given by

$$p = -\frac{\beta}{d\phi/dx} \qquad (9\text{-}47a)$$

where $\beta = 2\pi/\lambda$

λ = wavelength in free space

Both v in (9-47) and p in (9-47a) are useful where the phase velocity is a function of position.

9-6. Index of Refraction. In optics the *index of refraction* η is defined as the reciprocal of the relative phase velocity p. That is,

$$\eta = \frac{1}{p} = \frac{1}{v/c} = \frac{c}{v} = \sqrt{\mu_r \epsilon_r} \qquad (9\text{-}48)$$

For nonferrous media μ_r is very nearly unity so that

$$\eta = \sqrt{\epsilon_r} \qquad (9\text{-}49)$$

Example 1. Paraffin has a relative permittivity $\epsilon_r = 2.1$. Find the index of refraction for paraffin and also the phase velocity of a wave in an unbounded medium of paraffin.

Solution. The index of refraction

$$\eta = \sqrt{2.1} = 1.45$$

The phase velocity

$$v = \frac{c}{\sqrt{2.1}} = 2.07 \times 10^8 \text{ meters/sec}$$

Example 2. Distilled water has the constants $\sigma \simeq 0$, $\epsilon_r = 81$, $\mu_r = 1$. Find η and v.

Solution:

$$\eta = \sqrt{81} = 9$$

$$v = \frac{c}{\sqrt{81}} = 0.111c = 3.33 \times 10^7 \text{ meters/sec}$$

The index of refraction given for water in the above example is the value at low frequencies ($f \to 0$). At light frequencies, say for sodium light ($\lambda = 5,893$ angstroms), the index of refraction is observed to be about 1.33 instead of 9 as calculated on the basis of the relative permittivity. This difference was at one time cited as invalidating Maxwell's theory. The explanation for the difference is that the permittivity ϵ is not a constant but is a function of frequency. At zero frequency $\epsilon_r = 81$, but at light frequencies $\epsilon_r = 1.33^2 = 1.77$. The index of refraction and permittivity of many other substances also vary as a function of the frequency.

9-7. Group Velocity.[1]   Consider a plane wave traveling in the positive x direction as in Fig. 9-2.   Let the total electric field be given by

$$E_y = E_0 \cos (\omega t - \beta x) \qquad (9\text{-}50)$$

Suppose now that the wave has not one but two frequencies of equal amplitude expressed by

$$\omega_0 + \Delta\omega$$

and

$$\omega_0 - \Delta\omega$$

It follows that the β values corresponding to these two frequencies are

$$\beta_0 + \Delta\beta \text{ corresponding to } \omega_0 + \Delta\omega$$

and

$$\beta_0 - \Delta\beta \text{ corresponding to } \omega_0 - \Delta\omega$$

For frequency 1

$$E_y' = E_0 \cos \left[(\omega_0 + \Delta\omega)t - (\beta_0 + \Delta\beta)x\right] \qquad (9\text{-}51)$$

and for frequency 2

$$E_y'' = E_0 \cos \left[(\omega_0 - \Delta\omega)t - (\beta_0 - \Delta\beta)x\right] \qquad (9\text{-}52)$$

Adding gives the total field

$$E_y = E_y' + E_y'' \qquad (9\text{-}53)$$

or

$$E_y = E_0 \{\cos \left[(\omega_0 + \Delta\omega)t - (\beta_0 + \Delta\beta)x\right] \\ + \cos \left[(\omega_0 - \Delta\omega)t - (\beta_0 - \Delta\beta)x\right]\} \qquad (9\text{-}54)$$

Multiplying out (9-54) and by trigonometric transformation

$$E_y = 2E_0 \cos (\omega_0 t - \beta_0 x) \cos (\Delta\omega\, t - \Delta\beta\, x) \qquad (9\text{-}55)$$

The two cosine factors indicate the presence of beats, that is, a slow variation superimposed on a more rapid one.

For a *constant phase* point

$$\omega_0 t - \beta_0 x = \text{constant}$$

and

$$\frac{dx}{dt} = \frac{\omega_0}{\beta_0} = v = f_0 \lambda_0 \qquad (9\text{-}56)$$

where v = phase velocity.   Setting the argument of the second cosine factor equal to a constant,

$$\Delta\omega\, t - \Delta\beta\, x = \text{constant}$$

[1] Leon Brillouin, "Wave Propagation in Periodic Structures," McGraw-Hill Book Company, Inc., New York, 1946, Chap. 5.   J. A. Stratton, "Electromagnetic Theory," McGraw-Hill Book Company, Inc., New York, 1941, p. 330.

and

$$\frac{dx}{dt} = \frac{\Delta\omega}{\Delta\beta} = u = \Delta f \, \Delta\lambda \qquad (9\text{-}57)$$

where u is the phase velocity of the wave envelope, which is usually called the *group velocity*. In the above development we can consider $\omega_0 + \Delta\omega$ and $\omega_0 - \Delta\omega$ as the two side-band frequencies due to the modulation of a carrier frequency ω_0 by a frequency $\Delta\omega$, the carrier frequency being suppressed.

In nondispersive media the group velocity is the same as the phase velocity. Free space is an example of a lossless, nondispersive medium, and in free space $u = v = c$. However, in dispersive media the phase and group velocities differ.

A *dispersive medium* is one in which the phase velocity is a function of the frequency (and hence of the free-space wavelength). Dispersive media are of two types:

1. *Normally dispersive.* In these media the change in phase velocity with wavelength is positive, that is, $dv/d\lambda > 0$. For these media $u < v$.
2. *Anomalously dispersive.*[1] In these media the change in phase velocity with wavelength is negative, that is, $dv/d\lambda < 0$. For these media $u > v$.

The terms "normal" and "anomalous" are arbitrary, the significance being simply that anomalous dispersion is different from the type of dispersion described as "normal."

For a particular frequency (band width vanishingly small)

$$u = \lim_{\Delta\omega \to 0} \frac{\Delta\omega}{\Delta\beta} = \frac{d\omega}{d\beta} \qquad (9\text{-}58)$$

But $\omega = 2\pi f = 2\pi f \lambda/\lambda = \beta v$; so

$$u = \frac{d\omega}{d\beta} = \frac{d(\beta v)}{d\beta} = \beta \frac{dv}{d\beta} + v \qquad (9\text{-}59)$$

or

$$u = v + \beta \frac{dv}{d\beta} \qquad (9\text{-}60)$$

It may also be shown that

$$u = v - \lambda \frac{dv}{d\lambda} \qquad (9\text{-}61)$$

Equations (9-60) and (9-61) are useful in finding the group velocity for a given phase velocity function.

---

[1] A conductor is an example of an anomalously dispersive medium. However, conductors are absorptive (not lossless), and in media where the absorption is not small, the group velocity tends to lose its simple meaning.

Example.   A 1-Mc/sec (300 meters wavelength) plane wave traveling in a normally dispersive, lossless medium has a phase velocity at this frequency of 3×10^8 meters/sec.   The phase velocity as a function of wavelength is given by

$$v = k\sqrt{\lambda}$$

where k = constant.   Find the group velocity.
   Solution.   From (9-61) the group velocity is

$$u = v - \lambda \frac{dv}{d\lambda} = v - \frac{k}{2}\sqrt{\lambda}$$

or

$$u = v(1 - \tfrac{1}{2})$$

Hence

$$u = \frac{v}{2} = 1.5 \times 10^8 \text{ meters/sec}$$

To illustrate graphically the difference between phase and group velocity, let us consider a wave of the same phase velocity characteristics

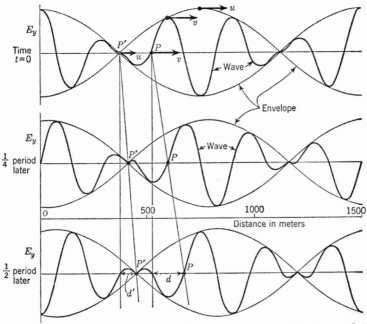

Fig. 9-6. Constant phase point P of the wave proper moves with phase velocity v, while point P' on the envelope moves with group velocity u.   In this example the group velocity is one-half the phase velocity.

as in the above example and assume, further, that the wave has two frequencies $f_0 + \Delta f$ and $f_0 - \Delta f$ of equal amplitude where $f_0 = 10^6$ cps and $\Delta f = 10^5$ cps.   This is equivalent to a 10^6-cps carrier modulated at 10^5 cps with the carrier suppressed.   From (9-55) graphs of the instantaneous magnitude of E_y as a function of distance (plotted in meters) are presented in Fig. 9-6 for three instants of time, $t = 0$, $t = T/4$, and $t = T/2$. The point P is a point of constant phase of the wave proper and moves with the phase velocity v. The point P' is a point of constant phase of the envelope enclosing the wave and moves with the group velocity u. It is apparent that in one-half period $(T/2)$ the point P' has moved a distance d' which is one-half the distance d moved by the point P. That is to say, the group velocity u is one-half the phase velocity v. The intelligence conveyed by the modulation moves with the velocity of the envelope, that is, at the group velocity.[1]

The difference between phase and group velocities is also illustrated by a crawling caterpillar. The humps on his back move forward with phase velocity, while the caterpillar as a whole progresses with group velocity.

For a single-frequency constant-amplitude (steady-state) wave the group velocity is not apparent. However, if the wave consists of two or more frequencies, or a frequency group, as in a modulated wave the group velocity may be observed because the wave amplitude is non-uniform and the individual waves appear to form groups that may be enclosed by an envelope, as in Fig. 9-6.

9-8. Impedance of Dielectric Media. Thus far our attention has been focused on the electric field E_y. Let us now consider also the magnetic field H_z of the same plane wave (see Fig. 9-2) and, in particular, find how H_z is related in magnitude to E_y. A solution of the wave equation (9-13) in H_z is

$$H_z = H_0 \sin (\omega t - \beta x) \tag{9-62}$$

This solution represents a wave traveling in the positive x direction. A solution for E_y representing a wave in the positive x direction is given by (9-31) as

$$E_y = E_0 \sin (\omega t - \beta x) \tag{9-63}$$

To find how H_z in (9-62) is related to E_y we recall from (9-8) that

$$\frac{\partial E_y}{\partial x} = -\mu \frac{\partial H_z}{\partial t} \tag{9-64}$$

Substituting (9-63) for E_y in (9-64), performing the indicated differentiation, and then integrating with respect to time yields

$$H_z = \frac{\beta}{\mu\omega} E_0 \sin (\omega t - \beta x) \tag{9-65}$$

Taking the ratio of E_y to H_z for a single traveling wave, as given by the ratio of (9-63) to (9-65), we obtain

$$\frac{E_y}{H_z} = \frac{E_0}{H_0} = \frac{\mu\omega}{\beta} = \frac{\mu}{\sqrt{\mu\epsilon}} = \sqrt{\frac{\mu}{\epsilon}} = \frac{E_0}{H_0} \tag{9-66}$$

[1] In a lossless medium the energy is also conveyed at the group velocity.

or

$$E_y = \sqrt{\frac{\mu}{\epsilon}} \, H_z \qquad (9\text{-}67)$$

For comparison we can now write

$$E_y = E_0 \sin(\omega t - \beta x) \qquad \text{volts/meter} \qquad (9\text{-}68)$$

and

$$H_z = \sqrt{\frac{\epsilon}{\mu}} \, E_0 \sin(\omega t - \beta x) \qquad \text{amp/meter} \qquad (9\text{-}69)$$

It is apparent that E_y and H_z are identical functions of x and t, but their magnitudes differ by a factor $\sqrt{\mu/\epsilon}$ or its reciprocal.

The dimensions of (9-66) expressed in mksc units are

$$\frac{\text{Volts/meter}}{\text{Amperes/meter}} = \frac{\text{volts}}{\text{ampere}} = \text{ohms}$$

Thus, $\sqrt{\mu/\epsilon}$ has the dimensions of an impedance, and we may write

$$Z = \sqrt{\frac{\mu}{\epsilon}} \qquad (9\text{-}70)$$

where Z is called the *intrinsic impedance* of the medium. For free space (vacuum)

$$Z = Z_0 = \sqrt{\frac{\mu_0}{\epsilon_0}} = 376.7 \simeq 120\pi \qquad \text{ohms} \qquad (9\text{-}71)$$

If E and H are in time phase, Z is a pure resistance. This is the case for free space and all lossless dielectric media. To emphasize the fact that the impedance is a pure resistance, one can speak of the *intrinsic resistance* (instead of impedance) of free space and of lossless dielectric media. If E and H are not in time phase, as in conducting media, the ratio of E to H is complex, so that the more general term *intrinsic impedance* must be used in connection with such media.

Introducing (9-70) in (9-66), we have

$$\frac{E_y}{H_z} = \frac{E_0}{H_0} = Z = \sqrt{\frac{\mu}{\epsilon}} \qquad (9\text{-}72)$$

Example. If the magnitude of **H** in a plane wave is 1 amp/meter, find the magnitude of **E** for a plane wave in free space.

Solution. From (9-72)

$$E = ZH = 376.7 \times 1 = 376.7 \text{ volts/meter}$$

The instantaneous values of E_y and H_z along the x axis for a plane wave progressing in the positive x direction are illustrated in Fig. 9-7. Figure 9-7a shows the condition at the time $t = 0$, while Fig. 9-7b shows the conditions one-quarter period later ($t = T/4$). The maximum values of E_y and H_z (E_0 and H_0) are shown to be equal. Hence, if the medium is free space, the scale in volts per meter along the y axis should be 377 times the scale in amperes per meter along the z axis. The scales would

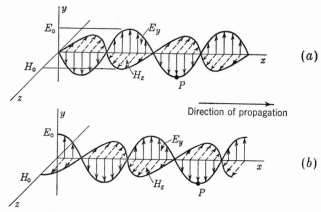

Fig. 9-7. Instantaneous values of E_y and H_z along x axis at time $t = 0$ (a) and $\frac{1}{4}$ period later (b). In this interval the point P has advanced $\frac{1}{4}$ wavelength to the right.

be equal, however, if the medium had an intrinsic impedance of 1 ohm. In Fig. 9-7 both the magnitudes and directions of E_y and H_z are shown for points along the x axis. Since we are considering a plane wave traveling in the direction of the x axis, the relations of E_y and H_z along all lines parallel to the x axis are the same as those shown.

9-9. Impedance of Transmission-line Cell. Imagine a plane wave traveling out of the page (toward the reader) with space divided up by

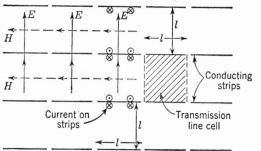

Fig. 9-8. Plane wave traveling out of page with space divided by conducting strips into transmission-line cells.

thin conducting strips into transmission-line cells as suggested in Fig. 9-8. The strips are normal to **E**, and they extend infinitely far normal to the page. The field **H** is parallel to the strips. At the surface of each strip there is a current sheet of linear density **K** (normal to the page) that is equal in magnitude to **H**. The currents on opposite sides of one strip are opposed as shown.   A plane (TEM) wave traveling through space divided up into line cells as in Fig. 9-8 has the same values of **E** and **H** everywhere as a wave in empty space (no strips present as in Fig. 9-2), it being assumed that the strips are of infinitesimal thickness.   Assuming also that the strip width and spacing are equal (both equal to l) so that the cell cross section is square and the edges of the strips are infinitesimally close together, the voltage V between two strips of one cell is

$$V = El \tag{9-73}$$

The total current I flowing on the bottom surface of the top strip of a cell (or top surface of the bottom strip of a cell) is given by

$$I = Hl \tag{9-74}$$

Dividing (9-73) by (9-74) yields

$$\frac{E}{H} = \frac{V}{I} = Z \tag{9-75}$$

Thus, for a single traveling wave the *intrinsic impedance* E/H of a wave is equal to the *characteristic impedance* V/I of a single transmission-line cell. Furthermore, from (9-72) we have

$$Z = \frac{E}{H} = \sqrt{\frac{\mu}{\epsilon}} \tag{9-76}$$

Now in the case of a transmission-line cell we have from (4-100) that the inductance of the line per unit depth (normal to the page) is equal to the permeability of the medium, that is,

$$\frac{L}{d} = \mu \tag{9-77}$$

while we have from (2-105) that the capacitance of the line cell per unit depth equals the permittivity of the medium, or

$$\frac{C}{d} = \epsilon \tag{9-78}$$

Accordingly, we can write

$$Z = \sqrt{\frac{\mu}{\epsilon}} = \sqrt{\frac{L/d}{C/d}} \tag{9-79}$$

where Z = characteristic impedance of line cell (ohms)

$\quad L/d$ = inductance per unit length of line cell (henrys/meter)

$\quad C/d$ = capacitance per unit length of line cell (farads/meter)

To summarize, *the characteristic impedance of a transmission line cell is equal to the intrinsic impedance of the medium filling the cell.*   If the medium is free space, $\mu = \mu_0$ and $\epsilon = \epsilon_0$; so the characteristic impedance of the line is

$$Z = \sqrt{\frac{\mu_0}{\epsilon_0}} = 376.7 \text{ ohms} \qquad (9\text{-}80)$$

9-10. Two Plane Waves Traveling in Opposite Directions. Standing Waves. Thus far, we have considered only a single traveling wave, such as a wave moving in the positive *or* the negative x direction. Let us now examine the situation which exists when there are two waves traveling in opposite directions, such as the negative *and* positive x directions.

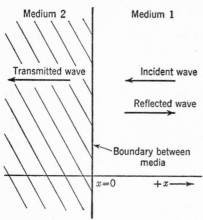

Assume that the two waves are of the same frequency and of sinusoidal form. The condition that the waves be of the same frequency and form is automatically fulfilled if one wave is a reflection of the other since both then originate from the same source.

Referring to Fig. 9-9, assume that space is divided into two media, 1 and 2, with a plane boundary between as shown. A wave originating in medium 1 and incident on the boundary is said to be the *incident wave*. The wave reflected from the boundary back into medium 1 is called the *reflected wave*. If the reflection of the incident wave at the boundary is not complete, some of the wave continues on into medium 2 and this wave is referred to as the *transmitted wave*.

FIG. 9-9. Relation of incident, reflected, and transmitted waves.

In the solution of the wave equation for E_y as given by (9-20) there are two terms, the first representing a wave in the negative x direction (to the left) and the second a wave in the positive x direction (to the right). Referring now to the exponential solution in Table 9-1, let the incident wave (traveling to the left) be given by

$$\dot{E}_{y0} = E_0 e^{j(\omega t + \beta x)} \qquad (9\text{-}81)$$

and the reflected wave (traveling to the right) by

$$\dot{E}_{y1} = E_1 e^{j(\omega t - \beta x + \delta)} \qquad (9\text{-}82)$$

where δ is the time-phase lead of $\dot{E}_{y1}$ with respect to $\dot{E}_{y0}$ at $x = 0$. That is, δ is the phase shift at the point of reflection. E_0 is the amplitude of the incident wave, and E_1 is the amplitude of the reflected wave. The dot (˙) is used here to indicate explicitly that $\dot{E}_{y0}$ and $\dot{E}_{y1}$ are complex functions of t, x, and δ†. The total electric field $\dot{E}_y$ is

$$\dot{E}_y = \dot{E}_{y0} + \dot{E}_{y1} \tag{9-83}$$

The instantaneous magnitude of the fields is obtained by taking either the real (Re) or imaginary (Im) parts of (9-81) and (9-82). Thus, taking the imaginary parts, the total instantaneous electric field is

$$E_y = \operatorname{Im} \dot{E}_y = E_0 \sin (\omega t + \beta x) + E_1 \sin (\omega t - \beta x + \delta) \tag{9-84}$$

To simplify the present discussion, assume that δ in (9-84) is either $0°$ or $180°$. Then, δ need not appear at all, E_1 being negative if $\delta = 180°$. On this basis, (9-84) may be expanded as follows:[1]

$$E_y = E_0 \sin \omega t \cos \beta x + E_0 \cos \omega t \sin \beta x$$
$$+ E_1 \sin \omega t \cos \beta x - E_1 \cos \omega t \sin \beta x \tag{9-85}$$

Collecting terms,

$$E_y = (E_0 + E_1) \sin \omega t \cos \beta x + (E_0 - E_1) \cos \omega t \sin \beta x \tag{9-86}$$

If medium 2 is a perfect conductor, the reflected wave is equal in magnitude to the incident wave. If $x = 0$ is taken to be at the boundary between media 1 and 2, the boundary relation for the tangential component of $\mathbf{E}$ requires that $E_y = 0$ so that $E_1 = -E_0$ at the boundary ($\delta = 180°$). Thus (9-86) becomes

$$E_y = 2E_0 \cos \omega t \sin \beta x \tag{9-87}$$

This represents a wave which is stationary in space. The values of E_y at a particular instant are a sine function of x. The instantaneous values at a particular point are a cosine function of t. The peak value of the wave is the sum of the incident and reflected peak values or $2E_0$. A stationary wave of this type for which $|E_1| = |E_0|$ is a *pure standing wave*. This type of wave is associated with resonators.

The space and time variations of E_y for a pure standing wave are shown by the curves of Fig. 9-10. It is to be noted that a constant phase point, such as P, does not move in the x direction but remains at a fixed position as time passes.

Now let us examine the conditions when the reflected wave is smaller than the incident wave, say one-half as large. Then, $E_1 = -0.5E_0$. Evaluating (9-86) for this case at four instants of time, the curves of Fig. 9-11 are obtained. The curves show the values of E_y as a function of βx at times equal to 0, $\frac{1}{8}$, $\frac{1}{4}$, and $\frac{3}{8}$ periods. The peak values of E_y range from $1.5E_0$ at $t = 0$ to $0.5E_0$ at $t = \frac{1}{4}$ period. The peak values as a func-

---

† However, both $\dot{E}_{y0}$ and $\dot{E}_{y1}$ are scalar space components of the total field vector $\mathbf{E}$. In the case being considered, $\mathbf{E}$ has only one component. Thus $\mathbf{E} = \mathbf{j}\dot{E}_y$.

[1] $\sin (a \pm b) = \sin a \cos b \pm \cos a \sin b$.

tion of x as observed over an interval of time greater than one cycle correspond to the envelope as indicated. This envelope remains stationary, but focusing our attention on a constant phase point P of the wave, we note that the total instantaneous wave travels to the left. It will also be noted that the velocity with which P moves is not constant. Between time 0 and $\frac{1}{8}$ period P moves about 0.05 wavelengths (0.1π),

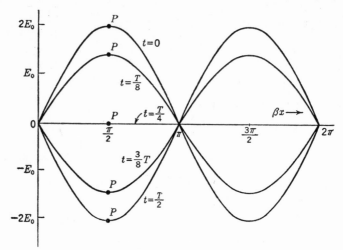

Fig. 9-10. Pure standing wave showing E_y at various instants of time.

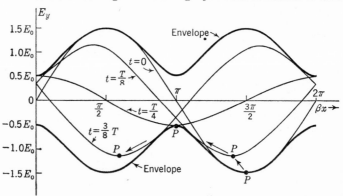

Fig. 9-11. Standing-wave envelope for $E_1 = -0.5E_0$ with associated (traveling) wave at four instants of time: $t = 0$, $t = T/8$, $t = T/4$, and $t = 3T/8$.

while in the next $\frac{1}{8}$ period P moves about four times as far, or about 0.2 wavelengths (0.4π). Although the average velocity of the constant phase point is the same as for a pure traveling wave, its instantaneous magnitude varies between values which are greater and less.

To summarize, there are two E_y waves, one traveling in the negative x direction and another one-half as large traveling in the positive x direction.   The waves reinforce each other at some points and subtract from each other at other points.   The resultant wave travels in the negative x direction.   This obviously must be the case since the larger wave is in the negative x direction.

The envelope of the instantaneous curves in Fig. 9-11 can be called a *standing-wave curve*, or *envelope*.   An instrument reading the rms values of E_y along the x axis would yield values proportional to those shown for the envelope.   At any position βx the maximum value of the field at some time during the cycle is equal to the ordinate value of the envelope.

To calculate the value of the standing-wave envelope, we may proceed as follows: In (9-86) put

$$A = (E_0 + E_1) \cos \beta x \qquad\qquad (9\text{-}88)$$
$$B = (E_0 - E_1) \sin \beta x \qquad\qquad (9\text{-}89)$$

Expanding $\sin \omega t$ and $\cos \omega t$ in terms of exponentials, it can be shown that

$$A \sin \omega t + B \cos \omega t = \sqrt{A^2 + B^2} \cos (\omega t - \delta) \qquad (9\text{-}90)$$

Equation (9-86) can then be written as

$$E_y = \sqrt{A^2 + B^2} \cos (\omega t - \delta) \qquad\qquad (9\text{-}91)$$

The value of δ is not significant in our application.

Expanding (9-91) by means of (9-88) and (9-89) yields

$$E_y = \sqrt{(E_0 + E_1)^2 \cos^2 \beta x + (E_0 - E_1)^2 \sin^2 \beta x} \cos (\omega t - \delta) \quad (9\text{-}92)$$

The maximum value of E_y at some position βx as observed over an interval of at least one period occurs when $\cos (\omega t - \delta) = 1$.   Thus for the shape of the standing-wave envelope of E_y we have

$$E_y = \sqrt{(E_0 + E_1)^2 \cos^2 \beta x + (E_0 - E_1)^2 \sin^2 \beta x} \qquad (9\text{-}93)$$

Ordinarily we are not so much interested in the shape of the standing-wave envelope as given by (9-93) as in the ratio of the maximum to minimum values for the envelope, which is called the *standing-wave ratio* (SWR).   The maximum value of the envelope corresponds to the sum of the amplitudes of the incident and reflected waves $(E_0 + E_1)$, while the minimum corresponds to the difference between the two $(E_0 - E_1)$.   With this information we can determine the fraction of the incident E_y wave which is reflected, forming the reflected wave, and also that which is transmitted (see Fig. 9-9).   As will be noted later on, this knowledge is of value in determining the nature of the conditions at the point of reflection.

Thus, for the standing-wave ratio we can write

$$\text{SWR} = \frac{E_{\max}}{E_{\min}} = \frac{E_0 + E_1}{E_0 - E_1} \qquad\qquad (9\text{-}94)$$

When the reflected wave is zero ($E_1 = 0$), the SWR is unity. When the reflected wave is equal to the incident ($E_1 = E_0$), the SWR is infinite. Hence for all intermediate values of the reflected wave, the standing-wave ratio lies between 1 and infinity.

The ratio of the reflected wave to the incident wave is defined as the *reflection coefficient.* Thus, at the point of reflection ($x = 0$) and at the time $t = 0$, the ratio of (9-82) to (9-81) is

$$\dot{\rho} = \frac{\dot{E}_{y1}}{\dot{E}_{y0}} = \frac{E_1 e^{j\delta}}{E_0} = \frac{E_1/\underline{\delta}}{E_0} = \rho/\underline{\delta} \tag{9-95}$$

The dot ($\cdot$) indicates that $\dot{\rho}$ is a complex function. Thus, in general, $\dot{\rho}$ expresses both the magnitude of the reflected wave with respect to the incident and also the phase shift δ at the point of reflection. The magnitude of $\dot{\rho}$ can range between 0 and 1 with phase angles between 0 and $\pm 180°$.

In this discussion, we are dealing with the values of the electric field. Hence, more specifically $\dot{\rho}$ may be called the field *reflection coefficient.*

Rewriting (9-94) and substituting (9-95),

$$\text{SWR} = \frac{1 + (E_1/E_0)}{1 - (E_1/E_0)} = \frac{1 + |\dot{\rho}|}{1 - |\dot{\rho}|} \tag{9-96}$$

Solving for $|\dot{\rho}|$ gives an expression for the magnitude of the reflection coefficient in terms of the standing-wave ratio. That is,

$$|\dot{\rho}| = \rho = \frac{\text{SWR} - 1}{\text{SWR} + 1} \tag{9-97}$$

In Fig. 9-12, standing-wave envelopes are presented for three magnitudes of the reflected wave as given by reflection coefficients, $\rho = 0, 0.5$, and 1. The amplitude of the incident wave is taken as unity. The curves show E_y as a function of position in terms of both βx and wavelength. For complete reflection ($\rho = 1$) we have a pure standing wave with a SWR of infinity. For zero reflection ($\rho = 0$), the SWR is unity, and E_y is constant as a function of position. For a reflection coefficient of 0.5, the curve varies between 1.5 and 0.5 so that SWR = 3. *In general*, the standing-wave envelope is *not* a sine curve, the minimum being sharper than the maximum. This is illustrated by the curve for $\rho = 0.5$. However, in the limiting condition of $\rho = 1$ the curve does have the form of a rectified sine function ($|\sin \beta x|$). Also, as the condition $\rho = 0$ is approached, the curve approximates a sinusoidal variation (see Prob. 9-15).

The standing-wave envelopes in Fig. 9-12 illustrate the peak magnitude of the electric field as a function of position. Figure 9-13 shows the time

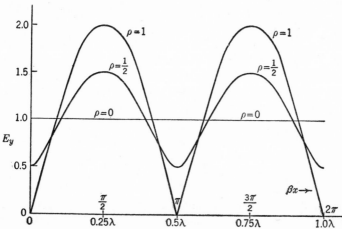

Fig. 9-12. Standing-wave envelopes for three magnitudes of reflection coefficient, $\rho = 0$, 0.5, and 1.

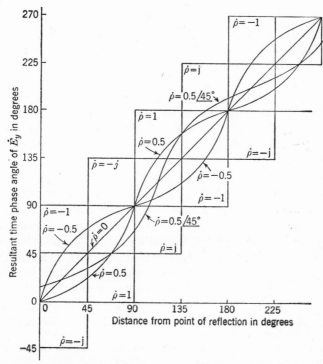

Fig. 9-13. Phase variation of total field as a function of distance from point of reflection for various conditions of reflection.

phase of the total field $\dot{E}_y$ as a function of distance from the point of reflection. Here the distance and time phase are expressed in degrees. The different curves show the phase variation for different conditions of reflection. When $\dot{\rho} = 0$, the phase variation is a linear function of distance and is shown as a straight line at a slope of 45°. For a reflection coefficient $\dot{\rho} = 1$ the phase variation is a step function which jumps in steps of 180° at distance intervals of 180°. For $\dot{\rho} = j$, which signifies a phase shift of 90° at reflection, we also have a step function which is displaced 45° in both time phase and distance from the curve for $\dot{\rho} = 1$. Likewise, $\dot{\rho} = -1$, and $\dot{\rho} = -j$ yield other displaced step functions. For reflection coefficients between zero and unity, the phase variation is given by smooth curves which fall between the straight line of $\dot{\rho} = 0$ and the step functions for which $\dot{\rho}$ equals unity. For example, note the curve for $\dot{\rho} = 0.5$. When ρ is fractional and δ is not equal to 0 or 180°, the curves are smooth but are displaced along the $\dot{\rho} = 0$ line, as illustrated by the curve for $\dot{\rho} = 0.5\underline{/45°} = 0.35 + j0.35$.

In a standing wave the velocity of a constant phase point is not uniform, as may be noted by the variable rate of progress of the point P in Fig. 9-11. From (9-47) the phase velocity as a function of position is inversely proportional to the slope $(d\phi/dx)$ of the phase-distance curve for the total field. The SWR in Fig. 9-11 is 3, and the corresponding reflection coefficient $\rho = 0.5$. Referring to the $\dot{\rho} = 0.5$ curve in Fig. 9-13 the phase velocity is seen to be largest where the slope of this curve is smallest, as at 0° and 180°, and vice versa.[1] The average phase velocity ω/β, in this instance, is inversely proportional to the average slope of the ϕ vs. x curve over an integral number of $\frac{1}{2}$ wavelength. This is seen to be the same as the slope of the $\dot{\rho} = 0$ line (SWR = 1) so that the average phase velocity in a standing wave is equal to the phase velocity for a pure traveling wave.

If the phase velocity is plotted as a function of position in a standing wave, a curve is obtained that oscillates between a maximum and a minimum value of velocity in a manner that is analogous to a standing-wave envelope for field in a wave, or voltage on a transmission line. Hence, by analogy we may call the ratio v_{max}/v_{min} the *standing-wave ratio for phase velocity*. It has been shown by Marsh[2] that, in a standing wave due to two waves of uniform but, in general, unequal amplitude traveling with equal velocity in opposite directions, the standing-wave ratio of the

[1] In this graph the abscissa is in degrees as obtained by multiplying the distance x by 360°/λ. The wavelength λ is always equal to the distance between any point and the next point having the same phase.

[2] J. A. Marsh, "A Study of Phase Velocity on Long Cylindrical Conductors," Ph.D. dissertation, Department of Electrical Engineering, Ohio State University, 1949; Measured Current Distributions on Helical Antennas, *Proc. I.R.E.*, **39**, 668–675, June, 1951. See Probs. 9–31 and 11–17 for more general relations.

phase velocity v as in (9-47) or of the relative phase velocity p as in (9-47a) *and* the standing-wave ratio for the field E or the voltage V are related by

$$p\text{SWR} = (V\text{SWR})^2 \tag{9-98}$$

where pSWR is the SWR for the velocity and VSWR is the SWR for the field or voltage. That is,

$$p\text{SWR} = \frac{v_{max}}{v_{min}} = \frac{p_{max}}{p_{min}} \tag{9-99}$$

where v_{max} = maximum phase velocity
$\quad v_{min}$ = minimum phase velocity
$\quad p_{max}$ = maximum relative phase velocity
$\quad p_{min}$ = minimum relative phase velocity
and

$$V\text{SWR} = \frac{E_{max}}{E_{min}} = \frac{E_0 + E_1}{E_0 - E_1} = \frac{V_{max}}{V_{min}} \tag{9-100}$$

where E_{max} = maximum resultant field
$\quad E_{min}$ = minimum resultant field
$\quad E_0$ = amplitude of first traveling wave
$\quad E_1$ = amplitude of second traveling wave
$\quad V_{max}$ = maximum resultant voltage
$\quad V_{min}$ = minimum resultant voltage

Example. The SWR of the envelope of the resultant wave in Fig. 9-11 is 3. This is also the SWR for the $\rho = \frac{1}{2}$ envelope in Fig. 9-12. Find the ratio of maximum to minimum phase velocity of the resultant wave corresponding to this SWR ($=3$).

Solution. From (9-98)

$$p\text{SWR} = (V\text{SWR})^2 = 3^2 = 9$$

Hence the maximum phase velocity (at E_{min}) is nine times the minimum phase velocity (at E_{max}).

9-11. Energy Relations in a Traveling Wave. From (2-67a) the energy density w_e at a point in an electric field is

$$w_e = \tfrac{1}{2}\epsilon E^2 \qquad \text{joules/meter}^3 \tag{9-101}$$

where ϵ = permittivity of medium (farads/meter)
$\quad E$ = electric field intensity (volts/meter)
From (4-110) the energy density w_m at a point in a magnetic field is

$$w_m = \tfrac{1}{2}\mu H^2 \qquad \text{joules/meter}^3 \tag{9-102}$$

where μ = permeability of medium (henrys/meter)
$\quad H$ = H field (amp/meter)
In a traveling wave

$$\frac{E}{H} = \sqrt{\frac{\mu}{\epsilon}} \tag{9-103}$$

Substituting for H from (9-103) in (9-102), we have

$$w_m = \tfrac{1}{2}\mu H^2 = \tfrac{1}{2}\epsilon E^2 = w_e \qquad (9\text{-}104)$$

Thus the electric and magnetic energy densities in a plane traveling wave are equal, and the total energy density w is the sum of the electric and magnetic energies. Thus

$$w = w_e + w_m = \tfrac{1}{2}\epsilon E^2 + \tfrac{1}{2}\mu H^2 \qquad (9\text{-}105)$$

or

$$w = \epsilon E^2 = \mu H^2 \qquad \text{joules/meter}^3 \qquad (9\text{-}106)$$

9-12. The Poynting Vector. Continuing the discussion of the preceding section, any increase in the energy per unit volume must be produced by an inflow of energy. Likewise any decrease must be equal to an outflow. Thus, for a small volume Δv the decrease in energy as a function of time may be expressed as

$$-\frac{\partial}{\partial t}\left(\frac{1}{2}\,\epsilon E^2 + \frac{1}{2}\,\mu H^2\right)\Delta v = \int_s \mathbf{S}\cdot d\mathbf{s} \qquad \text{watts} \qquad (9\text{-}107)$$

where $\mathbf{S}$ = energy per unit area passing per unit time through the surface of the volume Δv (watts/meter^2).

Dividing (9-107) by Δv and taking the limit as Δv approaches zero, we obtain

$$\boldsymbol{\nabla}\cdot\mathbf{S} = -\frac{\partial}{\partial t}\left(\frac{1}{2}\,\epsilon E^2 + \frac{1}{2}\,\mu H^2\right) \qquad (9\text{-}108)$$

The quantity $\mathbf{S}$ has the dimensions of power per unit area and is expressed in watts per square meter. It is a vector since it indicates not only the magnitude of the energy flow but also its direction. It is usually called the *Poynting vector.*[1]

Returning to Maxwell's equations for nonconducting media, we have

$$\boldsymbol{\nabla}\times\mathbf{H} = \frac{\partial\mathbf{D}}{\partial t} \qquad \text{and} \qquad \boldsymbol{\nabla}\times\mathbf{E} = -\frac{\partial\mathbf{B}}{\partial t} \qquad (9\text{-}109)$$

Writing the scalar product of the first equation with $\mathbf{E}$ and of the second with $\mathbf{H}$,

$$\mathbf{E}\cdot(\boldsymbol{\nabla}\times\mathbf{H}) = \mathbf{E}\cdot\frac{\partial\mathbf{D}}{\partial t} \qquad \text{and} \qquad \mathbf{H}\cdot(\boldsymbol{\nabla}\times\mathbf{E}) = -\mathbf{H}\cdot\frac{\partial\mathbf{B}}{\partial t} \qquad (9\text{-}110)$$

Subtracting the first from the second,

$$\mathbf{H}\cdot(\boldsymbol{\nabla}\times\mathbf{E}) - \mathbf{E}\cdot(\boldsymbol{\nabla}\times\mathbf{H}) = -\left(\mathbf{E}\cdot\frac{\partial\mathbf{D}}{\partial t} + \mathbf{H}\cdot\frac{\partial\mathbf{B}}{\partial t}\right) \qquad (9\text{-}111)$$

[1] J. H. Poynting, On the Transfer of Energy in the Electromagnetic Field, *Phil. Trans.*, **174**, 343, 1883. Oliver Heaviside, "Electromagnetic Theory," Ernest Benn, Ltd., London, 1893, Vol. 1, p. 78.

By means of the conversion formula

$$\mathbf{G} \cdot (\nabla \times \mathbf{F}) - \mathbf{F} \cdot (\nabla \times \mathbf{G}) = \nabla \cdot (\mathbf{F} \times \mathbf{G}) \qquad (9\text{-}112)$$

the two terms on the left side of (9-111) can be expressed as one. Thus

$$\nabla \cdot (\mathbf{E} \times \mathbf{H}) = - \left(\mathbf{E} \cdot \frac{\partial \mathbf{D}}{\partial t} + \mathbf{H} \cdot \frac{\partial \mathbf{B}}{\partial t} \right) \qquad (9\text{-}113)$$

For isotropic media, $\mathbf{D} = \epsilon\mathbf{E}$ and $\mathbf{B} = \mu\mathbf{H}$, and (9-113) takes the form

$$\nabla \cdot (\mathbf{E} \times \mathbf{H}) = - \left[\mathbf{E} \cdot \frac{\partial(\epsilon\mathbf{E})}{\partial t} + \mathbf{H} \cdot \frac{\partial(\mu\mathbf{H})}{\partial t} \right] \qquad (9\text{-}114)$$

Recalling from calculus that

$$w \frac{\partial w}{\partial t} = \frac{1}{2} \frac{\partial w^2}{\partial t} \qquad (9\text{-}115)$$

(9-114) can be written as

$$\nabla \cdot (\mathbf{E} \times \mathbf{H}) = - \left[\frac{\partial}{\partial t} \left(\frac{\epsilon E^2}{2} \right) + \frac{\partial}{\partial t} \left(\frac{\mu H^2}{2} \right) \right] \qquad (9\text{-}116)$$

Taking the time derivative operator outside the brackets,

$$\nabla \cdot (\mathbf{E} \times \mathbf{H}) = - \frac{\partial}{\partial t} \left(\frac{1}{2} \epsilon E^2 + \frac{1}{2} \mu H^2 \right) \qquad (9\text{-}117)$$

Comparing (9-117) with (9-108), it follows that

$$\mathbf{E} \times \mathbf{H} = \mathbf{S} \qquad (9\text{-}118)$$

where $\mathbf{E}$ = electric field intensity (volts/meter)
    $\mathbf{H}$ = $\mathbf{H}$ field (amp/meter)
    $\mathbf{S}$ = Poynting vector (watts/meter^2)
The dimensional form of (9-118) in mksc units is

$$\frac{\text{Volts}}{\text{Meter}} \times \frac{\text{amperes}}{\text{meter}} = \frac{\text{watts}}{\text{meter}^2}$$

In words, this important relation indicates that the rate of energy flow per unit area in a wave is directed normal to the plane containing $\mathbf{E}$ and $\mathbf{H}$ and has a magnitude in watts per square meter equal to $EH \sin \theta$, where θ is the angle between $\mathbf{E}$ and $\mathbf{H}$. It is often helpful to regard the Poynting vector as a *surface power density*.

For a plane wave traveling in the positive x direction, as in Fig. 9-2, (9-118) becomes

$$j E_y \times k H_z = i S_x = \mathbf{S} \qquad (9\text{-}119)$$

It should be mentioned that in some situations $\mathbf{E} \times \mathbf{H}$ does not represent energy flow, as, for example, in a static magnetic field superimposed on a static electric field. However, the integral of the normal component of $\mathbf{E} \times \mathbf{H}$ over a closed surface always gives the total power through the surface. That is,

$$\oint_s \mathbf{S} \cdot d\mathbf{s} = P \qquad \text{watts} \qquad (9\text{-}120)$$

where P = power flowing out of closed surface s. The Poynting vector $\mathbf{S}$ in the above relation is the instantaneous power density, and P in (9-120) is the instantaneous power.

When $\mathbf{E}$ and $\mathbf{H}$ are changing with time, we are often interested in the average power. This is obtained by integrating the instantaneous Poynting vector over one period and dividing by one period. It is also readily obtained using complex notation as follows: In complex notation the complex Poynting vector is given by

$$\mathbf{S} = \tfrac{1}{2}\mathbf{E} \times \mathbf{H}^* \qquad (9\text{-}121)$$

where $\mathbf{E} = \mathbf{a}_E \dot{E} = \mathbf{a}_E E_0 e^{j\omega t}$
   $\mathbf{a}_E$ = unit vector in $\mathbf{E}$ direction
   $\mathbf{H}^* = \mathbf{a}_H \dot{H}^* = \mathbf{a}_H H_0 e^{-j(\omega t - \xi)}$
   $\mathbf{a}_H$ = unit vector in $\mathbf{H}$ direction
   ξ = phase angle between $\dot{E}$ and $\dot{H}^*$
In (9-121) $\mathbf{H}^*$ is called the *complex conjugate* of $\mathbf{H}$, where

$$\mathbf{H} = \mathbf{a}_H H_0 e^{+j(\omega t - \xi)} \qquad (9\text{-}122)$$

The quantity $\mathbf{H}$ and its complex conjugate $\mathbf{H}^*$ have the same space direction and the same amplitude H_0, but they differ in sign in their phase factors. Assuming that the space directions of $\mathbf{E}$ and $\mathbf{H}$ (or $\mathbf{H}^*$) are normal to each other, the complex Poynting vector is normal to the plane containing $\mathbf{E}$ and $\mathbf{H}^*$ and is

$$\mathbf{S} = \tfrac{1}{2}\mathbf{a}_n E_0 H_0 e^{j\xi} \qquad (9\text{-}123)$$

where $\mathbf{a}_n$ = unit vector normal to $\mathbf{E}$ and $\mathbf{H}^*$.

Now the average Poynting vector $\mathbf{S}_{av}$ is given by the real part of the complex Poynting vector, or

$$\mathbf{S}_{av} = \text{Re } \mathbf{S} = \tfrac{1}{2}\mathbf{a}_n E_0 H_0 \cos \xi \qquad \text{watts/meter}^2 \qquad (9\text{-}124)$$

where ξ = time-phase angle between electric and magnetic fields. It is understood that E_0 and H_0 are the amplitudes or peak magnitudes of the fields. If, instead, one uses the rms values, the factor $\tfrac{1}{2}$ in (9-124) is omitted.

Taking the imaginary part of (9-123) yields the so-called "reactive" power per unit area.

The average power P_{av} flowing outward through a closed surface may now be expressed as

$$P_{av} = \oint_s \text{Re } \mathbf{S} \cdot d\mathbf{s} = \tfrac{1}{2} \oint_s \text{Re } (\mathbf{E} \times \mathbf{H}^*) \cdot d\mathbf{s} \qquad (9\text{-}125)$$

Dividing the Poynting vector by the energy density, we obtain a quantity with the dimensions of velocity. Thus

$$\frac{\text{Poynting vector}}{\text{Energy density}} = \text{velocity} \qquad (9\text{-}125a)$$

or in dimensional symbols

$$\frac{MT^{-3}}{ML^{-1}T^{-2}} = \frac{L}{T}$$

This is the *energy velocity* v_{en}. In nondispersive media the energy velocity is equal to the phase velocity v. In a nondispersive lossless medium we have

$$v_{en} = \frac{EH}{\epsilon E^2} = \frac{1}{\sqrt{\mu\epsilon}} = v$$

In dispersive media that are also lossless the energy velocity is equal to the group velocity. In absorbing media (not lossless) where the absorption is not small the group velocity tends to lose its simple significance. However, the energy velocity still has a simple, definite meaning.

Whereas the phase velocity (and also the group velocity) may assume values greater or less than the velocity of light, the energy velocity never exceeds the velocity of light (3×10^8 meters per sec).

Example 1. A plane traveling wave in free space has an average Poynting vector of 1 watt/meter^2. Find the average energy density.

Solution. The average energy density

$$w_{av} = \frac{S_{av}}{\text{velocity}} = \frac{1}{3} \times 10^{-8} \text{ joule/meter}^3$$
$$= \frac{1}{30} \text{ erg/meter}^3$$

The energy density w_{av} is an average value. The instantaneous value may be any value between zero and twice the average value. The difference between the average and instantaneous values is discussed in more detail in the following paragraphs.

Returning now to a further consideration of a plane wave traveling in the positive x direction in a lossless medium, let us substitute (9-68) and (9-69) in the Poynting-vector equation (9-119). This yields

$$S_x = \sqrt{\frac{\epsilon}{\mu}} \, E_0{}^2 \sin^2(\omega t - \beta x) \qquad \text{watts/meter}^2 \qquad (9\text{-}126)$$

This is the *instantaneous power per unit area*. At a fixed position, $\beta x = $ constant, this power pulsates with the passage of time as a sine squared function. The *peak power per unit area* occurs when

$$\sin^2(\omega t - \beta x) = 1$$

giving

$$\text{Peak } S_x = \sqrt{\frac{\epsilon}{\mu}} E_0^2 = \frac{E_0^2}{R} \qquad (9\text{-}127)$$

where R = intrinsic resistance of the medium.   To find the *average power
per unit area*, the instantaneous value given by (9-126) is integrated over
one period and divided by the length of one period, which yields[1]

$$\text{Average } S_x = \frac{1}{2}\sqrt{\frac{\epsilon}{\mu}} E_0^2 = \frac{E_0^2}{2R} \qquad (9\text{-}128)$$

Comparing (9-128) and (9-127), it follows that

$$\text{Peak } S_x = 2 \text{ (average } S_x) \qquad (9\text{-}129)$$

The energy flow per unit time per unit area, or power surface density,
of a plane wave traveling in the positive x direction is illustrated in Fig.
9-14.   Here the instantaneous values of S_x are shown at two instants of

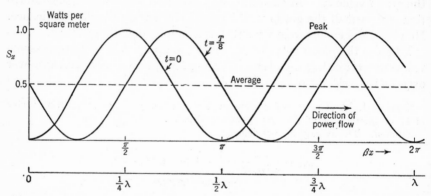

FIG. 9-14. Instantaneous Poynting-vector magnitude for plane wave traveling in
positive x direction at two instants of time: $t = 0$ and $\frac{1}{8}$ period later.

time $t = 0$ and $t = T/8$.   The values of the instantaneous power per
unit area are given over a distance of 1 wavelength in the x direction.
Confining our attention to one of the curves, say for $t = 0$, we note that
the power surface density is a pulsating quantity, with two pulses per
wavelength.   Hence, at a fixed position there are two pulses per period
or cycle.   Comparing the curves for $t = 0$ and $t = T/8$, we note that the
pulses move to the right a distance of $\frac{1}{8}$ wavelength in the interval of $\frac{1}{8}$
period, indicating a power flow in the positive x direction.

To obtain the instantaneous energy density of the wave, the instantaneous Poynting vector is divided by the velocity of the wave.   Thus

---

[1] The same result may be obtained from (9-124) by noting that in a lossless medium
$\xi = 0$.

the instantaneous energy density is given by

$$w = \frac{S}{v} = \frac{1}{v}\sqrt{\frac{\epsilon}{\mu}}\, E_0{}^2 \sin^2(\omega t - \beta x) \qquad (9\text{-}130)$$

Since $1/v = \sqrt{\epsilon\mu}$, (9-130) becomes

$$w = \epsilon E_0{}^2 \sin^2(\omega t - \beta x) \qquad \text{joules/meter}^3 \qquad (9\text{-}130a)$$

By steps similar to those for (9-127) and (9-128) the peak and average energy densities are

$$\text{Peak } w = \epsilon E_0{}^2 \qquad \text{joules/meter}^3 \qquad (9\text{-}131)$$
$$\text{Average } w = \tfrac{1}{2}\epsilon E_0{}^2 \qquad \text{joules/meter}^3 \qquad (9\text{-}132)$$

Table 9-2 summarizes the relations developed above for the Poynting vector and energy density of a single plane traveling wave.

TABLE 9-2
POYNTING-VECTOR AND ENERGY-DENSITY RELATIONS FOR A PLANE TRAVELING WAVE IN A DIELECTRIC MEDIUM

Condition	Poynting vector S, watts/meter^2	Total energy density w, joules/meter^3
Instantaneous......	$\sqrt{\dfrac{\epsilon}{\mu}}\, E_0{}^2 \sin^2(\omega t - \beta x)$	$\epsilon E_0{}^2 \sin^2(\omega t - \beta x)$
Peak..............	$\sqrt{\dfrac{\epsilon}{\mu}}\, E_0{}^2 = \sqrt{\dfrac{\mu}{\epsilon}}\, H_0{}^2$	$\epsilon E_0{}^2 = \mu H_0{}^2$
Average...........	$\dfrac{1}{2}\sqrt{\dfrac{\epsilon}{\mu}}\, E_0{}^2 = \dfrac{1}{2}\sqrt{\dfrac{\mu}{\epsilon}}\, H_0{}^2$	$\dfrac{1}{2}\epsilon E_0{}^2 = \dfrac{1}{2}\mu H_0{}^2$

The instantaneous energy-density distribution of the plane wave traveling in the positive x direction has the same form as the Poynting-vector curves shown in Fig. 9-14. The ordinate, however, for energy-density curves is expressed in joules per cubic meter.

From the energy point of view, it is interesting to consider the *energy per pulse* of the wave. Here we consider that 1 pulse is $\frac{1}{2}$ wavelength long. Its boundaries are defined by the positions where the energy density is zero. Since we are dealing with a plane wave of infinite extent, let us confine our attention to a volume 1 meter square (parallel to the wave front) by 1 pulse length (in the x direction). Since 1 pulse length is $\frac{1}{2}$ wavelength long, the energy in this volume (1 pulse long) is obtained by multiplying the average energy density by $\frac{1}{2}$ wavelength expressed in meters. Thus

$$\text{Energy} = (\text{average } w) \frac{\lambda}{2} \quad \text{joules} \tag{9-133}$$

where λ = wavelength.

Example 2. The average energy density of a plane traveling wave is 1 joule/meter³. If the wavelength is 0.5 meter, find the energy in a volume 1 pulse length by 1 meter².

Solution. From (9-133)

$$\text{Energy} = \tfrac{1}{4} \text{ joule}$$

This is the energy in a volume 1 meter square by 1 pulse length long, or the energy in a volume of 0.25 meter³.

It is to be noted that the instantaneous values of E_y and H_z have a sine distribution as a function of x. The Poynting vector **S** and the energy density w, however, have a sine squared distribution.

The energy density w which we have been discussing is the total energy density of the plane electromagnetic wave. This energy density in the case of the plane traveling wave is equally divided at all times between the electric energy density and the magnetic energy density. This relationship is given by (9-105).

Equation (9-126) for the Poynting vector of a plane traveling wave is written in terms of E. Since the power is equally divided between electric and magnetic forms, we can write

$$S'_e = \frac{1}{2} \sqrt{\frac{\epsilon}{\mu}} \, E_0{}^2 \sin^2 (\omega t - \beta x) \tag{9-134}$$

and

$$S'_m = \frac{1}{2} \sqrt{\frac{\mu}{\epsilon}} \, H_0{}^2 \sin^2 (\omega t - \beta x) \tag{9-135}$$

where S'_e = electric power per unit area

S'_m = magnetic power per unit area

The phase factors for both S'_e and S'_m are identical. Since $S'_e = S'_m$ for the plane traveling wave, the total power can be expressed as twice the value of S'_e. Thus

$$S = S'_e + S'_m = 2S'_e \tag{9-136}$$

where the Poynting vector S is equal to the total power per unit area.

Likewise, the energy density is equally divided between the electric (w_e) and magnetic (w_m) so that

$$w_e = \tfrac{1}{2}\epsilon E_0{}^2 \sin^2 (\omega t - \beta x) \tag{9-137}$$

and

$$w_m = \tfrac{1}{2}\mu H_0{}^2 \sin^2 (\omega t - \beta x) \tag{9-138}$$

Since $w_e = w_m$ for a plane traveling wave, the total w is twice w_e. Thus

$$w = w_e + w_m = 2w_e = 2w_m \qquad (9\text{-}139)$$

9-13. Energy Relations in a Standing Wave. Next let us consider the energy and power relations for two plane waves traveling in opposite directions. Assume that both waves are polarized with **E** in the y direction. Assume further that one wave travels in the negative x direction and has an amplitude E_0, while the other wave travels in the positive x direction and has an amplitude E_1. In this case the instantaneous value of E_y, resulting from the two waves, is given by

$$E_y = E_0 \sin (\omega t + \beta x) + E_1 \sin (\omega t - \beta x) \qquad (9\text{-}140)$$

We may find a corresponding relation for H_z as follows: Let us start with (9-8). That is,

$$\frac{\partial E_y}{\partial x} = -\mu \frac{\partial H_z}{\partial t} \qquad (9\text{-}141)$$

Substituting E_y from (9-140) into (9-141), differentiating with respect to x, and integrating with respect to t, we obtain

$$H_z = -\sqrt{\frac{\epsilon}{\mu}}\, E_0 \sin (\omega t + \beta x) + \sqrt{\frac{\epsilon}{\mu}}\, E_1 \sin (\omega t - \beta x) \qquad (9\text{-}142)$$

The magnitude of the Poynting vector is

$$S_x = E_y H_z \qquad (9\text{-}143)$$

Substituting (9-140) and (9-142) in (9-143) yields

$$S_x = -\sqrt{\frac{\epsilon}{\mu}}\, [E_0{}^2 \sin^2 (\omega t + \beta x) - E_1{}^2 \sin^2 (\omega t - \beta x)] \qquad (9\text{-}144)$$

According to (9-144) the net Poynting vector is in the negative x direction provided $E_0 > E_1$. Furthermore, the net Poynting vector is equal to the difference of the Poynting vectors for the two traveling waves. Suppose that the wave to the left is incident on a plane boundary at $x = 0$ (as in Fig. 9-9). The wave to the right then becomes a reflected wave. If the medium to the left of the boundary is a perfect conductor, we have the condition at the boundary that $E_1 = -E_0$, resulting in a pure standing wave to the right of the boundary. We note that for this condition the net Poynting vector is zero and, hence, no power is transmitted. Furthermore, it follows from (9-144) that, in general, *the larger the standing-wave ratio, the smaller the net power transmitted for a given value of E_0.* Conversely, the smaller the standing-wave ratio, the larger the net power transmitted for a given value of E_0.

It is interesting to examine the condition of a pure standing wave ($E_1 = -E_0$) in more detail, particularly from the standpoint of concentrations of energy. Accordingly, let us find the values of the electric and magnetic energy densities separately. Substituting (9-87) into (9-101), we obtain, for the electric energy density of a pure standing wave,

$$w_e = 2\epsilon E_0{}^2 \cos^2 \omega t \sin^2 \beta x \qquad (9\text{-}145)$$

Taking (9-142), expanding, collecting terms, and putting $E_1 \sqrt{\dfrac{\epsilon}{\mu}} = H_0$,

$$H_z = -2H_0 \sin \omega t \cos \beta x \qquad (9\text{-}146)$$

Substituting this in (9-102) yields the value of the magnetic energy density of a pure standing wave,

$$w_m = 2\mu H_0{}^2 \sin^2 \omega t \cos^2 \beta x \qquad (9\text{-}147)$$

Comparing (9-145) and (9-147), the electric energy density is a maximum when the magnetic is zero, and vice versa. Furthermore, the points

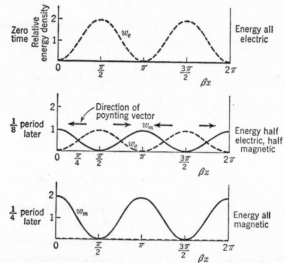

FIG. 9-15. Total electric and magnetic energy densities at three instants of time for a pure standing wave. Conditions are shown over a distance of 1 wavelength ($\beta x = 2\pi$). There is no net transmission of energy in a pure standing wave.

where they are maximum are $\frac{1}{4}$ wavelength apart. In other words, the electric and magnetic energy densities of a pure standing wave are in space and time quadrature. This condition is typical of a pure resonator. The energy oscillates back and forth from the electric form to the magnetic. Energy in this condition is often spoken of as reactive or stored energy. It is not transmitted but circulates from one form to the other. Simultaneously with the change from the electric to the magnetic form of energy there is a space motion of the energy back and forth over a distance of $\frac{1}{4}$ wavelength. These relations are shown graphically in Fig. 9-15.

Here the energy densities are shown at three instants of time, $t = 0$, $T/8$, and $T/4$. The dashed curves show the instantaneous electric energy density w_e as evaluated from (9-145) and the solid curves the instantaneous magnetic energy density w_m as evaluated from (9-147).

Finally, let us find an expression for the magnitude of the Poynting vector of a pure standing wave. To do this, we substitute (9-146) and (9-87) in (9-119), obtaining

$$S_x = -4E_0 H_0 \cos \omega t \sin \omega t \cos \beta x \sin \beta x \qquad (9\text{-}148)$$

Putting H_0 in terms of E_0,

$$S_x = -4 \sqrt{\frac{\epsilon}{\mu}} E_0^2 \cos \omega t \sin \omega t \cos \beta x \sin \beta x \qquad (9\text{-}149)$$

and the peak value of the Poynting vector is

$$\text{Peak } S_x = \sqrt{\frac{\epsilon}{\mu}} E_0^2 \qquad (9\text{-}150)$$

From an inspection of (9-149) it is clear that S_x is a maximum at $\omega t = \pi/4$ ($\frac{1}{8}$ period). At this instant the position of one maximum is at $\beta x = \pi/4$ ($\frac{1}{8}$ wavelength) and is directed to the left as shown by the arrow in Fig. 9-15. The other arrows indicate other Poynting-vector maxima and illustrate that at $t = T/8$ the energy is flowing from the regions of electric energy density to those of magnetic energy density.

Referring to Fig. 9-11, we note that in a standing wave, a constant phase point does not move with uniform velocity. As a result, the energy tends to bunch up or localize. This condition becomes extreme with a pure standing wave for which a constant phase point is stationary. Hence, localized concentrations of energy are associated with a nonuniform or stationary phase velocity.

9-14. Wave Polarization.[1] Consider a plane wave traveling out of the page (positive z direction) as in Fig. 9-16a, with the electric field at all times in the y direction. This wave is said to be *linearly polarized* in the y direction. As a function of time and position the electric field of a linearly polarized wave (as in Fig. 9-16a) traveling in the positive z direction (out of the page) is given by

$$E_y = E_2 \sin (\omega t - \beta z) \qquad (9\text{-}151)$$

In general, the electric field of a wave traveling in the z direction may have both a y component and an x component, as suggested in Fig. 9-16b. In the general situation, such a wave is said to be *elliptically polarized*.

[1] For a more detailed treatment of wave polarization see, for example, J. D. Kraus, "Antennas," McGraw-Hill Book Company, Inc., New York, 1950, pp. 464–484.

At a fixed value of z the electric field vector $\mathbf{E}$ rotates as a function of time, the tip of the vector describing an ellipse called the polarization ellipse. The ratio of the major to the minor axis of the polarization ellipse is called the *axial ratio* (AR). Thus, for the wave in Fig. 9-16b,

$$\text{AR} = \frac{E_2}{E_1} \tag{9-152}$$

The axial ratio of a linearly polarized wave is infinite.

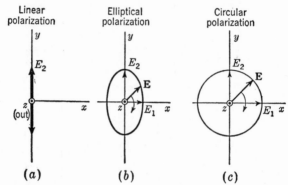

FIG. 9-16. Linear, elliptical, and circular polarization.

In general, an elliptically polarized wave may be expressed in terms of an x component given by

$$E_x = E_1 \sin (\omega t - \beta z) \tag{9-153}$$

and a y component given by

$$E_y = E_2 \sin (\omega t - \beta z + \delta) \tag{9-154}$$

where E_1 = amplitude of linearly polarized x-component wave
E_2 = amplitude of linearly polarized y-component wave
δ = time-phase angle by which E_y leads E_x (the "x wave" is taken as the reference for phase)
The instantaneous total vector field $\mathbf{E}$ resulting from the two linearly polarized component waves is

$$\mathbf{E} = \mathbf{i}E_1 \sin (\omega t - \beta z) + \mathbf{j}E_2 \sin (\omega t - \beta z + \delta) \tag{9-155}$$

Evaluating (9-155) as a function of time t at a fixed value of z and plotting the values for $\mathbf{E}$, the locus of the tip of $\mathbf{E}$ is obtained as a function of time. In general the locus is an ellipse. If $E_1 = E_2$ and $\delta = 90°$, the locus described by the tip of $\mathbf{E}$ is a circle (Fig. 9-16c) and the wave is said to be *circularly polarized*. On the other hand, if $\delta = 0°$ or $\pm 180°$ or if E_1 or E_2 equals zero, the wave is linearly polarized. Both linear and circular polarization may be regarded as special (limiting) cases of elliptical polarization.

The fact that the locus is in general an ellipse may be demonstrated by proving that (9-153) and (9-154) with $z = 0$ are the parametric equations of an ellipse.   Thus we have

$$E_x = E_1 \sin \omega t \qquad\qquad (9\text{-}156)$$
$$E_y = E_2 \sin (\omega t + \delta) \qquad\qquad (9\text{-}157)$$

where ωt is the independent variable.   The procedure used in the proof will be to eliminate ωt and rearrange the resulting expression into the form of the equation for an ellipse.   First we expand (9-157).   That is,

$$E_y = E_2 (\sin \omega t \cos \delta + \cos \omega t \sin \delta) \qquad\qquad (9\text{-}158)$$

From (9-156)

$$\sin \omega t = \frac{E_x}{E_1}$$

We also can write

$$\cos \omega t = \sqrt{1 - \sin^2 \omega t} = \sqrt{1 - \left(\frac{E_x}{E_1}\right)^2}$$

Substituting these relations for $\sin \omega t$ and $\cos \omega t$ in (9-158), rearranging, and squaring yields,

$$\frac{E_x^2}{E_1^2} - \frac{2 E_x E_y \cos \delta}{E_1 E_2} + \frac{E_y^2}{E_2^2} = \sin^2 \delta \qquad\qquad (9\text{-}159)$$

Dividing by $\sin^2 \delta$, this can be reduced to

$$a E_x^2 - b E_x E_y + c E_y^2 = 1 \qquad\qquad (9\text{-}160)$$

where $a = 1/(E_1^2 \sin^2 \delta)$
$\quad\ b = (2 \cos \delta)/(E_1 E_2 \sin^2 \delta)$
$\quad\ c = 1/(E_2^2 \sin^2 \delta)$

Equation (9-160) may be recognized as the equation for an ellipse in its most general form, the axes of the ellipse, in general, not coinciding with the x or y axis.

Finally, let us develop an expression for the average Poynting vector of an elliptically polarized wave.   For this it will be convenient to use complex notation and to indicate all complex quantities (phasors) explicitly by a dot ($\cdot$).

Now the complex Poynting vector is

$$\dot{S} = \tfrac{1}{2}\dot{E} \times \dot{H}^* \qquad\qquad (9\text{-}161)$$

and the average Poynting vector is the real part of it, or

$$S_{av} = \text{Re } \dot{S} = \tfrac{1}{2}\text{ Re } \dot{E} \times \dot{H}^* \qquad\qquad (9\text{-}162)$$

Referring to Fig. 9-16b, let the elliptically polarized wave have x and y components with a phase difference δ as given by

$$\dot{E}_x = E_1 e^{j(\omega t - \beta z)} \tag{9-163}$$
$$\dot{E}_y = E_2 e^{j(\omega t - \beta z + \delta)} \tag{9-164}$$

At $z = 0$ the total electric field (vector) is then

$$\dot{\mathbf{E}} = \mathbf{i}\dot{E}_x + \mathbf{j}\dot{E}_y = \mathbf{i}E_1 e^{j\omega t} + \mathbf{j}E_2 e^{j(\omega t + \delta)} \tag{9-165}$$

where $\mathbf{i}$ = unit vector in x direction

$\mathbf{j}$ = unit vector in y direction

Note that $\dot{\mathbf{E}}$ is a complex vector (phasor-vector) which is resolvable into two component complex vectors $\mathbf{i}\dot{E}_x$ and $\mathbf{j}\dot{E}_y$, where each component has a vector part (indicating space direction) and a complex part or phasor (indicating time phase). Thus, in $\mathbf{i}\dot{E}_x$, $\mathbf{i}$ is the vector and $\dot{E}_x$ is the phasor.

The **H**-field component associated with $\dot{E}_x$ is

$$\dot{H}_y = H_1 e^{j(\omega t - \beta z - \xi)} \tag{9-166}$$

where ξ = phase lag of $\dot{H}_y$ with respect to $\dot{E}_x$. The **H**-field component associated with $\dot{E}_y$ is

$$\dot{H}_x = H_2 e^{j(\omega t - \beta z + \delta - \xi)} \tag{9-167}$$

The total **H** field (vector) at $z = 0$ for a wave traveling in the positive z direction is then

$$\dot{\mathbf{H}} = \mathbf{j}\dot{H}_y - \mathbf{i}\dot{H}_x = \mathbf{j}H_1 e^{j(\omega t - \xi)} - \mathbf{i}H_2 e^{j(\omega t + \delta - \xi)} \tag{9-168}$$

Now the complex conjugate of $\dot{\mathbf{H}}$ is equal to (9-168) except for the sign of the exponents. That is,

$$\dot{\mathbf{H}}^* = \mathbf{j}H_1 e^{-j(\omega t - \xi)} - \mathbf{i}H_2 e^{-j(\omega t + \delta - \xi)} \tag{9-169}$$

Substituting (9-165) and (9-169) in (9-162) gives the average Poynting vector at $z = 0$ as

$$\begin{aligned}
\mathbf{S}_{\mathrm{av}} &= \tfrac{1}{2}\,\mathrm{Re}\,[(\mathbf{i} \times \mathbf{j})\dot{E}_x \dot{H}_y^* - (\mathbf{j} \times \mathbf{i})\dot{E}_y \dot{H}_x^*] \\
&= \tfrac{1}{2}\mathbf{k}\,\mathrm{Re}\,(\dot{E}_x \dot{H}_y^* + \dot{E}_y \dot{H}_x^*)
\end{aligned} \tag{9-170}$$

where $\mathbf{k}$ = unit vector in z direction (direction of propagation of wave). It follows that

$$\begin{aligned}
\mathbf{S}_{\mathrm{av}} &= \tfrac{1}{2}\mathbf{k}(E_1 H_1\,\mathrm{Re}\,e^{j\xi} + E_2 H_2\,\mathrm{Re}\,e^{j\xi}) \\
&= \tfrac{1}{2}\mathbf{k}(E_1 H_1 + E_2 H_2)\cos\xi
\end{aligned} \tag{9-171}$$

It is to be noted that $\mathbf{S}_{\mathrm{av}}$ is independent of δ.

In a lossless medium $\xi = 0$ (electric and magnetic fields in time phase) and $E_1/H_1 = E_2/H_2 = Z$, where Z, the intrinsic impedance of the medium, is real; so

$$\begin{aligned}
\mathbf{S}_{\mathrm{av}} &= \tfrac{1}{2}\mathbf{k}(E_1 H_1 + E_2 H_2) \\
&= \tfrac{1}{2}\mathbf{k}(H_1{}^2 + H_2{}^2)Z = \tfrac{1}{2}\mathbf{k}H^2 Z
\end{aligned} \tag{9-172}$$

where $H = \sqrt{H_1{}^2 + H_2{}^2}$ = amplitude of total $\mathbf{H}$ field. We can also write

$$\mathbf{S}_{av} = \frac{1}{2}\,\mathbf{k}\,\frac{E_1{}^2 + E_2{}^2}{Z} = \frac{1}{2}\,\mathbf{k}\,\frac{E^2}{Z} \tag{9-173}$$

where $E = \sqrt{E_1{}^2 + E_2{}^2}$ = amplitude of total $\mathbf{E}$ field.

Example. An elliptically polarized wave in air has x and y components

$$E_x = 3 \sin (\omega t - \beta z) \qquad \text{volts/meter}$$
$$E_y = 6 \sin (\omega t - \beta z + 75°) \qquad \text{volts/meter}$$

Find the average power per unit area conveyed by the wave.

Solution. The wave is traveling in the positive z direction. The average power per unit area is equal to the average Poynting vector, which from (9-173) has a magnitude

$$S_{av} = \frac{1}{2}\frac{E^2}{Z} = \frac{1}{2}\frac{E_1{}^2 + E_2{}^2}{Z}$$

From the stated conditions the amplitude $E_1 = 3$ volts/meter, and the amplitude $E_2 = 6$ volts/meter. Also for air $Z = 376.7$ ohms. Hence

$$S_{av} = \frac{1}{2}\frac{3^2 + 6^2}{376.7} = \frac{1}{2}\frac{45}{376.7} \simeq 0.06 \text{ watt/meter}^2$$

9-15. Cross-field. The discussion in the preceding sections has dealt with elliptical polarization and its two special limiting cases of linear and

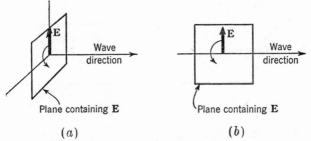

FIG. 9-17. Plane containing $\mathbf{E}$ for case of elliptical polarization (a), and plane containing $\mathbf{E}$ for case of cross-field (b).

circular polarization. In all of these cases the directions of the electric field vector at a given point are confined to a plane perpendicular to the direction of propagation, as indicated in Fig. 9-17a.

Another situation often occurs in which the electric vector rotates in a plane parallel to the propagation direction (Fig. 9-17b). This condition is called *cross-field*.[1] This situation can occur if there is a component of $\mathbf{E}$ in the direction of propagation. This situation never exists in the case

[1] A. Alford, J. D. Kraus, and E. C. Barkofsky, Chap. 9, "Very High Frequency Techniques," Radio Research Laboratory Staff, H. J. Reich (ed.), McGraw-Hill Book Company, Inc., New York, 1947, p. 200.

of a single plane wave in free space since such a wave has no field component in the direction of propagation. However, in the near field of an antenna there are field components in both the direction of propagation and normal to this direction so that cross-field is present (Fig. 9-18a).

Cross-field may also be present where two waves of the same frequency and traveling in different directions cross. Thus, in the region exposed to radiation from two antennas as in Fig. 9-18b there is cross-field. Both

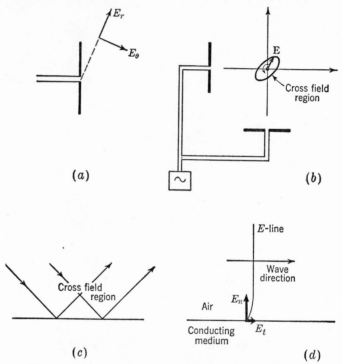

FIG. 9-18. Situations in which cross-field may be present.

antennas are linearly polarized in the plane of the page, and both are connected to the same generator so that both radiate the same frequency. In general, the tip of E describes a locus that is an ellipse in a manner similar to that in elliptical polarization except that E is confined to the plane containing the antennas (plane of the page).

As another illustration, cross-field is present wherever a wave is reflected so that waves of the same frequency and traveling in different directions cross (Fig. 9-18c). Still another situation in which cross-field is present is near the surface of a conducting medium along which a plane wave is traveling (Fig. 9-18d). If the medium is not infinitely conducting, the E line is tilted forward near the surface of the medium so that E has a component normal to the surface (E_n) and a component parallel to the surface (E_t).   Since, in general, these components are not in time phase there is elliptical cross-field present (see Sec. 12-7, Fig. 12-21).

In general, the tip of **E** describes an ellipse (elliptical cross-field).   In special cases the ellipse becomes a straight line (linear cross-field) or a circle (circular cross-field).   This may be shown as follows:

Consider two plane traveling waves linearly polarized in the plane of the page (Fig. 9-19), one wave traveling in the y direction (y wave) and a second wave in a direction making an angle ϕ with the y direction (ϕ wave).   The electric field of the y wave has only a component in the x direction with an instantaneous value

$$E_{xy} = E_1 \sin \omega t \qquad (9\text{-}174)$$

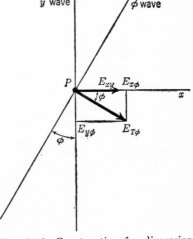

The instantaneous value of the total electric field of the ϕ wave is

$$E_{T\phi} = E_2 \sin (\omega t + \delta) \qquad (9\text{-}175)$$

where δ = phase lead of $E_{T\phi}$ over E_{xy}.   The total ϕ-wave field $E_{T\phi}$ can be resolved into two components, one in the x direction $E_{x\phi}$ and one in the y direction $E_{y\phi}$.   Thus

$$E_{x\phi} = E_{T\phi} \cos \phi$$
$$= E_2 \cos \phi \sin (\omega t + \delta) \qquad (9\text{-}176)$$

and

$$E_{y\phi} = E_{T\phi} \sin \phi$$
$$= E_2 \sin \phi \sin (\omega t + \delta) \qquad (9\text{-}177)$$

FIG. 9-19. Construction for discussion on cross-field ellipse.

Now adding the instantaneous fields in the x direction gives the x component E_x of the resultant field.   That is,

$$E_x = E_{xy} + E_{x\phi} = E_1 \sin \omega t + E_2 \cos \phi \sin (\omega t + \delta) \qquad (9\text{-}178)$$

Similarly we have for the y component E_y of the resultant field

$$E_y = -E_{y\phi} = -E_2 \sin \phi \sin (\omega t + \delta) \qquad (9\text{-}179)$$

Equations (9-178) and (9-179) are the parametric equations of an ellipse since by eliminating ωt they can be reduced to an equation for an ellipse of the form

$$A E_x{}^2 + B E_x E_y + C E_y{}^2 = 1 \qquad (9\text{-}180)$$

where $A = 1/(E_1{}^2 \sin^2 \delta)$

$$B = \frac{2(E_1 \cos \delta + E_2 \cos \phi)}{E_1{}^2 E_2 \sin^2 \delta \sin \phi}$$

$$C = \frac{E_1{}^2 + 2E_1 E_2 \cos \phi \cos \delta + E_2{}^2 \cos^2 \phi}{E_1{}^2 E_2{}^2 \sin^2 \phi \sin^2 \delta}$$

The steps required to arrive at (9-180) are left as an exercise for the student (see Prob. 9-26).

As a special case of (9-180) let the two wave directions be at right angles ($\phi = 90°$), of the same amplitude ($E_1 = E_2 = 1$), and in phase quadrature ($\delta = 90°$) at the point P. Then $A = 1$, $B = 0$, and $C = 1$ so that (9-180) reduces to

$$E_x{}^2 + E_y{}^2 = 1 \qquad (9\text{-}181)$$

This is the equation of a circle, and hence, under these conditions we have circular cross-field. Referring to Fig. 9-19, a linearly polarized receiving antenna in the plane of the page could be turned through 360° at the point P under these conditions and no change be observed in output. The rotation direction for **E** is counterclockwise for $\delta = 90°$ and clockwise for $\delta = -90°$.

As another special case let $\phi = 90°$ and $E_1 = E_2 = 1$, but let $\delta = 0°$. Then (9-180) reduces to

$$E_x = E_y \qquad (9\text{-}182)$$

which is the equation of a straight line of slope $+1$, that is, a line at an angle of $+45°$ with respect to the positive x axis. Therefore, in this case the cross-field ellipse has collapsed to a straight line and we have linear cross-field.

As a still more general situation consider the case where the two waves of Fig. 9-19 are not linearly polarized but are elliptically polarized. In such a situation we have a combination of elliptical polarization and elliptical cross-field called *space polarization*. If these two waves intersecting at P are of the same frequency, **E** will be confined to a single plane, the tip of **E** describing, in general, an ellipse.[1] The plane of the ellipse passes through the point P and, in general, may assume any orientation. If the plane is parallel to the page (Fig. 9-19), we have pure cross-field. When the two waves are elliptically polarized, the plane will lie, in general, at some angle with respect to the page. If the frequencies of the two waves are *not* the same, the tip of **E** vector will, in general, describe a three-dimensional Lissajous figure.

PROBLEMS

9-1. Find the velocity of a plane wave in a lossless medium having a relative permittivity of 5 and relative permeability of unity.   *Ans.:* 1.34×10^8 meters/sec.

9-2. (a) From Maxwell's curl equations derive the wave equation in E for a plane wave traveling in the positive y direction in an isotropic homogeneous lossless medium.

[1] C. W. Chandler, "Analysis and Measurement of Elliptically Polarized Electromagnetic Waves," master's thesis, department of electrical engineering, Ohio State University, 1948. M. G. Morgan and W. R. Evans, Synthesis and Analysis of Elliptic Polarization Loci in Terms of Space-quadrature Sinusoidal Components, *Proc. I.R.E.*, **39**, 552–556, May, 1951.

The electric field is in the z direction. (b) Assuming harmonic variation, state a solution of this equation, and prove that it is a solution.

9-3. A plane wave is traveling in the positive x direction in a lossless unbounded medium having a permeability the same as free space and a permittivity nine times that of free space. (a) Find the phase velocity of the wave. (b) If the electric field intensity $\mathbf{E}$ has only a y component with an amplitude of 10 volts/meter, find the amplitude and direction of the magnetic field intensity.

Ans.: (a) $v = 10^8$ meters/sec.; (b) $H_z = 0.08$ amp/meter.

9-4. A plane wave in a lossless dielectric medium has an electric field given by $E_y = E_0 \sin 2\pi(ft - x/\lambda)$, where f = frequency. Obtain an expression for the phase velocity of the wave.

9-5. Find the impedance of a lossless medium for which $\epsilon_r = 8$ and $\mu_r = 2$.

Ans.: 188 ohms.

9-6. A lossless medium has a relative dielectric constant of 81 and a relative permeability of unity. These conditions are closely met by distilled water. (a) Find the impedance of the medium. (b) Find the velocity of a low-frequency radio wave in the medium.

9-7. (a) Find the phase velocity of a wave in a medium having a relative permittivity of 9 and a relative permeability of unity. (b) Find the index of refraction of this medium. *Ans.* (a) $v = 10^8$ meters/sec.; (b) $\eta = 3$.

9-8. A plane 2,000-Mc/sec wave is incident normally on a slab of polystyrene ($\epsilon_r = 2.7$) of large extent. How thick must the slab be to retard the wave in phase by 90° behind a wave which passes through a large hole in the slab?

9-9. From Maxwell's curl equations derive the wave equation in E for a plane wave in free space traveling parallel to the x-y plane and at an angle of 45° with respect to the positive x axis. The electric field is in the z direction.

9-10. Compute and plot curves for the amplitude of the resultant electric field due to two plane waves traveling in the positive and negative x direction at three instants of time $t = 0$, $T/8$, and $T/4$. The waves have only E_y components. The wave in the positive x direction has an amplitude $E_0 = 1$ volt/meter and the other wave an amplitude $E_1 = \frac{1}{3}$ volt/meter. Extend the plot over a distance of at least one wavelength in the x direction. (a) In which direction does a constant phase point move? (b) What is the standing-wave ratio? (c) Assuming that the smaller wave is a reflection of the larger, what is the magnitude of the reflection coefficient?

9-11. A plane wave in free space is reflected at normal incidence from an infinite, perfectly conducting sheet producing a standing wave. The amplitude of $\mathbf{E}$ of the incident wave is 5 volts/meter. (a) How far from the sheet is the Poynting vector a maximum? (b) What is the average value of the Poynting vector? (c) What is the maximum value of the Poynting vector?

Ans.: (a) $(2n + 1)\lambda/8$, where $n = 0, 1, 2, 3$, etc.; (b) zero; (c) 6.63×10^{-2} watt/meter².

9-12. A plane wave is reflected at normal incidence from a boundary surface. The amplitude of $\mathbf{E}$ of the incident wave is 1 volt/meter and of the reflected wave is E_1. (a) Under what conditions is there a pure standing wave? (b) Find the standing-wave ratio when $E_1 = \frac{1}{5}$ volt/meter. (c) Find the value of E_{max} and E_{min} when

$$E_1 = \tfrac{3}{4} \text{ volt/meter}$$

9-13. (a) Find the average Poynting vector for a plane wave of amplitude

$$H_0 = 1 \text{ amp/meter}$$

in a homogeneous isotropic medium for which $\mu_r = 1$ and $\epsilon_r = 4$.   (b) Find the maximum energy density of this wave.

       Ans.: (a) 94.25 watts/meter²; (b) 1.26×10^{-6} joule/meter³.

9-14. The earth receives from the sun 2.2 g-cal/min/cm².   (a) What is the corresponding Poynting vector in watts per square meter?   (b) What is the power output of the sun assuming that it is an isotropic source?   (c) What would the rms electric field intensity be at the earth due to the sun's radiation, assuming that all of the sun's energy is at a single frequency?   *Note:* 1 watt = 14.3 g-cal/min.   Distance earth to sun = 149×10^6 km.

9-15. Show that when the incident wave amplitude E_0 is much greater than the reflected wave amplitude E_1, the standing-wave-envelope expression of (9-93) becomes approximately $E_y = E_0 + E_1 \cos 2\beta x$.

9-16. A 10-Mc/sec plane traveling wave in free space has an amplitude

$$E_0 = 1 \text{ volt/meter}$$

a. What is the average energy density of the wave?
b. What is the peak energy density?
c. What is the average Poynting vector?
d. What is the peak Poynting vector?
e. How much energy is contained in a cubical volume 10 km on a side?

9-17. Given a plane wave $E = E_0 \operatorname{Re} e^{i(\omega t - \beta x)}$. Show that the resultant of two waves of this type of equal amplitude and of two frequencies given by $\omega_0 + \omega_1$ and $\omega_0 - \omega_1$ (and two corresponding wave numbers given by $\beta_0 + \beta_1$ and $\beta_0 - \beta_1$) may be expressed $E = 2E_0 \cos (\omega_0 t - \beta_0 x) \cos (\omega_1 t - \beta_1 x)$.

9-18. The group velocity $u = d\omega/d\beta$. Show that u can also be expressed in the following forms,

$$u = v + \beta \frac{dv}{d\beta} = v - \lambda \frac{dv}{d\lambda} = \frac{df}{d(1/\lambda)}$$

where v = phase velocity.

9-19. Find the group velocity of a wave 10 meters long in a normally dispersive, lossless medium for which the phase velocity v is given by $v = 2 \times 10^7 \lambda^{\frac{3}{2}}$ meters/sec.

9-20. Show that, for a plane wave in a dielectric medium, the energy velocity can be expressed as $1/\epsilon Z$ or Z/μ, where Z = intrinsic impedance of the medium.

9-21. A wave traveling normally out of the page (toward the reader) has two linearly polarized components $E_x = 2 \cos \omega t$, $E_y = 3 \cos (\omega t + 90°)$.   (a) What is the axial ratio of the resultant wave?   (b) In what direction is the major axis of the polarization ellipse?   (c) Does **E** rotate clockwise or counterclockwise?

       Ans.: (a) AR = 1.5; (b) y direction; (c) clockwise.

9-22. A wave traveling normally outward from the page (toward the reader) is the resultant of two elliptically polarized waves, one with components of **E** given by

$$E_y' = 2 \cos \omega t$$
$$E_x' = 6 \cos \left(\omega t + \frac{\pi}{2} \right)$$

and the other with components given by

$$E_y'' = 1 \cos \omega t$$
$$E_x'' = 3 \cos \left(\omega t - \frac{\pi}{2} \right)$$

(a) What is the axial ratio of the resultant wave?   (b) Does **E** rotate clockwise or counterclockwise?

9-23. An elliptically polarized plane wave traveling normally out of the page (toward the reader) has linearly polarized components E_x and E_y. Let $E_x = E_y = 1$ volt/meter and E_y lead E_x in the time phase by 72°. (a) Calculate and draw the polarization ellipse. (b) What is the axial ratio? (c) What is the angle between the major axis and the x axis?   Ans.: (b) AR = 1.38; (c) 45°.

9-24. Answer the same questions as in Prob. 9-23 for the case where E_y leads E_x by 72° as before but $E_x = 2$ volts/meter and $E_y = 1$ volt/meter.

9-25. The resultant magnitude of **E** for a cross-field ellipse is given by

$$E = \sqrt{[E_x \sin{(\omega t + 45°)}]^2 + (E_y \sin{\omega t})^2}$$

Show that E is a maximum when

$$\omega t = \arctan\left[\left(\frac{E_y}{E_x}\right)^2 \pm \sqrt{\left(\frac{E_y}{E_x}\right)^4 + 1}\right]$$

9-26. Confirm (9-180) and the values given for A, B, and C.

9-27. Two circularly polarized waves of equal magnitude intersect at the origin. One (y wave) is traveling in the positive y direction with **E** rotating clockwise as observed from a point on the positive y axis. The other (x wave) is traveling in the positive x direction with **E** rotating clockwise as observed from a point on the positive x axis. At the origin, **E** for the y wave is in the positive z direction at the same instant as **E** for the x wave is in the negative z direction. What is the locus of the resulting **E** at the origin?

Ans.: Straight line (linear space polarization) in x-y plane at angle of 45° with respect to x axis.

9-28. Prove that the instantaneous Poynting vector of a plane traveling wave is a constant when the wave is circularly polarized.

9-29. Prove that the average Poynting vector of a circularly polarized wave is twice that of a linearly polarized wave if the maximum field intensity is the same for both waves.

9-30 Show that by taking the absolute value of $\dot{E}_y$ in (9-83) the standing-wave envelope is obtained as given in (9-93). That is, show that $|\dot{E}_y|$ gives the standing-wave envelope as a function of position.

9-31. The resultant field of a standing wave due to two traveling waves is given by $\dot{E} = E_0 e^{j(\omega t + \beta x)} + E_1 e^{j(\omega t - \beta x)}$, where $E_1 \leq E_0$. Marsh[1] has shown that the phase velocity v as a function of position (x) is given by

$$v = -\frac{(E_0^2 + E_1^2 + 2E_0 E_1 \cos 2\beta x)}{(E_0^2 - E_1^2)} \frac{\omega}{\beta}$$

(a) Confirm this result. (b) Also confirm Marsh's relation (9-98) that

$$\frac{v_{max}}{v_{min}} = \left(\frac{E_0 + E_1}{E_0 - E_1}\right)^2 = (VSWR)^2$$

Hint for (a): Note that $\phi = \arctan B/A$, where $B = \text{Im } \dot{E}$ and $A = \text{Re } \dot{E}$. Note also that

$$\frac{d\phi}{dx} = \frac{A(dB/dx) - B(dA/dx)}{A^2 + B^2}$$

[1] J. A. Marsh, "A Study of Phase Velocity on Long Cylindrical Conductors," Ph.D. dissertation, Department of Electrical Engineering, Ohio State University, 1949; Measured Current Distributions on Helical Antennas, *Proc. I.R.E.*, **39**, 668–675, June, 1951.

9-32. Two uniform waves of the same frequency and velocity and of amplitudes E_0 and E_1 traveling in opposite directions form a standing wave. If $E_1 = 0.5E_0$, make a graph showing the standing-wave envelope for the resultant field as a function of distance (abscissa) for several wavelengths. Also draw a curve on the same graph showing the velocity of the resultant field as a function of distance (see Prob. 9-31).

9-33. Show that in a standing wave the average phase velocity of the resultant field is equal to the geometric mean of the maximum and minimum velocities. That is, $v_{av} = \sqrt{v_{max}v_{min}}$.

9-34. A plane traveling wave is incident at an angle of 45° to an infinite, perfectly conducting flat sheet. The electric field is everywhere contained in a plane normal to the sheet and parallel to the direction of wave propagation. Plot the axial ratio of the cross-field ellipse as a function of distance from the sheet for a distance of 1 wavelength.

9-35. An elliptically polarized wave in an unbounded lossless medium of relative permittivity 4 has **H**-field components (normal to the direction of propagation and normal to each other) of amplitude 2 and 3 amp/meter. Find the power conveyed through an area of 10 meters² normal to the direction of propagation.

CHAPTER 10

PLANE WAVES IN CONDUCTING MEDIA

10-1. Conductors and Dielectrics. In Chap. 9 the discussion was confined to waves in nonconducting or lossless media, that is, the conductivity σ was assumed to be zero. Let us now consider the more general situation where σ is not zero.

Assume that a plane traveling wave strikes the boundary of a conducting medium at normal incidence as shown in Fig. 10-1. A portion of the

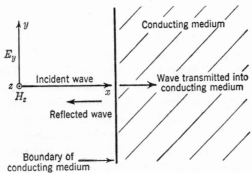

FIG. 10-1. Plane wave entering conducting medium at normal incidence.

incident energy is reflected, while the remainder enters the conducting medium. Let us disregard the reflected wave and focus our attention on the transmitted wave.

According to Maxwell's first curl equation,

$$\nabla \times \mathbf{H} = \mathbf{J} + \frac{\partial \mathbf{D}}{\partial t} \qquad (10\text{-}1)$$

In nonconducting media $\mathbf{J} = 0$, but in conducting media $\mathbf{J}$ may not be negligible. Recalling that $\mathbf{J} = \sigma\mathbf{E}$, (10-1) becomes

$$\nabla \times \mathbf{H} = \sigma\mathbf{E} + \frac{\partial \mathbf{D}}{\partial t} \qquad (10\text{-}2)$$

For a linearly polarized plane wave traveling in the x direction with $\mathbf{E}$ in the y direction, the vector equation (10-2) reduces to the following scalar equation involving the field components E_y and H_z:

$$-\frac{\partial H_z}{\partial x} = \sigma E_y + \epsilon \frac{\partial E_y}{\partial t} \qquad (10\text{-}3)$$

This equation has two terms in E_y. Assuming that E_y is a harmonic function of time, that is, $E_y = E_0 e^{j\omega t}$, (10-3) becomes

$$-\frac{\partial H_z}{\partial x} = \sigma E_y + j\omega\epsilon E_y \qquad (10\text{-}4)$$

The terms in (10-4) each have the dimensions of current density, which is expressed in amperes per square meter. The term σE_y represents the *conduction current density*, while the term $j\omega\epsilon E_y$ represents the *displacement current density*.[1] Thus, according to (10-4) the space rate of change of H_z equals the sum of the conduction and displacement current densities. If the conductivity is zero ($\sigma = 0$), the conduction current term vanishes and we have the condition considered in Chap. 9. If σ is not equal to zero, there are three conditions, which can be listed as follows:

1. $\omega\epsilon \gg \sigma$
2. $\omega\epsilon \sim \sigma$
3. $\omega\epsilon \ll \sigma$

When the displacement current is much greater than the conduction current, as in condition 1, the medium behaves like a dielectric. If $\sigma = 0$, the medium is a perfect, or lossless, dielectric. For σ not equal to zero the medium is a lossy, or imperfect, dielectric. However, if $\omega\epsilon \gg \sigma$, it behaves more like a dielectric than anything else and may, for practical purposes, be classified as a *dielectric*. On the other hand, when the conduction current is much greater than the displacement current, as in condition 3, the medium may be classified as a *conductor*. Under conditions midway between these two, when the conduction current is of the same order of magnitude as the displacement current, the medium may be classified as a *quasi conductor*.

We can be even more specific and arbitrarily classify media as belonging to one of three types according to the value of the ratio $\sigma/\omega\epsilon$ as follows:

$$\text{Dielectrics:} \quad \frac{\sigma}{\omega\epsilon} < \frac{1}{100}$$

$$\text{Quasi conductors:} \quad \frac{1}{100} < \frac{\sigma}{\omega\epsilon} < 100$$

$$\text{Conductors:} \quad 100 < \frac{\sigma}{\omega\epsilon}$$

where σ = conductivity of medium (mhos/meter)

ϵ = permittivity of medium (farads/meter)

ω = radian frequency ($= 2\pi f$, where f is the frequency)

The ratio $\sigma/\omega\epsilon$ is dimensionless.

---

[1] The operator $j(= \sqrt{-1})$ in the displacement current term indicates that the displacement current leads the conduction current by 90° in time phase.

It is to be noted that frequency is an important factor in determining whether a medium acts like a dielectric or a conductor. For example, take the case of average rural ground (Ohio) for which $\epsilon_r = 14$ (at low frequencies) and $\sigma = 10^{-2}$ mho per meter. Assuming no change in these values as a function of frequency, the ratio $\sigma/\omega\epsilon$ at three different frequencies is as tabulated below.

Frequency, cps	Ratio $\sigma/\omega\epsilon$
10^3	1.3×10^4
10^7	1.3
$3 \times 10^{10} (\lambda = 1 \text{ cm})$	4.3×10^{-4}

At 1 kc per sec (10^3 cps) rural ground behaves like a conductor, while at the microwave frequency of 30,000 mc per sec (3×10^{10} cps) it acts like a dielectric. At 10 mc per sec (10^7 cps) its behavior is that of a quasi conductor.

As another example, consider the case of copper, which is ordinarily regarded as an excellent conductor. Taking $\sigma = 5.8 \times 10^7$ mhos per meter and $\epsilon_r = 1$, the ratio $\sigma/\omega\epsilon$ is very large at ordinary radio frequencies. Even at 30,000 mc per sec the ratio is 3.5×10^7, which still classes copper as a good conductor. However, at a frequency of 10^{20} cps corresponding to short X rays, the ratio $\sigma/\omega\epsilon$ is about 10^{-2}, which classifies copper as a dielectric. In other words, copper behaves like a dielectric for X rays, which is a crude way of explaining why X rays can penetrate considerable thicknesses of a metal such as copper.[1]

In Fig. 10-2 the ratio $\sigma/\omega\epsilon$ is plotted as a function of frequency for a number of common media. In preparing Fig. 10-2 the constants were assumed to maintain their low-frequency values at all frequencies. The curves in Fig. 10-2 should therefore not be regarded as accurate above the microwave region since the constants of media may vary with frequency, particularly at frequencies of the order of 10^9 cps and higher. A list of the low-frequency constants for the media of Fig. 10-2 is presented in Table 10-1.

TABLE 10-1
TABLE OF CONSTANTS FOR SOME COMMON MEDIA

Medium	Relative permittivity ϵ_r (dimensionless)	Conductivity σ, mhos/meter
Copper.................	1	5.8×10^7
Sea water..............	80	4
Rural ground (Ohio)......	14	10^{-2}
Urban ground...........	3	10^{-4}
Fresh water.............	80	10^{-3}

[1] The penetration of X rays occurs because the wavelength is comparable with or smaller than the atomic spacing.

Referring to Fig. 10-2, we note that copper behaves like a conductor at frequencies far above the microwave region. On the other hand, fresh water acts like a dielectric at frequencies above about 10 mc per sec. The $\sigma/\omega\epsilon$ ratios for sea water, rural ground, and urban ground are between the extremes of copper and fresh water.

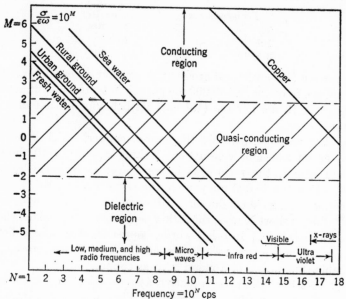

Fig. 10-2. Ratio $\sigma/\omega\epsilon$ as a function of frequency for some common media (log-log plot).

10-2. Wave Equation for Conducting Media.

An electromagnetic wave is rapidly attenuated in a conducting medium. In fact, in a good conductor the attenuation is so rapid that at high radio frequencies the wave penetrates the conductor only to a very small depth.

This depth of the penetration is a matter of considerable interest. To calculate it, let us first develop a wave equation in E_y for a plane wave in a conducting medium. From a solution of this equation, an expression for the depth of penetration is then obtained.

From Maxwell's curl equations we have for a linearly polarized wave traveling in the x direction with $\mathbf{E}$ in the y direction

$$-\frac{\partial H_z}{\partial x} = \sigma E_y + \epsilon \frac{\partial E_y}{\partial t} \tag{10-5}$$

and

$$\frac{\partial E_y}{\partial x} = -\mu \frac{\partial H_z}{\partial t} \tag{10-6}$$

Differentiating (10-5) with respect to t and (10-6) with respect to x, we obtain

$$\frac{\partial}{\partial t}\left(\frac{\partial H_z}{\partial x}\right) = -\sigma\frac{\partial E_y}{\partial t} - \epsilon\frac{\partial^2 E_y}{\partial t^2} \qquad (10\text{-}7)$$

and

$$-\frac{1}{\mu}\frac{\partial^2 E_y}{\partial x^2} = \frac{\partial}{\partial x}\left(\frac{\partial H_z}{\partial t}\right) \qquad (10\text{-}8)$$

Since the order of differentiation is immaterial, the left side of (10-7) is equal to the right side of (10-8) so that

$$\frac{1}{\mu}\frac{\partial^2 E_y}{\partial x^2} - \epsilon\frac{\partial^2 E_y}{\partial t^2} - \sigma\frac{\partial E_y}{\partial t} = 0 \qquad (10\text{-}9)$$

This is the wave equation in E_y for a plane wave in a conducting medium. It is more general than the wave equation (9-12), developed for the case of a nonconducting medium. Whereas (9-12) has two terms, (10-9) has three, the third one involving the conductivity.

Assuming harmonic variation of E_y with respect to t, we may write

$$E_y = E_0 e^{j\omega t} \qquad (10\text{-}10)$$

Taking the first and second derivatives of (10-10) with respect to t and substituting these values in (10-9),

$$\frac{1}{\mu}\frac{\partial^2 E_y}{\partial x^2} + \omega^2\epsilon E_y - j\omega\sigma E_y = 0 \qquad (10\text{-}11)$$

Rearranging terms, this becomes

$$\frac{\partial^2 E_y}{\partial x^2} - (j\omega\mu\sigma - \omega^2\mu\epsilon)E_y = 0 \qquad (10\text{-}11a)$$

Let

$$\gamma^2 = j\omega\mu\sigma - \omega^2\mu\epsilon \qquad (10\text{-}12)$$

Then (10-11a) reduces to

$$\frac{\partial^2 E_y}{\partial x^2} - \gamma^2 E_y = 0 \qquad (10\text{-}13)$$

This equation is a simplified form of (10-9). The time t does not appear explicitly, harmonic variation with time being assumed.

A solution of (10-13) for a wave traveling in the positive x direction is

$$E_y = E_0 e^{-\gamma x} \qquad (10\text{-}14)$$

For conductors, $\sigma \gg \omega\epsilon$ so that (10-12) reduces to

$$\gamma^2 \simeq j\omega\mu\sigma \qquad (10\text{-}15)$$

and[1]

$$\gamma \simeq \sqrt{j\omega\mu\sigma} = (1 + j)\sqrt{\frac{\omega\mu\sigma}{2}} \qquad (10\text{-}15a)$$

Thus, γ has a real and imaginary part. Putting $\gamma = \alpha + j\beta$, α, the real part, is associated with attenuation, and β, the imaginary part, is associated with phase.

Substituting the value of γ from (10-15a) in (10-14),

$$E_y = E_0 e^{-(1+j)\sqrt{\frac{\omega\mu\sigma}{2}}x} = E_0 e^{-\sqrt{\frac{\omega\mu\sigma}{2}}x} e^{-j\sqrt{\frac{\omega\mu\sigma}{2}}x} \qquad (10\text{-}16)$$

In (10-16) the *attenuation factor* is given by

$$e^{-\sqrt{\frac{\omega\mu\sigma}{2}}x} \qquad (10\text{-}17)$$

and the *phase factor* by

$$e^{-j\sqrt{\frac{\omega\mu\sigma}{2}}x} \qquad (10\text{-}18)$$

where ω = radian frequency ($=2\pi f$) (reciprocal seconds)

μ = permeability of medium (henrys/meter)

σ = conductivity of medium (mhos/meter)

x = distance (meters)

j = complex operator (dimensionless)

Equation (10-16) is a solution of the wave equation for a plane wave traveling in the positive x direction in a conducting medium. It gives the variation of E_y in both magnitude and phase as a function of x. The field attenuates exponentially and is retarded linearly in phase with increasing x.

10-3. Depth of Penetration. Continuing the discussion of the preceding section, let us now obtain a quantitative measure of the penetration of a wave in a conducting medium. Referring to Fig. 10-1, consider the wave that penetrates the conducting medium, that is, the transmitted wave. Let $x = 0$ at the boundary of the conducting medium so that x increases positively into the conducting medium.

Let (10-16) be written in the following form,

$$E_y = E_0 e^{-x/\delta} e^{-j(x/\delta)} \qquad (10\text{-}19)$$

where $\delta = \sqrt{2/\omega\mu\sigma}$. At $x = 0$, $E_y = E_0$. This is the amplitude of the field at the surface of the conducting medium. Now δ in (10-19) has the

[1] *Note:*

$$\sqrt{j} = \sqrt{\frac{2j}{2}} = \sqrt{\frac{1 + 2j - 1}{2}} = \sqrt{\frac{(1 + j)^2}{2}}$$
$$= \frac{1 + j}{\sqrt{2}} = 1/45°$$

dimension of distance.[1]   At a distance $x = \delta$ the amplitude of the field is

$$|E_y| = E_0 e^{-1} = E_0 \frac{1}{e} \tag{10-20}$$

Thus, E_y decreases to $1/e$ (36.8 per cent) of its initial value, while the wave penetrates to a distance δ.   Hence δ is called the $1/e$ *depth of penetration*.

As an example, consider the depth of penetration of a plane electromagnetic wave incident normally on a good conductor, such as copper. Since $\omega = 2\pi f$, the $1/e$ depth becomes

$$\delta = \frac{1}{\sqrt{f \pi \mu \sigma}} \tag{10-21}$$

For copper $\mu_r = 1$ so that $\mu = 1.26 \times 10^{-6}$ henry per meter.   The conductivity $\sigma = 5.8 \times 10^7$ mhos per meter.   Putting these values in (10-21), we obtain for copper,

$$\delta = \frac{6.6 \times 10^{-2}}{\sqrt{f}} \tag{10-22}$$

where $\delta = 1/e$ depth of penetration (meters)
   f = frequency (cps)
Evaluating (10-22) at specific frequencies, it is found that

At 60 cps, $\delta = 8.5 \times 10^{-3}$ meter
At 1 Mc/sec, $\delta = 6.6 \times 10^{-5}$ meter
At 30,000 Mc/sec, $\delta = 3.8 \times 10^{-7}$ meter

Thus, while at 60 cps the $1/e$ depth of penetration is 8.5 mm, the penetration decreases in inverse proportion to the square root of the frequency. At 1 cm wavelength (30,000 Mc/sec) the penetration is only 0.00038 mm, or less than $\frac{1}{2}$ micron.   This phenomenon is often called *skin effect*.

Thus, a high-frequency field is damped out as it penetrates a conductor in a shorter distance than a low-frequency field.[2]

In addition to the $1/e$ depth of penetration, we can speak of other depths for which the electric field decreases to an arbitrary fraction of its original value.   For example, consider the depth at which the field is 0.01 (1 per cent) of its original value.   This depth is obtained by multiplying the $1/e$ depth by 4.6 and may be called the 1 *per cent depth of penetration*.

Phase velocity is given by the ratio ω/β.   In the present case, $\beta = 1/\delta$

[1] In dimensional symbols δ is given by

$$\sqrt{T \frac{Q^2}{ML} \frac{ML^3}{TQ^2}} = L$$

[2] This is analogous to the way in which a rapid temperature variation at the surface of a thermal conductor penetrates a shorter distance than a slow temperature variation.

so that the phase velocity in the conductor is

$$v_c = \omega\delta = \sqrt{\frac{2\omega}{\sigma\mu}} \qquad (10\text{-}23)$$

Since the $1/e$ depth is small, the phase velocity in conductors is small. It is apparent from (10-23) that the velocity is a function of the frequency and, hence, of the wavelength. In this case, $dv/d\lambda$ is negative, where λ is the free-space wavelength. Hence, conductors are anomalously dispersive media (Sec. 9-7).

The ratio of the velocity of a wave in free space to that in the conducting medium is the index of refraction for the conducting medium. At low frequencies the index for conductors is very large.

To find the wavelength λ_c in the conductor, we have from (10-23) that $f\lambda_c = \omega\delta$, or

$$\lambda_c = 2\pi\delta \qquad (10\text{-}24)$$

In (10-24), both λ_c and δ are in the same units of length. Hence the wavelength in the conductor is 2π times the $1/e$ depth. Since the $1/e$ depth is small for conductors, the wavelength in conductors is small.

Values of the $1/e$ depth, 1 per cent depth, wavelength, velocity, and refractive index for a medium of copper are given in Table 10-2 for three frequencies.

TABLE 10-2

TABLE OF PENETRATION DEPTHS, WAVELENGTH, VELOCITY, AND REFRACTIVE INDEX FOR COPPER

Frequency	60 cps	10^6 cps	3×10^{10} cps
Wavelength in free space λ (meters)	5,000 km	300 meters	1 cm
$1/e$ depth, meters	8.5×10^{-3}	6.6×10^{-5}	3.8×10^{-7}
1 per cent depth, meters	3.9×10^{-2}	3×10^{-4}	1.7×10^{-6}
Wavelength in conductor λ_c, meters	5.3×10^{-2}	4.1×10^{-4}	2.4×10^{-6}
Velocity in conductor v_c, meters/sec	3.2	4.1×10^2	7.1×10^4
Index of refraction (dimensionless)	9.5×10^7	7.3×10^5	4.2×10^3

It is interesting to note that the electric field is damped to 1 per cent of its initial amplitude in about $\frac{3}{4}$ wavelength in the metal.

Since the penetration depth is inversely proportional to the square root of the frequency, a thin sheet of conducting material can act as a low-pass filter for electromagnetic waves.

10-4. Relaxation Time. Thus far, the behavior of electromagnetic waves in conducting media has been discussed from the standpoint of depth of penetration, velocity, and so forth. It is instructive to consider the problem from another point of view, namely, from that of the behavior of a charge configuration placed in the conducting medium.

Consider a conducting medium of infinite extent, in which is placed a charge of arbitrary shape and density. Imagine that the charge is released and, because of the mutual repulsion of the like charges of which it is composed, spreads out through the conducting medium. Now let us determine how long it takes for such a charge of density ρ to decrease in density to $1/e$ of its original value.

According to (3-58) the continuity relation between current density and charge density is

$$\nabla \cdot \mathbf{J} = -\frac{\partial \rho}{\partial t} \tag{10-25}$$

From Maxwell's equation $\nabla \cdot \mathbf{D} = \rho$, and from $\mathbf{D} = \epsilon \mathbf{E}$.

$$\nabla \cdot \mathbf{E} = \frac{\rho}{\epsilon} \tag{10-26}$$

But $\mathbf{J} = \sigma \mathbf{E}$ so that (10-26) becomes

$$\nabla \cdot \mathbf{J} = \frac{\rho\sigma}{\epsilon} \tag{10-27}$$

From (10-25) and (10-27) it follows that

$$\frac{\partial \rho}{\partial t} + \frac{\sigma}{\epsilon}\rho = 0 \tag{10-28}$$

A solution of this equation is

$$\rho = \rho_0 e^{-(\sigma/\epsilon)t} \tag{10-29}$$

as may be readily verified by taking the first derivative with respect to time and substituting in (10-28).

Let us put

$$T_r = \frac{\epsilon}{\sigma} \tag{10-30}$$

T_r has the dimension of time. At $t = 0$, $\rho = \rho_0$, which is the initial charge density. When $t = T_r$,

$$\rho = \rho_0 e^{-1} = \rho_0 \frac{1}{e} \tag{10-31}$$

Thus, T_r is the time required for the charge density to decrease to $1/e$ of its initial value. The quantity T_r is called the *relaxation time*.

In a perfect dielectric $\sigma = 0$ so that T_r is infinite. Hence the charge maintains its original density indefinitely. On the other hand, for a conductor such as copper for which $\sigma = 5.8 \times 10^7$ mhos per meter and $\epsilon = 8.85 \times 10^{-12}$ farad per meter, we find that

$$T_r = 1.5 \times 10^{-19} \text{ sec}$$

This very short interval corresponds to the length of one period for X rays. Thus, at radio and microwave frequencies the relaxation time is much less than the period. The result of the short relaxation time is that the conductor cannot maintain a charge configuration long enough to permit propagation of a wave more than a very short distance into the conductor. When the frequency is sufficiently high, of the order of 10^{19} cps, the relaxation time is about the same length as the period and propagation is possible. This is another way of looking at the phenomenon of X-ray penetration of metals. We noted in an earlier section that copper begins to act like a dielectric when the frequency is raised to about 10^{20} cps.

10-5. Impedance of Conducting Media. The behavior of conducting media toward plane electromagnetic waves can be considered from yet another point of view. This is from the standpoint of impedance.

A solution of the wave equation for the electric field of a linearly polarized plane wave traveling in the x direction in a conducting medium with **E** in the y direction is of the form

$$\dot{E}_y = E_0 e^{j\omega t - \gamma x} \tag{10-32}$$

while for the magnetic field a solution is

$$\dot{H}_z = H_0 e^{j(\omega t - \xi) - \gamma x} \tag{10-33}$$

where ξ is the lag in time phase of $\dot{H}_z$ with respect to $\dot{E}_y$ or the lead of $\dot{E}_y$ with respect to $\dot{H}_z$.†

Taking the ratio of (10-32) to (10-33) yields the intrinsic impedance $\dot{Z}_c$ of the conducting medium. Thus

$$\dot{Z}_c = \frac{\dot{E}_y}{\dot{H}_z} = \frac{E_0}{H_0 e^{-j\xi}} = \frac{E_0}{H_0 / -\xi} = \frac{E_0/\xi}{H_0} = Z_c/\underline{\xi} \tag{10-34}$$

According to (10-34) the magnitude or modulus of the intrinsic impedance is equal to the ratio of the electric to the magnetic field, and the phase angle of the impedance is equal to ξ.‡

To evaluate $\dot{Z}_c$ in terms of the constants of the conducting medium, we proceed as follows: Maxwell's equation from Faraday's law for a plane wave with components $\dot{E}_y$ and $\dot{H}_z$ is

$$\frac{\partial \dot{E}_y}{\partial x} = -\mu \frac{\partial \dot{H}_z}{\partial t} \tag{10-35}$$

Taking the x derivative of (10-32) and the t derivative of (10-33) and substituting in (10-35) yields

$$\gamma \dot{E}_y = j\mu\omega \dot{H}_z$$

† The dot (˙) is used to indicate explicitly that $\dot{E}_y$ and $\dot{H}_z$ are complex functions of t, x, and ξ. The instantaneous values of the field components are given by either the real or the imaginary parts of $\dot{E}_y$ and $\dot{H}_z$.

‡ The dot on $\dot{Z}_c$ indicates explicitly that the impedance is also a complex quantity. However, it is a complex function only of the phase angle ξ.

The intrinsic impedance $\dot{Z}_c$ is then given by

$$\dot{Z}_c = \frac{\dot{E}_y}{\dot{H}_z} = \frac{j\mu\omega}{\gamma} \qquad (10\text{-}36)$$

Recalling from (10-15a) that for a good conductor

$$\gamma \simeq (1+j)\sqrt{\frac{\omega\mu\sigma}{2}}$$

(10-36) becomes

$$\dot{Z}_c = \frac{\dot{E}_y}{\dot{H}_z} = \frac{1+j}{\sqrt{2}}\sqrt{\frac{\mu\omega}{\sigma}} = (1+j)\frac{1}{\sigma\delta} \qquad (10\text{-}37)$$

Since

$$\frac{1+j}{\sqrt{2}} = 1\underline{/45^\circ}$$

the intrinsic impedance can also be expressed as

$$\dot{Z}_c = Z_c\underline{/\xi} = \sqrt{\frac{\mu\omega}{\sigma}}\ \underline{/45^\circ} \qquad (10\text{-}38)$$

It follows that the magnitude of the intrinsic impedance of a conductor is given by

$$Z_c = \sqrt{\frac{\mu\omega}{\sigma}} = \frac{E_0}{H_0} \qquad (10\text{-}39)$$

and the phase angle by

$$\xi = 45^\circ \qquad (10\text{-}39a)$$

Whereas the intrinsic impedance of a perfect dielectric medium is a pure resistance ($\dot{E}_y$ and $\dot{H}_z$ in time phase), we note from (10-38) that the intrinsic impedance of a conductor is a complex quantity, $\dot{H}_z$ lagging $\dot{E}_y$ in time phase by very nearly 45°. This is analogous to the situation in a circuit having resistance and inductance in series where the current lags the applied voltage. Therefore the conducting medium behaves like an inductive impedance. This may be expressed explicitly by writing $\dot{Z}_c$ in terms of its resistive, or real, part R and its reactive, or imaginary, part X. That is,

$$\dot{Z}_c = R + jX = \sqrt{\frac{\mu\omega}{2\sigma}} + j\sqrt{\frac{\mu\omega}{2\sigma}} \qquad (10\text{-}40)$$

The intrinsic impedance may be expressed in yet another form, as follows: Multiplying and dividing in (10-37) by ϵ, ϵ_0, and μ_0,

$$\dot{Z}_c = \frac{1+j}{\sqrt{2}}\sqrt{\frac{\mu_0\,\epsilon_0}{\epsilon_0\ \epsilon}\frac{\mu}{\mu_0}\frac{\omega\epsilon}{\sigma}} \qquad (10\text{-}41)$$

Substituting ϵ_r and μ_r for the ratios in (10-41),

$$\dot{Z}_c = \frac{1+j}{\sqrt{2}} \sqrt{\frac{\mu_0}{\epsilon_0}} \sqrt{\frac{\mu_r}{\epsilon_r}} \sqrt{\frac{\omega\epsilon}{\sigma}} \qquad (10\text{-}42)$$

But $\sqrt{\mu_0/\epsilon_0}$ is the intrinsic resistance of free space, which equals 376.7 ohms, so that

$$\dot{Z}_c = \frac{1+j}{\sqrt{2}} \times 376.7 \sqrt{\frac{\mu_r}{\epsilon_r}} \sqrt{\frac{\omega\epsilon}{\sigma}} \qquad \text{ohms} \qquad (10\text{-}43)$$

where μ_r = relative permeability of medium (dimensionless)
ϵ_r = relative permittivity of medium (dimensionless)
ω = radian frequency (= $2\pi f$) (reciprocal seconds)
ϵ = permittivity of medium (farads/meter)
σ = conductivity of medium (mhos/meter)

The magnitude or modulus of $\dot{Z}_c$ is

$$Z_c = |\dot{Z}_c| = 376.7 \sqrt{\frac{\mu_r}{\epsilon_r}} \sqrt{\frac{\omega\epsilon}{\sigma}} \qquad (10\text{-}44)$$

The ratio $\omega\epsilon/\sigma$ or its reciprocal was discussed in Sec. 10-1. For good conductors $\omega\epsilon/\sigma$ is very small ($\sigma/\omega\epsilon$ very large). Take, for instance, copper. At a frequency of 3,000 Mc/sec (wavelength 10 cm),

$$\frac{\omega\epsilon}{\sigma} = 2.9 \times 10^{-9}$$

Taking μ_r and ϵ_r as unity, the intrinsic impedance of copper at 10 cm is

$$\dot{Z}_c = \frac{1+j}{\sqrt{2}} \times 376.7 \times 5.4 \times 10^{-5}$$

or

$$\dot{Z}_c = \frac{1+j}{\sqrt{2}} \times 0.02 = 0.02\underline{/45°} \text{ ohms}$$

The magnitude of the intrinsic impedance of copper is

$$Z_c = |\dot{Z}_c| = 0.02 \text{ ohm}$$

These results indicate that for a conducting medium such as copper the ratio of E_y to H_z is much less than for free space. If σ were infinite (perfect conductor), then $Z_c = 0$ and E vanishes. The small value of Z_c for copper suggests that the conducting medium behaves like a short circuit to the electromagnetic field.

In the above discussion on the impedance of conducting media, we introduced a value of γ into (10-36) based on the assumption that $\sigma \gg \omega\epsilon$. However, in the case of a dielectric medium $\omega\epsilon \gg \sigma$, and

$\gamma = j\beta = j\omega \sqrt{\mu\epsilon}$. Substituting this value of γ into (10-36) gives the intrinsic impedance for a dielectric medium equal to $\sqrt{\mu/\epsilon}$ as obtained in Chap. 9.

Some of the important relations for conductors developed in this and preceding sections are summarized in Table 10-3.

TABLE 10-3

PENETRATION DEPTHS, VELOCITY, WAVELENGTH, INDEX OF REFRACTION, IMPEDANCE, AND RELAXATION TIME IN CONDUCTING MEDIA $(\sigma \gg \omega\epsilon)$†

$$\frac{1}{e}\,\text{depth} = \delta = \frac{1}{\sqrt{\pi f \mu\sigma}} = \sqrt{\frac{2}{\omega\mu\sigma}} \quad \text{meters}$$

$$1 \text{ per cent depth} = 4.6\delta \quad \text{meters}$$

$$\text{Phase velocity} = v_c = \omega\delta = \sqrt{\frac{2\omega}{\sigma\mu}} \quad \text{meters/sec}$$

$$\text{Wavelength} = \lambda_c = 2\pi\delta \quad \text{meters}$$

$$\text{Index of refraction} = \eta = \frac{c}{v_c} = \frac{c}{\omega\delta} = \sqrt{\frac{\sigma}{2\omega\epsilon_0}} \quad \text{(dimensionless)}$$

$$\text{Relaxation time} = T_r = \frac{\epsilon}{\sigma} \quad \text{sec}$$

$$\text{Impedance} = \dot{Z}_c = \sqrt{\frac{\mu\omega}{\sigma}} \,\underline{/45^\circ} \quad \text{ohms}$$

† In the table

$\omega = 2\pi f$ = radian frequency

f = frequency (cps)

μ = permeability ($\simeq 4\pi \times 10^{-7}$ henry/meter if no ferromagnetic material is present)

ϵ = permittivity (farads/meter)

σ = conductivity (mhos/meter)

10-6. Reflection and Transmission of Waves at a Boundary. The situation of a plane traveling wave incident normally on a boundary between two media of infinite extent is discussed in this section. Let the wave be linearly polarized and traveling in the positive x direction with **E** in the y direction and **H** in the z direction. Assume that the incident traveling wave has field components $\dot{E}_i$ and $\dot{H}_i$ at the boundary as in Fig. 10-3a. At the boundary between the two media part of the incident wave is, in general, reflected while another part is transmitted into the second medium. The reflected traveling wave has field components $\dot{E}_r$ and $\dot{H}_r$ at the boundary. The transmitted wave has field components $\dot{E}_t$ and $\dot{H}_t$ at the boundary.[1]

[1] The dot (˙) on $\dot{E}_i$, $\dot{E}_r$, $\dot{E}_t$, $\dot{H}_i$, $\dot{H}_r$, and $\dot{H}_t$ indicates explicitly that, *in general*, they are complex functions of t, x, and δ or ξ (that is, phasors), where δ is the time-phase difference between E_r and E_i (same as between reflected and incident waves in Sec. 9-10) and ξ is the time-phase difference between E_t and H_t. Taking the fields at the boundary ($x = 0$) and at $t = 0$, they are functions only of δ and ξ.

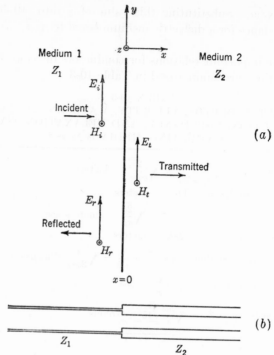

Fig. 10-3. Plane wave incident normally on boundary (a) and analogous transmission line (b).

From the continuity of the tangential field components at a boundary,

$$\dot{E}_i + \dot{E}_r = \dot{E}_t \tag{10-45}$$

and

$$\dot{H}_i + \dot{H}_r = \dot{H}_t \tag{10-46}$$

The electric and magnetic fields of a plane wave are related by the intrinsic impedance of the medium. Thus

$$\frac{\dot{E}_i}{\dot{H}_i} = \dot{Z}_1 \qquad \frac{\dot{E}_r}{\dot{H}_r} = -\dot{Z}_1 \qquad \frac{\dot{E}_t}{\dot{H}_t} = \dot{Z}_2 \tag{10-47}$$

The impedance of the reflected wave (traveling in the negative x direction) is taken to be negative $\dot{Z}_1$ and of the incident wave, positive $\dot{Z}_1$. From (10-46) and (10-47)

$$\dot{H}_t = \frac{\dot{E}_t}{\dot{Z}_2} = \frac{\dot{E}_i}{\dot{Z}_1} - \frac{\dot{E}_r}{\dot{Z}_1} \tag{10-48}$$

or

$$\dot{E}_t = \frac{\dot{Z}_2}{\dot{Z}_1} \dot{E}_i - \frac{\dot{Z}_2}{\dot{Z}_1} \dot{E}_r \tag{10-49}$$

Multiplying (10-45) by $\dot{Z}_2/\dot{Z}_1$,

$$\frac{\dot{Z}_2}{\dot{Z}_1} \dot{E}_t = \frac{\dot{Z}_2}{\dot{Z}_1} \dot{E}_i + \frac{\dot{Z}_2}{\dot{Z}_1} \dot{E}_r \qquad (10\text{-}50)$$

Adding (10-49) and (10-50),

$$\dot{E}_t \left(1 + \frac{\dot{Z}_2}{\dot{Z}_1} \right) = \frac{2\dot{Z}_2}{\dot{Z}_1} \dot{E}_i \qquad (10\text{-}51)$$

or

$$\dot{E}_t = \frac{2\dot{Z}_2}{\dot{Z}_2 + \dot{Z}_1} \dot{E}_i = \dot{\tau}\dot{E}_i \qquad (10\text{-}52)$$

where $\dot{\tau}$ is called the *transmission coefficient*. It follows that

$$\dot{\tau} = \frac{\dot{E}_t}{\dot{E}_i} = \frac{2\dot{Z}_2}{\dot{Z}_2 + \dot{Z}_1} \qquad (10\text{-}53)$$

Subtracting (10-49) from (10-50),

$$\dot{E}_t \left(\frac{\dot{Z}_2}{\dot{Z}_1} - 1 \right) = \frac{2\dot{Z}_2}{\dot{Z}_1} \dot{E}_r \qquad (10\text{-}54)$$

Substituting $\dot{E}_t$ from (10-52) into (10-54) and solving for $\dot{E}_r$,

$$\dot{E}_r = \frac{\dot{Z}_2 - \dot{Z}_1}{\dot{Z}_2 + \dot{Z}_1} \dot{E}_i = \dot{\rho}\dot{E}_i \qquad (10\text{-}55)$$

where $\dot{\rho}$ is called the *reflection coefficient*.[1] It follows that

$$\dot{\rho} = \frac{\dot{E}_r}{\dot{E}_i} = \frac{\dot{Z}_2 - \dot{Z}_1}{\dot{Z}_2 + \dot{Z}_1} \qquad (10\text{-}56)$$

The situation (Fig. 10-3a) of a plane wave incident normally on a boundary between two different media of infinite extent, with intrinsic impedances Z_1 and Z_2, is analogous to the situation of a guided wave on an infinite transmission line having an abrupt change in impedance from Z_1 to Z_2 (Fig. 10-3b). The transmission and reflection coefficients for voltage across the transmission line are identical to those given in (10-53) and (10-56) if the intrinsic impedance Z_1 of medium 1 is taken to be the characteristic impedance of the line to the left of the junction (Fig. 10-3b) and the intrinsic impedance Z_2 of medium 2 is taken to be the characteristic impedance of the line to the right of the junction. This is discussed further in Chap. 11.

The above relations apply to any media, conducting or dielectric (lossless), the nature of the medium being specified in every case by its intrinsic impedance Z.

---

[1] This is the same as the reflection coefficient $\dot{\rho}$ discussed in Sec. 9-10.

Returning now to the case of a plane wave incident normally on the boundary between two media of infinite extent as in Fig. 10-3a, let us consider several special cases.

Case 1.   Assume that medium 1 is air and medium 2 is a conductor so that $Z_1 \gg Z_2$.   Then, from (10-52) we have the approximate relation

$$\dot{E}_t \simeq \frac{2\dot{Z}_2}{\dot{Z}_1} \dot{E}_i \tag{10-57}$$

But from (10-47) this becomes

$$\dot{H}_t \dot{Z}_2 \simeq \frac{2\dot{Z}_2}{\dot{Z}_1} \dot{H}_i \dot{Z}_1 \tag{10-58}$$

from which

$$\dot{H}_t \simeq 2\dot{H}_i \tag{10-59}$$

Thus, for a plane wave in air incident normally on a conducting medium, the magnetic field is, to a good approximation, doubled in intensity at the boundary.   It also follows that $\dot{H}_r \simeq \dot{H}_i$ so that there is a nearly pure standing wave to the left of the boundary (in medium 1).

Case 2.   Consider now the opposite situation where medium 1 is a conductor and medium 2 is air so that $Z_1 \ll Z_2$.   Then, from (10-52) we have approximately

$$\dot{E}_t \simeq 2\dot{E}_i \tag{10-60}$$

Thus, for a wave leaving a conducting medium, the electric field is nearly doubled at the boundary.   It follows that $\dot{E}_r \simeq \dot{E}_i$ so that there is a nearly pure standing wave (SWR $= \infty$) immediately to the left of the boundary (in medium 1).   However, owing to the attenuation of waves in medium 1, the SWR decreases rapidly as one moves away from the boundary (to the left).

Case 3.   In Case 1 it is assumed that $Z_1 \gg Z_2$.   Consider now that $Z_2 = 0$ (medium 2 a perfect conductor).   Then from (10-56) the reflection coefficient $\rho = -1$, and from (10-53) the transmission coefficient $\tau = 0$.   Thus, the wave is completely reflected, and no field is transmitted into medium 2.   Further $\dot{E}_r = -\dot{E}_i$, and $\dot{H}_r = \dot{H}_i$ so that the magnetic field intensity exactly doubles at the boundary.   This situation is analogous to a short-circuited transmission line.

Case 4.   In Case 2 it is assumed that $Z_1 \ll Z_2$.   Consider now the hypothetical situation where Z_2 is infinite.[1]   Then from (10-56) $\rho = +1$ and from (10-53) $\tau = 2$.   Thus the wave is completely reflected, but $E_r = +E_i$ so that the electric field intensity at the boundary is exactly doubled.   This situation is analogous to an open-circuited transmission line.

---

[1] It is to be noted that for free space the intrinsic impedance is only 377 ohms.   To obtain a higher impedance would require that $\mu_r > 1$ such as in ferromagnetic media.

Case 5.   Take now the case where $\dot{Z}_2 = \dot{Z}_1$. Then $\rho = 0$, and $\tau = 1$ so that the wave propagates into medium 2 without any reflection. This situation is similar to that on a continuous transmission line of uniform characteristic impedance.

10-7. The Terminated Wave.[1]   In the preceding section we considered various reflection and transmission situations at a boundary. In all cases there was a reflected wave except where the two media were of the same impedance, and in this case the wave was entirely transmitted. No case was considered in which the incident wave is terminated so that

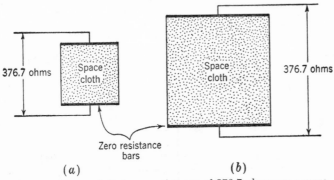

(a)   (b)

Fig. 10-4. Space cloth has a resistance of 376.7 ohms per square.

no wave will be transmitted or reflected. This case deserves special mention and is considered in this section.

The intrinsic impedance of free space is 376.7 ohms. This concept of an impedance for free space takes on more physical significance if we consider the properties of a resistive sheet having a resistance of 376.7 *ohms per square*. Material so treated is often called *space paper* or *space cloth*. It should be noted that the resistance is not per square centimeter or per square meter but simply *per square*. This is equivalent to saying that the resistance between the edges of any square section of the material is the same. Hence the resistance between the opposite edges of the small square of space cloth in Fig. 10-4*a* is 376.7 ohms, as is also the resistance between the edges of the large square in Fig. 10-4*b*. In this illustration it is assumed that the edges are

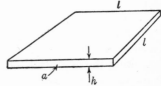

Fig. 10-5. Square of space cloth of thickness h.

clamped with zero-resistance bars and that the impedance of the leads is negligible.

The conductivity of the material required for a sheet of the space cloth

[1] S. Ramo and J. R. Whinnery, "Fields and Waves in Modern Radio," John Wiley & Sons, Inc., New York, 1944, p. 277.

depends on the thickness of the sheet.   Thus the resistance R of a square section as in Fig. 10-5 is expressed by

$$R = \frac{l}{\sigma a} = \frac{l}{\sigma h l} = \frac{1}{\sigma h} \quad \text{ohms} \tag{10-61}$$

where l = length of side (meters)
    a = area of edge (meters^2)
    h = thickness of sheet (meters)
    σ = conductivity of sheet (mhos/meter)
It follows that the required conductivity is

$$\sigma = \frac{1}{Rh} = \frac{1}{376.7h} \quad \text{mhos/meter} \tag{10-62}$$

Consider now the behavior of a sheet of space cloth placed in the path of a plane wave.   Suppose, as shown in Fig. 10-6a, that a plane wave in

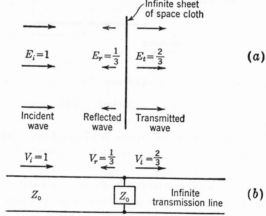

Fig. 10-6. (a) Plane wave traveling to right incident normally on sheet of space cloth, and (b) analogous transmission-line arrangement.

free space traveling to the right is incident normally on a sheet of space cloth of infinite extent.

Taking the amplitude of the incident wave as 1 volt per meter, we have from (10-53) that there is a transmitted wave continuing to the right of the sheet of amplitude

$$E_t = \tau E_i = \frac{2 \times 188.3}{188.3 + 376.7} = \frac{2}{3} \text{ volt/meter}$$

and from (10-56) that there is a reflected wave to the left of the sheet of amplitude

$$E_r = \rho E_i = \frac{188.3 - 376.7}{188.3 + 376.7} = -\frac{1}{3} \text{ volt/meter}$$

It is to be noted that the impedance presented to the incident wave at the sheet is the resultant of the space cloth in parallel with the impedance of the space behind it. This is one-half of 376.7, or 188.3 ohms.

It is apparent that a sheet of space cloth by itself is insufficient to terminate a wave. This may also be seen by considering the analogous transmission arrangement as shown in Fig. 10-6b.

In order completely to absorb or terminate the incident wave without reflection or transmission,[1] let an infinite, perfectly conducting sheet be placed parallel to the space cloth and $\frac{1}{4}$ wavelength behind it, as por-

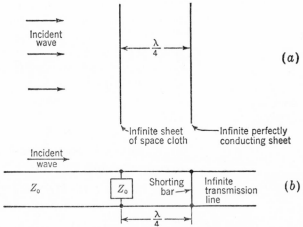

FIG. 10-7. (a) Plane wave traveling to right incident normally on sheet of space cloth backed by conducting sheet is absorbed without reflection. (b) Wave traveling to right on transmission line is absorbed without reflection by analogous arrangement.

trayed in Fig. 10-7a. Now the impedance presented to the incident wave at the sheet of space cloth is 376.7 ohms, being the impedance of the sheet in parallel with an infinite impedance. As a consequence, this arrangement results in the total absorption of the wave by the space cloth, with no reflection to the left of the space cloth. There is, however, a standing-wave and energy circulation between the cloth and the conducting sheet. The analogous transmission-line arrangement is illustrated in Fig. 10-7b.

In the case of the plane wave, the perfectly conducting sheet effectively isolates the region of space behind it from the effects of the wave. In a roughly analogous manner, the shorting bar on the transmission line reduces the wave beyond it to a small value.

A transmission line may also be terminated by placing an impedance across the line which is equal to the characteristic impedance of the line,

[1] This result may also be approximated by the use of a large stack of parallel sheets of suitable resistance and spacing extending an appreciable distance, as measured in wavelengths, in the direction of travel of the incident wave, the wave being gradually absorbed as it penetrates the stack.

as in Fig. 10-6b, and disconnecting the line beyond it. Although this provides a practical method of terminating a transmission line, there is no analogous counterpart in the case of a wave in space, because it is not possible to "disconnect" the space to the right of the termination. A region of space may only be isolated or shielded, as by a perfectly conducting sheet.

10-8. The Poynting Vector in Conducting Media. Assume that a plane wave is traveling in a uniform conducting medium. Let us find the value of the Poynting vector **S** for the wave. Suppose that the wave is linearly polarized and traveling in the positive x direction with **E** in the y direction and **H** in the z direction, as in Fig. 10-8. Let the boundary of the conducting medium be at $x = 0$, and let

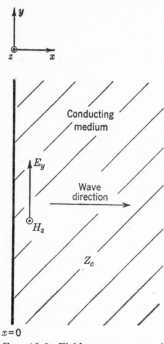

$$\dot{E}_y = E_0 e^{j\omega t} \qquad (10\text{-}63a)$$

and

$$\dot{H}_z = H_0 e^{j(\omega t - \xi)} \qquad (10\text{-}63b)$$

From (9-124) the scalar magnitude of the average Poynting vector is

$$S_{av} = \text{Re } \dot{S} = \tfrac{1}{2} \text{ Re } \dot{E}_y \dot{H}_z^* = \tfrac{1}{2} E_0 H_0 \text{ Re } e^{j\xi} \qquad (10\text{-}64)$$

or

$$S_{av} = \tfrac{1}{2} E_0 H_0 \cos \xi \qquad \text{watts/meter}^2 \qquad (10\text{-}65)$$

where E_0 = amplitude of electric field (volts/meter)

H_0 = amplitude of magnetic field (amp/meter)

ξ = phase difference between electric and magnetic fields (rad or deg)

FIG. 10-8. Field components of wave in conducting medium.

The Poynting vector is entirely in the x direction in this case. If E_0 and H_0 are rms values, the factor $\tfrac{1}{2}$ in (10-65) is omitted. For a conducting medium, ξ is very nearly 45°. Returning to a further consideration of the average Poynting vector, the intrinsic impedance $\dot{Z}_c$ is equal to $\dot{E}_y/\dot{H}_z$ so that (10-64) can be expressed

$$S_{av} = \tfrac{1}{2} \text{ Re } \dot{H}_z \dot{H}_z^* \dot{Z}_c = \tfrac{1}{2} |\dot{H}_z|^2 \text{ Re } \dot{Z}_c = \tfrac{1}{2} H_0{}^2 \text{ Re } \dot{Z}_c \qquad \text{watts/meter}^2 \qquad (10\text{-}66)$$

This is a very useful relation since, if the intrinsic impedance $\dot{Z}_c$ of a conducting medium and also the magnetic field H_0 at the surface are known, it gives the average Poynting vector (or average power per unit area) into the conducting medium.

Example. A plane 1,000 Mc/sec traveling wave in air with peak electric field intensity of 1 volt/meter is incident normally on a large copper sheet. Find the average power absorbed by the sheet per square meter of area.

Solution. First let the intrinsic impedance of copper be calculated at 1,000 Mc/sec. From (10-43)

$$\dot{Z}_c = \frac{1+j}{\sqrt{2}}\, 376.7\, \sqrt{\frac{\mu_r}{\epsilon_r}}\, \sqrt{\frac{\omega\epsilon}{\sigma}}$$

For copper $\mu_r = \epsilon_r = 1$ and $\sigma = 5.8 \times 10^7$ mhos/meter. Hence the real part of $\dot{Z}_c$ is

$$\text{Re } \dot{Z}_c = (\cos 45°)(376.7)\, \sqrt{\frac{2\pi \times 10^9 \times 8.85 \times 10^{-12}}{5.8 \times 10^7}}$$

$$= 8.2 \times 10^{-3}\ \text{ohm}$$

Next we find the value of H_0 at the sheet (tangent to the surface). This is very nearly double H for the incident wave. Thus

$$H_0 = 2\frac{E}{Z} = \frac{2 \times 1}{376.7}\ \text{amp/meter}$$

From (10-66) the average power per square meter into the sheet is then

$$S_{\text{av}} = \frac{1}{2}\left(\frac{2}{376.7}\right)^2 8.2 \times 10^{-3} = 1.16 \times 10^{-7}\ \text{watt/meter}^2$$

The power from a wave absorbed by a conducting medium may also be conveniently regarded in terms of the current induced in the medium. Since $\mathbf{J} = \sigma\mathbf{E}$, the current density $\mathbf{J}$ in the medium varies in the same manner as the electric field $\mathbf{E}$. Thus for a plane wave incident normally on a conducting medium, as in Fig. 10-8, the current-density variation is expressed by

$$J = J_0 e^{-x/\delta} e^{-j(x/\delta)} \qquad \text{amp/meter}^2 \qquad (10\text{-}67)$$

where J_0 = current density at surface of the medium ($x = 0$). The variation of the magnitude of J (or E) as a function of the distance x is portrayed by the exponential curve in Fig. 10-9. Assuming that the conducting medium extends infinitely far in the positive x direction, the total current per unit width (in z direction) induced in the conducting medium by the wave is given by the integral of the magnitude of J from the surface of the medium ($x = 0$) to infinity. That is,

$$K = \int_0^\infty |J|\, dx = J_0 \int_0^\infty e^{-x/\delta}\, dx = J_0\delta \qquad (10\text{-}68)$$

where K = current per unit width (sheet current density) (amp/meter)
J_0 = current density at surface (amp/meter^2)
δ = $1/e$ depth of penetration (meters)

Thus the area under the exponential curve in Fig. 10-9 is equal to the area under the step curve. It follows that the total current K per unit width is equal to what would be obtained if J maintained the constant ampli-

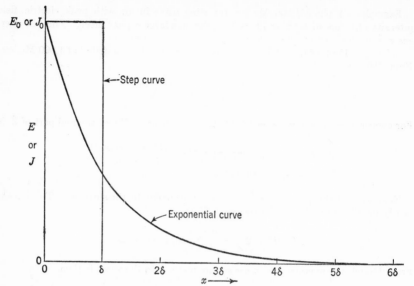

Fig. 10-9. Relative magnitude of electric field **E** or current density **J** as a function of depth of penetration δ for a plane wave traveling in x direction into conducting medium. The abscissa gives the penetration distance x and is expressed in $1/e$ depths (δ). The wavelength in the conductor equals $2\pi\delta$.

tude J_0 from the surface to a depth δ and was zero elsewhere.   This gives added significance to the $1/e$ depth of penetration δ.

Now the average power absorbed per unit area of the conducting medium is, from (10-66),

$$S_{av} = \tfrac{1}{2}H_0{}^2 \operatorname{Re} \dot{Z}_c \qquad (10\text{-}69)$$

or since $H_0 = K$ and $\operatorname{Re} \dot{Z}_c = R$,

$$S_{av} = \tfrac{1}{2}K^2R \qquad \text{watts/meter}^2 \qquad (10\text{-}70)[1]$$

where $K = J_0\delta$ = current per unit width, as in (10-68) (amp/meter)

$R = 1/\sigma\delta$ = resistance of a square sheet of conducting medium of thickness δ (ohms per square)

The resistance R in (10-70) is sometimes referred to as the *skin resistance*, since at high frequencies the current may be confined to a very thin layer.   Referring to Fig. 10-5, R is the resistance of a square sheet of the medium of thickness $\delta = h$ as measured between two opposite edges.

10-9. Circuit Application of the Poynting Vector.   In field theory we deal with point functions such as **E**, **H**, and **S**.   Thus, **E** and **H** give the electric and magnetic fields at a point and **S** the power density at a point. In dealing with waves in space it is convenient to use such point func-

---

[1] Note the similarity between (10-70) and the circuit relation for the power dissipated in an impedance with a real part (resistance) R as given by $P = \tfrac{1}{2}I_0{}^2R$ watts.

tions. On the other hand, in dealing with circuits it is usually more convenient to employ integrated quantities such as V, I, and P. That is, V is the voltage between two points and is equal to the line integral of $\mathbf{E}$ between the points, or

$$V = \int_1^2 \mathbf{E} \cdot d\mathbf{l} \qquad (10\text{-}71)$$

The quantity I is the current through a conductor which is equal to the integral of $\mathbf{H}$ around the conductor or

$$I = \oint \mathbf{H} \cdot d\mathbf{l} \qquad (10\text{-}72)$$

The quantity P is, for example, the power dissipated in a load and is equal to the integral of the Poynting vector over a surface enclosing the load, or

$$P = \oint_s \mathbf{S} \cdot d\mathbf{s} \qquad (10\text{-}73)$$

As an illustration let us find the average power flowing into a load of impedance Z, using the field approach. Suppose that the load is a long, slender, rod-shaped device, as suggested in Fig. 10-10. Let an imaginary cylindrical surface be constructed, as indicated, that encloses the load. The average power in the load is, from (9-125),

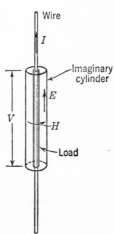

Fig. 10-10. The power in a load is equal to the integral of the normal component of the Poynting vector over a surface enclosing the load.

$$P_{av} = \oint_s \operatorname{Re} \mathbf{S} \cdot d\mathbf{s} = \tfrac{1}{2} \oint_s \operatorname{Re} (\mathbf{E} \times \mathbf{H}^*) \cdot d\mathbf{s} \qquad (10\text{-}74)$$

From the geometry $\mathbf{E}$ and $\mathbf{H}$ are normal to each other and both tangent to the curved surface of the imaginary cylinder. The contribution of the flat end surfaces of the cylinder to (10-74) is zero since $\mathbf{E}$ is normal to these surfaces. Thus, the total average power P_{av} in the load is given by the surface integral of the real part of the complex Poynting vector over the curved surface of the cylinder. From the geometry this reduces to the real part of the line integral of $\mathbf{E}$ between the ends of the cylinder multiplied by the line integral of $\mathbf{H}^*$ around the cylinder. That is,[1]

$$P_{av} = -\tfrac{1}{2} \operatorname{Re} \int \mathbf{E} \cdot d\mathbf{l} \oint \mathbf{H}^* \cdot d\mathbf{l} \qquad (10\text{-}75)$$

or

$$P_{av} = -\tfrac{1}{2} \operatorname{Re} V I^* \qquad \text{watts} \qquad (10\text{-}76)$$

where $V = \int \mathbf{E} \cdot d\mathbf{l} =$ voltage between the ends of the cylinder (or load) (volts)

$I^* = \oint \mathbf{H}^* \cdot d\mathbf{l} =$ current through load (amp)

[1] $\mathbf{E}$, $\mathbf{H}^*$, V, and I^* are complex quantities (phasors). For simplicity the dot (·) is omitted.

The negative sign in (10-75) and (10-76) results from the fact that **E** x **H*** on the cylindrical surface is inward, making **S** negative with respect to d**s**. Thus, from the field point of view the power entering a load is negative power. Conversely, the power leaving a generator is positive power. Omitting the negative sign and noting that I^* in (10-76) is the complex conjugate of I, we have

$$P_{av} = \tfrac{1}{2}V_0 I_0 \operatorname{Re} e^{j\xi} = \tfrac{1}{2}V_0 I_0 \cos\xi \qquad \text{watts} \qquad (10\text{-}77)$$

where ξ = time phase angle between current and voltage. Note that $V = V_0 e^{j\omega t}$ and $I^* = I_0 e^{-j(\omega t - \xi)}$. In (10-77) V_0 and I_0 are amplitudes (peak values). If rms values are used, the factor $\tfrac{1}{2}$ is omitted. Equation (10-77) is a familiar circuit relation. It has been developed here as a special case of the more general field relation of (10-74).

The quantity $\cos\xi$ in (10-77) is called the *power factor*. Hence, by analogy $\cos\xi$ in (10-65) may be called the *power factor of the medium*.

Since the load impedance $Z = V/I$, we also have from (10-76) (omitting the negative sign) that

$$P_{av} = \tfrac{1}{2}I_0^2 \operatorname{Re} Z = \tfrac{1}{2}I_0^2 R \qquad (10\text{-}78)$$

where R = resistance of load (real part of Z) (ohms).

10-10. General Development of the Wave Equation. In this chapter and in Chap. 9, we have dealt entirely with plane waves traveling in the x direction. The wave equation was developed for this special case, and appropriate solutions were obtained. A more general development of the wave equation will now be given, and it will be shown that for a plane wave it reduces to the expressions obtained previously.

Maxwell's curl equations are

$$\nabla \times \mathbf{H} = \mathbf{J} + \frac{\partial \mathbf{D}}{\partial t} = \sigma\mathbf{E} + \epsilon\frac{\partial \mathbf{E}}{\partial t} \qquad (10\text{-}79)$$

and

$$\nabla \times \mathbf{E} = -\frac{\partial \mathbf{B}}{\partial t} = -\mu\frac{\partial \mathbf{H}}{\partial t} \qquad (10\text{-}80)$$

Taking the curl of (10-80) and introducing the value of $\nabla \times \mathbf{H}$ from (10-79),

$$\nabla \times (\nabla \times \mathbf{E}) = -\mu\frac{\partial(\nabla \times \mathbf{H})}{\partial t} = -\mu\frac{\partial}{\partial t}\left(\sigma\mathbf{E} + \epsilon\frac{\partial \mathbf{E}}{\partial t}\right) \qquad (10\text{-}81)$$

But by a vector identity, meaningful only in rectangular coordinates, the left-hand side of (10-81) can be expressed

$$\nabla \times (\nabla \times \mathbf{E}) = \nabla(\nabla \cdot \mathbf{E}) - \nabla^2\mathbf{E} \qquad (10\text{-}82)$$

Equating (10-82) and (10-81), and noting that in space having no free charge $\nabla \cdot \mathbf{E} = 0$,

$$\nabla^2\mathbf{E} = \mu\epsilon\frac{\partial^2\mathbf{E}}{\partial t^2} + \mu\sigma\frac{\partial \mathbf{E}}{\partial t} \qquad (10\text{-}82a)$$

Assuming harmonic variation of the field with time, (10-82a) reduces to

$$\nabla^2 \mathbf{E} = (-\omega^2 \mu \epsilon + j\omega\mu\sigma)\mathbf{E} = \gamma^2 \mathbf{E} \qquad (10\text{-}83a)$$

or

$$\nabla^2 \mathbf{E} - \gamma^2 \mathbf{E} = 0 \qquad (10\text{-}83b)$$

From (10-82) we can also write

$$\nabla \times \nabla \times \mathbf{E} + \gamma^2 \mathbf{E} = 0 \qquad (10\text{-}83c)$$

All of the above four equations are vector wave equations in $\mathbf{E}$. In (10-82a) the time is explicit, while in the other three it is implicit, harmonic variation with time being assumed. The equations (10-83) incorporate all four of Maxwell's equations. Maxwell's two curl equations are the starting point for the wave equation, and the equations of (10-83) satisfy them. Maxwell's two divergence equations are also satified.

For a plane wave traveling in the x direction with $\mathbf{E}$ in the y direction ($\mathbf{E} = \mathbf{j}E_y$) Eq. (10-82a) reduces to

$$\frac{\partial^2 E_y}{\partial x^2} = \mu\epsilon \frac{\partial^2 E_y}{\partial t^2} + \mu\sigma \frac{\partial E_y}{\partial t} \qquad (10\text{-}84)$$

which is the same as (10-9). If $\sigma = 0$,

$$\frac{\partial^2 E_y}{\partial x^2} = \mu\epsilon \frac{\partial^2 E_y}{\partial t^2} \qquad (10\text{-}85)$$

which is the same as obtained for a lossless medium in Chap. 9. These are scalar wave equations.

If $\mathbf{E}$ does not change with time ($\mathbf{E}$ static),

$$\nabla^2 \mathbf{E} = 0 \qquad (10\text{-}86)$$

If $\mathbf{E}$ is a harmonic function of time, then (10-84) becomes

$$\frac{\partial^2 E_y}{\partial x^2} = -\omega^2 \mu\epsilon E_y + j\omega\mu\sigma E_y \qquad (10\text{-}87)$$

or

$$\frac{\partial^2 E_y}{\partial x^2} - \gamma^2 E_y = 0 \qquad (10\text{-}88)$$

which is the same as (10-13).

PROBLEMS

10-1. A medium has a conductivity $\sigma = 10^{-1}$ mho/meter and a relative permittivity $\epsilon_r = 50$. Assume that these values do not change with frequency and that $\mu_r = 1$. Does the medium behave like a conductor or a dielectric at a frequency of (a) 50 kc/sec; (b) 10^4 Mc/sec?

   Ans.: (a) $\sigma/\omega\epsilon = 720 =$ conductor; (b) $\sigma/\omega\epsilon = 3.6 \times 10^{-3} =$ dielectric.

10-2. A plane 1,590-Mc/sec wave is traveling in a medium for which $\epsilon_r = \mu_r = 1$ and $\sigma = 0.1$ mho/meter. If the rms electric field intensity of the wave is 10 volts/meter, what are (a) the conduction current density, (b) the displacement current density, and (c) the total current density?

10-3. What is the $1/e$ depth of penetration of a 159-Mc/sec wave into a medium for which $\sigma = 10^6$ mhos/meter and $\mu_r = 1$?　　　　　　*Ans.:* 4×10^{-5} meter.

10-4. Determine the $1/e$ depths and the 1 per cent depths of penetration of a wave into an infinite medium for which $\sigma = 10^6$ mhos/meter and $\mu_r = 2$ at the following frequencies: (a) 60 cps; (b) 2 Mc/sec; (c) 3,000 Mc/sec.

10-5. (a) Develop the wave equation in E for a plane wave traveling in the y direction in a conducting medium. Take E in the z direction. Assume harmonic variation of E. (b) State a solution for a wave traveling in the negative y direction. Prove that it is a solution.

10-6. A plane 159-Mc/sec wave is traveling in a medium for which $\epsilon_r = \mu_r = 1$ and $\sigma = 10^5$ mhos/meter. How far must the wave travel to decrease in amplitude to 13.5 per cent $(1/e^2)$ of its original value?

10-7. How long does it take for the charge density in a medium, with constants $\sigma = 10^6$ mhos/meter, $\epsilon_r = \mu_r = 1$, to decrease to 1 per cent of its original value?
　　　　　　Ans.: 4.07×10^{-17} second.

10-8. What is the intrinsic impedance of the medium of Prob. 10-7 for a 30,000-Mc/sec wave?

10-9. A 159-Mc/sec plane wave traveling in a lossless dielectric medium with $\epsilon_r = 4$ and $\mu_r = 1$ is incident normally on a large, thick conducting sheet. The constants for the sheet are $\sigma = 10^5$ mhos/meter and $\epsilon_r = \mu_r = 1$. If the amplitude of the incident traveling wave is 10 volts/meter, what is the average Poynting vector into the sheet?

10-10. A half space of air and a half space of a lossless dielectric medium M are separated by a sheet of copper. A plane 1,000-Mc/sec traveling wave in the air space is incident normally on the copper sheet. The amplitude of the electric field intensity of the incident traveling wave is 100 volts/meter. The copper sheet has a thickness of 9.6×10^{-6} meter and has constants $\sigma = 5.8 \times 10^7$ mhos/meter and $\epsilon_r = \mu_r = 1$. The constants for the dielectric medium M are $\epsilon_r = 4$ and $\mu_r = 1$. Determine (a) the rms value of the electric field in the copper sheet just inside the surface adjacent to the dielectric medium M; (b) the rms value of the electric field at a point in the dielectric medium M at a distance of 1 meter from the copper sheet; (c) the rms value of the magnetic field H at a point in the dielectric medium M at a distance of 1 meter from the copper sheet.

10-11. A plane traveling wave with an rms electric field intensity of 1 volt/meter is incident normally on a large body of salt water with constants $\sigma = 4$ mhos/meter, $\epsilon_r = 80$, and $\mu_r = 1$. At what depths is the rms field intensity equal to 10 μv/meter at frequencies of (a) 100 kc/sec and (b) 10 Mc/sec?
　　　　　　Ans.: (a) 4.3 meters; (b) 0.62 meter.

10-12. A plane traveling wave in air with magnetic field amplitude H_1 is incident normally on the boundary of a large conducting medium. The frequency and the constants of the medium are such that $\dot{Z}_c = 0.02\underline{/45°}$ ohms for the conducting medium. Calculate without approximation the magnitude of the magnetic field H_2 at the conducting boundary, and compare with the approximation that $H_2 = 2H_1$. What is the error involved in the approximation?

10-13. Calculate the conductivity required for a sheet of space cloth $\frac{1}{2}$ mm in thickness.

10-14. A medium has the constants $\mu = 4\pi \times 10^{-7}$ henry/meter, $\epsilon = 10^{-11}$ farad/meter, and $\sigma = 10^{-5}$ mho/meter. At a frequency of 159 Mc/sec find (a) the intrinsic impedance of the medium; (b) the phase velocity of a plane wave in the medium.

CHAPTER 11

TRANSMISSION LINES

11-1. Introduction. As mentioned in Chap. 10, there is a close analogy between plane waves in unbounded media and guided waves on transmission lines. The subject of transmission lines is considered further in this chapter, and additional comparisons are made between waves in space and waves on transmission lines.

A *transmission line* may be defined as a device for transmitting or guiding energy from one point to another. Usually it is desired that the energy be conveyed with maximum efficiency, losses in heat or radiation being as small as possible.

Transmission lines may be of many forms and shapes. It will be convenient to classify transmission lines on the basis of the field configurations, or *modes*, which they can transmit. Thus transmission lines may be divided into two main groups, (1) those capable of transmitting transverse electromagnetic (TEM) modes and (2) those able to transmit only higher-order modes. In a TEM mode both the electric and the magnetic fields are entirely transverse to the direction of propagation. There is no component of either **E** or **H** in the direction of transmission. Higher-order modes, on the other hand, always have at least one field component in the direction of transmission. All two-conductor lines such as coaxial or two-wire transmission lines are examples of TEM-mode types, while hollow single-conductor wave guides (see Chap. 12) or dielectric rods are examples of higher mode types.

To summarize, transmission lines may be classified as follows:

1. TEM-mode type: **E** and **H** entirely transverse
   Examples: All two-conductor types such as coaxial and two-wire lines
2. Higher mode type: **E** or **H** or both have components in the direction of transmission
   Examples: Hollow single-conductor wave guides and dielectric rods

In the above discussion we have used the term "transmission line" as a general, all-inclusive expression. In common present-day usage, however, the term "line" or "transmission line" is usually restricted to those devices which can transmit TEM modes, while the term "guide" or

417

"wave guide" is employed for those devices which can transmit *only* higher-order modes. The remainder of this chapter deals specifically with transmission lines of the two-conductor type, wave guides being discussed in Chap. 12.

11-2. Coaxial, Two-wire, and Infinite-plane Transmission Lines. The most common forms of TEM-mode transmission lines are the coaxial

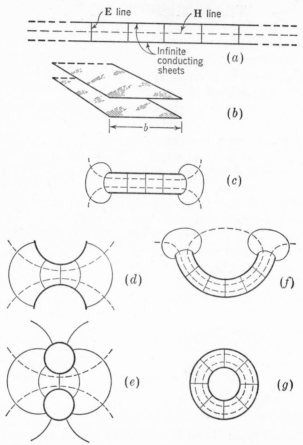

FIG. 11-1. Evolution of two-wire and coaxial transmission lines from infinite-parallel-plane type by means of transitional forms.

and two-wire types. Many other forms, in fact an infinite variety of them, are also possible. However, all may be regarded as derived from a basic or parent form. Thus let us consider the infinite-parallel-plane transmission line as the basic two-conductor type. This type consists of two parallel-plane conducting sheets of infinite extent. A cross section through such a line is shown in Fig. 11-1a. Considering only a TEM wave, **E** is everywhere normal and **H** everywhere parallel to the sheets.

An approximation to the infinite-parallel-plane transmission line is provided by the parallel-strip line shown in perspective in Fig. 11-1b. Here the sheets have been reduced to form long parallel strips of width b. A cross section of this line is portrayed by Fig. 11-1c. In the region between the strips E and H are oriented the same as for the infinite-sheet line. However, E and H also extend outside the region between the strips, the H lines forming loops that enclose each strip.

Now let the strips of the line of Fig. 11-1c be curved away from each other at the edges, as suggested by Fig. 11-1d. Continuing this process, we end up with the two-conductor transmission line shown in Fig. 11-1e.

As another variation, let the strips of the line of Fig. 11-1c be bent in the same direction, as suggested in Fig. 11-1f. Continuing this process, we arrive at the coaxial transmission line portrayed in Fig. 11-1g.

Thus we may regard both the two-wire transmission line (Fig. 11-1e) and the coaxial line (Fig. 11-1g) as forms that can be derived from the parallel-plane type.

In the following sections of this chapter the properties of two-conductor transmission lines are developed by an extension of ordinary circuit theory to take into account the finite velocity of propagation along the line, and comparisons are made with corresponding relations for plane waves in space. The development applies to coaxial, two-wire, or any two-conductor type of transmission line carrying only TEM waves.

11-3. The Infinite Uniform Transmission Line. Consider the uniform two-wire transmission line shown in Fig. 11-2. In earlier chapters expressions were developed for the capacitance and inductance per unit length of such a line. If the line is not lossless, the line will also have a series resistance and a shunt conductance that may need to be considered. The net effect of the series resistance and inductance can be expressed by the *series impedance* Z per unit length. Thus[1]

$$Z = R + j\omega L = R + jX \qquad \text{ohms/meter} \qquad (11\text{-}1)$$

where R = series resistance (ohms/meter)
L = series inductance (henrys/meter)
ω = radian frequency (= $2\pi f$)
X = series reactance (ohms/meter)

The net effect of the shunt conductance and capacitance may be expressed by the *shunt admittance* Y per unit length. Thus

$$Y = G + j\omega C = G + jB \qquad \text{mhos/meter} \qquad (11\text{-}2)$$

---

[1] In previous chapters such quantities as the series inductance are expressed as L/d or L/l, where L is inductance and d or l is length. However, to simplify the equations, L will be understood here to mean inductance per length.

where G = shunt conductance (mhos/meter)

 C = shunt capacitance (farads/meter)

 ω = radian frequency ($= 2\pi f$)

 B = shunt susceptance (mhos/meter)

Consider now an infinitesimal section dx of the line, and let a harmonically varying wave be present on the line. Let the voltage across the line be V and the current through the line be I (Fig. 11-2). The voltage

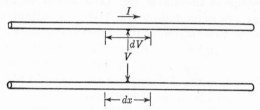

Fig. 11-2. Two-wire transmission line.

drop dV over the length of the section dx is equal to the IZ drop per unit length multiplied by the length of the section, or

$$dV = IZ\,dx \tag{11-3}$$

where I = line current. Thus

$$\frac{dV}{dx} = IZ \tag{11-4}$$

The change in current dI between the ends of the section dx is equal to the shunt current VY flowing across the line from one wire to the other, multiplied by the length of the section, or

$$dI = VY\,dx \tag{11-5}$$

where V = voltage across the line. Thus

$$\frac{dI}{dx} = VY \tag{11-6}$$

Differentiating (11-4) and (11-6) with respect to x, we obtain

$$\frac{d^2V}{dx^2} = I\frac{dZ}{dx} + Z\frac{dI}{dx} = I\frac{dZ}{dx} + ZVY \tag{11-7}$$

$$\frac{d^2I}{dx^2} = V\frac{dY}{dx} + Y\frac{dV}{dx} = V\frac{dY}{dx} + YIZ \tag{11-8}$$

On a uniform line Z and Y are independent of x (do not vary along the line), and so dZ/dx and dY/dx are zero.[1]   Thus, for a *uniform* line (11-7) and (11-8) reduce to

$$\frac{d^2V}{dx^2} - ZYV = 0 \qquad (11\text{-}13)$$

and

$$\frac{d^2I}{dx^2} - ZYI = 0 \qquad (11\text{-}14)$$

Equations (11-13) and (11-14) are the basic differential equations or wave equations for a uniform transmission line. In mathematical terminology they are linear differential equations of the second order with constant coefficients. They are the most general way of expressing the natural law relating the variation of voltage and current with distance along a uniform transmission line. However, they tell us nothing specifically about the voltage or current distribution on a particular transmission line. For this we must first obtain a solution appropriate to the imposed conditions. As a trial solution of (11-13) let us substitute

$$V = e^{\gamma x} \qquad (11\text{-}15)$$

from which

$$\frac{d^2V}{dx^2} = \gamma^2 e^{\gamma x} \qquad (11\text{-}16)$$

Thus, (11-13) becomes

$$(\gamma^2 - ZY)e^{\gamma x} = 0 \qquad (11\text{-}17)$$

and

$$\gamma^2 - ZY = 0 \qquad (11\text{-}18)$$

---

[1] For a nonuniform (tapered) transmission line the terms with dZ/dx and dY/dx must be retained.   From (11-4)

$$I = \frac{1}{Z}\frac{dV}{dx} \qquad (11\text{-}9)$$

so that the first term on the right side of (11-7) can be written

$$I\frac{dZ}{dx} = \frac{1}{Z}\frac{dZ}{dx}\frac{dV}{dx} = \frac{d(\ln Z)}{dx}\frac{dV}{dx} \qquad (11\text{-}10)$$

Substituting (11-10) in (11-7),

$$\frac{d^2V}{dx^2} - \frac{d(\ln Z)}{dx}\frac{dV}{dx} - ZYV = 0 \qquad (11\text{-}11)$$

In a like manner (11-8) becomes

$$\frac{d^2I}{dx^2} - \frac{d(\ln Y)}{dx}\frac{dI}{dx} - ZYI = 0 \qquad (11\text{-}12)$$

Equations (11-11) and (11-12) are basic differential equations for a *nonuniform* transmission line.   For a uniform line they reduce to (11-13) and (11-14).

Equation (11-18), known as the auxiliary equation, has two unequal roots $+\sqrt{ZY}$ and $-\sqrt{ZY}$, so that the general solution for (11-13) is

$$V = C_1 e^{\sqrt{ZY}\,x} + C_2 e^{-\sqrt{ZY}\,x} \tag{11-19}$$

where C_1 and C_2 are constants.

If (11-14) is solved in the same fashion as (11-13), we obtain a solution for I similar in form to (11-19) but having two more constants. Instead of solving for I in this manner, let us proceed along another avenue of approach and obtain a solution for I from (11-19). To do this, let (11-19) be differentiated with respect to x. Recalling also (11-4), we obtain

$$\frac{dV}{dx} = C_1 \sqrt{ZY}\, e^{\sqrt{ZY}\,x} - C_2 \sqrt{ZY}\, e^{-\sqrt{ZY}\,x} = IZ \tag{11-20}$$

from which it follows that

$$I = \frac{C_1}{\sqrt{Z/Y}}\, e^{\sqrt{ZY}\,x} - \frac{C_2}{\sqrt{Z/Y}}\, e^{-\sqrt{ZY}\,x} \tag{11-21}$$

This is a solution for the current. To evaluate the constants, we note from (11-19) that when $x = 0$

$$V = C_1 + C_2 \tag{11-22}$$

where V is the instantaneous voltage at the point $x = 0$ on the line. We may regard this voltage as the sum of two voltages which, in general, are unequal in amplitude and vary harmonically with time. Let V_1 and V_2 be the amplitudes of the voltages. The quantities C_1 and C_2 are constants with respect to x but may be regarded as variables with respect to time. Thus we may put

$$C_1 = V_1 e^{j\omega t} \tag{11-23}$$

and

$$C_2 = V_2 e^{j\omega t} \tag{11-24}$$

Therefore (11-22) becomes

$$V = V_1 e^{j\omega t} + V_2 e^{j\omega t} \tag{11-25}$$

at $x = 0$. Substituting (11-23) and (11-24) into (11-19) and (11-21) yields

$$V = V_1 e^{j\omega t} e^{\sqrt{ZY}\,x} + V_2 e^{j\omega t} e^{-\sqrt{ZY}\,x} \tag{11-26}$$

and

$$I = \frac{V_1 e^{j\omega t}}{\sqrt{Z/Y}}\, e^{\sqrt{ZY}\,x} - \frac{V_2 e^{j\omega t}}{\sqrt{Z/Y}}\, e^{-\sqrt{ZY}\,x} \tag{11-27}$$

The quantity $\sqrt{ZY} = \gamma$ is called the *propagation constant*. In general it is complex, with a real part α called the *attenuation constant* and an imaginary part β called the *phase constant.* Thus

$$\gamma = \sqrt{ZY} = \alpha + j\beta \tag{11-28}$$

or

$$\alpha = \text{Re }\sqrt{ZY} \tag{11-28a}$$

and

$$\beta = \text{Im }\sqrt{ZY} \tag{11-28b}$$

Introducing (11-28) into (11-26) and (11-27) and rearranging, we obtain

$$V = V_1 e^{\alpha x} e^{j(\omega t + \beta x)} + V_2 e^{-\alpha x} e^{j(\omega t - \beta x)} \tag{11-29}$$

and

$$I = \frac{V_1}{\sqrt{Z/Y}} e^{\alpha x} e^{j(\omega t + \beta x)} - \frac{V_2}{\sqrt{Z/Y}} e^{-\alpha x} e^{j(\omega t - \beta x)} \tag{11-30}$$

Equation (11-29) is the solution for the voltage on the transmission line. The solution has two terms. The first term, involving $\omega t + \beta x$, represents a wave traveling in the *negative* x direction along the line. The magnitude of this wave at $x = 0$ and $t = 0$ is V_1, and the factor $e^{\alpha x}$ indicates that this wave decreases in magnitude as it proceeds in the negative x direction. The second term, involving $\omega t - \beta x$, represents a wave traveling in the positive x direction along the line. The magnitude of this wave at $x = 0$ and $t = 0$ is V_2, and the factor $e^{-\alpha x}$ indicates that this wave decreases in magnitude as it proceeds in the positive x direction. The factors $e^{\alpha x}$ and $e^{-\alpha x}$ are *attenuation factors,* α being the *attenuation constant.* The factors $e^{j(\omega t + \beta x)}$ and $e^{j(\omega t - \beta x)}$ are *phase factors,* β being the *phase constant.*

If the voltages in (11-29) were replaced by electric fields, the equation would apply to two traveling waves in a conducting medium.[1]

The solution for I in (11-30) also has two terms, the first term representing a current wave traveling in the negative x direction and the second term a current wave traveling in the positive x direction. The total current at any point is the resultant of the two traveling-wave components.

Confining our attention now to a single wave traveling in the negative x direction as represented by the first terms of (11-29) and (11-30), we note that V and I are identical functions of x and t. The amplitudes differ. Taking the ratio of the voltage V across the line to the current I through the line for a single traveling wave, we obtain the impedance, Z_0, which is called the *characteristic,* or *surge, impedance* of the line. That is,

$$\frac{V}{I} = \sqrt{\frac{Z}{Y}} = Z_0 \qquad \text{ohms} \tag{11-31}$$

---

[1] For a wave in a conducting medium ($\sigma \gg \omega\epsilon$) we have $\alpha = \beta = 1/\delta$, where α is the attenuation constant, β the phase constant, and δ the $1/e$ depth of penetration. Compare (10-16).

This impedance is a function of the series impedance Z per unit length and shunt admittance Y per unit length. Expanding Z and Y as in (11-1) and (11-2), we obtain, from (11-31),

$$Z_0 = \sqrt{\frac{R + j\omega L}{G + j\omega C}} \quad \text{ohms} \tag{11-32}$$

Where R and G are small or where the frequency is large so that $\omega L \gg R$ and $\omega C \gg G$, (11-32) reduces to

$$Z_0 = \sqrt{\frac{L}{C}} \quad \text{ohms} \tag{11-33}$$

where Z_0 = characteristic impedance (ohms)

L = series inductance (henrys/meter)

C = shunt capacitance (farads/meter)

In (11-33) Z_0 is entirely real, or resistive, so that in this case we may, to be explicit, speak of the *characteristic resistance* R_0 of the line. That is, for this case

$$Z_0 = \sqrt{\frac{L}{C}} = R_0 \quad \text{ohms} \tag{11-34}$$

In general, where R and G cannot be neglected, Z_0 is complex and the term "characteristic impedance" should be used. However, if R and G are negligible, Z_0 is real ($= R_0$) and the term "characteristic resistance" may be used.

When R and G are small, but not negligible, (11-32) may be reexpressed approximately in the following form:

$$Z_0 = \sqrt{\frac{L}{C}} \left[1 + j \left(\frac{G}{2\omega C} - \frac{R}{2\omega L} \right) \right] \tag{11-35}$$

Thus Z_0 for this case is, in general, complex. However, if

$$\frac{G}{C} = \frac{R}{L} \tag{11-35a}$$

Z_0 is real.

The relations developed above for the characteristic impedance of a uniform transmission line are summarized in Table 11-1.

TABLE 11-1

CHARACTERISTIC IMPEDANCE OF TRANSMISSION LINES

Condition	Characteristic impedance, ohms
General case........................	$Z_0 = \sqrt{\dfrac{Z}{Y}} = \sqrt{\dfrac{R + j\omega L}{G + j\omega C}}$
Small losses........................	$Z_0 = \sqrt{\dfrac{L}{C}} \left[1 + j \left(\dfrac{G}{2\omega C} - \dfrac{R}{2\omega L} \right) \right]$
Lossless case,† $R = 0, G = 0$........	$Z_0 = \sqrt{\dfrac{L}{C}} = R_0$

† This case also applies where the losses are not zero but $\omega L \gg R$ and $\omega C \gg G$.

The phase velocity v of a wave traveling on the line is given by ω/β. That is,

$$v = \frac{\omega}{\beta} = \frac{\omega}{\text{Im } \gamma} = \frac{\omega}{\text{Im } \sqrt{ZY}} \qquad (11\text{-}36)$$

If the line is lossless or $R \ll \omega L$ and $G \ll \omega C$,

$$v = \frac{\omega}{\omega \sqrt{LC}} = \frac{1}{\sqrt{LC}} \qquad \text{meters/sec} \qquad (11\text{-}36a)$$

where L = series inductance (henrys/meter)
$\quad\ \ C$ = shunt capacitance (farads/meter)

11-4. Comparison of Circuit and Field Quantities. It is interesting to compare some of the relations for transmission lines developed in the preceding section with corresponding relations for waves developed in earlier chapters. For example, consider the transmission-line equations

$$\frac{dV}{dx} = ZI = (R + j\omega L)I \qquad \text{volts/meter} \qquad (11\text{-}37)$$

and

$$\frac{dI}{dx} = YV = (G + j\omega C)V \qquad \text{amp/meter} \qquad (11\text{-}38)$$

The corresponding relations for a plane wave traveling in the x direction with **E** in the y direction, as obtained from Maxwell's two curl equations, are

$$\frac{dE_y}{dx} = -j\omega\mu H_z \qquad \text{volts/meter}^2 \qquad (11\text{-}39)$$

and

$$\frac{dH_z}{dx} = (\sigma + j\omega\epsilon)E_y \qquad \text{amp/meter}^2 \qquad (11\text{-}40)$$

In these relations harmonic variation with time is assumed, and the differentiations with respect to time have been performed.

Comparing (11-37) with (11-39), we note that $j\omega\mu$ in the wave case corresponds to $Z = R + j\omega L$ for the line. Comparing (11-38) with (11-40), we see that $\sigma + j\omega\epsilon$ for the wave corresponds to $Y = G + j\omega C$ for the line.

Further comparisons of the circuit relations used for lines and the field relations employed for waves are made in Table 11-2. The first column gives the circuit quantity and the last column the corresponding field quantity. The center column indicates the mksc units, which are the same for corresponding circuit and field relations.

TABLE 11-2

COMPARISON OF CIRCUIT AND FIELD RELATIONS

Circuit relation for transmission line	mksc units	Field relation for space wave
$Z = R + j\omega L$	ohms/meter	$j\omega\mu$
$Y = G + j\omega C$	mhos/meter	$\sigma + j\omega\epsilon$
Characteristic impedance $= \sqrt{\dfrac{L}{C}}$	ohms	Intrinsic impedance $= \sqrt{\dfrac{\mu}{\epsilon}}$
Velocity $= \dfrac{1}{\sqrt{LC}}$	meters/sec	Velocity $= \dfrac{1}{\sqrt{\mu\epsilon}}$
Series inductance $= L$	henrys/meter	Permeability $= \mu$
Shunt capacitance $= C$	farads/meter	Permittivity $= \epsilon$
$\dfrac{\text{Voltage}}{\text{Distance}} = \dfrac{V}{x}$	volts/meter	Electric field $= \mathbf{E}$
$\dfrac{\text{Current}}{\text{Distance}} = \dfrac{I}{x}$	amp/meter	Magnetic field $= \mathbf{H}$

11-5. Characteristic-impedance Determinations. The correspondence of L to μ and C to ϵ (see Table 11-2) is of particular interest. Thus, if space is divided up into transmission-line cells, μ is the series inductance per unit length (or depth) of a cell, while ϵ is the shunt capacitance per unit length (or depth) of a cell.[1]

The transmission-line-cell concept (see Secs. 4-20 and 9-9) is of considerable value in connection with the determi-

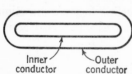

Inner conductor   Outer conductor

Fig. 11-3. Coaxial transmission line of noncircular cross section.

nation of the characteristic impedance of lossless transmission lines operating in the TEM mode. For instance, consider the transmission line portrayed in Fig. 11-3. Let the space between the conductors be divided into curvilinear squares by graphical-field-mapping methods. Each square represents the end of a transmission-line cell of characteristic impedance $Z_0' = \sqrt{\mu/\epsilon}$. Then, the characteristic impedance of the line is given by

$$Z_0 = \frac{N}{n} Z_0' \quad \text{ohms} \tag{11-41}$$

where $N =$ number of cells in series

$n =$ number of cells in parallel

$Z_0' =$ characteristic impedance of one cell $(= \sqrt{\mu/\epsilon}$, where μ is permeability and ϵ is permittivity of medium filling line)

[1] In earlier discussions (see, for example, Secs. 2-27, 4-20, 5-19, and also 9-9) series inductance in henrys per meter is written as L/l or L/d, while shunt capacitance in farads per meter is written as C/l or C/d. To simplify the equations in this chapter, the letter L by itself is understood to be the series inductance in henrys per meter and the letter C the shunt capacitance in farads per meter.

This method may be applied to two-conductor transmission lines of any shape. The characteristic impedance of lossless high-frequency lines of any shape can also be obtained by a simple d-c measurement. For example, if we wish to find the characteristic impedance (or resistance) of the line shown in Fig. 11-3 by this method, the conductor cross section is drawn to scale[1] with conducting paint (such as silver paint) on a sheet of resistance cloth or paper of uniform resistance R_s per square as suggested in Fig. 11-4.[2] Then by connecting the terminals of an ohmmeter to the inner and outer conductors, as indicated, a d-c resistance R_m is measured.[3] The characteristic impedance of the line is then

$$Z_0 = k R_m \quad \text{ohms} \quad (11\text{-}42)$$

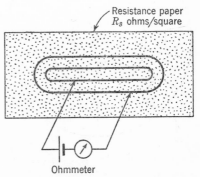

Fig. 11-4. Determination of characteristic impedance of transmission line by simple d-c measurement.

where $k = Z_0'/R_s = \sqrt{\mu/\epsilon}/R_s$ (dimensionless). The quantity k is a constant factor that is equal to the ratio of the intrinsic impedance $\sqrt{\mu/\epsilon}$ of the medium in the line to the resistance R_s per square of the resistance cloth or paper used in the measurement. Thus, if the line is air-filled, $Z_0' = 376.7$ ohms and (11-42) becomes

$$Z_0 = \frac{376.7}{R_s} R_m \quad \text{ohms} \quad (11\text{-}43)$$

Hence, if space cloth ($R_s = 376.7$) is used as the resistance cloth,

$$Z_0 = R_m \quad \text{ohms} \quad (11\text{-}44)$$

and the *ohmmeter reads directly the characteristic impedance of the line.*

Example 1. Find the characteristic impedance (or resistance) of the lossless coaxial line shown in Fig. 11-5. The line is air-filled.

Solution. Dividing the space between the conductors into curvilinear squares or cells by graphical field mapping, we obtain a total of 18.3 squares in parallel and 2 in

---

[1] Since only the shape is important, the cross section may be scaled to any convenient size.

[2] It is important that there be good contact between the conductor cross section and the resistance material. One of the simplest ways of ensuring this is by the use of silver paint.

[3] Supposing that the resistance paper between the conductors were marked off in curvilinear squares, R_m would be given by $R_m = (N/n)R_s$, where N = number of squares in series, n = number of squares in parallel, and R_s = resistance per square (that is, resistance of one square).

series.   The characteristic impedance of each cell is 376.7 ohms.   Hence, from (11-41), the characteristic impedance of the line of Fig. 11-5 is

$$Z_0 = \frac{N}{n} Z_0' = \frac{2}{18.3} 376.7 = 41.2 \text{ ohms}$$

If a cross section of this line is drawn to scale with conducting paint on a sheet of space cloth, the value 41.2 ohms would be measured directly on an ohmmeter connected between the inner and outer conductors.

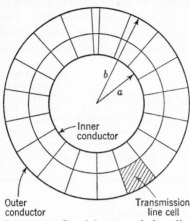

FIG. 11-5. Coaxial transmission line with 18.3 transmission-line cells in parallel and 2 in series.

When the above resistance-measurement method is applied to open types of line, such as a two-wire line, the sheet of resistance material should extend out to a distance that is large compared with the line cross section if accurate results are to be obtained.

Although the graphical and d-c measurement methods can be applied to two-conductor lines of any shape, there are some configurations that yield to a simple calculation.   Thus, for the case under consideration where the characteristic impedance

$$Z_0 = \sqrt{\frac{L}{C}} \qquad \text{ohms} \tag{11-45}$$

the value of Z_0 can be determined by a knowledge of L and C for the line. Thus, obtaining L from (4-67) and C from (2-81), the characteristic impedance of a *coaxial line* (as in Fig. 11-5) is given by

$$Z_0 = \frac{1}{2\pi} \sqrt{\frac{\mu}{\epsilon}} \ln \frac{b}{a} = 0.367 \sqrt{\frac{\mu}{\epsilon}} \log \frac{b}{a} \qquad \text{ohms} \tag{11-46}$$

If there is no ferromagnetic material present, $\mu = \mu_0$ and (11-46) reduces to

$$Z_0 = \frac{138}{\sqrt{\epsilon_r}} \log \frac{b}{a} \qquad \text{ohms} \tag{11-47}$$

where ϵ_r = relative permittivity of medium filling line
    a = outside radius of inner conductor
    b = inside radius of outer conductor
    $\log$ = logarithm to base 10 = 0.4343 natural logarithm ($\ln$)
For an air-filled line $\epsilon_r = 1$, and (11-47) becomes

$$Z_0 = 138 \log \frac{b}{a} \qquad \text{ohms} \tag{11-48}$$

Example 2. The air-filled coaxial line in Fig. 11-5 has a radius ratio $b/a = 2$. Find its characteristic impedance.

Solution. From (11-48)

$$Z_0 = 138 \log 2 = 41.4 \text{ ohms}$$

The value obtained previously by graphical methods agrees well with this exact value.

In a similar way, the characteristic impedance may be obtained for a *two-wire line*, as in Fig. 11-6. Thus, if $D \gg a$, we have

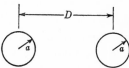

FIG. 11-6. Two-wire transmission line.

$$Z_0 = \frac{1}{\pi} \sqrt{\frac{\mu}{\epsilon}} \ln \frac{D}{a} = 0.73 \sqrt{\frac{\mu}{\epsilon}} \log \frac{D}{a} \qquad \text{ohms}$$

$$(11\text{-}49)$$

If there is no ferromagnetic material present, $\mu = \mu_0$ and (11-49) reduces to

$$Z_0 = \frac{276}{\sqrt{\epsilon_r}} \log \frac{D}{a} \qquad \text{ohms} \qquad (11\text{-}50)$$

where ϵ_r = relative permittivity of medium

  D = center-to-center spacing (see Fig. 11-6)

  a = radius of conductor (in same units as D)

If the medium is air, $\epsilon_r = 1$ and (11-50) becomes

$$Z_0 = 276 \log \frac{D}{a} \qquad \text{ohms} \qquad (11\text{-}51)$$

The characteristic impedances obtained above are summarized in Table 11-3.

TABLE 11-3

CHARACTERISTIC IMPEDANCE OF COAXIAL AND TWO-WIRE LINES

Type of line	*Characteristic impedance, ohms†*
Coaxial (filled with medium of relative permittivity ϵ_r)	$Z_0 = \dfrac{138}{\sqrt{\epsilon_r}} \log \dfrac{b}{a}$ (see Fig. 11-5)
Coaxial (air-filled)	$Z_0 = 138 \log \dfrac{b}{a}$ (see Fig. 11-5)
Two-wire (in medium of relative permittivity ϵ_r) ($D \gg a$)	$Z_0 = \dfrac{276}{\sqrt{\epsilon_r}} \log \dfrac{D}{a}$ (see Fig. 11-6)
Two-wire (in air) ($D \gg a$)	$Z_0 = 276 \log \dfrac{D}{a}$ (see Fig. 11-6)

† Logarithms are to base 10.

It is assumed throughout this section that the line is lossless (or $R \ll \omega L$ and $G \ll \omega C$) and also that the currents are confined to the conductor surfaces to which the radii refer. This condition is approximated at high frequencies owing to the small depth of penetration. This condition may also be approximated at low frequencies by the use of thinwalled tubes. It is also assumed that the lines are operating in the TEM mode.

11-6. The Terminated Uniform Transmission Line. In Sec. 11-3 the line was considered to be of infinite length. Let us now analyze the situation where a line of characteristic impedance Z_0 is terminated in a load impedance Z_L as in Fig. 11-7. The load is at $x = 0$, and positive

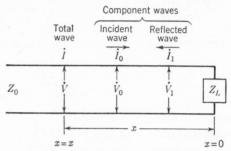

FIG. 11-7. Terminated transmission line.

distance x is measured to the left along the line. The total voltage and total current are expressed as the resultant of two traveling waves moving in opposite directions as on an infinite transmission line. However, on the terminated line the wave to the right may be regarded as the incident wave and the wave to the left as the reflected wave, with the reflected wave related to the incident wave by the load impedance Z_L.

At a point on the line at a distance x from the load let the voltage between the wires and the current through one wire due to the incident wave traveling to the right be designated $\dot{V}_0$ and $\dot{I}_0$, respectively.[1] Let $\dot{V}_1$ and $\dot{I}_1$ be the voltage and current due to the wave traveling to the left that is reflected from the load. The resultant voltage $\dot{V}$ at a point on the line is equal to the sum of the voltages $\dot{V}_0$ and $\dot{V}_1$ at the point. That is,

$$\dot{V} = \dot{V}_0 + \dot{V}_1 \tag{11-52}$$

where $\dot{V}_0 = V_0 e^{\gamma x}$ (the factor $e^{j\omega t}$ is understood to be present)
$\dot{V}_1 = V_1 e^{-\gamma x + j\xi}$ (the factor $e^{j\omega t}$ is understood to be present)
γ = propagation constant = $\alpha + j\beta$
ξ = phase shift at load

---

[1] The dot (˙) indicates explicitly that $\dot{V}_0$ and $\dot{I}_0$ are complex functions of position (phasors). The modulus, or absolute value, of $\dot{V}_0$ is V_0 (that is, $V_0 = |\dot{V}_0|$). Likewise the absolute value of $\dot{I}_0$ is I_0 (that is, $I_0 = |\dot{I}_0|$).

At the load ($x = 0$) we have $\dot{V}_0 = V_0$ and $\dot{V}_1 = V_1 e^{j\xi} = V_1 / \xi$ so that *at* *the load*

$$\frac{\dot{V}_1}{\dot{V}_0} = \frac{V_1}{V_0} \big/\xi = \dot{\rho}_v \tag{11-53}$$

where $\dot{\rho}_v$ = *reflection coefficient for voltage* (dimensionless). It follows that

$$\dot{V} = V_0(e^{\gamma x} + \dot{\rho}_v e^{-\gamma x}) \tag{11-54}$$

The resultant current $\dot{I}$ at a point on the line is equal to the sum of the currents $\dot{I}_0$ and $\dot{I}_1$ at the point. That is,

$$\dot{I} = \dot{I}_0 + \dot{I}_1 \tag{11-55}$$

where $\dot{I}_0 = I_0 e^{\gamma x - j\delta}$
$\dot{I}_1 = I_1 e^{-\gamma x + j(\xi - \delta)}$
δ = phase difference between current and voltage

At the load

$$\frac{\dot{I}_1}{\dot{I}_0} = \frac{I_1}{I_0} \big/\xi = \dot{\rho}_i \tag{11-56}$$

where $\dot{\rho}_i$ = *reflection coefficient for current* (dimensionless). It follows that

$$\dot{I} = I_0 e^{-j\delta}(e^{\gamma x} + \dot{\rho}_i e^{-\gamma x}) \tag{11-57}$$

Now $\dot{\rho}_v$ and $\dot{\rho}_i$ may be expressed in terms of the characteristic impedance Z_0 and the load impedance Z_L.[1] Thus we note that at any point on the line

$$Z_0 = \frac{\dot{V}_0}{\dot{I}_0} = \frac{V_0}{I_0} \big/\delta = -\frac{\dot{V}_1}{\dot{I}_1} = -\frac{V_1}{I_1} \big/\delta \tag{11-58}$$

while at the load ($x = 0$)

$$Z_L = \frac{\dot{V}}{\dot{I}} \tag{11-59}$$

It follows from (11-55) that at the load

$$\frac{\dot{V}}{Z_L} = \frac{\dot{V}_0}{Z_0} - \frac{\dot{V}_1}{Z_0} = \frac{\dot{V}_0 - \dot{V}_1}{Z_0} \tag{11-60}$$

But $\dot{V} = \dot{V}_0 + \dot{V}_1$; so we have

$$\frac{\dot{V}_0 + \dot{V}_1}{Z_L} = \frac{\dot{V}_0 - \dot{V}_1}{Z_0} \tag{11-61}$$

[1] Although the impedances Z_L and Z_0 are (in general) also complex quantities, the dot over the letter will, for simplicity, be omitted. If it becomes necessary to indicate the absolute value, or modulus, of Z_L, this will be done by the use of bars (thus the absolute value of Z_L equals $|Z_L| = \sqrt{R_L{}^2 + X_L{}^2}$).

Solving for $\dot{V}_1/\dot{V}_0$ yields

$$\frac{\dot{V}_1}{\dot{V}_0} = \frac{Z_L - Z_0}{Z_L + Z_0} = \dot{\rho}_v \qquad (11\text{-}62)$$

For real load impedances Z_L ranging from 0 to ∞, $\dot{\rho}_v$ ranges from -1 to $+1$ in value.

In a similar way it can be shown that

$$\dot{\rho}_i = -\frac{Z_L - Z_0}{Z_L + Z_0} = -\dot{\rho}_v \qquad (11\text{-}63)$$

Now the ratio $\dot{V}/\dot{I}$ at any point x on the line gives the impedance Z_x at the point looking toward the load.   Taking this ratio and introducing the relation (11-63) in (11-57) for $\dot{I}$, we obtain

$$Z_x = \frac{\dot{V}}{\dot{I}} = \frac{V_0}{I_0} \underline{/\delta}\, \frac{e^{\gamma x} + \dot{\rho}_v e^{-\gamma x}}{e^{\gamma x} - \dot{\rho}_v e^{-\gamma x}} \qquad (11\text{-}64)$$

Noting (11-58) and (11-62), this can be reexpressed as

$$Z_x = Z_0 \frac{Z_L + Z_0 \tanh \gamma x}{Z_0 + Z_L \tanh \gamma x} \qquad \text{ohms} \qquad (11\text{-}65)$$

where Z_x = impedance at distance x looking toward load (ohms)
$\quad Z_0$ = characteristic impedance of line (ohms)
$\quad Z_L$ = load impedance (ohms)
$\quad \gamma$ = propagation constant $(\alpha + j\beta)$
$\quad x$ = distance from load
This is the general expression for the impedance Z_x at a distance x from the load.

If the line is open-circuited, $Z_L = \infty$ and (11-65) reduces to

$$Z_x = \frac{Z_0}{\tanh \gamma x} = Z_0 \coth \gamma x \qquad (11\text{-}66)$$

If the line is short-circuited, $Z_L = 0$ and (11-65) reduces to

$$Z_x = Z_0 \tanh \gamma x \qquad (11\text{-}67)$$

It is to be noted that, in general, γ is complex $(= \alpha + j\beta)$.   Thus[1]

$$\tanh \gamma x = \frac{\sinh \alpha x \cos \beta x + j \cosh \alpha x \sin \beta x}{\cosh \alpha x \cos \beta x + j \sinh \alpha x \sin \beta x} \qquad (11\text{-}68)$$

or

$$\tanh \gamma x = \frac{\tanh \alpha x + j \tan \beta x}{1 + j \tanh \alpha x \tan \beta x} \qquad (11\text{-}69)$$

It is to be noted that the product of the impedance of the line when it is open-circuited and when it is short-circuited equals the square of the

[1] See Appendix for other hyperbolic relations.

characteristic impedance. That is,

$$Z_0{}^2 = Z_{oc}Z_{sc} \tag{11-70}$$

where $Z_{oc} = Z_x$ for open-circuited line ($Z_L = \infty$)

$Z_{sc} = Z_x$ for short-circuited line ($Z_L = 0$)

If the line is *lossless* ($\alpha = 0$), the above relations reduce to the following: In general,

$$Z_x = Z_0 \frac{Z_L + jZ_0 \tan \beta x}{Z_0 + jZ_L \tan \beta x} \tag{11-71}$$

When the line is open-circuited ($Z_L = \infty$),

$$Z_x = \frac{Z_0}{j \tan \beta x} = -jZ_0 \cot \beta x \tag{11-72}$$

When the line is short-circuited ($Z_L = 0$),

$$Z_x = jZ_0 \tan \beta x \tag{11-73}$$

We note that (11-70) is also fulfilled on the lossless line. Furthermore, the impedance for an open- or short-circuited lossless line is a pure reactance.

The impedance relations developed above apply to all uniform two-conductor lines, such as coaxial and two-wire lines. They give the input impedance Z_x of a uniform transmission line

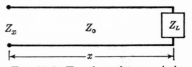

FIG. 11-8. Terminated transmission line.

of length x and characteristic impedance Z_0 terminated in a load Z_L (see Fig. 11-8). These relations are summarized in Table 11-4.

TABLE 11-4
INPUT IMPEDANCE OF TERMINATED TRANSMISSION LINE†

Load condition	General case ($\alpha \neq 0$)	Lossless case ($\alpha = 0$)
Any value of load Z_L	$Z_x = Z_0 \dfrac{Z_L + Z_0 \tanh \gamma x}{Z_0 + Z_L \tanh \gamma x}$	$Z_x = Z_0 \dfrac{Z_L + jZ_0 \tan \beta x}{Z_0 + jZ_L \tan \beta x}$
Open-circuited line ($Z_L = \infty$)	$Z_x = Z_0 \coth \gamma x$	$Z_x = -jZ_0 \cot \beta x$
Short-circuited line ($Z_L = 0$)	$Z_x = Z_0 \tanh \gamma x$	$Z_x = jZ_0 \tan \beta x$

† In the table $\gamma = \alpha + j\beta$, where α = attenuation constant (nepers/meter) and $\beta = 2\pi/\lambda$ = phase constant (rad/meter), where λ is the wavelength.

On a lossless line the *standing-wave ratio* (SWR) is given by

$$\text{SWR} = \frac{V_{\max}}{V_{\min}} = \frac{I_{\max}}{I_{\min}} \tag{11-74}$$

It follows that

$$\text{SWR} = \frac{V_0 + V_1}{V_0 - V_1} = \frac{1 + (V_1/V_0)}{1 - (V_1/V_0)} \tag{11-75}$$

But

$$\frac{V_1}{V_0} = |\dot{\rho}_v| \tag{11-76}$$

and so

$$\text{SWR} = \frac{1 + |\dot{\rho}_v|}{1 - |\dot{\rho}_v|} \tag{11-77}$$

where $\dot{\rho}_v$ = reflection coefficient for voltage. This relation is identical with that given by (9-96) for the SWR of plane waves. Solving (11-77) for the magnitude of the reflection coefficient,

$$|\dot{\rho}_v| = \frac{\text{SWR} - 1}{\text{SWR} + 1} \tag{11-78}$$

It is often of interest to know the voltage $\dot{V}$ at the load in terms of the voltage $\dot{V}_0$ of the incident wave. This is given by the *transmission coefficient for voltage* $\dot{\tau}_v$. That is, at the load

$$\dot{V} = \dot{\tau}_v \dot{V}_0 \qquad \text{or} \qquad \dot{\tau}_v = \frac{\dot{V}}{\dot{V}_0} \tag{11-79}$$

The load impedance may be a lumped element as suggested in Fig. 11-7 or Fig. 11-8, or it may be the impedance presented by another line of

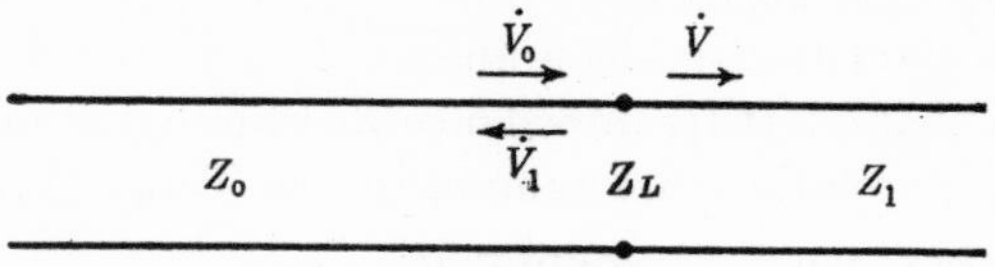

FIG. 11-9. Junction of transmission lines of different characteristic impedance.

characteristic impedance Z_1 as suggested in Fig. 11-9. In the latter case (11-79) gives the voltage $\dot{V}$ of the wave transmitted beyond the junction. It may be shown that the coefficient $\dot{\tau}_v$ is related to Z_L and Z_0 by

$$\dot{\tau}_v = \frac{2Z_L}{Z_L + Z_0} = 1 + \dot{\rho}_v \tag{11-80}$$

where Z_L = load impedance presented to line of characteristic impedance Z_0

$\dot{\rho}_v$ = reflection coefficient for voltage

As Z_L ranges from 0 to ∞, $\dot{\tau}_v$ ranges from 0 to 2.

It also follows that the *transmission coefficient for current* $\dot{\tau}_i$ is given by

$$\dot{\tau}_i = \frac{\dot{I}}{\dot{I}_0} = \frac{2Z_0}{Z_0 + Z_L} = 1 + \dot{\rho}_i \tag{11-81}$$

As Z_L ranges from 0 to ∞, $\dot{\tau}_i$ varies from 2 to 0.

The relations for reflection and transmission coefficients developed in this section are summarized in Table 11-5.

TABLE 11-5
RELATIONS FOR REFLECTION AND TRANSMISSION COEFFICIENTS

Reflection coefficient for voltage	$\dot{\rho}_v = \dfrac{Z_L - Z_0}{Z_L + Z_0}$
Reflection coefficient for current	$\dot{\rho}_i = \dfrac{Z_0 - Z_L}{Z_0 + Z_L}$
Transmission coefficient for voltage	$\dot{\tau}_v = \dfrac{2Z_L}{Z_0 + Z_L} = 1 + \dot{\rho}_v$
Transmission coefficient for current	$\dot{\tau}_i = \dfrac{2Z_0}{Z_0 + Z_L} = 1 + \dot{\rho}_i$
Standing-wave ratio (SWR)	$\dfrac{1 + |\dot{\rho}_v|}{1 - |\dot{\rho}_v|} = \dfrac{1 + |\dot{\rho}_i|}{1 - |\dot{\rho}_i|}$
Magnitude of reflection coefficient	$|\dot{\rho}_v| = |\dot{\rho}_i| = \dfrac{\text{SWR} - 1}{\text{SWR} + 1}$

11-7. Transmission-line Charts. Transmission-line calculations are often tremendously facilitated by the use of transmission-line charts. In particular, the rectangular and the Smith impedance charts are extremely useful in making calculations on uniform lossless transmission lines.

A rectangular impedance chart is illustrated in Fig. 11-10.[1] The rectangular coordinates on this chart give the normalized resistance R_n as abscissa and the normalized reactance X_n as ordinate for points on the transmission line, while the closed circles indicate the SWR on the line and the partial circles the distance in wavelengths from the load. The normalized resistance R_n is equal to the actual resistance R divided by the characteristic resistance R_0 of the line. That is,

$$R_n = \frac{R}{R_0} \qquad \text{(dimensionless)} \qquad (11\text{-}82)$$

The normalized reactance X_n is equal to the actual reactance X divided by R_0, or

$$X_n = \frac{X}{R_0} \qquad \text{(dimensionless)} \qquad (11\text{-}83)$$

Thus, the normalized impedance Z_n is related to the actual impedance Z by

$$Z_n = \frac{Z}{R_0} = \frac{R}{R_0} + j\frac{X}{R_0} \qquad \text{(dimensionless)} \qquad (11\text{-}84)$$

[1] For methods of constructing this chart see, for example, M.I.T. Radar School Staff, "Principles of Radar," J. F. Reintjes (ed.), McGraw-Hill Book Company, Inc., New York, 1946, pp. 8–64.

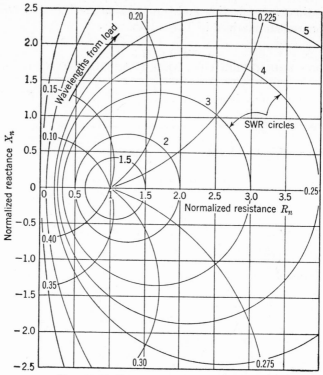

FIG. 11-10. Rectangular impedance chart.

The chart may also be used for admittances, the normalized admittance Y_n being given by

$$Y_n = G_n + jB_n = YR_0 = \frac{R_0}{Z} \qquad \text{(dimensionless)} \qquad (11\text{-}85)$$

An example will be given to illustrate the use of the rectangular chart.

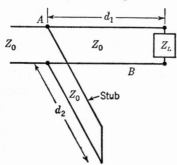

FIG. 11-11. Terminated transmission line with single matching stub. Both the stub position (d_1) and its length (d_2) are adjustable.

Example 1. Referring to the terminated transmission line with short-circuited stub shown in Fig. 11-11, the load $Z_L = 150 + j50$ ohms. The line and stubs have a characteristic impedance $Z_0 = R_0 = 100$ ohms. Find values for d_1 and d_2 such that there is no reflected wave at A (SWR = 1).

Solution. The normalized value of the load is

$$Z_n = \frac{Z_L}{R_0} = \frac{150 + j50}{100} = 1.5 + j0.5$$

The chart is then entered at the point $1.5 + j0.5$ as indicated by P_1 in Fig. 11-12. For clarity most of the rectangular and circular coordinate lines are omitted in this figure. Point P_1 is on the SWR circle for which SWR = 1.77. Hence, the SWR at B is 1.77. Now, moving along the SWR = 1.77 circle away from the load (clockwise), we proceed to the point P_2. This is just $\frac{1}{4}$ wavelength (90 electrical degrees) from the point P_3 that lies on the SWR = 1.77 circle at $R_n = 1$. At P_2, which is 0.194 wavelength from the load, the normalized impedance is 0.78 − $j0.41$. Moving $\frac{1}{4}$ wavelength farther on the chart gives the impedance $\frac{1}{4}$ wavelength farther from the load *or* the admittance at the same location (0.194 wavelength from the load).

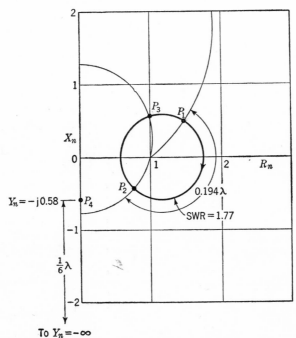

Fig. 11-12. Worked example using rectangular impedance chart.

Since the stub is connected in parallel to the line, it is convenient to deal in admittances. To do this, the chart is now considered to be an admittance chart, the point P_3 giving the normalized admittance at a distance of 0.194 wavelength from the load as

$$Y_n = 1.0 + j0.58$$

The actual admittance is $1/R_0$ times this value, or

$$0.01 + j0.0058 \text{ mhos}$$

For there to be no reflection at A (Fig. 11-11) requires that the stub present a normalized admittance to the line of $-j0.58$, so that the resultant $Y_n = 1.0 + j0$ and, hence, the impedance looking to the right at the junction is $100 + j0$ ohms. A normalized admittance $Y_n = -j0.58$ (pure susceptance) is indicated at P_4, and we note that the distance required from a short circuit ($Y_n = \pm \infty$) to obtain this value is $\frac{1}{8}$ wavelength. Thus the required stub length

$$d_2 = \frac{1}{8} = 0.167 \text{ wavelength}$$

The required distance of the stub from the load as obtained above is

$$d_1 = 0.194 \text{ wavelength}$$

438 ELECTROMAGNETICS [Chap. 11

A Smith chart[1] is illustrated in Fig. 11-13. In this chart the rectangular diagram has been transformed (see Prob. 14-11) so that all impedance values fall within the circular periphery. The chart coordinates give the normalized resistance and reactance. The SWR circles are usually not included but may be constructed as needed with a compass centered on the center point of the chart. For example, the SWR = 2 circle is shown in Fig. 11-13. The SWR is unity at the center of the

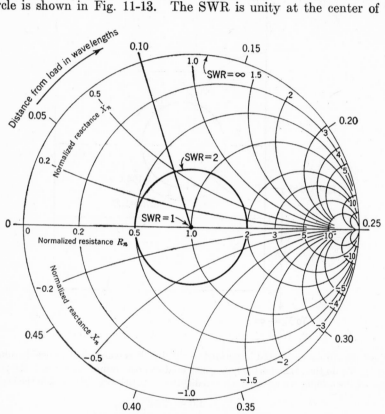

Fig. 11-13. Smith impedance chart.

chart and infinity at the periphery. The distance from the load is indicated around the periphery of the chart. For instance, at a distance of $\frac{1}{10}$ wavelength from a load for which $R_n < 1$ and $X_n = 0$ the impedance must correspond to some value on the straight line constructed from the center of the chart to the peripheral point marked 0.1 wavelength as indicated in Fig. 11-13. The fact that distance is proportional to angular position around the periphery is one of the principal advantages of this type of chart.

[1] P. H. Smith, Transmission Line Calculator, *Electronics*, **12**, 29–31, January, 1939.

An example will be given to illustrate the use of the Smith chart.

Example 2. Consider the terminated line with two short-circuited stubs portrayed in Fig. 11-14. The position at which the stubs connect to the line is fixed, as shown, but the stub lengths, d_1 and d_2, are adjustable. This kind of arrangement is called a *double-stub tuner*. The load $Z_L = 50 + j100$ ohms. The line and stubs have a characteristic impedance $Z_0 = R_0 = 100$ ohms. Find the shortest values of d_1 and d_2 such that there is no reflected wave at A.

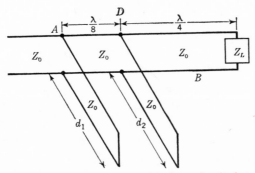

FIG. 11-14. Double-stub tuner with short-circuited stubs.

Solution. The normalized value of the load impedance is

$$Z_n = \frac{50 + j100}{100} = 0.5 + j1.0$$

The chart (Fig. 11-15) is entered at this normalized impedance as indicated by the point P_1. Constructing a SWR curve through P_1, we note that the SWR at B (Fig. 11-14) is 4.6. Next, constructing the diametric line through P_1, we locate P_2 halfway around the constant SWR circle from P_1. Thus, the normalized load admittance is $0.4 - j0.8$. Now, moving clockwise along the constant SWR circle from P_2 a distance of $\frac{1}{4}$ wavelength away from the load (toward the generator), we arrive back at P_1. Thus at the point D the normalized admittance of the main line (looking toward the load) is $0.5 + j1.0$. Since the reflection at A must be zero, we may anticipate the fact that the admittance of the main line at A (without the stub of length d_1 connected) must fall on the circle marked C_1 (Fig. 11-15). Therefore, at the junction of the stub of length d_2 the admittance must fall on this circle rotated back (counterclockwise) $\frac{1}{8}$ wavelength to the position indicated by the circle marked C_2.

The admittance added by the stub of length d_2 will cause the total admittance to move from P_1 along a constant conductance line. In order to end up on the circle C_2, we can move either to the left, arriving at P_3, or to the right, arriving at P_4. Moving to P_3 results in shorter stubs; so we will make the stub of such length as to bring the total admittance to P_3. This requires a stub admittance (pure susceptance) of

$$Y_n = -j(1.0 - 0.14) = -j0.86$$

A short-circuited stub has an infinite SWR so that the admittance at points along the stub are on the circle at the periphery of the chart. At the short circuit the admittance is infinite (point P_5). Therefore, in order to present a value

$$Y_n = -j0.86 \text{ (point } P_6)$$

the stub length must be given by

$$d_2 = 0.388 - 0.25 = 0.138 \text{ wavelength}$$

Next, moving along the constant SWR curve from P_3 to P_7, we find that the line admittance at A is $Y_n = 1.0 + j0.73$. Hence a stub admittance of $Y_n = -j0.73$ is

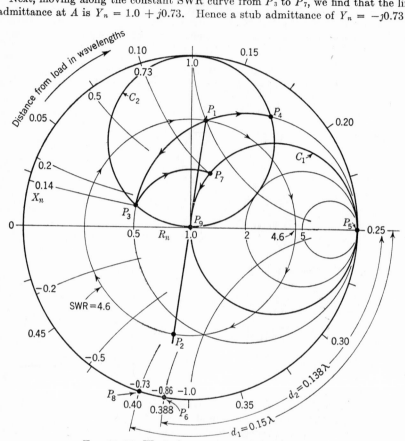

FIG. 11-15. Worked example using Smith chart.

required in order to make the total normalized admittance at A equal to $1.0 + j0$, and therefore the actual impedance at A equal to $100 + j0$ ohms. A value

$$Y_n = -j0.73$$

falls at point P_8. Therefore the length of the stub is given by

$$d_1 = 0.40 - 0.25 = 0.15 \text{ wavelength}$$

Connecting this stub brings the total admittance (or impedance) to the center of the chart (point P_9).

To summarize, the required stub lengths are

$$d_1 = 0.15 \text{ wavelength}$$
$$d_2 = 0.138 \text{ wavelength}$$

If we had moved to P_4 instead of to P_3, we would have ended up with longer stubs, namely,

$$d_1 = 0.443 \text{ wavelength}$$
$$d_2 = 0.364 \text{ wavelength}$$

11-8. One-fourth-wavelength Transformer. There are many situations where a section of transmission line $\frac{1}{4}$ wavelength long may be useful. Such a section is called a $\frac{1}{4}$-*wavelength transformer*.

Consider, for instance, that we wish to connect a transmission line of 100 ohms characteristic impedance to a load of $200 + j0$ ohms, as shown in Fig. 11-16. This may be done with a $\frac{1}{4}$-wavelength transformer of

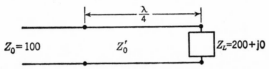

$$Z_0 = 100 \qquad Z_0' \qquad Z_L = 200 + j0$$

FIG. 11-16. One-fourth-wavelength transformer.

suitable characteristic impedance Z_0'. From (11-71) we note that when $x = \frac{1}{4}$ wavelength $(\beta x = \pi/2)$

$$Z_x = \frac{(Z_0')^2}{Z_L} \qquad \text{or} \qquad Z_0' = \sqrt{Z_L Z_x} \qquad (11\text{-}86)^1$$

In the present example $Z_L = 200 + j0$ ohms, while Z_x must be equal to $100 + j0$ ohms. It follows that

$$Z_0' = \sqrt{200 \cdot 100} = 141 \text{ ohms}$$

Therefore, a $\frac{1}{4}$-wavelength section of line of characteristic impedance $Z_0' = R_0' = 141$ ohms provides the desired transformation, eliminating a reflected wave on the 100-ohm line.

Although the reflected wave is eliminated at the design frequency (or wavelength), there will be reflection at slightly different frequencies. In other words, the transformer is a frequency-sensitive device. All transformers or matching devices are frequency-sensitive although some are more so than others. Those devices which can provide approximately the desired transformation over a considerable band of frequencies are called *broad-band* transformers, while those which can do it over only a small band are called *narrow-band* transformers.

An interesting application of the $\frac{1}{4}$-wavelength transformer principle is to the $\frac{1}{4}$-*wavelength plate*, which can be used to eliminate plane wave reflection. Thus, for example, a plane wave in air incident normally on a half space filled with a lossless dielectric medium of relative permittivity $\epsilon_r = 4$ will be partially reflected and partially transmitted. The reflec-

---

[1] Z_0' here is the *geometric mean* of Z_L and Z_x.

tion may be eliminated, as shown in Fig. 11-17, by placing a plate of $\frac{1}{4}$ wavelength thickness[1] between the air and the dielectric medium provided the plate has an intrinsic impedance

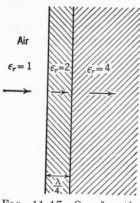

$$Z'_0 = \sqrt{Z_0 Z_1} \qquad (11\text{-}87)$$

where Z_0 = intrinsic impedance of air

Z_1 = intrinsic impedance of dielectric medium

In the present example,

$$Z_0 = \sqrt{\frac{\mu_0}{\epsilon_0}} = 376.7 \text{ ohms}$$

$$Z_1 = \frac{Z_0}{\sqrt{\epsilon_r}} = \frac{376.7}{\sqrt{4}} = 188 \text{ ohms}$$

Fig. 11-17. One-fourth-wavelength plate.

Therefore the intrinsic impedance of the plate must be

$$Z'_0 = \sqrt{Z_0 Z_1} = 266 \text{ ohms}$$

and hence its relative permittivity must be

$$\epsilon_r = \left(\frac{Z_0}{Z'_0} \right)^2 = 2$$

It is assumed in this illustration that no ferromagnetic material is present and so $\mu = \mu_0$.

PROBLEMS

11-1. A transmission line of 100 ohms characteristic resistance is terminated in an impedance of $150 - j100$ ohms. Calculate the impedance at a point on the line $\frac{3}{8}$ wavelength from the load. The calculation should be checked using an impedance chart.

11-2. The SWR on a lossless line is 5. Find the magnitude of the reflection coefficients.

11-3. A line of 100 ohms characteristic impedance is terminated in a load of $100 + j100$ ohms. Find the reflection and transmission coefficients for voltage. Also find the SWR

11-4. Confirm Eq. (11-35).

11-5. A uniform transmission line has constants

$$R = 10^{-2} \text{ ohm/meter}$$
$$G = 10^{-6} \text{ mho/meter}$$
$$L = 10^{-6} \text{ henry/meter}$$
$$C = 10^{-9} \text{ farad/meter}$$

At a frequency of 1,590 cps find (a) the characteristic impedance of the line; (b) the phase velocity of wave propagation on the line; (c) the percentage to which the voltage of a traveling wave decreases in 1 km.

Ans.: (a) $37.5\underline{/-20°}$; (b) 2.96×10^7 meters/sec; (c) 85 percent.

[1] It is to be noted that the plate thickness is measured in terms of the wavelength *in the plate.*

11-6. Find the high-frequency characteristic impedance of an air-filled coaxial transmission line having a radius ratio $b/a = 4$, where b is the inside radius of the outer conductor and a is the outside radius of the inner conductor.

11-7. Find the high-frequency characteristic impedance of a two-wire transmission line in air with a conductor radius of 1 mm and a center-to-center spacing of 5 cm.

11-8. A transmission line consists of two parallel wires of diameter d symmetrically located inside of a cylindrical conductor or shield. The wires are separated by a center-to-center distance of $2d$. The inside diameter of the outer conductor or shield is $5d$. Find the high-frequency character-istic impedance of this line for two different TEM modes of operation, (a) with the generator connected between the wires (shield not connected), as suggested in Fig. 11-18a; and (b) with the generator connected between both wires and the shield, as in Fig. 11-18b.

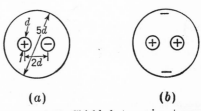

(a)   **(b)**

Fig. 11-18. Shielded two-wire transmission line with two TEM modes of operation.

11-9. The maximum electric field intensity in a coaxial cable is 10,000 volts/meter when a constant voltage of 100 volts is applied between the conductors. If the outside radius of the inner conductor is 1 cm, find the inside radius of the outer conductor.
                                          Ans.: 2.7 cm.

11-10. A coaxial transmission line consists of an inner conductor of diameter d and a symmetrically situated outer conductor having the cross section of an equilateral triangle with a side length of $2.5d$. Find the high-frequency characteristic imped-ance of this line when it is air-filled and when it is filled with polystyrene.

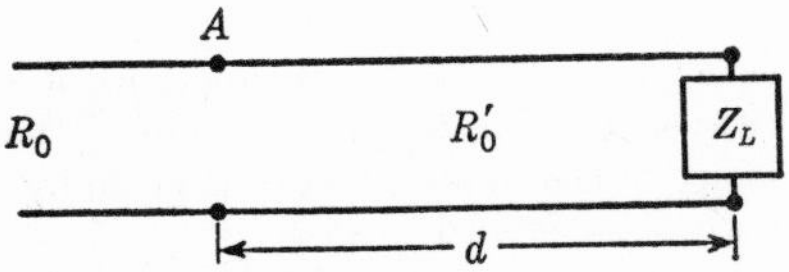

Fig. 11-19. Illustration for Prob. 11-11.

11-11. Referring to Fig. 11-19, $R_0 = 100$ ohms, and $Z_L = 150 + j50$ ohms. Find d and R_0' such that there is no reflected wave at A.
                                          Ans.: $d = 0.348\lambda$; $R_0' = 141$ ohms.

11-12. Referring to Fig. 11-20, $R_0 = 200$ ohms, $R_0' = 100$ ohms, and $Z_L = 50 + j50$ ohms. Find Z_x when the wavelength is 5 meters.

11-13. Confirm the fact that when $d_1 = 0.443$ wavelength and $d_2 = 0.364$ wavelength there is also no reflection at A for the double-stub tuner of Fig. 11-14.

11-14. Referring to the double-stub tuner of Fig. 11-21, $Z_0 = R_0 = 50$

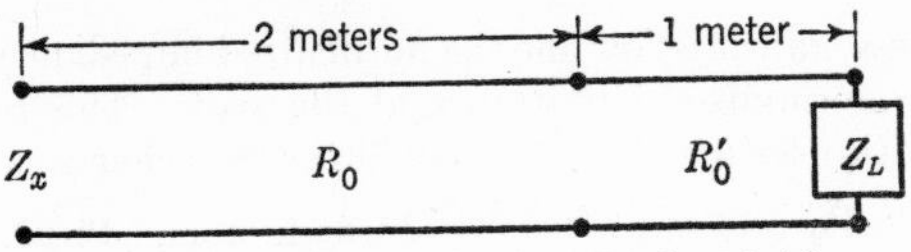

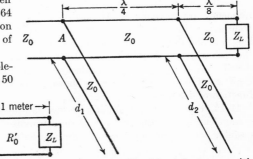

Fig. 11-20. Illustration for Prob. 11-12.

Fig. 11-21. Double-stub tuner with open-circuited stubs for Prob. 11-14.

ohms and $Z_L = 125 - j65$ ohms. Find the shortest lengths d_1 and d_2 so that there is no reflected wave at A. Note that the stubs are open-circuited.

11-15. A plane 300-Mc/sec wave is incident normally on a large slab of material having $\mu_r = 1$ and $\epsilon_r = 6$. Find the thickness (in meters) and relative permittivity required for a plate placed on the slab in order to eliminate reflection of a wave incident normally on the slab.

11-16. Show that when the series resistance R and the shunt conductance G of a transmission line are small, but not negligible, the attenuation constant may be expressed by

$$\alpha \simeq \frac{R}{2}\sqrt{\frac{C}{L}} + \frac{G}{2}\sqrt{\frac{L}{C}}$$

and the phase constant by $\beta \simeq \omega \sqrt{LC}$.

11-17. Consider that the resultant current distribution along a transmission system is the resultant of two traveling waves of different mode but of the same frequency as given by

$$I = I_0 e^{j(\omega t - \beta_0 x)} + I_1 e^{j(\omega t - \beta_1 x - \delta)}$$

where I_0 = amplitude of first wave
I_1 = amplitude of second wave
$\beta_0 = 2\pi/\lambda_0$
λ_0 = wavelength of wave 1
$\beta_1 = 2\pi/\lambda_1$
λ_1 = wavelength of wave 2
$\omega = 2\pi f$
f = frequency
δ = phase angle (arbitrary)

Confirm Marsh's result[1] that in the general case where I_0 and I_1 are functions of x and where β_0 and β_1 may be of opposite sign (waves in opposite directions) or of the same sign (waves in same direction), phase velocity of the resultant wave is given by

$$v = \frac{\omega A}{B + C}$$

where $A = I_0{}^2 + I_1{}^2 + 2I_0I_1 \cos D$
$B = I_0{}^2\beta_0 + I_1{}^2\beta_1 + I_0I_1(\beta_1 + \beta_0) \cos D$
$C = \left(I_0 \dfrac{dI_1}{dx} - I_1 \dfrac{dI_0}{dx}\right) \sin D$
$D = (\beta_1 - \beta_0)x + \delta$

11-18. Two traveling waves (different modes) of constant amplitude and the same frequency are traveling in the positive x direction with different velocities along a transmission line. Let the current amplitude due to the first wave be I_0 and its wavelength λ_0 and the amplitude due to the second wave be I_1 and its wavelength λ_1. For the case where $\beta_1 = \frac{4}{3}\beta_0$ and $I_1 = 0.5I_0$ make a graph showing the resultant current distribution $|I|$ as a function of x (abscissa) for a distance of several wavelengths. Also draw a curve on the same graph showing the velocity of the resultant wave as a function of distance.

11-19. Prove that for a uniform lossless transmission line the normalized impedance $\frac{1}{4}$ wavelength from the load equals the normalized admittance at the load. This is useful in converting impedances to admittances (or vice versa) on impedance charts.

[1] J. A. Marsh, "A Study of Phase Velocity on Long Cylindrical Conductors," Ph.D. dissertation, Department of Electrical Engineering, Ohio State University, 1949; Measured Current Distributions on Helical Antennas, *Proc. I.R.E.*, **39**, 668–675, June, 1951.

CHAPTER 12

WAVE GUIDES

12-1. Introduction. In Chap. 11 we considered the subject of two-conductor transmission lines which are capable of guiding energy from point to point in TEM modes. This chapter deals with the transmission of energy in higher-order modes. Those devices which can transmit energy *only* in higher-order modes are usually called *wave guides*.

Although waves can be guided along two-conductor transmission lines in higher-order modes, we shall not consider this type of operation except in the case of the infinite-parallel-plane transmission line, and it will be convenient to use this type of line transmitting a higher-order mode as the starting point for our discussion of wave guides.

12-2. TE Wave in the Infinite-parallel-plane Transmission Line. Consider the two conducting sheets in Fig. 12-1 representing a portion of an infinite-parallel-plane transmission line. As discussed in Chap. 11,

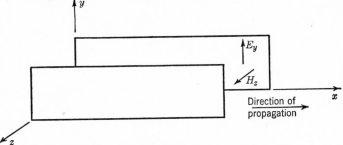

Fig. 12-1. Infinite-parallel-plane transmission line.

these sheets can transmit a TEM wave with **E** in the z direction. They may also be used to transmit higher-order modes provided the wavelength is sufficiently short.

Let us consider the higher-order mode where the electric field is everywhere in the y direction, with transmission in the x direction. That is, the electric field has only an E_y component. Since E_y is transverse to the direction of transmission, this mode may be designated as a *transverse electric*, or TE, mode. Although **E** is everywhere transverse, **H** has longitudinal, as well as transverse, components. Assuming perfectly conducting sheets, boundary conditions require that E_y vanish *at the*

445

sheets. However, E_y need not be zero at points removed from the sheets. It is possible to determine the properties of a TE wave of the type under discussion by regarding it as made up of two plane TEM waves reflected obliquely back and forth between the sheets.

First, however, let us consider the situation that exists when two plane TEM waves of the same frequency traveling in free space intersect at an angle, as suggested in Fig. 12-2. It is assumed that the waves are linearly polarized with **E** normal to the page. Wave fronts or surfaces of constant phase are indicated for the two waves.

The solid lines (marked "max") show where the field is a maximum with **E** directed out from the page. These lines may be regarded as

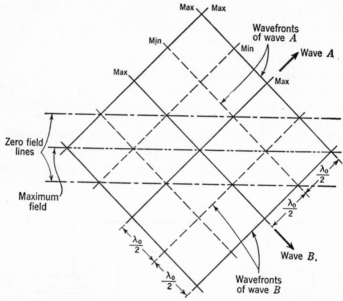

FIG. 12-2. Two plane TEM waves traveling in free space in different directions.

representing the crests of the waves. The dashed lines (marked "min") show where the field is a minimum, that is, where **E** is of maximum absolute magnitude but directed into the page. These lines may be regarded as representing the troughs of the waves. Now wherever the crest of one wave coincides with the trough of the other wave there is cancellation, and the resultant **E** at that point is zero. Wherever crest coincides with crest or trough with trough there is reinforcement, and the resultant **E** at that point doubles. Referring to Fig. 12-2, it is therefore apparent that at all points along the dash-dot lines the field is always zero, while along the line indicated by dash and double dots the field will be reinforced and will have its maximum value.

Since **E** is zero along the dash-dot lines, boundary conditions will be satisfied at plane, perfectly conducting sheets placed along these lines normal to the page. The waves, however, will now be reflected at the sheets with an angle of reflection equal to the angle of incidence, and waves incident from the outside will not penetrate to the region between the sheets. But if two plane waves (A and B) are launched between the sheets from the left end, they will travel to the right via multiple reflections between the sheets, as suggested by the wave paths in Fig. 12-3a.

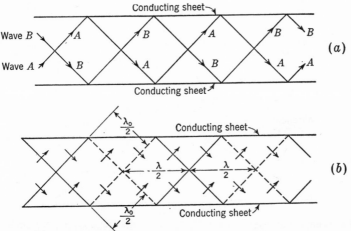

FIG. 12-3. (a) Wave paths and (b) wave fronts between infinite parallel conducting sheets acting as a wave guide.

The wave fronts (normal to the wave paths) for these waves are as indicated in Fig. 12-3b. Here the field between the sheets is the same as in Fig. 12-2, with solid lines indicating that **E** is outward (a maximum) and dashed lines that **E** is inward (a minimum). At the sheets the resultant **E** is always zero.

Although the two component waves we have been considering are plane TEM-mode waves, the *resultant wave* belongs to a higher-order TE mode. It is an important property of the TE-mode wave that it will not be transmitted unless the wavelength is sufficiently short. The critical wavelength at which transmission is no longer possible is called the *cutoff wavelength*. It is possible by a very simple analysis, which will now be given, to calculate the cutoff wavelength as a function of the sheet spacing.

Referring to Fig. 12-4, let the TE wave be resolved into two component waves traveling in the x' and x'' directions. These directions make an angle θ with respect to the conducting sheets (and the x axis). The electric field is in the y direction (normal to the page). The spacing between the sheets is b. From Fig. 12-4 we note that E_y' of the x' wave and E_y'' of the x'' wave cancel at a point such as A at the conducting sheet and reinforce at point B midway between the sheets provided that the distance

$$CB = BD = C'B = \frac{\lambda_0}{4} \qquad (12\text{-}1)$$

where λ_0 = wavelength of TEM wave in unbounded space filled with same medium as between the sheets. Thus, if E_y'' is into the page (negative) at the point C and E_y' is out of the page (positive) at the point D, the two waves will cancel at A. They will also reinforce at B since by the

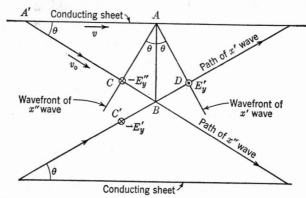

Fig. 12-4. Component waves between infinite-parallel-plane conducting sheets acting as a wave guide.

time the field $-E_y''$ moves from C to B the field $-E_y'$ will have moved from C' to B. More generally we may write

$$CB = \frac{n\lambda_0}{4} \qquad (12\text{-}2)$$

where n = an integer $(1, 2, 3, \ldots)$.[1] It follows that

$$AB \sin \theta = \frac{b}{2} \sin \theta = \frac{n\lambda_0}{4} \qquad (12\text{-}3)$$

or

$$\lambda_0 = \frac{2b}{n} \sin \theta \qquad (12\text{-}4)$$

where λ_0 = wavelength (meters)
$\quad b$ = spacing of conducting sheets (meters)
$\quad n$ = 1, 2, 3, . . .
$\quad \theta$ = angle between component wave direction and conducting sheets

According to (12-4) we note that for a given sheet separation b the longest wavelength that can be transmitted in a higher-order mode occurs when

[1] For n even, the field halfway between the sheets is zero, with maximum fields either side of the center line.

$\theta = 90°$. This wavelength is the cutoff wavelength λ_{oc} of the higher-order mode. Thus, for $\theta = 90°$,

$$\lambda_{oc} = \frac{2b}{n} \qquad (12\text{-}5)$$

Each value of n corresponds to a particular higher-order mode. When $n = 1$, we find that

$$\lambda_{oc} = 2b \qquad (12\text{-}6)$$

This is the longest wavelength which can be transmitted between the sheets in a higher-order mode. That is, the spacing b must be at least $\frac{1}{2}$ wavelength for a higher-order mode to be transmitted.

When $n = 1$, the wave is said to be the lowest of the higher-order types. When $n = 2$, we have the next higher-order mode and for this case

$$\lambda_{oc} = b \qquad (12\text{-}7)$$

Thus the spacing b must be at least 1 wavelength for the $n = 2$ mode to be transmitted. For $n = 3$, $\lambda_{oc} = \frac{2}{3}b$, etc.

Introducing (12-5) in (12-4) yields

$$\sin \theta = \frac{\lambda_0}{\lambda_{oc}} \qquad (12\text{-}8)$$

or

$$\theta = \arcsin \frac{\lambda_0}{\lambda_{oc}} \qquad (12\text{-}9)$$

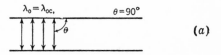

(a)

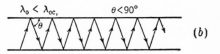

(b)

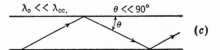

(c)

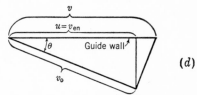

(d)

FIG. 12-5. (a, b, c) Reflection of waves between walls of wave guide. (d) Triangle showing relative magnitude of phase velocity v, group velocity u, and energy velocity v_{en} in the guide, to phase velocity v_0 of the component wave (equal to phase velocity of wave in an unbounded medium).

Hence, at cutoff for any mode ($\lambda_0 = \lambda_{oc}$) the angle $\theta = 90°$. Under these conditions the component waves for this mode are reflected back and forth between the sheets, as in Fig. 12-5a, and do not progress in the x direction. Hence there is a standing wave between the sheets, and no energy is propagated. If the wavelength λ_0 is slightly less than λ_{oc}, θ is less than $90°$ and the wave progresses in the x direction although making many reflections from the sheets, as in Fig. 12-5b. As the wavelength is further reduced, θ becomes less, as in Fig. 12-5c, until at very short wavelengths the transmission for this mode approaches the conditions in an unbounded medium.

It is apparent from Fig. 12-4 that a constant phase point of the TE wave moves in the x direction with a velocity v that is greater than that of the component waves. The phase velocity v_0 of the component waves is the same as for a wave in an unbounded medium of the same kind as fills the space between the conducting sheets. That is,

$$v_0 = \frac{1}{\sqrt{\mu\epsilon}} \qquad \text{meters/sec} \qquad (12\text{-}10)$$

where μ = permeability of medium (henrys/meter)
ϵ = permittivity of medium (farads/meter)
From Fig. 12-4 it follows that

$$\frac{v_0}{v} = \frac{A'C}{A'A} = \cos\theta \qquad (12\text{-}11)$$

or

$$v = \frac{v_0}{\cos\theta} = \frac{1}{\sqrt{\mu\epsilon}\,\cos\theta} \qquad \text{meters/sec} \qquad (12\text{-}12)$$

According to (12-12) the phase velocity v of a TE wave approaches an infinite value as the wavelength is increased toward the cutoff value. On the other hand, v approaches the phase velocity v_0 in an unbounded medium as the wavelength becomes very short. Thus, the phase velocity of a higher-order mode wave in the guide formed by the sheets is always equal to or greater than the velocity in an unbounded medium. The energy, however, is propagated with the velocity of the zigzag component wave. Thus $v_{en} = v_0 \cos\theta$. Accordingly, the energy velocity v_{en} is always equal to or less than the velocity in an unbounded medium.[1] When, for instance, the wavelength approaches cutoff, the phase velocity becomes infinite, while the energy velocity approaches zero. This is another way of saying that the wave degenerates into a standing wave and does not propagate energy at the cutoff wavelength or longer wavelengths. The relative magnitudes of the various velocities are shown by the triangle in Fig. 12-5d.

Since the wavelength is proportional to the phase velocity, the wavelength λ of the higher-order mode in the guide is given in terms of the wavelength λ_0 in an unbounded medium by

$$\lambda = \frac{\lambda_0}{\cos\theta} \qquad (12\text{-}13)$$

[1] The waveguide behaves like a lossless dispersive medium. It follows that

$$u = v_{en} = \frac{v_0^2}{v},$$

where u = group velocity, v_{en} = energy velocity, v_0 = phase velocity in an unbounded medium, v = phase velocity in guide.

The infinite-parallel-plane transmission line we have been considering is obviously not a type that can be applied in practice.   Actual wave guides for higher-order modes usually take the form of a single hollow conductor.   The hollow rectangular guide is a common form.   The above analysis for the infinite-parallel-plane transmission line is of practical value, however, because the properties of TE-mode waves, such as are discussed above, are the same in a rectangular guide of width b as between two infinite parallel planes separated by a distance b.   This follows from the fact that if infinitely conducting sheets are introduced normal to **E** between the parallel planes the field is not disturbed.   Thus,

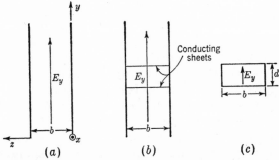

FIG. 12-6. (a) Infinite-parallel-plane transmission line acting as a wave guide for TE wave. **E** is in y direction. (b) Sheets introduced normal to E_y. (c) Hollow rectangular wave guide.

if a TE-mode wave with electric field in the y direction is traveling in the x direction as indicated in Fig. 12-6a, the introduction of sheets normal to E_y, as in Fig. 12-6b, does not disturb the field.   The conducting sheets now form a complete enclosure of rectangular shape.   Proceeding a step further, let the sheets beyond the rectangular enclosure be removed, leaving the hollow rectangular wave guide shown in Fig. 12-6c.   The cutoff wavelengths for the TE modes as given by (12-5) for the infinite-parallel-plane line also apply for this rectangular guide if the width b is the same as the spacing between the planes.   For the type of TE modes we have thus far considered (E_y component only) the dimension d (Fig. 12-6c) is not critical.

Although the above simple analysis yields information about cutoff wavelength, phase velocity, etc., it gives little information concerning the field configuration and fails to consider more complex higher-order modes in which, for example, **E** is transverse but with both y and z components. To obtain complete information concerning the waves in a hollow wave guide, we shall solve the wave equation subject to the boundary conditions for the guide.   This is done for the hollow rectangular guide in the next section.

12-3. The Hollow Rectangular Wave Guide.[1] In Sec. 12-2 certain properties of an infinite-parallel-plane transmission line and of a hollow rectangular guide were obtained by considering that the higher mode wave consists of two plane TEM component waves and then applying the boundary condition that the tangential component of the resultant **E** must vanish at the perfectly conducting walls of the guide. This method may be extended to provide more complete information about the waves in a hollow wave guide. However, in this section we shall use another approach, which involves the solution of the wave equation subject to the above-mentioned boundary condition for the tangential component of **E**.

In this method we start with Maxwell's equations and develop a wave equation in rectangular coordinates. This choice of coordinates is made in order that the boundary conditions for the rectangular guide can be easily applied later. The restrictions are then introduced of harmonic variation with respect to time and a wave traveling in the x direction (direction of guide). Next a choice is made of the type of higher-order mode to be analyzed. Thus we may consider a transverse electric (TE) wave for which $E_x = 0$ or a transverse magnetic (TM) wave for which $H_x = 0$. If, for example, we select the TE type, we know that there must be an H_x component since a higher mode wave always has a longitudinal field component and E_x being zero means that H_x must have a value. It is then convenient to write the remaining field components in terms of H_x. Next a solution of a scalar wave equation in H_x is obtained that fits the boundary conditions of the rectangular guide. This solution is substituted back into the equations for the other field components (E_y, E_z, H_y, and H_z). In this way we end up with a set of equations giving the variation of each field component with respect to space and time. This method of solution is very general and may be applied to many problems.

We shall develop the method in detail for TE waves in a hollow rectangular wave guide. First, however, the procedure will be outlined in step form as follows:

1. Start with Maxwell's equations.
2. Apply restriction of harmonic variation with respect to time.
3. Apply restriction of harmonic variation and attenuation with respect to x.
4. Select the type or mode of wave (TE in this case; so $E_x = 0$ and $H_x \neq 0$).

---

[1] L. J. Chu and W. L. Barrow, Electromagnetic Waves in Hollow Metal Tubes of Rectangular Cross Section, *Proc. I.R.E.*, **26**, 1520–1555, December, 1938. See also references in Bibliography.

5. Find equations for other four field components (E_y, E_z, H_y, and H_z) in terms of H_x.
6. Develop scalar wave equation for H_x.
7. Solve this wave equation for H_x subject to boundary conditions of wave guide.
8. Substitute H_x back into equations of step 5, giving a set of equations expressing each field component as a function of space and time. This constitutes the complete solution of the problem.

Beginning now with step 1 of the procedure, we have from Maxwell's curl equations in rectangular coordinates the following set of six scalar equations:

$$\frac{\partial H_z}{\partial y} - \frac{\partial H_y}{\partial z} - \sigma E_x - \epsilon \frac{\partial E_x}{\partial t} = 0 \tag{12-14}$$

$$\frac{\partial H_x}{\partial z} - \frac{\partial H_z}{\partial x} - \sigma E_y - \epsilon \frac{\partial E_y}{\partial t} = 0 \tag{12-15}$$

$$\frac{\partial H_y}{\partial x} - \frac{\partial H_x}{\partial y} - \sigma E_z - \epsilon \frac{\partial E_z}{\partial t} = 0 \tag{12-16}$$

$$\frac{\partial E_z}{\partial y} - \frac{\partial E_y}{\partial z} + \mu \frac{\partial H_x}{\partial t} = 0 \tag{12-17}$$

$$\frac{\partial E_x}{\partial z} - \frac{\partial E_z}{\partial x} + \mu \frac{\partial H_y}{\partial t} = 0 \tag{12-18}$$

$$\frac{\partial E_y}{\partial x} - \frac{\partial E_x}{\partial y} + \mu \frac{\partial H_z}{\partial t} = 0 \tag{12-19}$$

From Maxwell's divergence equations in rectangular coordinates we have in space free from charge the following two scalar equations:

$$\frac{\partial E_x}{\partial x} + \frac{\partial E_y}{\partial y} + \frac{\partial E_z}{\partial z} = 0 \tag{12-20}$$

$$\frac{\partial H_x}{\partial x} + \frac{\partial H_y}{\partial y} + \frac{\partial H_z}{\partial z} = 0 \tag{12-21}$$

Let us assume now that any field component varies harmonically with time and distance and also may attenuate with distance. Thus, confining our attention to waves traveling in the positive x direction, we have, for instance, that the field component E_y is expressed by

$$E_y = E_1 e^{j\omega t - \gamma x} \tag{12-22}$$

where γ = propagation constant = $\alpha + j\beta$. Introducing the restriction of (12-22) into the equations, (12-14) through (12-21) reduce to

$$\frac{\partial H_z}{\partial y} - \frac{\partial H_y}{\partial z} - (\sigma + j\omega\epsilon)E_x = 0 \tag{12-23}$$

$$\frac{\partial H_x}{\partial z} + \gamma H_z - (\sigma + j\omega\epsilon)E_y = 0 \tag{12-24}$$

$$-\gamma H_y - \frac{\partial H_z}{\partial y} - (\sigma + j\omega\epsilon)E_z = 0 \qquad (12\text{-}25)$$

$$\frac{\partial E_z}{\partial y} - \frac{\partial E_y}{\partial z} + j\omega\mu H_x = 0 \qquad (12\text{-}26)$$

$$\frac{\partial E_x}{\partial z} + \gamma E_z + j\omega\mu H_y = 0 \qquad (12\text{-}27)$$

$$-\gamma E_y - \frac{\partial E_x}{\partial y} + j\omega\mu H_z = 0 \qquad (12\text{-}28)$$

$$-\gamma E_x + \frac{\partial E_y}{\partial y} + \frac{\partial E_z}{\partial z} = 0 \qquad (12\text{-}29)$$

$$-\gamma H_x + \frac{\partial H_y}{\partial y} + \frac{\partial H_z}{\partial z} = 0 \qquad (12\text{-}30)$$

The above eight equations may be simplified by introducing a series impedance Z and shunt admittance Y, analogous to a transmission line (see Table 11-2), where

$$Z = -j\omega\mu \qquad \text{ohms/meter} \qquad (12\text{-}31)$$
$$Y = \sigma + j\omega\epsilon \qquad \text{mhos/meter} \qquad (12\text{-}32)$$

Substituting these relations in (12-23) through (12-30) yields

$$\frac{\partial H_z}{\partial y} - \frac{\partial H_y}{\partial z} - YE_x = 0 \qquad (12\text{-}33)$$

$$\frac{\partial H_x}{\partial z} + \gamma H_z - YE_y = 0 \qquad (12\text{-}34)$$

$$-\gamma H_y - \frac{\partial H_x}{\partial y} - YE_z = 0 \qquad (12\text{-}35)$$

$$\frac{\partial E_z}{\partial y} - \frac{\partial E_y}{\partial z} - ZH_x = 0 \qquad (12\text{-}36)$$

$$\frac{\partial E_x}{\partial z} + \gamma E_z - ZH_y = 0 \qquad (12\text{-}37)$$

$$-\gamma E_y - \frac{\partial E_x}{\partial y} - ZH_z = 0 \qquad (12\text{-}38)$$

$$-\gamma E_x + \frac{\partial E_y}{\partial y} + \frac{\partial E_z}{\partial z} = 0 \qquad (12\text{-}39)$$

$$-\gamma H_x + \frac{\partial H_y}{\partial y} + \frac{\partial H_z}{\partial z} = 0 \qquad (12\text{-}40)$$

These are the general equations for the steady-state field of a wave traveling in the x direction. No restrictions have as yet been made as to the mode of the wave or the shape of the guide. We are now ready to proceed with step 4 and introduce the condition for a TE wave that $E_x = 0$. The equations then reduce to

$$\frac{\partial H_z}{\partial y} - \frac{\partial H_y}{\partial z} = 0 \tag{12-41}$$

$$\frac{\partial H_x}{\partial z} + \gamma H_z - Y E_y = 0 \tag{12-42}$$

$$-\gamma H_y - \frac{\partial H_x}{\partial y} - Y E_z = 0 \tag{12-43}$$

$$\frac{\partial E_z}{\partial y} - \frac{\partial E_y}{\partial z} - Z H_x = 0 \tag{12-44}$$

$$\gamma E_z - Z H_y = 0 \tag{12-45}$$
$$-\gamma E_y - Z H_z = 0 \tag{12-46}$$
$$\frac{\partial E_y}{\partial y} + \frac{\partial E_z}{\partial z} = 0 \tag{12-47}$$

$$-\gamma H_x + \frac{\partial H_y}{\partial y} + \frac{\partial H_z}{\partial z} = 0 \tag{12-48}$$

Proceeding to step 5, let us rewrite these equations so that each field component is expressed in terms of H_x. To do this, we note from (12-45) and (12-46) that

$$\frac{E_z}{H_y} = -\frac{E_y}{H_z} = \frac{Z}{\gamma} \qquad \text{ohms} \tag{12-49}$$

The ratio E_z/H_y or E_y/H_z is a quantity which corresponds, in the case of a wave guide, to the characteristic impedance of a transmission line. Since (12-49) involves only transverse field components, it may be called the *transverse impedance* Z_{yz} of the wave guide.[1] Thus

$$Z_{yz} = \frac{E_y}{H_z} = -\frac{E_z}{H_y} = -\frac{Z}{\gamma} = \frac{j\omega\mu}{\gamma} \qquad \text{ohms} \tag{12-50}$$

Introducing (12-50) into (12-43) and solving for H_y yields

$$H_y = \frac{-1}{\gamma - Y Z_{yz}} \frac{\partial H_x}{\partial y} \tag{12-51}$$

In a like manner we have, from (12-42),

$$H_z = \frac{-1}{\gamma - Y Z_{yz}} \frac{\partial H_x}{\partial z} \tag{12-52}$$

Now, substituting (12-52) into (12-50), we obtain

$$E_y = \frac{-Z_{yz}}{\gamma - Y Z_{yz}} \frac{\partial H_x}{\partial z} \tag{12-53}$$

and substituting (12-51) into (12-50)

$$E_z = \frac{Z_{yz}}{\gamma - Y Z_{yz}} \frac{\partial H_x}{\partial y} \tag{12-54}$$

[1] Z_{yz} is also often called the "characteristic impedance" (of the guide).

Equations (12-51) through (12-54) express the four transverse field components in terms of H_x. This completes step 5.

Proceeding now to step 6, we can obtain a wave equation in H_x by taking the y derivative of (12-51), the z derivative of (12-52), and substituting both in (12-48). This yields

$$-\gamma H_x - \frac{1}{\gamma - YZ_{yz}}\left(\frac{\partial^2 H_x}{\partial y^2} + \frac{\partial^2 H_x}{\partial z^2}\right) = 0 \qquad (12\text{-}55)$$

or

$$\frac{\partial^2 H_x}{\partial y^2} + \frac{\partial^2 H_x}{\partial z^2} + \gamma(\gamma - YZ_{yz})H_x = 0 \qquad (12\text{-}56)$$

Putting $k^2 = \gamma(\gamma - YZ_{yz})$, (12-56) reduces to

$$\frac{\partial^2 H_x}{\partial y^2} + \frac{\partial^2 H_x}{\partial z^2} + k^2 H_x = 0 \qquad (12\text{-}57)$$

This is a partial differential equation of the second order and first degree. It is a scalar wave equation in H_x. It applies to a TE wave in a guide of any cross-sectional shape. This completes step 6.

Step 7 is to find a solution of (12-57) that satisfies the boundary conditions for the wave guide under consideration, which is a hollow rectangular

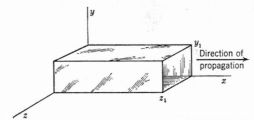

Fig. 12-7. Coordinates for hollow rectangular wave guide.

type as shown in Fig. 12-7. The width of the guide is z_1, and the height is y_1. Assuming that the walls are perfectly conducting, the tangential component of **E** must vanish at the guide surface. Thus, at the side walls E_y must be zero, and at the top and bottom surfaces E_z must be zero. The problem now is to find a solution of (12-57) subject to these boundary conditions. The method of "separation of variables" may be employed in obtaining the solution. Thus, H_x in (12-57) is a function of y and z. Hence we may seek a solution of the form

$$H_x = YZ \qquad (12\text{-}58)$$

where Y = a function of y only, that is, $Y = f(y)$
   Z = a function of z only[1]

---

[1] Sometimes the notation $f(y)$ or $Y(y)$ is used to represent a function of y only, and $F(z)$ or $Z(z)$ a function of z only. However, to simplify notation, the symbols Y and

Substituting (12-58) in (12-57) gives

$$Z \frac{d^2Y}{dy^2} + Y \frac{d^2Z}{dz^2} + k^2 YZ = 0 \qquad (12\text{-}59)$$

Dividing by YZ to separate variables,

$$\frac{1}{Y} \frac{d^2Y}{dy^2} + \frac{1}{Z} \frac{d^2Z}{dz^2} = -k^2 \qquad (12\text{-}60)$$

The first term is a function of y alone, the second term is a function of z alone, while k^2 is a constant. For the two terms (each involving a different independent variable) to equal a constant requires that each term be a constant. Thus we can write

$$\frac{1}{Y} \frac{d^2Y}{dy^2} = -A_1 \qquad (12\text{-}61)$$

and

$$\frac{1}{Z} \frac{d^2Z}{dz^2} = -A_2 \qquad (12\text{-}62)$$

where A_1 and A_2 are constants. It follows that

$$A_1 + A_2 = k^2 \qquad (12\text{-}63)$$

Equations (12-61) and (12-62) each involves but one independent variable. A solution of (12-61) is

$$Y = c_1 \sin b_1 y \qquad (12\text{-}64)$$

Substituting (12-64) in (12-61) yields

$$b_1 = \sqrt{A_1} \qquad (12\text{-}65)$$

Hence (12-64) is a solution provided (12-65) is fulfilled. Another solution is

$$Y = c_2 \cos b_1 y \qquad (12\text{-}66)$$

If (12-64) and (12-66) are each a solution for Y, their sum is also a solution, or

$$Y = c_1 \sin \sqrt{A_1}\, y + c_2 \cos \sqrt{A_1}\, y \qquad (12\text{-}67)$$

In the same manner a solution may be written for Z as

$$Z = c_3 \sin \sqrt{A_2}\, z + c_4 \cos \sqrt{A_2}\, z \qquad (12\text{-}68)$$

Substituting (12-67) and (12-68) into (12-58), we obtain the solution for H_x as

$$H_x = c_1 c_3 \sin \sqrt{A_1}\, y \sin \sqrt{A_2}\, z + c_2 c_3 \cos \sqrt{A_1}\, y \sin \sqrt{A_2}\, z$$
$$+ c_1 c_4 \sin \sqrt{A_1}\, y \cos \sqrt{A_2}\, z + c_2 c_4 \cos \sqrt{A_1}\, y \cos \sqrt{A_2}\, z \qquad (12\text{-}69)$$

Z are used in Eqs. (12-58) to (12-68), inclusive, to indicate functions only of y or z, respectively. Y and Z in these equations should not be confused with admittance and impedance, for which these symbols are also used.

Equation (12-69) is a solution for H_x, but any term is also a solution. Taking the last term as the solution, we note that on introducing this solution for H_x into (12-53) and (12-54) the boundary conditions for the hollow rectangular guide can be satisfied provided that

$$\sqrt{A_1} = \frac{n\pi}{y_1} \tag{12-70}$$

and

$$\sqrt{A_2} = \frac{m\pi}{z_1} \tag{12-71}$$

where m and n are integers $(0, 1, 2, 3, \ldots)$.   They may be equal to the same integer or to different integers.   The solution for H_x now assumes the form

$$H_x = H_0 \cos \frac{n\pi y}{y_1} \cos \frac{m\pi z}{z_1} \tag{12-72}$$

where $H_0 = c_2 c_4 = $ a constant.   If (12-72) is multiplied by a constant factor, it is still a solution.   That is, the factor should not involve y or z although it may involve x and the time (t).   Accordingly, (12-72) may be multiplied by the exponential factor in (12-22) since this gives the variation assumed for the fields with respect to x and t.   The complete solution for H_x then becomes

$$H_x = H_0 \cos \frac{n\pi y}{y_1} \cos \frac{m\pi z}{z_1} e^{j\omega t - \gamma x} \tag{12-73}$$

This completes step 7.   To perform step 8, Eq. (12-73) is substituted into (12-51) through (12-54), giving the solutions for the transverse field components as

$$H_y = \frac{\gamma H_0}{k^2} \frac{n\pi}{y_1} \sin \frac{n\pi y}{y_1} \cos \frac{m\pi z}{z_1} e^{j\omega t - \gamma x} \tag{12-74}$$

$$H_z = \frac{\gamma H_0}{k^2} \frac{m\pi}{z_1} \cos \frac{n\pi y}{y_1} \sin \frac{m\pi z}{z_1} e^{j\omega t - \gamma x} \tag{12-75}$$

$$E_y = \frac{\gamma Z_{yz} H_0}{k^2} \frac{m\pi}{z_1} \cos \frac{n\pi y}{y_1} \sin \frac{m\pi z}{z_1} e^{j\omega t - \gamma x} \tag{12-76}$$

$$E_z = - \frac{\gamma Z_{yz} H_0}{k^2} \frac{n\pi}{y_1} \sin \frac{n\pi y}{y_1} \cos \frac{m\pi z}{z_1} e^{j\omega t - \gamma x} \tag{12-77}$$

Equations (12-73) to (12-77), inclusive, to which may be added $E_x = 0$, are the solutions that we have sought for the field components of a TE mode in a hollow rectangular guide of width z_1 and height y_1.   This completes step 8.

Turning our attention now to an interpretation of the solutions for the field components, let us consider the significance of the integers m and n. It is apparent that for $m = 1$ and $n = 0$ we have only three field components H_x, H_z, and E_y and, further, that each of these components has no variation with respect to y but each has a half-cycle variation with respect to z. For example, E_y has a sinusoidal variation across the guide (in the z direction), being a maximum in the center and zero at the walls, and has no variation as a function of y.

If $m = 2$, there is a variation of two half cycles (full cycle variation) of each field component as a function of z. When $n = 1$, there is a half-cycle variation of each field component with respect to y. Hence we may conclude that the value of m or n indicates the number of half-cycle variations of each field component with respect to z and y, respectively. Each combination of m and n values represents a different field configuration or mode in the guide. Since we are dealing here with TE modes, it is convenient to designate them by adding the subscript mn so that, in general, any TE mode can be designated by the notation TE_{mn}, where m = number of half-cycle variations in the z direction (usually taken as the larger transverse dimension of the guide) and n = number of half-cycle variations in the y direction (usually taken as the smaller transverse dimension of the guide).

Thus, for a TE_{10} mode $m = 1$, and $n = 0$, and we have, as mentioned above, only three components E_y, H_x, and H_z that are not zero. The six field components for the TE_{10} mode are

$$\left.\begin{aligned}
E_x &= 0 \\
E_y &= \frac{\gamma Z_{yz} H_0}{k^2} \frac{\pi}{z_1} \sin \frac{\pi z}{z_1} e^{j\omega t - \gamma x} \\
E_z &= 0 \\
H_x &= H_0 \qquad\quad \cos \frac{\pi z}{z_1} e^{j\omega t - \gamma x} \\
H_y &= 0 \\
H_z &= \frac{\gamma H_0}{k^2} \frac{\pi}{z_1} \qquad \sin \frac{\pi z}{z_1} e^{j\omega t - \gamma x}
\end{aligned}\right\} \qquad (12\text{-}78)$$

The variation of these components as a function of z is portrayed in Fig. 12-8a. There is no variation with respect to y. This mode has the longest cutoff wavelength of any higher order mode, and hence the lowest frequency of transmission in a hollow rectangular wave guide must be in the TE_{10} mode.

The variation of the field components as a function of z for the TE_{20} mode ($m = 2$, $n = 0$) is shown in Fig. 12-8b.

In Fig. 12-9a the field configuration of the TE_{10} mode is illustrated for a guide cross section and in Fig. 12-9b for a longitudinal section of the guide (top view). The field configuration for a TE_{20} mode is shown in cross section in Fig. 12-9c and in longitudinal section (top view) in Fig. 12-9d.

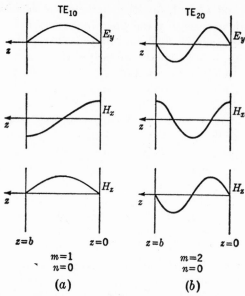

FIG. 12-8. Variation of field components for TE_{10} and TE_{20} modes in a hollow rectangular wave guide. (Wave traveling out of page.)

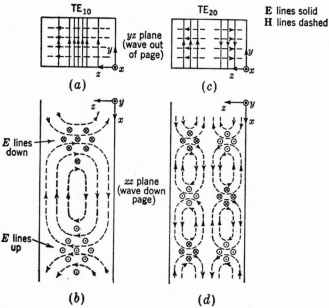

FIG. 12-9. Field configurations for TE_{10} and TE_{20} modes in a hollow rectangular wave guide.

Consider next the TE_{11} mode ($m = 1$, $n = 1$). The field components are given by

$$E_x = 0$$

$$E_y = \frac{\gamma Z_{yz} H_0}{k^2} \frac{\pi}{z_1} \quad \cos\frac{\pi y}{y_1} \sin\frac{\pi z}{z_1} e^{j\omega t - \gamma x}$$

$$E_z = -\frac{\gamma Z_{yz} H_0}{k^2} \frac{\pi}{y_1} \sin\frac{\pi y}{y_1} \cos\frac{\pi z}{z_1} e^{j\omega t - \gamma x}$$

$$H_x = H_0 \qquad\qquad \cos\frac{\pi y}{y_1} \cos\frac{\pi z}{z_1} e^{j\omega t - \gamma x} \qquad (12\text{-}79)$$

$$H_y = \frac{\gamma H_0}{k^2} \frac{\pi}{y_1} \qquad \sin\frac{\pi y}{y_1} \cos\frac{\pi z}{z_1} e^{j\omega t - \gamma x}$$

$$H_z = \frac{\gamma H_0}{k^2} \frac{\pi}{z_1} \qquad \cos\frac{\pi y}{y_1} \sin\frac{\pi z}{z_1} e^{j\omega t - \gamma x}$$

For this mode five field components have a value, only E_x being everywhere and always zero. The variation of the five field components with respect to z and y is shown in Fig. 12-10. It is assumed that the guide has a square cross section ($y_1 = z_1$). The field configuration for the TE_{11} mode in a square guide is illustrated in cross section in Fig. 12-11a and in longitudinal section (side view) in Fig. 12-11b.

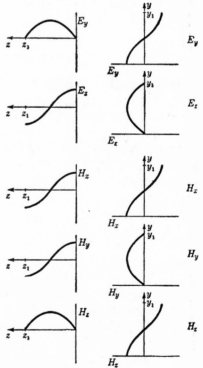

The solution we have obtained tells us what modes are possible in the hollow rectangular wave guide. However, the particular mode or modes that are actually present in any case depend on the guide dimensions, the method of exciting the guide, and the irregularities or discontinuities in the guide. The resultant field in the guide is equal to the sum of the fields of all modes present.

Returning now to a consideration of the general significance of the solution, we have from (12-63), (12-70), and (12-71) that

$$\left(\frac{n\pi}{y_1}\right)^2 + \left(\frac{m\pi}{z_1}\right)^2 = k^2 \quad (12\text{-}80)$$

Fig. 12-10. Variation of field components for TE_{11} mode in a square wave guide. (Wave traveling out of page.)

462 ELECTROMAGNETICS [Chap. 12

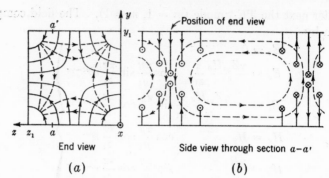

End view   Side view through section a–a'

(a) (b)

Fig. 12-11. Field configurations for TE_{11} mode in a square wave guide. **E** lines are solid, and **H** lines are dashed.

From (12-56), (12-31) and (12-32) k^2 is given by

$$k^2 = \gamma^2 - j\omega\mu(\sigma + j\omega\epsilon) \qquad (12\text{-}81)$$

Assuming a lossless dielectric medium in the guide, we can put $\sigma = 0$. Then equating (12-80) and (12-81) and solving for γ yields

$$\gamma = \sqrt{\left(\frac{n\pi}{y_1}\right)^2 + \left(\frac{m\pi}{z_1}\right)^2 - \omega^2\mu\epsilon} \qquad (12\text{-}82)$$

At sufficiently low frequencies the last term in (12-82) is smaller than the sum of the first two terms under the square-root sign. It follows that for this condition γ is real and, therefore, that the wave is attenuated. Under this condition it is said that the wave (or mode) is not propagated.

At sufficiently high frequencies the last term in (12-82) is larger than the sum of the first two terms under the square-root sign. Under this condition γ is imaginary, and therefore the wave is propagated without attenuation.

At some intermediate frequency the right-hand side of (12-82) is zero, and hence $\gamma = 0$. This frequency is called the *cutoff frequency* for the mode under consideration. At frequencies higher than cutoff this mode propagates without attenuation, while at frequencies lower than cutoff the mode is attenuated.

To summarize:

At low frequencies, ω small, γ real, guide opaque

At cutoff, ω intermediate, $\gamma = 0$, transition condition

At high frequencies, ω large, γ imaginary, guide transparent

Referring to (12-82), it is to be noted that $\sqrt{\omega^2\mu\epsilon}$ is equal to the phase constant β_0 for a wave traveling in an unbounded medium of the same dielectric material as fills the guide. Thus we can write

$$\gamma = \sqrt{k^2 - \beta^2_0} \qquad \text{reciprocal meters} \qquad (12\text{-}83)$$

where $\beta_0 = \sqrt{\omega^2 \mu \epsilon} = 2\pi/\lambda_0$ = phase constant in an unbounded medium

λ_0 = wavelength in an unbounded medium

$$k = \sqrt{\left(\frac{n\pi}{y_1}\right)^2 + \left(\frac{m\pi}{z_1}\right)^2}$$

Thus, at frequencies higher than cutoff $\beta_0 > k$, and

$$\gamma = \sqrt{k^2 - \beta_0{}^2} = j\beta \tag{12-84}$$

where $\beta = 2\pi/\lambda$ = phase constant in guide

λ = wavelength in guide

At sufficiently high frequencies $(\beta_0 \gg k)$ we note that the phase constant β in the guide approaches the phase constant β_0 in an unbounded medium. On the other hand, at frequencies less than cutoff $\beta_0 < k$, and

$$\gamma = \sqrt{k^2 - \beta_0{}^2} = \alpha \tag{12-85}$$

where α = attenuation constant.

At sufficiently low frequencies $(\beta_0 \ll k)$ we note that the attenuation constant α approaches a constant value k.

At the cutoff frequency, $\beta_0 = k$, and $\gamma = 0$. Thus, at cutoff

$$\omega^2 \mu \epsilon = \left(\frac{n\pi}{y_1}\right)^2 + \left(\frac{m\pi}{z_1}\right)^2 \tag{12-86}$$

It follows that the *cutoff frequency* is

$$f_c = \frac{1}{2\sqrt{\mu\epsilon}} \sqrt{\left(\frac{n}{y_1}\right)^2 + \left(\frac{m}{z_1}\right)^2} \qquad \text{cps} \tag{12-87}$$

and the *cutoff wavelength* is

$$\lambda_{oc} = \frac{2\pi}{\sqrt{(n\pi/y_1)^2 + (m\pi/z_1)^2}} = \frac{2}{\sqrt{(n/y_1)^2 + (m/z_1)^2}} \qquad \text{meters} \tag{12-88}$$

where λ_{oc} = wavelength in an unbounded medium at the cutoff frequency (or, more concisely, the *cutoff wavelength*).[1] *Equations* (12-87) *and* (12-88) *give the cutoff frequency and cutoff wavelength for any* TE_{mn} *mode in a hollow rectangular guide.* For instance, the cutoff wavelength of a TE_{10} mode is

$$\lambda_{oc} = 2z_1 \tag{12-89}$$

This is identical with the value found in the last section since $z_1 = b$.

At frequencies above cutoff $(\beta_0 > k)$

$$\beta = \sqrt{\beta_0{}^2 - k^2} = \sqrt{\omega^2 \mu \epsilon - \left(\frac{n\pi}{y_1}\right)^2 - \left(\frac{m\pi}{z_1}\right)^2} \tag{12-90}$$

---

[1] Note that $k = 2\pi/\lambda_{oc}$. Introducing this value of k, (12-84) can be used to relate λ, λ_0, and λ_{oc} when $\lambda_0 < \lambda_{oc}$.

It follows that the phase velocity v in the guide is equal to

$$v = \frac{\omega}{\beta} = \frac{v_0}{\sqrt{1 - (n\lambda_0/2y_1)^2 - (m\lambda_0/2z_1)^2}} \quad \text{meters/sec} \quad (12\text{-}91)$$

or

$$v = \frac{v_0}{\sqrt{1 - (\lambda_0/\lambda_{oc})^2}} \quad (12\text{-}92)$$

where $v_0 = 1/\sqrt{\mu\epsilon}$ = phase velocity in an unbounded medium (for air
$v_0 = 3 \times 10^8$ meters/sec)

λ_0 = wavelength in an unbounded medium (in same units as y_1 and z_1)

λ_{oc} = cutoff wavelength (in same units as λ_0)

The ratio v/v_0 as a function of the wavelength λ_0 is shown in Fig. 12-12 for several TE modes in a hollow wave guide of square cross section ($y_1 = z_1$).

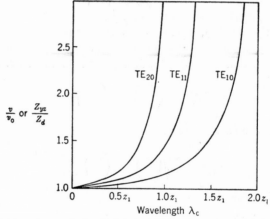

Fig. 12-12. Relative phase velocity (v/v_0) or relative transverse impedance (Z_{yz}/Z_d) as a function of the wavelength λ_0 for TE modes in a hollow square guide (height y_1 equal to width z_1).

In the above analysis there is no attenuation whatsoever at frequencies above cutoff. This results from the assumption of perfectly conducting guide walls and a lossless dielectric medium filling the guide. However, if the walls are not perfectly conducting or the medium is not lossless, or both, there is attenuation.[1] Thus, in actual wave guides there is attenuation at frequencies greater than cutoff although it is usually small compared with the attenuation at frequencies less than cutoff.

If the guide is filled with air, the dielectric loss is usually negligible compared with losses in the guide walls, so that the attenuation at frequencies

[1] That γ may have both a real and an imaginary part at frequencies greater than cutoff may be shown by solving (12-81) for γ under these conditions, with σ not equal to zero.

greater than cutoff is mainly determined by the conductivity of the guide walls. The fact that the guide walls are not perfectly conducting means that the tangential component E_t of the electric field is not zero at the walls but has a finite value. However, for walls made of a good conductor, such as copper, E_t will generally be so small that the above analysis (based on $E_t = 0$) is not affected to any appreciable extent. However, as a result of the finite wall conductivity α is not zero. Thus, in most practical problems where the wall conductivity is high (but not infinite) the field configuration in the guide, the wavelength λ, the phase constant β, the phase velocity v, etc., can all be calculated with high accuracy on the assumption that the walls have infinite conductivity, as done earlier in this section. The small (but not zero) attenuation may then be calculated separately, using (10-66) to find the power lost per unit area in the guide wall, it being assumed that the H-field distribution is the same as with perfectly conducting walls.

Finally, let us determine the value of the transverse impedance Z_{yz} for TE modes in a rectangular hollow guide. Thus, from (12-50),

$$Z_{yz} = \frac{j\omega\mu}{\gamma} \qquad (12\text{-}93)$$

At frequencies higher than cutoff $\gamma = j\beta$; so

$$Z_{yz} = \frac{\omega\mu}{\beta} = \frac{Z_d}{\sqrt{1 - (\lambda_0/\lambda_{oc})^2}} \qquad \text{ohms} \qquad (12\text{-}94)$$

where Z_d = intrinsic impedance of dielectric medium filling guide ($= \sqrt{\mu/\epsilon}$) (for air, $Z_d = 376.7$ ohms)

   λ_0 = wavelength in an unbounded medium

   λ_{oc} = cutoff wavelength (in same units as λ_0)

The ratio of Z_{yz} (transverse impedance) to Z_d (intrinsic impedance) as a function of the wavelength λ_0 is shown in Fig. 12-12 for several TE modes in a hollow wave guide of square cross section ($y_1 = z_1$).

Thus far only TE-mode waves have been considered. To find the field relations for transverse magnetic (TM) mode waves we proceed precisely as in the eight-step list given earlier in this section except that where TE appears we substitute TM and where E_x appears we substitute H_x, and vice versa. In the TM wave $H_x = 0$, and the longitudinal field component is E_x. This analysis will not be carried through here (see Prob. 12-6). However, it may be mentioned that (12-88) for the cutoff wavelength applies to both TE and TM waves as does (12-91) for the phase velocity, but this is not the case with (12-94) for the transverse impedance (see Prob. 12-8). The notation for any TM mode, in general, is TM_{mn} where m and n are integers $(1, 2, 3, \ldots)$. It is to be noted that neither m nor n may be equal to zero for TM waves. Thus, the lowest frequency

TM wave that will be transmitted by a rectangular wave guide is the
TM$_{11}$ mode.

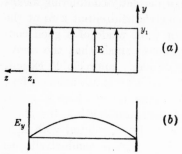

FIG. 12-13. Rectangular wave guide with TE$_{10}$ mode only.

We have seen that each mode in a wave guide has a particular cutoff wavelength, velocity, and impedance. When the frequency is high enough to permit the transmission of more than one mode, the resultant field is the sum of the fields of the individual mode fields in the guide. If the fields of one mode are much stronger than those of the others, this mode predominates. Whether a certain mode will predominate or not, when a guide can also transmit other modes, depends largely on the method of excitation and on the symmetry of the guide.[1]

For example, suppose that a rectangular wave guide, as shown in cross section in Fig. 12-13a, is excited in the TE$_{10}$ mode. The variation of E_y across the guide is sinusoidal, as shown in Fig. 12-13b. Suppose now that z_1 exceeds 1 wavelength so that the TE$_{20}$ mode can also be transmitted.[2] If only the TE$_{10}$ mode is excited, no TE$_{20}$ will appear provided that the guide is perfectly regular. However, in practice certain asymmetries and irregularities will be present, and these will tend to convert some of the TE$_{10}$-mode energy into TE$_{20}$-mode energy. Thus, if an asymmetrically located screw projects into the guide as in Fig. 12-14a, the total E_y field will tend to become asymmetrical, as suggested in Fig. 12-14b. This total field may be resolved into TE$_{10}$ and TE$_{20}$ components as shown in Fig. 12-14c and d.

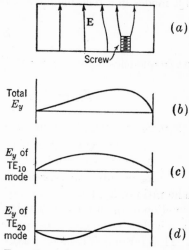

FIG. 12-14. Rectangular wave guide with TE$_{20}$ mode induced from TE$_{10}$ mode by asymmetrically placed projection (screw).

If both TE$_{10}$ and TE$_{20}$ modes can be transmitted, the field in the guide beyond the screw location will have energy in both modes. In effect

---

[1] Nonpropagating modes may also be present (near irregularities or discontinuities) in addition to the propagating modes, but the nonpropagating modes attenuate rapidly with distance. The lowest frequency mode that a guide can transmit is often called the *dominant mode*. However, if the frequency is high enough to transmit other modes the dominant mode does not necessarily predominate.

[2] But $y_1 < \lambda_0/2$ so that no TE$_{01}$ mode (E in z direction) is transmitted.

the screw is a receiving antenna that extracts energy from the incident TE_{10}-mode wave and reradiates it so as to excite the TE_{20} mode. However, if the frequency is decreased so that only the TE_{10} wave can be transmitted, the asymmetric field (Fig. 12-14b) will exist only in the vicinity of the screw and farther down the guide the field will be entirely in the TE_{10} mode. To avoid the problems of multiple-mode transmission, a wave guide is usually operated so that only one mode is capable of transmission. For instance, to ensure transmission only in the TE_{10} mode, z_1 must be less than 1 wavelength and y_1 less than $\frac{1}{2}$ wavelength. But to allow transmission of the TE_{10} mode, z_1 must exceed $\frac{1}{2}$ wavelength. Hence z_1 must be between $\frac{1}{2}$ and 1 wavelength, and a value of 0.7 wavelength is often used since this is well below 1 wavelength and yet enough more than $\frac{1}{2}$ wavelength so that the velocity and transverse impedance values are not too critical a function of frequency. We

TABLE 12-1

RELATIONS FOR TE_{mn} MODES IN HOLLOW RECTANGULAR WAVE GUIDES[†]

Name of relation	Relation
Cutoff frequency	$f_c = \dfrac{1}{2\sqrt{\mu\epsilon}} \sqrt{\left(\dfrac{n}{y_1}\right)^2 + \left(\dfrac{m}{z_1}\right)^2}$ cps
Cutoff wavelength	$\lambda_{oc} = \dfrac{2}{\sqrt{\left(\dfrac{n}{y_1}\right)^2 + \left(\dfrac{m}{z_1}\right)^2}}$ meters
Phase velocity	$v = \dfrac{v_0}{\sqrt{1 - \left(\dfrac{n\lambda_0}{2y_1}\right)^2 - \left(\dfrac{m\lambda_0}{2z_1}\right)^2}}$ $= \dfrac{v_0}{\sqrt{1 - \left(\dfrac{\lambda_0}{\lambda_{oc}}\right)^2}}$ meters/sec where $v_0 = 1/\sqrt{\mu\epsilon}$
Transverse impedance	$Z_{yz} = \dfrac{Z_d}{\sqrt{1 - \left(\dfrac{n\lambda_0}{2y_1}\right)^2 - \left(\dfrac{m\lambda_0}{2z_1}\right)^2}}$ $= \dfrac{Z_d}{\sqrt{1 - \left(\dfrac{\lambda_0}{\lambda_{oc}}\right)^2}}$ ohms where $Z_d = \sqrt{\mu/\epsilon}$

[†] All of the relations also apply to TM_{mn} modes except for the transverse-impedance relation. The velocity and impedance relations involving $(\lambda_0/\lambda_{oc})^2$ apply not only to rectangular guides but also to TE modes in hollow single-conductor guides of any shape.

recall that at cutoff ($z_1 = \frac{1}{2}$ wavelength) the velocity and impedance approach infinite values. The height y_1 may be as small as desired without preventing transmission of the TE_{10} mode. Too small a value of y_1, however, increases attenuation (because of power lost in the guide walls) and also reduces the power-handling capabilities of the guide. It is often the practice to make $y_1 = z_1/2$.

The relations derived in this section for TE modes in a hollow rectangular wave guide (see Fig. 12-7) are summarized in Table 12-1.

12-4. Hollow Wave Guides of Other Shape. In Sec. 12-3 we considered the rectangular wave guide. This is only one of an infinite variety of forms in which single-conductor hollow wave guides may be made. For example, the wave guide could have a circular[1] cross section as in Fig. 12-15c, an elliptical[2] cross section as in Fig. 12-15d, or a reentrant[3] cross section as in 12-15f.

All of these forms and many others may be regarded as derivable from the rectangular type (Fig. 12-15a). Thus the square cross section (Fig. 12-15b) is a special case of the rectangular guide. By bending out the walls the square guide may be transformed to the circular shape (Fig. 12-15c). By flattening the circular guide the elliptical form of Fig. 12-15d is obtained. On the other hand, by bending the top and bottom surfaces of the rectangular wave guide inward the form shown in Fig. 12-15e is obtained. A still further modification is the reentrant form in Fig. 12-15f. The value of regarding these as related forms is that often certain properties of a guide of a particular shape may be interpolated approximately from the known properties of wave guides of closely related shape.

For example, the longest wavelength that the square guide (Fig. 12-15b) will transmit is equal to $2b$. This is for the TE_{10} mode. This information may be used to predict with fair accuracy the longest wavelength that a circular guide can transmit. Thus, if the cross-sectional area of the square guide is taken equal to the area of the circular guide,

$$b^2 = \pi \left(\frac{d}{2}\right)^2 \tag{12-95}$$

where d = diameter of circular guide. It follows that

$$d = 1.13b \tag{12-96}$$

Since $\lambda_{oc} = 2b$ for the square wave guide, we obtain as the cutoff wave-

---

[1] G. C. Southworth, Some Fundamental Experiments with Wave Guides, *Proc. I.R.E.*, **25**, 807–822, July, 1937.

[2] L. J. Chu, Electromagnetic Waves in Hollow Elliptic Pipes of Metal, *J. Applied Phys.*, **9**, September, 1938.

[3] S. B. Cohn, Properties of Ridge Wave Guide, *Proc. I.R.E.*, **35**, 783–789, August, 1947.

length for the circular wave guide

$$\lambda_{oc} = \frac{2}{1.13} d = 1.77d \tag{12-97}$$

This approximate value exceeds the exact value by 4 per cent.

The procedure for carrying out a complete analysis of the properties of a wave guide of any shape is formally the same as in Sec. 12-3 for the rectangular guide. It is usually most convenient, however, to set up the equations in a coordinate system such that the wave-guide surfaces can

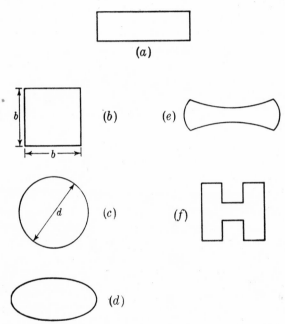

FIG. 12-15. Forms of hollow single-conductor wave guides.

be specified by a fixed value of a coordinate. Thus, as we have seen, a rectangular guide is conveniently handled with rectangular coordinates, the guide surfaces being specified by $y = 0$, $y = y_1$, $z = 0$, and $z = z_1$. Likewise, a circular wave guide is readily analyzed using cylindrical coordinates, the guide surface being specified by $r = r_1$. Referring to Fig. 12-15d and e, these shapes can be analyzed using elliptical-hyperbolic coordinates. However, if the guide surface cannot be specified in a simple manner, as in the above-mentioned cases, the application of the boundary condition ($E_t = 0$) may become so difficult as to make an exact mathematical analysis of prohibitive complexity.

12-5. Attenuation at Frequencies Less than Cutoff. It has been shown that at frequencies less than cutoff, waves are not transmitted through hollow single-conductor guides but are attenuated. Let us now calculate the magnitude of this attenuation. From (12-85) the attenuation constant for a rectangular guide at frequencies less than cutoff is

$$\alpha = \sqrt{\left(\frac{n\pi}{y_1}\right)^2 + \left(\frac{m\pi}{z_1}\right)^2 - \left(\frac{2\pi}{\lambda_0}\right)^2} \qquad (12\text{-}98)$$

Noting (12-88), this can be reexpressed as

$$\alpha = \frac{2\pi}{\lambda_0} \sqrt{\left(\frac{\lambda_0}{\lambda_{oc}}\right)^2 - 1} = \beta_0 \sqrt{\left(\frac{\lambda_0}{\lambda_{oc}}\right)^2 - 1} \qquad \text{nepers/meter} \qquad (12\text{-}99)$$

where λ_0 = wavelength in an unbounded medium (meters)
   λ_{oc} = cutoff wavelength (meters)

The attenuation constant α as given in (12-99) applies not only to rectangular guides but to hollow single-conductor guides of any cross-sectional shape.

If the frequency is much less than cutoff $(\lambda_0 \gg \lambda_{oc})$, Eq. (12-99) reduces to the approximate relation

$$\alpha \simeq \frac{2\pi}{\lambda_{oc}} \qquad \text{nepers/meter} \qquad (12\text{-}100)$$

where λ_{oc} = cutoff wavelength (meters). Since, in dealing with voltage, 1 neper equals 8.68 decibels (db),[1]

$$\alpha \simeq \frac{2\pi \times 8.68}{\lambda_{oc}} = \frac{54.5}{\lambda_{oc}} \qquad \text{db/meter} \qquad (12\text{-}101)$$

Example. A certain wave guide has a cutoff wavelength λ_{oc} of 10 cm. Find the attenuation per meter along the guide for an applied wavelength λ_0 of 1 meter.
Solution. Since $\lambda_0 \gg \lambda_{oc}$, Eq. (12-100) or (12-101) can be used, yielding

$$\alpha = 20\pi \text{ nepers/meter, or 545 db/meter}$$

This is a very high rate of attenuation, the applied field falling to a negligible value in a very short distance.

A simple attenuator operating at frequencies less than cutoff is illustrated in longitudinal section in Fig. 12-16. A metal tube, acting as a wave guide, has loops arranged at each end, as shown, to couple from coaxial transmission lines into and out of the wave guide. One of the loops is mounted on a movable plunger so that the distance between the loops is variable. If the applied wavelength λ_0 is much longer than the cutoff wavelength λ_{oc} of the guide, and the loops are not in too close proximity, the attenuation is as given by (12-100) or (12-101). For

---

[1] Note that a 1-neper attenuation means a reduction to $1/e$ of the original value. Conversely, an increase of 1 neper means an increase to $e(=2.7183)$ times the original value. Hence, for voltages 1 neper is equal to $20 \log_{10} e = 8.68$ db.

instance, if $\lambda_{oc} = 10$ cm and λ_0 is much greater (1 meter or more), the attenuation increases 5.45 db per centimeter of outward movement of the plunger. This type of attenuator is very useful but has the disadvantage of a high insertion loss, that is, a large initial attenuation when inserted in a coaxial line. Since $\beta = 0$, there is no change in phase with change in plunger position.

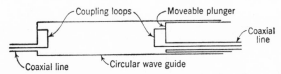

Fig. 12-16. Attenuator for use at frequencies less than cutoff.

12-6. Attenuation at Frequencies Greater than Cutoff. If the wave guide has perfectly conducting walls and the medium filling the guide is lossless, there is no attenuation at frequencies greater than cutoff. Thus, $\alpha = 0$, and from (12-84) we have for a rectangular guide that

$$\gamma = j\beta = \sqrt{\left(\frac{n\pi}{y_1}\right)^2 + \left(\frac{m\pi}{z_1}\right)^2 - \left(\frac{2\pi}{\lambda_0}\right)^2} \qquad (12\text{-}102)$$

or

$$\beta = \frac{2\pi}{\lambda_0}\sqrt{1 - \left(\frac{\lambda_0}{\lambda_{oc}}\right)^2} = \beta_0\sqrt{1 - \left(\frac{\lambda_0}{\lambda_{oc}}\right)^2} \qquad (12\text{-}103)$$

The phase constant β as given in (12-103) applies not only to rectangular guides but to hollow single-conductor guides of any cross-sectional shape.

The behavior of the phase constant β for this case and for the case discussed in Sec. 12-5 is compared on the composite graph in Fig. 12-17. Here the propagation constant γ is shown as ordinate vs. the wavelength λ_0 in an unbounded medium as abscissa. The real part of γ ($=\alpha$) is plotted as the solid curve above the x axis and the imaginary part ($=\beta$) as the dashed curve below the axis. At very short wavelengths ($\lambda_0 \to 0$), α is zero, and β approaches an infinite value that is equal to β_0 for an unbounded medium. As λ_0 increases, β decreases until at cutoff ($\lambda_0 = \lambda_{oc}$) β is zero. At still longer wavelengths, β remains zero, but α does not. At sufficiently long wavelengths ($\lambda_0 \gg \lambda_{oc}$), α approaches a value of $2\pi/\lambda_{oc}$ as indicated. This diagram applies to lossless hollow single-conductor guides with cross sections of any shape.

Actual guides are not lossless so that α is not zero for $\lambda_0 < \lambda_{oc}$ as indicated in Fig. 12-17. However, for air-filled guides of a good conducting material, such as copper, β is substantially as indicated for $\lambda_0 < \lambda_{oc}$, while α is small but not necessarily negligible. To calculate α for this case, we note (see Fig. 12-18) that the average power in the guide

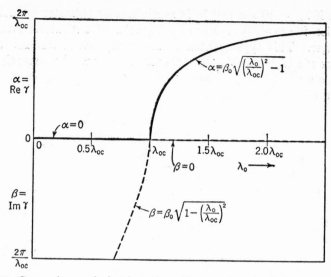

FIG. 12-17. Composite graph showing attenuation constant α and phase constant β for a lossless hollow single-conductor waveguide as a function of the wavelength λ_0 in an unbounded medium.

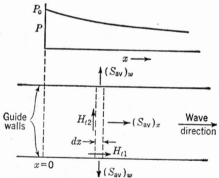

FIG. 12-18. Power lost in walls of wave guide results in attenuation.

varies with the distance x in the direction of transmission as given by

$$P = P_0 e^{-2\alpha x} \qquad \text{watts} \qquad (12\text{-}104)$$

where average P_0 = power at reference point ($x = 0$)

x = distance in direction of transmission through guide (meters)

The factor 2 in the exponent is present because power is proportional to field squared. It follows that

$$\alpha = \frac{1}{2} \frac{-dP/dx}{P} \qquad \text{nepers/meter} \qquad (12\text{-}105)$$

In (12-105) $-dP/dx$ represents the decrease in power per unit distance along the guide at a particular location, while P is the power transmitted through the guide at that location.[1]

Thus, in words the attenuation constant in nepers per unit distance is expressed by

$$\alpha = \frac{\text{power lost per unit distance}}{\text{twice the power transmitted}}$$

If the medium filling the guide is lossless, the decrease in power per unit distance is equal to the power lost per unit distance in the walls of the guide. This is

$$-\frac{dP}{dx} = \frac{1}{dx} \iint (S_{av})_w \, ds = \int (S_{av})_w \, dl \qquad (12\text{-}106)$$

where $(S_{av})_w$ = average Poynting vector into wall (average with respect to time). The surface integral in (12-106) is taken over a strip of length dx of the interior surface of the wave guide (Fig. 12-18). The line integral in (12-106) is taken around the inside of the guide (same path as that for strip). In general, the average Poynting vector is

$$\mathbf{S}_{av} = \tfrac{1}{2} \, \text{Re} \, \mathbf{E} \times \mathbf{H}^* \qquad (12\text{-}107)$$

Since $\mathbf{E}$ and $\mathbf{H}$ are normal, the magnitude of the average Poynting vector into the conducting wall medium is (see Fig. 12-18)

$$(S_{av})_w = \tfrac{1}{2} \, \text{Re} \, H_{t1} H_{t1}^* Z_c = \tfrac{1}{2} |H_{t1}|^2 \, \text{Re} \, Z_c \qquad (12\text{-}108)$$

where $|H_{t1}|$ = absolute value (or magnitude) of the component of $\mathbf{H}$ tangent to the conducting surface of the guide walls

$\text{Re} \, Z_c$ = real part of the intrinsic impedance of the conducting wall medium $(= \sqrt{\mu\omega/2\sigma})$

Introducing (12-108) in (12-106) yields

$$-\frac{dP}{dx} = \frac{\text{Re} \, Z_c}{2} \int |H_{t1}|^2 \, dl \qquad (12\text{-}109)$$

Now the power traveling through the guide (in x direction) is

$$P = \iint (S_{av})_x \, ds \qquad \text{watts} \qquad (12\text{-}110)$$

where in this case the surface integral is taken over the guide cross section. It follows that

$$P = \tfrac{1}{2} \, \text{Re} \, Z_{yz} \iint |H_{t2}|^2 \, ds \qquad (12\text{-}111)$$

---

[1] It is to be noted that the attenuation in this case is due to an actual power loss (Joule heating of guide walls), whereas at frequencies less than cutoff no Joule heating effect is involved, the attenuation being due to the inability of the guide to transmit the higher-order mode.

where $|H_{t2}|$ = absolute value of component of **H** tangent to a cross-
   sectional plane through the guide (Fig. 12-18)
Re Z_{yz} = real part of transverse impedance of guide
Therefore, the attenuation constant α is, in general, given by

$$\alpha = \frac{\text{Re } Z_c \int |H_{t1}|^2 \, dl}{2 \, \text{Re } Z_{yz} \int\!\!\int |H_{t2}|^2 \, ds} \qquad \text{nepers/meter} \qquad (12\text{-}112)$$

where Re Z_c = real part of the intrinsic impedance of guide walls (conductor)
   Re Z_{yz} = real part of transverse impedance of guide
   $|H_{t1}|$ = absolute value of component of **H** tangent to the conduct-
   ing surface of the guide walls (integrated around interior
   surface of guide)
   $|H_{t2}|$ = absolute value of component of **H** tangent to plane of
   cross section through guide (integrated over the cross-
   sectional area)
Equation (12-112) applies to any mode in any guide. For each mode the
attenuation constant must be calculated using (12-112), with values of
$|H_{t1}|$ and $|H_{t2}|$ corresponding to the field distribution for that mode. If
the guide walls are of good conducting material, we may assume, with but
little error, that the **H**-field distribution used in (12-112) is the same as for
perfectly conducting walls. The following example illustrates an application of (12-112) to a simple problem.

Example. Find the attenuation constant for a 300-Mc/sec TEM wave in an
infinite-parallel-plane transmission line with a spacing between planes of 10 cm. The
planes or walls are made of copper, and the medium between the planes is air.
   Solution. For a TEM wave the transverse impedance equals the intrinsic impedance; so (12-112) becomes

$$\alpha = \frac{2 \, \text{Re } Z_c \int_0^{y_1} |H_{t1}|^2 \, dy}{2 \, \text{Re } Z_d \int_0^{y_1} \int_0^{z_1} |H_{t2}|^2 \, dz \, dy} \qquad (12\text{-}113)$$

where y_1 = arbitrary distance along conducting wall (see **Fig. 12-1**)
   z_1 = spacing between walls (meters)
   Re Z_c = real part of intrinsic impedance of conducting walls (ohms)
   Re Z_d = real part of intrinsic impedance of dielectric medium between walls
   (Z_d is entirely real for lossless medium)
The integral with H_{t1} involves the power lost in one wall of the line. The total power
lost in both walls is twice this; hence the factor 2 in the numerator. For a TEM wave
H is everywhere parallel to the walls and normal to the direction of propagation so
that both H_{t1} and H_{t2} are perpendicular to the page instead of as suggested in Fig.
12-18. It follows that $|H_{t1}| = |H_{t2}|$ = a constant. Hence, (12-113) reduces to

$$\alpha = \frac{\text{Re } Z_c \, y_1}{\text{Re } Z_d \, y_1 z_1} = \frac{\text{Re } Z_c}{z_1 \, \text{Re } Z_d} \qquad (12\text{-}114)$$

For copper at 300 Mc/sec, Re Z_c = 4.55 × 10⁻³ ohm, while for air Re Z_d = 376.7 ohms. Therefore

$$\alpha = 1.2 \times 10^{-4} \text{ neper/meter}$$

or

$$\alpha = 1.04 \times 10^{-3} \text{ db/meter}$$

Thus, the attenuation amounts to about 1 db for 1,000 meters of line.

12-7. Waves Traveling Parallel to a Plane Boundary. In the previous section we considered the attenuation of a guided wave due to the power lost in the walls of the wave guide. In this section some of the phenomena associated with this power loss or power flow are discussed in more detail.

Consider the plane boundary between two media shown in Fig. 12-19a, assuming that medium 1 is air and medium 2 is a perfect conductor.

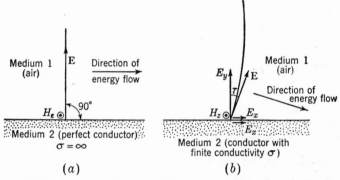

FIG. 12-19. TEM wave traveling to right along surface of perfectly conducting medium.

From the boundary condition that the tangential component of the electric field vanishes at the surface of a perfect conductor, the electric field of a TEM wave traveling parallel to the boundary must be exactly normal to the boundary as portrayed in the figure. However, if medium 2 has a finite conductivity σ there will be a tangential electric field E_x at the boundary, and, as a result, the electric field of a wave traveling along the boundary has a *forward tilt*, as suggested in Fig. 12-19b. From the continuity relation for tangential electric fields, the field on both sides of the boundary is E_x.

The direction and magnitude of the power flow per unit area are given by the Poynting vector. The average value (with respect to time) of the Poynting vector is

$$\mathbf{S}_{av} = \tfrac{1}{2} \operatorname{Re} \mathbf{E} \times \mathbf{H}^* \qquad \text{watts/meter}^2 \qquad (12\text{-}115)$$

At the surface of the conducting medium (Fig. 12-19b) the power into the conductor is in the negative y direction, and from (12-115) its average value per unit area is[1]

$$S_y = -\tfrac{1}{2} \operatorname{Re} E_x H_z^* \tag{12-116}$$

The space relation of E_x, H_z (or H_z^*), and S_y is shown in Fig. 12-20a. But

$$\frac{E_x}{H_z} = Z_c \tag{12-117}$$

where Z_c = intrinsic impedance of conducting medium, so that (12-116) can be written

$$S_y = -\tfrac{1}{2} H_z H_z^* \operatorname{Re} Z_c = -\tfrac{1}{2} H_{z0}{}^2 \operatorname{Re} Z_c \tag{12-118}$$

where $H_z = H_{z0} e^{j(\omega t - \xi) - \gamma x}$

$H_z^* = H_{z0} e^{-[j(\omega t - \xi) - \gamma x]}$ = complex conjugate of H_z

ξ = phase lag of H_z with respect to E_x

The relation for the Poynting vector in (12-118) is the same as given in (12-108).

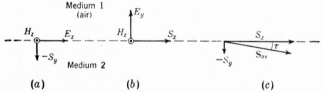

Fig. 12-20. Fields and Poynting vector at surface of a conducting medium with wave traveling parallel to surface.

At the surface of the conducting medium (Fig. 12-19b) the power per unit area flowing parallel to the surface (x direction) is

$$S_x = \tfrac{1}{2} \operatorname{Re} E_y H_z^* \tag{12-119}$$

The space relation of E_y, H_z (or H_z^*), and S_x is illustrated by Fig. 12-20b. But

$$\frac{E_y}{H_z} = Z_d \tag{12-120}$$

where Z_d = intrinsic impedance of dielectric medium (air). It follows that

$$S_x = \tfrac{1}{2} H_{z0}{}^2 \operatorname{Re} Z_d \tag{12-121}$$

The total average Poynting vector is then

$$\mathbf{S}_{av} = \mathbf{i} S_x + \mathbf{j} S_y = \frac{H_{z0}{}^2}{2} (\mathbf{i} \operatorname{Re} Z_d - \mathbf{j} \operatorname{Re} Z_c) \tag{12-122}$$

The relation of $\mathbf{S}_{av}$ to its x and y components is illustrated in Fig. 12-20c. It is to be noted that the average power flow (per unit area) is not parallel

[1] The component of the average Poynting vector in the y direction is $(S_{av})_y$, but to simplify notation we shall write S_y for $(S_{av})_y$.

to the surface but inward at an angle τ.   This angle is also the same as the angle of forward tilt of the average electric field (see Fig. 12-19b).   If medium 2 were perfectly conducting, τ would be zero.

It is of interest to evaluate the tilt angle τ for a couple of practical situations.   This is done in the following examples.

Example 1.   Find the forward tilt angle τ for a vertically polarized 3,000-Mc/sec wave traveling in air along a sheet of copper.
Solution.   From (12–122) the tilt angle τ is given by

$$\tau = \arctan \frac{\text{Re } Z_c}{\text{Re } Z_d} \qquad (12\text{-}123)$$

At 3,000 Mc/sec, we have for copper that Re $Z_c = 1.44 \times 10^{-2}$ ohms.   The intrinsic impedance of air is independent of frequency.   (Re $Z_d = 376.7$ ohms.)   Thus

$$\tau = \arctan \frac{1.44 \times 10^{-2}}{376.7} = 0.0022°$$

Although τ is not zero in the above example, it is very small, so that **E** is nearly normal to the copper surface and **S** nearly parallel to it.   This small value of tilt is typical at most air-conductor boundaries but accounts for the power flow into the conducting medium.   If the conductivity of medium 2 is very low or if it is a dielectric medium, τ may amount to a few degrees.   Thus the forward tilt of a vertically polarized radio wave propagating along poor ground is sufficient to produce an appreciable horizontal electric field component.   In the Beverage or wave antenna this horizontal component is utilized to induce emfs along a horizontal wire oriented parallel to the direction of transmission of the wave.

In contrast to Example 1, in which medium 2 is copper, the following example considers the case of fresh water as medium 2.

Example 2.   Find the forward tilt angle τ for a vertically polarized 3,000-Mc/sec wave traveling in air along the surface of a smooth fresh-water lake.
Solution.   At 3,000 Mc/sec the conduction current in fresh water is negligible compared with the displacement current (see Fig. 10-2), so that the lake may be regarded as a dielectric medium of relative permittivity $\epsilon_r = 80$.   Thus

$$\tau = \arctan \frac{1}{\sqrt{80}} = 6.4°$$

In this case the forward tilt of 6.4° is sufficient to be readily detected by a direct measurement of the direction of the electric field.

The angle τ discussed above is an average value.   In general, the instantaneous direction of the electric field varies as a function of time.   In the case of a wave in air traveling along a copper sheet, E_y and E_z are in phase octature (45° phase difference), so that at one instant of time the total field **E** may be in the y direction and $\frac{1}{8}$ period later it will be in the x

direction.   As a function of time the locus of the tip of **E** describes a cross-field ellipse (see Sec. 9-15), as portrayed in Fig. 12-21, for a 3,000 Mc per sec wave in air traveling along a copper sheet (in the x direction) as in Example 1.[1]   The ellipse is not to scale, the abscissa values being mag-

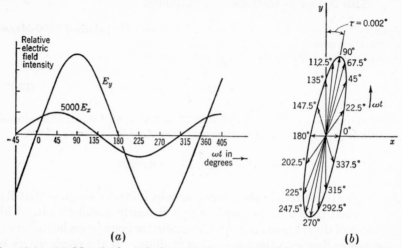

(a)   (b)

Fig. 12-21.   (a) Magnitude variation with time of E_y and E_x components of **E** in air at the surface of a copper region for a 3,000-Mc/sec TEM wave traveling parallel to the surface.   (b) Resultant values of **E** (space vector) at 22.5° intervals over one cycle, illustrating elliptical cross-field at the surface of the copper region.   The wave is traveling to the right.   Abscissa values are magnified 5,000 times as compared to the ordinate values.

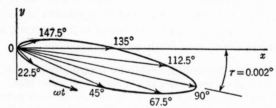

Fig. 12-22.   Poynting vector in air at a point on the surface of a copper region for a 3,000-Mc/sec TEM wave traveling along the surface (to right).   The Poynting vector is shown at 22.5° intervals over one-half cycle.   The ordinate values are magnified 5,000 times as compared to the abscissa values.

nified 5,000 times.   The positions of **E** for various values of ωt are indicated.   The variation of the instantaneous Poynting vector for this case is shown in Fig. 12-22.   Here the ordinate values are magnified 5,000 times.   It is to be noted that the tip of the Poynting vector travels around the ellipse twice per cycle.

[1] P. Epstein, Kraftliniendiagramme für die Ausbreitung der Wellen in der drahtlosen Telegraphie bei Berücksichtigung der Bodenschaffenheit, *Jarhb. drahtlosen T. u. T.,* **4,** 176–187, 1910.

Whereas copper has a complex intrinsic impedance, fresh water, at the frequency considered in Example 2, has a real intrinsic impedance. It follows that the E_x and E_y components of the total field **E** are in time phase so that the cross-field ellipse in this case collapses to a straight line (linear cross-field) with a forward tilt of 6.4°.

12-8. The Single-wire Open Wave Guide. In the previous section we have seen that a wave traveling along an air-conductor or air-dielectric boundary has a longitudinal (E_z) component of the electric field, resulting in a forward tilt of the total electric field. Hence the Poynting vector is not entirely parallel to the boundary but has a component directed from the air into the adjacent medium, as suggested in Fig. 12-20c. This tends to keep the energy in the wave from spreading out and to concentrate it near the surface, resulting in a *bound wave*, or *surface wave*. The phase velocity of such a bound wave is always less than the velocity in free space. Although the field of this guided wave extends to infinity, such a large proportion of the energy may be confined within a few wavelengths of the surface that the surface can be regarded as an open type of wave guide. It should be noted, however, that even though the forward-tilt effect is present along all finitely conducting surfaces, the bound wave may be of negligible importance without a launching device of relatively large dimensions (several wavelengths across) to initiate the wave. If the surface is perfectly smooth and perfectly conducting, the tangential component of the electric field vanishes, there is no forward tilt of the electric field, and no tendency whatever for the wave to be bound to the surface.

In 1899 Sommerfeld[1] showed that a wave could be guided along a round wire of finite conductivity. Zenneck[2] pointed out that for similar reasons a wave traveling along the earth's surface would tend to be guided by the surface. More recently Goubau[3] has shown that the guiding action of a single round conducting wire can be greatly enhanced by a thin dielectric coating, the radial extent of the strong field being sufficiently small that the coated wire forms a relatively efficient open type of wave guide. Modification of the surface, as by corrugation, can also enhance the guiding action. However, to initiate the guided wave along the wire with good efficiency requires a relatively large launching device, its function being to excite a mode, closely related in form to the guided mode, over a

[1] A. Sommerfeld, Fortpflanzung elektrodynamischer Wellen an einem zylindrischen Leiter, *Ann. Phys. u. Chem.*, **67**, 233, December, 1899.

[2] J. Zenneck, Uber die Fortpflanzung ebener elecktromagnetischer Wellen langs einer ebenen Leiterflache und ihre Beziehung zur drahtlosen Telegraphie, *Ann. Physik.*, Ser. 4, **23**, 846–866, Sept. 20, 1907.

[3] G. Goubau, Surface Waves and Their Application to Transmission Lines, *J. Applied Phys.*, **21**, 1119–1128, November, 1950.

diameter of perhaps several wavelengths. Hence this type of guide is practical only at very high frequencies.

A dielectric-coated single-wire wave guide with typical dimensions is illustrated in Fig. 12-23. The dielectric coat consists of a layer of enamel of relative permittivity $\epsilon_r = 3$ having a thickness of only 0.0005 wavelength. The wire diameter is 0.02 wavelength. The configuration of the electric field lines in the launcher and along the wire guide is suggested in the figure. The mode on the wire is a TM type, but it is like a plane TEM wave to a considerable distance from the wire.

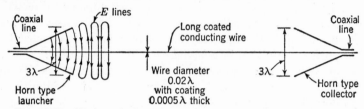

FIG. 12-23. Single coated-wire open wave guide. *(After G. Goubau.)*

Wires wound in the form of long helices are also effective single-conductor open-type wave guides. Helix diameters as large as 0.4 wavelengths can be used successfully.

A linear wire made of a nonconducting dielectric material also may form an effective open type of wave guide,[1] the guiding action being associated with the forward tilt of the electric field at the air-dielectric boundary. If the dielectric wire is of sufficiently small diameter (in terms of wavelengths), most of the energy is guided in the air outside the wire. However, if the wire or rod is sufficiently large in diameter, most of the energy may be conveyed inside the rod. For rods of moderate permittivity (say $\epsilon_r = 2.5$) diameters of the order of 1 wavelength or more are required to confine most of the energy to the inside of the rod. Hollow dielectric wires or tubes are also feasible as wave guides, but larger diameters may be required for effective guiding action.

PROBLEMS

12-1. An air-filled hollow rectangular conducting wave guide has cross-sectional dimensions $y_1 = 6$ cm and $z_1 = 10$ cm. Find the cutoff frequencies for the following modes: TEM, TE_{10}, TE_{20}, TE_{01}, TE_{11}, and TE_{21}.

Ans.: TEM not passed; TE_{10} 1,500 Mc/sec; TE_{20} 3,000 Mc/sec; TE_{01} 2,500 Mc/sec; TE_{11} 2,920 Mc/sec; TE_{21} 3,905 Mc/sec.

12-2. An air-filled hollow rectangular conducting wave guide has cross-sectional dimensions $y_1 = 8$ cm and $z_1 = 10$ cm. (a) How many TE modes will this guide transmit at frequencies below 4,000 Mc/sec? (b) How are these modes designated, and what are their cutoff frequencies?

[1] D. Hondros and P. Debye, Elektromagnetische Wellen an dielektrischen Drahten, *Ann. Physik.*, **32**, 465–476, 1910. R. M. Whitmer, Fields in Non-metallic Guides, *Proc. I.R.E.*, **36**, 1105–1109, September, 1948.

12-3. Find the phase velocity of the TE_{10}-mode wave in Prob. 12-1 at a frequency of 1.5 times its cutoff frequency. *Ans.:* 4×10^8 meters/sec.

12-4. Find the reflection angle θ of the TE_{10}-mode wave in Prob. 12-1 at a frequency of 2.5 times its cutoff frequency.

12-5. A plane 1,590-Mc/sec wave in air is traveling parallel to the boundary of a conducting medium with **H** parallel to the boundary. The constants for the conducting medium are $\sigma = 10^8$ mhos/meter and $\epsilon_r = \mu_r = 1$. If the rms field intensity of the traveling wave is 5 volts/meter, find the average power per unit area lost in the conducting medium. *Ans.:* 1.4×10^{-6} watt/meter².

12-6. Show that the field components for a TM wave in a hollow rectangular single conductor wave guide (see Fig. 12-7) are given by

$$E_x = E_0 \sin \frac{n\pi y}{y_1} \sin \frac{m\pi z}{z_1} e^{j\omega t - \gamma x}$$

$$E_y = \frac{-\gamma E_0}{k^2} \frac{n\pi}{y_1} \cos \frac{n\pi y}{y_1} \sin \frac{m\pi z}{z_1} e^{j\omega t - \gamma x}$$

$$E_z = \frac{-\gamma E_0}{k^2} \frac{m\pi}{z_1} \sin \frac{n\pi y}{y_1} \cos \frac{m\pi z}{z_1} e^{j\omega t - \gamma x}$$

$$H_x = 0$$

$$H_y = \frac{-\gamma Y_{yz} E_0}{k^2} \frac{m\pi}{z_1} \sin \frac{n\pi y}{y_1} \cos \frac{m\pi z}{z_1} e^{j\omega t - \gamma x}$$

$$H_z = \frac{\gamma Y_{yz} E_0}{k^2} \frac{n\pi}{y_1} \cos \frac{n\pi y}{y_1} \sin \frac{m\pi z}{z_1} e^{j\omega t - \gamma x}$$

12-7. Show that the transverse impedance of a TE wave in a rectangular guide is equal to $Z_{yz} = Z_0(\lambda/\lambda_0)$, where Z_0 is the intrinsic impedance of the medium, λ the wavelength in the guide, and λ_0 the wavelength in an unbounded medium of the same material as fills the guide.

12-8. Show that the transverse impedance of a TM wave in a rectangular guide is equal to

$$Z_{yz} = Z_0 \sqrt{1 - \left(\frac{n\lambda_0}{2y_1}\right)^2 - \left(\frac{m\lambda_0}{2z_1}\right)^2} = Z_0 \sqrt{1 - \left(\frac{\lambda_0}{\lambda_{oc}}\right)^2}$$

12-9. Show that the attenuation constant for a TE_{10} wave at frequencies **above** cutoff in an infinite-parallel-plane transmission line or guide is

$$\alpha = \frac{2 \operatorname{Re} Z_c}{d \operatorname{Re} Z_d} \frac{(\lambda_0/2d)^2}{\sqrt{1 - (\lambda_0/2d)^2}} \quad \text{nepers/meter}$$

where $\operatorname{Re} Z_c$ = real part of intrinsic impedance of wall medium (conductor), $\operatorname{Re} Z_d$ = real part of intrinsic impedance of medium filling guide (dielectric), d = wall spacing, and λ_0 = wavelength in unbounded medium.

12-10. Show that the attenuation constant for a TE_{mo} wave at frequencies above cutoff in an infinite-parallel-plane transmission line of spacing d is

$$\alpha = \frac{\operatorname{Re} Z_c}{d \operatorname{Re} Z_d} \frac{2(\lambda_0/\lambda_{oc})^2}{\sqrt{1 - (\lambda_0/\lambda_{oc})^2}}$$

where λ_{oc} = cutoff wavelength.

12-11. A TEM wave is traveling in air parallel to the plane boundary of a conducting medium. Show that if $K = \rho_s v$, where K = sheet current density (amp/meter), ρ_s = surface charge density, and v = velocity of wave, it follows that $K = H$, where H is the magnitude of the **H** field of the wave.

12-12. Write the equations giving the variation of each field component with y and z for a TE_{12} wave in a square conducting guide ($y_1 = z_1$).

12-13. Sketch the variation of the field components as functions of y and z for the guide and mode of Prob. 12-12.

12-14. In an infinite-parallel-plane air-filled transmission line of 2 cm spacing find the attenuation constant α for a TEM wave and for a TE_{10} wave at 10,000 Mc/sec. The planes are made of copper.

12-15. Find the attenuation constant α for a hollow single-conductor wave guide at an applied frequency of 0.75 of the lowest cutoff frequency for the guide.

12-16. In an infinite-parallel-plane transmission line show that at a wavelength λ_0, less than cutoff, the attenuation constant for a TM_{10} mode is

$$\alpha' = \frac{2\alpha}{\sqrt{1 - (\lambda_0/2b)^2}}$$

where α = attenuation constant for TEM wave.

12-17. An air-filled hollow rectangular wave guide has cross-sectional dimensions $y_1 = 6$ cm and $z_1 = 10$ cm. Find the cutoff frequencies for the following modes: TM_{10}, TM_{20}, TM_{11}, TM_{21}.

Ans.: TM_{10} and TM_{20} not passed; TM_{11} 2,920 Mc/sec; TM_{21} 3,907 Mc/sec.

12-18. A hollow rectangular wave guide of dimensions $y_1 = 3$ cm and $z_1 = 10$ cm is filled with a lossless dielectric of relative permittivity 2. (a) Find the transverse impedance for a TE_{20} mode at twice its cutoff frequency. (b) Find the phase velocity of the TE_{20} mode at twice its cutoff frequency.

12-19. A TEM wave is traveling in an infinite-parallel-plane transmission line with 10 cm wall separation. Given that the peak value (in time) of the electric field is 100 volts/meter and that the wall conductivity is 5.7×10^7 mhos/meter, find (a) the average Poynting vector into the walls; (b) the attenuation constant in decibels per meter. The frequency is 300 Mc/sec.

12-20. Show that the solutions for the field components of a TE mode in a rectangular guide satisfy Maxwell's equations.

12-21. A 100-Mc/sec TEM traveling wave in an infinite air-filled parallel-plane transmission line with 5 cm separation has an electric field intensity of 100 volts/meter at a point P. If the guide walls have an intrinsic impedance whose real part is 0.1 ohm, (a) find the average power at P in the direction of transmission per meter width of guide; (b) find the average Poynting vector into one wall at P; (c) find the electric field intensity at a point 500 meters from P in the direction of transmission.

12-22. In a hollow rectangular wave guide with TE_{10} mode show that the ratio of the voltage V between the top and bottom of the guide (at the middle) to the longitudinal current I on the upper or lower inside surface is an impedance given by $Z = V/I = (\pi y_1/2z_1)Z_{yz}$, where y_1 = height of guide, z_1 = width of guide, and Z_{yz} = transverse impedance.

12-23. Show that the attenuation constant for a TE_{mo} wave at frequencies above cutoff in a hollow rectangular wave guide of height y_1 and width z_1 is

$$\alpha = \frac{2 \operatorname{Re} Z_c[(\lambda_0/\lambda_{oc})^2 + (z_1/2y_1)]}{z_1 \operatorname{Re} Z_d \sqrt{1 - (\lambda_0/\lambda_{oc})^2}}$$

12-24. Show that the group velocity u in a hollow rectangular single-conductor wave guide (equal to the velocity of energy transport) is given by

$$u = v_0 \sqrt{1 - \left(\frac{n\lambda_0}{2y_1}\right)^2 - \left(\frac{m\lambda_0}{2z_1}\right)^2}$$

$$= v_0 \sqrt{1 - \left(\frac{\lambda_0}{\lambda_{oc}}\right)^2}$$

where λ_0 = wavelength in unbounded medium and λ_{oc} = cutoff wavelength.   Both λ_0 and λ_{oc} should be distinguished from λ, the wavelength in the guide.

Note that it follows that $uv = v_0^2$, where v = phase velocity in guide and v_0 = phase velocity in an unbounded medium.

CHAPTER 13

ANTENNAS

13-1. Introduction. In previous chapters our attention has been focused on situations where the energy is confined within a system or is guided along it. No consideration has been given to *radiation*, that is, the loss of energy from a system into free space. While transmission lines or wave guides are usually made so as to minimize radiation, antennas are designed to radiate energy as effectively as possible. In fact, radiation is the primary function of a transmitting antenna.

In general, a *transmitting antenna may be defined as the structure associated with the region of transition between a guided wave and a free-space wave,* or vice versa for a receiving antenna. In this chapter a few of the fundamental properties of antennas are discussed.[1]

13-2. Propagation Time and Wavelength. The wave radiated from an antenna spreads out in all directions much like an expanding spherical soap bubble having the antenna at its center. The time it takes this wave to reach a distance r from the antenna (or source) is

$$\frac{r}{c} \quad \text{seconds}$$

where r = distance (meters)
   c = velocity of light ($= 3 \times 10^8$ meters/sec)
The quantity r/c is the propagation time for the wave.

All points at a distance r from the antenna have the same phase.[2] Other points of identical phase are situated at a radial distance of 1 wavelength (or integral multiples thereof) as suggested in Fig. 13-1, the wavelength being given by

$$\lambda = \frac{c}{f} = cT \quad \text{meters} \tag{13-1}$$

where c = velocity of light ($=3 \times 10^8$ meters/sec)
   f = frequency (cycles/sec)
   $T = 1/f$ = period (sec)

[1] For a more detailed treatment of antennas see, for example, J. D. Kraus, "Antennas," McGraw-Hill Book Company, Inc., New York, 1950.

[2] It is assumed that r is large compared with the size of the antenna and also that r is measured from the phase center of the antenna.

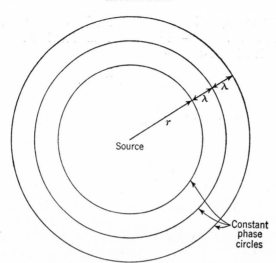

FIG. 13-1. Constant phase circles of field radiated from source.

13-3. Retarded Potentials. In dealing with antennas or radiating systems the propagation time is a matter of great importance. Thus, if an alternating current is flowing in the short element in Fig. 13-2, the effect of the current is not felt instantaneously at the point P but only after an interval equal to the time required for the disturbance to propagate over the distance r.

Accordingly, instead of writing the current I as

$$I = I_0 \sin \omega t \qquad (13\text{-}2)$$

which implies instantaneous propagation of the effect of the current, we can introduce the time of propagation (or retardation time[1]), as done by Lorentz, and write

$$[I] = I_0 \sin \omega \left(t - \frac{r}{c} \right) \qquad (13\text{-}3)$$

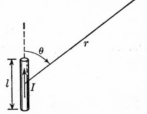

FIG. 13-2. Short current-carrying element.

where $[I]$ is called the *retarded current*. The brackets [ ] may be added, as here, to indicate explicity that the current is retarded.

Equation (13-3) is a statement of the fact that the disturbance at a time t and at a distance r from the element is caused by a current $[I]$ that occurred at an earlier time $t - (r/c)$. The time difference r/c is the interval required for the disturbance to travel the distance r.

It is to be noted that we dealt with retarded quantities in Chap. 9 in connection with wave propagation, although the term "retarded" was

[1] Called *retardation time* because the phase of the wave at P is retarded with respect to the phase of the current in the element by an angle $\omega r/c$.

not used. For example, in Chap. 9 a solution of the wave equation is given that involves $\sin(\omega t - \beta x)$ which is similar in form to the trigonometric function in (13-3) since[1]

$$\sin \omega \left(t - \frac{r}{c} \right) = \sin(\omega t - \beta r)$$

where $\beta = \omega/c = 2\pi/\lambda$ = phase constant

In complex form (13-2) is[2]

$$[I] = I_0 e^{j\omega\left(t-\frac{r}{c}\right)} = I_0 e^{j(\omega t - \beta r)} \tag{13-4}$$

In the more general situation where the current is distributed we may write for the retarded current density

$$[\mathbf{J}] = \mathbf{J}_0 e^{j\omega\left(t-\frac{r}{c}\right)} = \mathbf{J}_0 e^{j(\omega t - \beta r)} \tag{13-5}$$

Introducing this value of current density in (4-176) for the vector potential, we obtain a *retarded vector potential* that is applicable in time-varying situations where the distances involved are significant in terms of the wavelength. That is, the retarded vector potential is

$$[\mathbf{A}] = \frac{\mu_0}{4\pi} \int_v \frac{[\mathbf{J}]}{r} \, dv = \frac{\mu_0}{4\pi} \int_v \frac{\mathbf{J}_0 e^{j\omega\left(t-\frac{r}{c}\right)}}{r} \cdot dv \tag{13-6}$$

Likewise the *scalar potential* V may be put in the retarded form

$$[V] = \frac{1}{4\pi\epsilon_0} \int_v \frac{[\rho]}{r} \, dv \tag{13-7}$$

where $[V]$ = retarded scalar potential

$$[\rho] = \rho_0 e^{j\omega\left(t-\frac{r}{c}\right)} = \text{retarded charge density (coulombs/meter}^3)$$

13-4. The Small Loop Antenna.[3] In Chap. 8 it was shown that the inductance L of an inductor that is very small compared with the wavelength is

$$L = \oint \frac{\mathbf{A}}{I} \cdot d\mathbf{l} \qquad \text{henrys} \tag{13-8}$$

---

[1] The expression $\sin(\omega t - \beta x)$ in Chap. 9 refers to a plane wave traveling in the x direction. The relation $\sin \omega(t - r/c)$ or $\sin(\omega t - \beta r)$ refers to a spherical wave traveling in the radial direction. An important point of difference between a plane and a spherical wave is that a plane wave suffers no attenuation (in a lossless medium) but a spherical wave does because it expands over a larger and larger region as it propagates.

[2] It is understood that the instantaneous value of current is given either by the imaginary (Im) or the real (Re) part of the exponential expression in (13-4).

[3] S. Ramo and J. R. Whinnery, "Fields and Waves in Modern Radio," John Wiley & Sons, Inc., New York, 1944, p. 189.

where $\mathbf{A}/I$ is integrated along the entire length of the conductor of which the inductor is made.   This relation neglects the effects of propagation time.

Suppose that the inductor consists of a single-turn wire loop situated in air as illustrated in Fig. 13-3.   At low frequencies, where the loop circumference is very small compared with the wavelength, the inductance L is as given by (13-8).   Assuming that the wire is perfectly conducting, the loop has zero resistance, and therefore the impedance Z appearing at the loop terminals is a pure reactance (that is, $Z = j\omega L$).

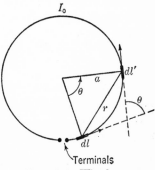

Fig. 13-3. Wire loop.

Consider now that the frequency is raised sufficiently so that the loop circumference is a significant fraction of a wavelength (say of the order of $\frac{1}{8}$ wavelength or more).   As it stands, (13-8) is not adequate for this situation since it neglects the propagation time.   However, by replacing $\mathbf{A}$ by the retarded vector potential $[\mathbf{A}]$, as given in (13-6), Eq. (13-8) may be applied to this situation.   It is assumed that the loop is small enough so that the current is substantially of uniform amplitude and in phase around the loop.   This is a good approximation for a small loop with a circumference of less than $\frac{1}{3}$ wavelength.   Thus, (13-8) becomes

$$L = \oint \frac{[\mathbf{A}]}{I} \cdot d\mathbf{l} \qquad \text{henrys} \tag{13-9}$$

where $[\mathbf{A}] = \dfrac{\mu_0}{4\pi} \displaystyle\int_v \dfrac{\mathbf{J}_0 e^{j(\omega t - \beta r)}}{r}\, dv \qquad$ henry-amp/meter

$\qquad I = I_0 e^{j\omega t} \qquad$ amp

For the case of a wire loop with current of amplitude I_0, $[\mathbf{A}]$ reduces to

$$[\mathbf{A}] = \frac{\mu_0 I_0}{4\pi} \oint \frac{e^{j(\omega t - \beta r)}}{r}\, d\mathbf{l}' \tag{13-10}$$

where the integration is carried out around the entire loop.   The infinitesimal element of path length $d\mathbf{l}'$ is at a distance r from the element $d\mathbf{l}$, appearing in (13-9), as shown in Fig. 13-3.

Substituting (13-10) for $[\mathbf{A}]$ in (13-9) yields

$$L = \frac{\mu_0}{4\pi} \oint\oint \frac{e^{-j\beta r}}{r}\, d\mathbf{l}' \cdot d\mathbf{l} \tag{13-11}$$

or

$$L = \frac{\mu_0}{4\pi} \oint\oint \frac{e^{-j\beta r}}{r} \cos\theta\, dl'\, dl \tag{13-12}$$

Expressing $e^{-j\beta r}$ in terms of its real and imaginary parts,

$$L = \frac{\mu_0}{4\pi} \oint\oint \frac{\cos \beta r - j \sin \beta r}{r} \cos \theta \, dl' \, dl \qquad (13\text{-}13)$$

When a is much smaller than the wavelength $(r \ll \lambda)$, βr is much less than unity $(\beta r \ll 1)$. It follows that $\cos \beta r$ then approaches unity, and $\sin \beta r$ approaches zero, so that

$$L = \frac{\mu_0}{4\pi} \oint\oint \frac{1}{r} \cos \theta \, dl' \, dl \qquad \text{henrys} \qquad (13\text{-}14)$$

This is Neumann's low-frequency inductance formula for a wire loop. This relation is actually (13-8) applied to a wire loop.

However, at higher frequencies βr may become significant so that it is seen from (13-13) that L has both real and imaginary parts. That is,

$$L = L' + jL'' \qquad \text{henrys} \qquad (13\text{-}15)$$

where $L' = \operatorname{Re} L$
$L'' = \operatorname{Im} L$

It follows that the terminal impedance of the loop is

$$Z = j\omega L = -\omega L'' + j\omega L' \qquad \text{ohms} \qquad (13\text{-}16)$$

Thus, the real part of L $(= L')$ is the true inductance, while ω times the imaginary part of L $(= \omega L'')$ is a resistance. This resistance is not due to the resistivity of the wire of the loop but is *in addition* to any such resistance. In fact, in the present discussion the resistivity of the wire is assumed to be zero $(\sigma = \infty)$. Therefore $\omega L''$ is called a *radiation resistance*, since the power dissipated in this resistance $(= \frac{1}{2}I_0^2 \omega L''$ watts) is equal to the power radiated into space.

Let us now proceed to find the value of this radiation resistance for a loop that is small but not negligibly small compared with the wavelength (circumference about $\frac{1}{3}$ wavelength or less). From (13-16) this radiation resistance is given by

$$R = -\omega \operatorname{Im} L = \frac{\omega \mu_0}{4\pi} \oint\oint \frac{\sin \beta r}{r} \cos \theta \, dl' \, dl \qquad (13\text{-}17)$$

Using the first two terms of the series expansion for $\sin \beta r$,

$$R = \frac{\omega \mu_0}{4\pi} \oint\oint \left(\beta - \frac{\beta^3 r^2}{3!} \right) \cos \theta \, dl' \, dl \qquad (13\text{-}18)$$

Noting that $r = 2a \sin (\theta/2)$ and that $dl' = a \, d\theta$,

$$R = \frac{\omega \mu_0}{4\pi} \oint \int_0^{2\pi} \frac{-4(\beta a)^3}{3!} \sin^2 \frac{\theta}{2} \cos \theta \, d\theta \, dl \qquad (13\text{-}19)$$

or

$$R = \frac{\omega\mu_0(\beta a)^3}{12} \oint dl \qquad\qquad (13\text{-}20)$$

Also, since $dl = a\,d\theta$,

$$R = \frac{\omega\mu_0(\beta a)^3}{12} \int_0^{2\pi} a\,d\theta = \frac{\pi\omega\mu_0\beta^3 a^4}{6} \qquad (13\text{-}21)$$

or

$$R = 31{,}171 \left(\frac{A}{\lambda^2}\right)^2 \quad \text{ohms} \qquad\qquad (13\text{-}22)$$

where $A = \pi a^2$ = area of loop (meters^2)
$\qquad \lambda$ = wavelength (meters)

Equation (13-22) gives the radiation resistance of a small loop antenna. It is about 2 per cent in error when the loop area is 0.01 wavelength^2 (circumference about $\frac{1}{3}$ wavelength). For smaller loops the error decreases. Equation (13-22) was developed here for a circular loop. However, it also applies to loops of other shape (square, triangular, etc.) provided the area is equal to A.

Example. Find the radiation resistance of a single-turn circular loop with a circumference of $\frac{1}{4}$ wavelength.

Solution. The area of the loop is

$$A = \pi a^2 = \pi \left(\frac{\lambda}{8\pi}\right)^2 = 0.00497\lambda^2$$

Hence the radiation resistance is

$$R = 31{,}171\,(0.00497)^2 = 0.77 \text{ ohm}$$

This is a small value of radiation resistance. However, if the resistance of the loop due to the resistivity of the wire is small compared with the radiation resistance, the loop may be an efficient radiator. As the frequency is decreased (circumference in wavelengths less), the radiation resistance rapidly reduces to such a small value that for practical purposes radiation is negligible.

The change in behavior of the loop as the frequency is increased may also be explained qualitatively as follows. Consider the small square wire loop shown in Fig. 13-4. The loop is in the x-y plane with its center at the origin. Assuming that the loop is small compared with the wavelength ($l \ll \lambda$), an alternating emf applied at the terminals will cause an alternating current I of uniform amplitude at all points of the loop. According to (7-151) this time-changing current produces an electric field **E**. At a large distance x_1 along the x axis the total electric field is the resultant of contributions E_1 and E_3 caused by the current in sides 1 and 3.[1] These component fields are substantially equal in magnitude

[1] Sides 2 and 4 yield no field at x_1.

but opposite in phase as indicated by the phase diagram in Fig. 13-5a, so that the total field is negligible.

Suppose now that the size of the loop is not negligible compared with the wavelength but that each side is, say, $\frac{1}{12}$ wavelength long. It is still

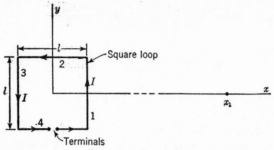

Fig. 13-4. Square loop.

assumed that the instantaneous current is uniform around the loop. In this case the field component E_3 at x_1 is not in opposite phase with respect to E_1 but is retarded by 30° (= 360°/12), as indicated in Fig. 13-5b. This retardation results from the fact that side 3 of the loop is farther from x_1 than side 1, so that the component field E_3 takes longer to reach x_1 and hence is delayed in time or retarded in phase with respect to E_1. The resultant electric field E is not negligible and represents a field

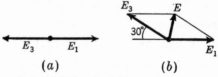

$$(a) \qquad\qquad (b)$$

Fig. 13-5. (a) Phase relation of electric fields at x_1 due to square loop (Fig. 13-4) when l is small compared with a wavelength and (b) when l is about $\frac{1}{12}$ wavelength (0.083λ).

that is *radiated* by the loop. In this case the loop may be regarded as an antenna.

The above picture is oversimplified, but it serves to illustrate the fact that although radiation is negligible when the loop is small compared to the wavelength ($l \ll \lambda$), the radiated field may be significant when the loop perimeter is $\frac{1}{3}$ wavelength. If the perimeter (and area) is increased further the radiated field becomes even more important.

13-5. The Short Dipole Antenna. A short linear conductor is often called a short *dipole*. In the following discussion, a short dipole is always of finite length even though it may be very short. If the dipole is vanishingly short, it is an infinitesimal dipole.

Any linear antenna may be regarded as composed of a large number of short dipoles connected in series. Thus, a knowledge of the properties of the short dipole is useful in determining the properties of longer dipoles or conductors of more complex shape such as are commonly used in practice.

Let us consider a short dipole such as shown in Fig. 13-6a. The length l is very short compared with the wavelength ($l \ll \lambda$). Plates at the ends of the dipole provide capacitance loading. The short length and the

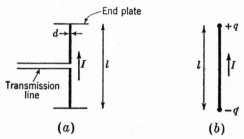

FIG. 13-6. (a) Short dipole antenna and (b) its equivalent.

presence of these plates result in a uniform current I along the entire length l of the dipole. The dipole may be energized by a balanced transmission line, as shown. It is assumed that the transmission line does not radiate, and its presence will therefore be disregarded. Radiation from the end plates is also considered to be negligible. The diameter d of the dipole is small compared with its length ($d \ll l$). Thus, for purposes of analysis we may consider that the short dipole appears as in Fig. 13-6b. Here it consists simply of a thin conductor of length l with a uniform current I and point charges q at the ends. According to (3-61) the current and charge are related by

$$\frac{dq}{dt} = I \qquad (13\text{-}23)$$

Let us now proceed to find the fields everywhere around a short dipole. Let the dipole of length l be placed coincident with the z axis and with its center at the origin as in Fig. 13-7. At any point P the electric field has, in general,

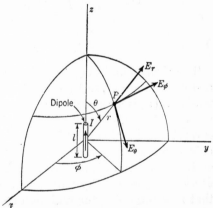

FIG. 13-7. Relation of dipole to coordinates.

three components, E_θ, E_ϕ, and E_r, as shown. It is assumed that the medium surrounding the dipole is air or vacuum.

From (7-151) the electric field intensity $\mathbf{E}$ at any point P is expressed by

$$\mathbf{E} = -\boldsymbol{\nabla}V - \frac{\partial \mathbf{A}}{\partial t} \qquad \text{volts/meter} \qquad (13\text{-}24)$$

where V = electric scalar potential at point P (volts)

       A = vector potential at point P (henry-amp/meter)

From (4-168) the magnetic field H at any point P is

$$H = \frac{1}{\mu_0} \nabla \times A \qquad \text{amp/meter} \qquad (13\text{-}25)$$

where μ_0 = permeability of air

       A = vector potential at point P (henry-amp/meter)

If the scalar potential V and the vector potential A at the point P are known, the electric and magnetic fields E and H at P can then be determined by means of (13-24) and (13-25). Since we are interested in the fields not only at points near the dipole but also at distances that are comparable to and larger than the wavelength, we must use the retarded potentials given in (13-6) and (13-7). Thus we have

$$E = -\nabla[V] - \frac{\partial[A]}{\partial t} = -\nabla[V] - j\omega[A] \qquad \text{volts/meter} \quad (13\text{-}26)$$

and

$$H = \frac{1}{\mu_0} \nabla \times [A] \qquad \text{amp/meter} \qquad (13\text{-}27)$$

where

$$[V] = \frac{1}{4\pi\epsilon_0} \int_v \frac{\rho_0 e^{j\omega\left(t - \frac{r}{c}\right)}}{r}\, dv \qquad \text{volts}$$

$$[A] = \frac{\mu_0}{4\pi} \int_v \frac{J_0 e^{j\omega\left(t - \frac{r}{c}\right)}}{r}\, dv \qquad \text{henry-amp/meter}$$

The electric and magnetic fields due to any configuration of currents and charges are given by (13-26) and (13-27), where the retarded scalar potential $[V]$ is a quantity that depends only on the charges (stationary), and the retarded vector potential $[A]$ is a quantity that depends only on the currents. Equation (13-27) indicates that the magnetic field H depends only on the currents, while (13-26) indicates that the electric field E depends on *both* the currents and the charges. However, the effect of the charges decreases more rapidly with distance than the effect of the currents so that in determining the radiation field (at large distances from a current and charge distribution) only the currents need be considered. Since the retarded potentials will be used exclusively in the following development the brackets will be omitted for the sake of simplicity, it being understood that the potentials are retarded.

We shall now proceed to find the electric and magnetic fields everywhere from a short dipole by first determining the retarded vector and scalar potentials and then substituting these values in (13-26) and (13-27) and performing the indicated operations.

Referring to Fig. 13-7 or 13-8, the current is entirely in the z direction. Hence, it follows that the retarded vector potential has only a z component. Its value is

$$A_z = |\mathbf{A}| = \frac{\mu_0 I_0}{4\pi} \int_{-l/2}^{l/2} \frac{e^{j(\omega t - \beta s)}}{s} \, dz \qquad (13\text{-}28)$$

where I_0 = amplitude (peak value in time) of current (same at all points along dipole) (amp)

μ_0 = permeability of free space ($= 4\pi \times 10^{-7}$ henry/meter)

dz = element of length of conductor (meters)

ω = radian frequency ($= 2\pi f$ where f = frequency in cps)

t = time (sec)

s = distance from dz to point P (see Fig. 13-8) (meters)

β = phase constant (rad/meter) ($= 2\pi/\lambda$, where λ = wavelength in meters)

If the distance from the dipole is large compared with its length ($r \gg l$) and if the wavelength is large compared with the length ($\lambda \gg l$) we can put $s = r$ and neglect the magnitude and phase differences of the contributions from the different parts of the wire.[1] Thus (13-28) becomes

$$A_z = \frac{\mu_0 I_0 l e^{j(\omega t - \beta r)}}{4\pi r} \qquad (13\text{-}29)$$

The electric charge is confined to the ends of the dipole; so turning our attention now to the retarded scalar potential, its value is

$$V = \frac{q_0}{4\pi\epsilon_0} \left[\frac{e^{j(\omega t - \beta s_1)}}{s_1} - \frac{e^{j(\omega t - \beta s_2)}}{s_2} \right] \quad \text{volts} \qquad (13\text{-}30)$$

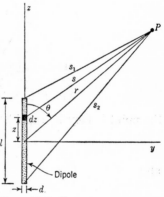

FIG. 13-8. Geometry for short dipole.

where q_0 = amplitude (peak value in time) of charge at ends of dipole (coulombs)

s_1 = distance from upper end of dipole to P

s_2 = distance from lower end of dipole to P

From (13-23)

$$q = \int I \, dt = \frac{I}{j\omega} \qquad (13\text{-}31)$$

---

[1] If r is large compared with l but λ is not large compared with l, we may put $s = r$ in the denominator in (13-28) and neglect the differences in magnitude. However, in such cases we should retain s in the exponential expression since the difference in phase of the contributions may be significant.

where $q = q_0 e^{j(\omega t - \beta s)}$ = retarded charge (coulombs)

$I = I_0 e^{j(\omega t - \beta s)}$ = retarded current (amp)

It follows that

$$q_0 = \frac{I_0}{j\omega} \tag{13-32}$$

so that (13-30) can be reexpressed

$$V = \frac{I_0}{4\pi\epsilon_0 j\omega}\left[\frac{e^{j(\omega t - \beta s_1)}}{s_1} - \frac{e^{j(\omega t - \beta s_2)}}{s_2}\right] \tag{13-33}$$

When $r \gg l$, the lines of length s_1 and s_2 from the ends of the dipole to

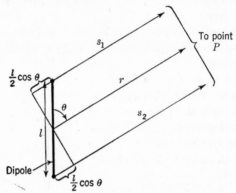

FIG. 13-9. Relations for short dipole when $r \gg l$.

the point P may be considered parallel, as shown in Fig. 13-9, so that

$$s_1 = r - \frac{l}{2}\cos\theta \tag{13-34}$$

and

$$s_2 = r + \frac{l}{2}\cos\theta \tag{13-35}$$

Substituting (13-34) and (13-35) into (13-33) and clearing fractions yields

$$V = \frac{I_0 e^{j(\omega t - \beta r)}}{4\pi\epsilon_0 j\omega}\left[\frac{[r + (l/2)\cos\theta]e^{j\frac{\beta l}{2}\cos\theta} - [r - (l/2)\cos\theta]e^{-j\frac{\beta l}{2}\cos\theta}}{r^2}\right] \tag{13-36}$$

where the term $(l^2\cos^2\theta)/4$ in the denominator has been neglected in comparison with r^2 since $r \gg l$. By de Moivre's theorem, (13-36) becomes

$$V = \frac{I_0 e^{j(\omega t - \beta r)}}{4\pi\epsilon_0 j\omega r^2}\left[\left(\cos\frac{\beta l\cos\theta}{2} + j\sin\frac{\beta l\cos\theta}{2}\right)\left(r + \frac{l}{2}\cos\theta\right)\right.$$
$$\left. - \left(\cos\frac{\beta l\cos\theta}{2} - j\sin\frac{\beta l\cos\theta}{2}\right)\left(r - \frac{l}{2}\cos\theta\right)\right] \tag{13-37}$$

Since it is assumed that the wavelength is much greater than the length of the dipole ($\lambda \gg l$),

$$\cos \frac{\beta l \cos \theta}{2} = \cos \frac{\pi l \cos \theta}{\lambda} \simeq 1 \qquad (13\text{-}38)$$

and

$$\sin \frac{\beta l \cos \theta}{2} \simeq \frac{\beta l \cos \theta}{2} \qquad (13\text{-}39)$$

Introducing (13-38) and (13-39) into (13-37), the expression for the scalar potential reduces to

$$V = \frac{I_0 l e^{j(\omega t - \beta r)} \cos \theta}{4\pi\epsilon_0 c} \left(\frac{1}{r} + \frac{c}{j\omega} \frac{1}{r^2} \right) \qquad \text{volts} \qquad (13\text{-}40)[1]$$

where I_0 = amplitude (peak value in time) of current (amp)
  l = length of dipole (meters)
  ω = radian frequency ($= 2\pi f$, where f = frequency in cps)
  β = phase constant (rad/meter) ($= 2\pi/\lambda$, where λ = wavelength in meters)
  t = time (sec)
  θ = angle between dipole and radius vector of length r to point P (dimensionless)
  ϵ_0 = permittivity of free space ($= 8.85 \times 10^{-12}$ farad/meter)
  c = velocity of light ($= 3 \times 10^8$ meters/sec)
  j = complex operator ($= \sqrt{-1}$)
  r = distance from center of dipole to point P (meters)

Equation (13-40) gives the retarded scalar potential and (13-29) the retarded vector potential at a distance r and at an angle θ from a short dipole. The only restrictions are that $r \gg l$ and $\lambda \gg l$. Before substituting these values in (13-26) and (13-27) let us express **E** in polar coordinates. Thus, in polar coordinates (see Fig. 13-7),

$$\mathbf{E} = \mathbf{a}_r E_r + \mathbf{a}_\theta E_\theta + \mathbf{a}_\phi E_\phi \qquad (13\text{-}41)$$

Now in polar coordinates

$$\mathbf{A} = \mathbf{a}_r A_r + \mathbf{a}_\theta A_\theta + \mathbf{a}_\phi A_\phi \qquad (13\text{-}42)$$

Fig. 13-10. Resolution of vector potential into A_r and A_θ components.

In our case **A** has only a z component so that $A_\phi = 0$, and from Fig. 13-10

$$A_r = A_z \cos \theta \qquad (13\text{-}43)$$
$$A_\theta = -A_z \sin \theta \qquad (13\text{-}44)$$

In polar coordinates we also have for the gradient of the scalar potential

$$\nabla V = \mathbf{a}_r \frac{\partial V}{\partial r} + \mathbf{a}_\theta \frac{1}{r} \frac{\partial V}{\partial \theta} + \mathbf{a}_\phi \frac{1}{r \sin \theta} \frac{\partial V}{\partial \phi} \qquad (13\text{-}45)$$

[1] Note that $1/\epsilon_0 c = \mu_0 c = \sqrt{\mu_0/\epsilon_0} = 376.7$ ohms.

It follows from (13-26) and the above relations that the components of $\mathbf{E}$ are

$$E_r = -j\omega A_r - \frac{\partial V}{\partial r} = -j\omega A_z \cos\theta - \frac{\partial V}{\partial r} \qquad (13\text{-}46)$$

$$E_\theta = -j\omega A_\theta - \frac{1}{r}\frac{\partial V}{\partial \theta} = j\omega A_z \sin\theta - \frac{1}{r}\frac{\partial V}{\partial \theta} \qquad (13\text{-}47)$$

$$E_\phi = -j\omega A_\phi - \frac{1}{r\sin\theta}\frac{\partial V}{\partial \phi} = -\frac{1}{r\sin\theta}\frac{\partial V}{\partial \phi} \qquad (13\text{-}48)$$

Now introducing the value of A_z from (13-29) and V from (13-40) into these equations, we find that $E_\phi = 0$ (since V is independent of ϕ so that $\partial V/\partial\phi = 0$) and also that

$$E_r = \frac{I_0 l e^{j(\omega t - \beta r)}\cos\theta}{2\pi\epsilon_0}\left(\frac{1}{cr^2} + \frac{1}{j\omega r^3}\right) \qquad (13\text{-}49)$$

and

$$E_\theta = \frac{I_0 l e^{j(\omega t - \beta r)}\sin\theta}{4\pi\epsilon_0}\left(\frac{j\omega}{c^2 r} + \frac{1}{cr^2} + \frac{1}{j\omega r^3}\right) \qquad (13\text{-}50)$$

Turning our attention now to the magnetic field, this may be calculated by (13-27). In polar coordinates the curl of $\mathbf{A}$ is

$$\nabla \times \mathbf{A} = \frac{\mathbf{a}_r}{r\sin\theta}\left[\frac{\partial(\sin\theta\, A_\phi)}{\partial\theta} - \frac{\partial(A_\theta)}{\partial\phi}\right]$$
$$+ \frac{\mathbf{a}_\theta}{r\sin\theta}\left[\frac{\partial A_r}{\partial\phi} - \frac{\partial(r\sin\theta)A_\phi}{\partial r}\right] + \frac{\mathbf{a}_\phi}{r}\left[\frac{\partial(rA_\theta)}{\partial r} - \frac{\partial A_r}{\partial\theta}\right] \qquad (13\text{-}51)$$

Since $A_\phi = 0$, the first and fourth terms of (13-51) are zero. From (13-29), (13-43), and (13-44) we note that A_r and A_θ are independent of ϕ, so that the second and third terms of (13-51) are also zero. Thus, only the last two terms in (13-51) contribute so that $\nabla \times \mathbf{A}$ has only a ϕ component. Introducing (13-43) and (13-44) into (13-51), performing the indicated operations, and substituting this result into (13-27), we find that $H_r = H_\theta = 0$ and that

$$H_\phi = |\mathbf{H}| = \frac{I_0 l e^{j(\omega t - \beta r)}\sin\theta}{4\pi}\left(\frac{j\omega}{cr} + \frac{1}{r^2}\right) \qquad (13\text{-}52)$$

Thus the electric and magnetic fields from the dipole have only three components E_r, E_θ, and H_ϕ. The components E_ϕ, H_r, and H_θ are everywhere zero.

When r is very large, the terms involving $1/r^2$ and $1/r^3$ in (13-49), (13-50), and (13-52) can be neglected in comparison with terms in $1/r$. Thus, in the *far field* E_r is negligible and we have effectively only two field components, E_θ and H_ϕ, given by

$$E_\theta = \frac{j\omega I_0 l e^{j(\omega t - \beta r)} \sin \theta}{4\pi\epsilon_0 c^2 r} = j\,\frac{30 I_0 \beta l}{r}\, e^{j(\omega t - \beta r)} \sin \theta \qquad (13\text{-}53)$$

$$H_\phi = \frac{j\omega I_0 l e^{j(\omega t - \beta r)} \sin \theta}{4\pi c r} = j\,\frac{I_0 \beta l}{4\pi r}\, e^{j(\omega t - \beta r)} \sin \theta \qquad (13\text{-}54)$$

Taking the ratio of E_θ to H_ϕ as given by (13-53) and (13-54), we obtain

$$\frac{E_\theta}{H_\phi} = \frac{1}{\epsilon_0 c} = \sqrt{\frac{\mu_0}{\epsilon_0}} = 376.7 \text{ ohms} \qquad (13\text{-}55)$$

This is the intrinsic impedance of free space.

It is to be noted that E_θ and H_ϕ are in time phase in the far field. Thus, **E** and **H** in the far field of the spherical wave from the dipole are related in the same manner as in a plane traveling wave. Both are also proportional to $\sin \theta$. That is, both are maximum when $\theta = 90°$ and a minimum when $\theta = 0$ (in the direction of the dipole axis). This variation of E_θ (or H_ϕ) with angle may be portrayed by a *field pattern* as in Fig. 13-11, the length ρ of the radius vector being proportional to the value of the far field (E_θ or H_ϕ) in that direction from the dipole. The pattern in Fig. 13-11a is one-half of a three-dimensional pattern and illustrates that the fields are a function of θ but are independent of ϕ. The pattern in Fig. 13-11b is two-dimensional and represents a cross section through the three-dimensional pattern. The three-dimensional far-field pattern of the short dipole is doughnut-shaped, while the two-dimensional pattern has the shape of a figure of eight.

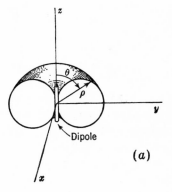

(a)

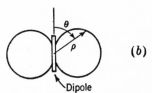

(b)

Fig. 13-11. (a) Three-dimensional and (b) two-dimensional field pattern of far field (E_θ or H_ϕ) from a short dipole.

From (13-49), (13-50), and (13-52) we note that for a small value of r the electric field has two components, E_r and E_θ, both of which are in time phase quadrature with the magnetic field H_ϕ. Thus, in the *near field*, **E** and **H** are related as in a standing wave. At intermediate distances, E_θ and E_r can approach time phase quadrature with each other so that the total electric field vector rotates in a plane parallel to the direction of propagation, exhibiting the phenomenon of cross-field (see Sec. 9-15).

In the far field the energy flow is real. That is, the energy flow is always radially outward. This energy is radiated. As a function of angle it is maximum at the equator ($\theta = 90°$). In the near field the energy flow is largely reactive. That is, energy flows out and back twice per cycle without being radiated. There is also angular energy flow (in the θ direction). This energy picture is suggested by Fig. 13-12,

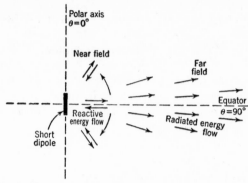

FIG. 13-12. Energy flow in near and far regions of short dipole.

where the arrows represent the direction of energy flow at successive instants.[1]

Let us now consider the situation at very low frequencies. This will be referred to as the *quasi-stationary* case. Noting (13-32), the field components can be expressed

$$E_r = \frac{q_0 l e^{j(\omega t - \beta r)} \cos \theta}{2\pi\epsilon_0} \left(\frac{j\omega}{cr^2} + \frac{1}{r^3} \right) \qquad (13\text{-}56)$$

$$E_\theta = \frac{q_0 l e^{j(\omega t - \beta r)} \sin \theta}{4\pi\epsilon_0} \left(-\frac{\omega^2}{c^2 r} + \frac{j\omega}{cr^2} + \frac{1}{r^3} \right) \qquad (13\text{-}57)$$

$$H_\phi = \frac{I_0 l e^{j(\omega t - \beta r)} \sin \theta}{4\pi} \left(\frac{j\omega}{cr} + \frac{1}{r^2} \right) \qquad (13\text{-}58)$$

As the frequency approaches zero ($\omega \to 0$), the terms with ω in the numerator can be neglected. Also $e^{j(\omega t - \beta r)}$ approaches unity. Thus, for the quasi-stationary (or d-c) case[2] the field components become

$$E_r = \frac{q_0 l \cos \theta}{2\pi\epsilon_0 r^3} \qquad (13\text{-}59)$$

$$E_\theta = \frac{q_0 l \sin \theta}{4\pi\epsilon_0 r^3} \qquad (13\text{-}60)$$

$$H_\phi = \frac{I_0 l \sin \theta}{4\pi r^2} \qquad (13\text{-}61)$$

[1] The instantaneous direction and time rate of energy flow per unit area is given by the instantaneous Poynting vector ($= \mathbf{E} \times \mathbf{H}$).

[2] For this case the wavelength is very large ($\lambda \to \infty$) so that $\lambda >>> l$. We also have $r \gg l$ and hence in *this* case $\lambda \gg r$.

The electric field components, (13-59) and (13-60), are the same as (2-9) and (2-10) for a static electric dipole, while the magnetic field component H_ϕ in (13-61) is equivalent to (4-7) for a current element. Since these fields vary as $1/r^2$ or $1/r^3$, they are effectively confined to the vicinity of the dipole and radiation is negligible. At high frequencies in the far field, however, we note from (13-53) and (13-54) that the fields (E_θ and H_ϕ) vary as $1/r$. These fields are radiated and hence are often called the *radiation fields* of the dipole.

The expressions for the fields from a short dipole, developed above, are summarized in Table 13-1. In the table the restriction applies that $r \gg l$ and $\lambda \gg l$. The three field components not listed are everywhere zero, that is, $E_\phi = H_r = H_\theta = 0$.

TABLE 13-1

FIELDS OF A SHORT DIPOLE

Component	General expression	Far field	Quasi-stationary
E_r	$\dfrac{I_0 l e^{i(\omega t - \beta r)} \cos\theta}{2\pi\epsilon_0}\left[\dfrac{1}{cr^2} + \dfrac{1}{j\omega r^3}\right]$	0	$\dfrac{q_0 l \cos\theta}{2\pi\epsilon r^3}$
E_θ	$\dfrac{I_0 l e^{i(\omega t - \beta r)} \sin\theta}{4\pi\epsilon_0}\left[\dfrac{j\omega}{c^2 r} + \dfrac{1}{cr^2} + \dfrac{1}{j\omega r^3}\right]$	$\dfrac{j60\pi I_0 e^{i(\omega t - \beta r)} \sin\theta}{r} \dfrac{l}{\lambda}$	$\dfrac{q_0 l \sin\theta}{4\pi\epsilon r^3}$
H_ϕ	$\dfrac{I_0 l e^{i(\omega t - \beta r)} \sin\theta}{4\pi}\left[\dfrac{j\omega}{cr} + \dfrac{1}{r^2}\right]$	$\dfrac{jI_0 e^{i(\omega t - \beta r)} \sin\theta}{2r} \dfrac{l}{\lambda}$	$\dfrac{I_0 l \sin\theta}{4\pi r^2}$

If we had been interested only in the far field, the development following (13-29) could have been much simplified. The scalar potential V does not contribute to the far field so that both **E** and **H** may be determined from **A** alone. Thus, from (13-26), E_θ and H_ϕ of the far field may be obtained very simply from

$$E_\theta = |\mathbf{E}| = -j\omega A_\theta \qquad (13\text{-}62)$$

and

$$H_\phi = |\mathbf{H}| = \frac{E_\theta}{Z_0} = -\frac{j\omega}{Z_0} A_\theta \qquad (13\text{-}63)$$

where $Z_0 = \sqrt{\mu_0/\epsilon_0} = 376.7$ ohms. Or H_ϕ may be obtained directly from (13-27) and E_θ from this. Thus

$$H_\phi = |\mathbf{H}| = \frac{1}{\mu_0}\boldsymbol{\nabla}\times\mathbf{A} \qquad (13\text{-}64)$$

and neglecting terms in $1/r^2$,

$$E_\theta = |\mathbf{E}| = ZH_\phi = \frac{Z}{\mu_0}\boldsymbol{\nabla}\times\mathbf{A} \qquad (13\text{-}65)$$

The field relations in Table 13-1 are those for a short dipole. Longer linear antennas or large antennas of other shape may be regarded as made up of many such short dipoles. Hence the fields of these larger antennas may be obtained by integrating the field contributions from all the small dipoles making up the antenna.

13-6. Radiation Resistance of a Short Dipole. By taking the surface integral of the average Poynting vector over any surface enclosing an antenna the total power radiated by the antenna is obtained. Thus

$$P = \int_s \mathbf{S}_{av} \cdot d\mathbf{s} \qquad \text{watts} \tag{13-66}$$

where P = power radiated (watts)

$\mathbf{S}_{av}$ = average Poynting vector (watts/meter^2)

The simplest surface we might choose is a sphere with the antenna in question at the center. Since the far-field equations for an antenna are simpler than the near-field relations, it will be to our advantage to make the radius of the sphere large compared with the dimensions of the antenna. In this way the surface of the sphere lies in the far field, and only the far-field components need be considered.

Assuming no losses, the power radiated by the antenna is equal to the average power delivered to the antenna terminals. This is equal to $\frac{1}{2}I_0^2R$, where I_0 is the amplitude (peak value in time) of the current at the terminals and R is the *radiation resistance* appearing at the terminals. Thus

$$P = \tfrac{1}{2}I_0^2R \tag{13-67}$$

and the radiation resistance is

$$R = \frac{2P}{I_0^2} \qquad \text{ohms} \tag{13-68}$$

where P = radiated power (watts).

Let us now carry through the calculation, as outlined above, in order to find the radiation resistance of a short dipole. The power radiated is

$$P = \int \mathbf{S}_{av} \cdot d\mathbf{s} = \tfrac{1}{2} \int_s \text{Re}\ (\mathbf{E} \times \mathbf{H}^*) \cdot d\mathbf{s} \tag{13-69}$$

In the far field only E_θ and H_ϕ are not zero so that (13-69) reduces to

$$P = \tfrac{1}{2} \int_s \text{Re}\ E_\theta H_\phi^* \mathbf{a}_r \cdot d\mathbf{s} \tag{13-70}$$

where $\mathbf{a}_r$ = unit vector in radial direction. Thus the power flow in the far field is entirely radial (normal to surface of sphere of integration). But $\mathbf{a}_r \cdot d\mathbf{s} = ds$; so

$$P = \tfrac{1}{2} \int_s \text{Re}\ E_\theta H_\phi^*\ ds \tag{13-71}$$

where E_θ and H_ϕ^* are complex, H_ϕ^* being the complex conjugate of H_ϕ. Now $E_\theta = H_\phi Z$; so (13-71) becomes

$$P = \tfrac{1}{2} \int_s \text{Re } H_\phi H_\phi^* Z \, ds = \tfrac{1}{2} \int_s |H_\phi|^2 \text{ Re } Z \, ds \qquad (13\text{-}72)$$

Since $\text{Re } Z = \sqrt{\mu_0/\epsilon_0}$ and $ds = r^2 \sin\theta \, d\theta \, d\phi$,[1]

$$P = \frac{1}{2}\sqrt{\frac{\mu_0}{\epsilon_0}} \int_0^{2\pi} \int_0^\pi |H_\phi|^2 r^2 \sin\theta \, d\theta \, d\phi \qquad (13\text{-}73)$$

where the angles θ and ϕ are as shown in Fig. 13-7 and $|H_\phi|$ is the absolute value (or amplitude) of the H field. From (13-54) this is

$$|H_\phi| = \frac{\omega I_0 l \sin\theta}{4\pi c r} \qquad (13\text{-}74)$$

Substituting this into (13-73), we have

$$P = \frac{1}{32}\sqrt{\frac{\mu_0}{\epsilon_0}}\left(\frac{\beta I_0 l}{\pi}\right)^2 \int_0^{2\pi}\int_0^\pi \sin^3\theta \, d\theta \, d\phi \qquad (13\text{-}75)$$

Upon integration (13-75) becomes

$$P = \sqrt{\frac{\mu_0}{\epsilon_0}}\frac{(\beta I_0 l)^2}{12\pi} \quad \text{watts} \qquad (13\text{-}76)$$

This is the power radiated by the short dipole.

Substituting the power P from (13-76) into (13-68) yields for the radiation resistance of the short dipole

$$R = \sqrt{\frac{\mu_0}{\epsilon_0}}\frac{(\beta l)^2}{6\pi} \quad \text{ohms} \qquad (13\text{-}77)$$

Since $\sqrt{\mu_0/\epsilon_0} = 376.7 \simeq 120\pi$ ohms, (13-77) reduces to

$$R = 20(\beta l)^2 = 80\pi^2 \left(\frac{l}{\lambda}\right)^2 \quad \text{ohms} \qquad (13\text{-}78)$$

Example. Find the radiation resistance of a dipole antenna $\frac{1}{10}$ wavelength long. *Solution.* From (13-78)

$$R = 80\pi^2(\tfrac{1}{10})^2 = 7.9 \text{ ohms}$$

The radiation resistance of antennas other than the short dipole can be calculated as above provided the far field is known as a function of angle. Thus, from (13-68) and (13-72) the radiation resistance at the terminals

[1] Since $\sqrt{\mu_0/\epsilon_0} \simeq 120\pi \simeq E_\theta/H_\phi$ we may also write

$$P = \frac{1}{240\pi}\int_0^{2\pi}\int_0^\pi |E_\theta|^2 r^2 \sin\theta \, d\theta \, d\phi$$

of an antenna is given by

$$R = \frac{120\pi}{I_0{}^2} \int_s |H|^2 \, ds \qquad \text{ohms} \qquad (13\text{-}79)$$

where $|H|$ = amplitude of far H field (amp/meter)

I_0 = amplitude of terminal current (amp)

In Sec. 13-4 the radiation resistance of a small loop antenna was obtained by a vector potential integration. If the far field of the loop is known, the radiation resistance can also be obtained from (13-79).

If we integrate the complex Poynting vector $(= \frac{1}{2}\mathbf{E} \times \mathbf{H}^*)$ over a surface enclosing an antenna, we shall obtain, in general, both a real part equal to the power radiated and an imaginary part equal to the reactive power. Whereas the real part, or radiated power, is the same for *any* surface enclosing the antenna, the imaginary, or reactive, power obtained depends on the size and shape of the surface enclosing the antenna. For a large surface lying only in the far field the reactive power is zero, but for a surface lying in the near field it may be of considerable magnitude. In the case of a very thin linear antenna, it turns out that if the surface of integration is collapsed so as to coincide with the surface of the antenna the complex power so obtained divided by the square of the terminal current yields the terminal impedance $(R + jX)$, where R is the radiation resistance.

13-7. Directivity and Gain. The power radiated by an antenna is equal to the surface integral of the average Poynting vector over a surface enclosing the antenna, as given by (13-66). Consider that the surface is a large sphere in the far field with the antenna at the center. Then (13-66) may be written

$$P = \iint S_r r^2 \sin\theta \, d\theta \, d\phi \qquad \text{watts} \qquad (13\text{-}80)$$

where S_r = radial component of average Poynting vector (watts/meter²)

r = radius of sphere (meters)

The angles θ and ϕ are as shown in Fig. 13-7. Now S_r varies as $1/r^2$ so that the product $S_r r^2$ is independent of r. This product $S_r r^2$ is called the *radiation intensity U*. That is,

$$\text{Radiation intensity} = U = S_r r^2 \qquad (13\text{-}81)$$

Whereas S_r has the dimensions of power per area and is expressed in watts per square meter, the radiation intensity U has the dimensions of power and is expressed in watts per unit solid angle (watts per square radian or steradian).[1] Thus, (13-80) becomes

$$P = \iint U \, d\Omega \qquad \text{watts} \qquad (13\text{-}81a)$$

where $d\Omega$ = element of solid angle $(= \sin\theta \, d\theta \, d\phi$ steradians).

[1] Since radians are dimensionless, U has the dimensions of power.

Confining our attention, as above, to the far field, U is independent of r but, in general, is a function of angle (θ and ϕ).

Antennas are often applied to concentrate energy in a certain direction. A quantitative measure of an antenna's ability to perform this function is given by its directivity, which is defined as the ratio of the maximum radiation intensity to the average radiation intensity. That is,

$$\text{Directivity} = D = \frac{\text{maximum radiation intensity}}{\text{average radiation intensity}} \qquad (13\text{-}82)$$

If the radiation intensity is the same in all directions from the antenna[1] and equal to U_0, the power radiated is

$$P = \iint U_0 \, d\Omega = 4\pi U_0 \qquad (13\text{-}83)$$

Now U_0 is also the same as the *average* radiation intensity. Therefore the directivity is given by

$$D = \frac{U_m}{U_0} \quad \text{(dimensionless)} \qquad (13\text{-}84)$$

where U_m = maximum radiation intensity
      U_0 = average radiation intensity
But from (13-83), $U_0 = P/4\pi$ so that (13-84) becomes

$$D = \frac{4\pi U_m}{P} = \frac{4\pi \, (\text{maximum radiation intensity})}{\text{power radiated}} \qquad (13\text{-}85)$$

or, in general,

$$D = \frac{4\pi U_m}{\iint U \, d\Omega} \qquad (13\text{-}86)$$

Any of the above relations (13-84), (13-85), or (13-86) may be used to calculate the directivity of an antenna.

Example. Calculate the directivity of a short dipole.
Solution. From (13-81) and (13-72)

$$U = S_r r^2 = 60\pi |H_\phi|^2 r^2 \qquad (13\text{-}87)$$

where from (13-74)

$$|H_\phi| = \frac{\omega I_0 l \sin \theta}{4\pi c r} \qquad (13\text{-}88)$$

Substituting this in (13-87),

$$U = 60\pi \left(\frac{\omega I_0 l}{4\pi c}\right)^2 \sin^2 \theta \qquad (13\text{-}89)$$

and the maximum value of U is given by

$$U_m = 60\pi \left(\frac{\omega I_0 l}{4\pi c}\right)^2 \qquad (13\text{-}90)$$

---

[1] An antenna having a uniform radiation intensity in all directions is called an *isotropic* antenna. It is a hypothetical type. The directivity of an isotropic antenna is unity. This is the smallest value that the directivity can attain.

Introducing (13-89) and (13-90) into (13-86) yields for the directivity

$$D = \frac{4\pi}{\displaystyle\int_0^{2\pi}\int_0^{\pi} \sin^3 \theta \, d\theta \, d\phi} = \frac{4\pi}{\frac{8}{3}\pi} = \frac{3}{2} \tag{13-91}$$

Hence, the directivity of a short dipole is $\frac{3}{2}$. That is, the maximum radiation intensity is 1.5 times as much as if the power were radiated uniformly in all directions.

Directivity is based entirely on the shape of the far- (or radiated-) field pattern. The antenna efficiency is not involved. However, the power gain, or simply the *gain*, of an antenna does involve the efficiency. It is defined as follows:

$$\text{Gain} = G = \frac{\text{maximum radiation intensity}}{\begin{array}{c}\text{maximum radiation intensity from a refer-}\\ \text{ence antenna with the same power input}\end{array}} \tag{13-92}$$

Any convenient type of antenna may be taken as the reference. If the reference antenna is a lossless isotropic type (radiation intensity uniform in all directions), then the gain (designated G_0) is given by

$$G_0 = \frac{U_m'}{U_0} \tag{13-93}$$

where U_m' = maximum radiation intensity from antenna under consideration
U_0 = radiation intensity from a lossless (100 per cent efficient) isotropic antenna with same power input.

Now U_m' is related to the radiation intensity U_m of a 100 per cent efficient antenna by a radiation efficiency factor k. Thus,

$$G_0 = \frac{kU_m}{U_0} = kD \tag{13-95}$$

Thus, the gain of an antenna over a lossless isotropic type equals the directivity if the antenna is 100 per cent efficient ($k = 1$) but is less than the directivity if any losses are present in the antenna ($k < 1$).

The directivity D is never less than unity. Its value must lie between 1 and infinity ($1 \leq D \leq \infty$). On the other hand, the gain (G or G_0) may lie between 0 and infinity.

13-8. Receiving Antennas and Aperture. A transmitting antenna radiates energy. A receiving antenna, on the other hand, collects energy. In this connection it is often useful to consider that the receiving antenna possesses an aperture or equivalent area over which it extracts energy from a passing radio wave.

Thus, suppose that a receiving antenna is immersed in the field of a plane traveling wave as suggested in Fig. 13-13a. The antenna is terminated in a load of impedance $Z_T = R_T + jX_T$. Let the *effective* aperture A_e of the antenna be defined as the ratio of the received power to the power density (or Poynting vector) of the incident wave. The received power is equal to I^2R_T, where I is the terminal current. Therefore

$$A_e = \frac{I^2R_T}{S} = \frac{\text{received power}}{\text{power density of incident wave}} \qquad (13\text{-}96)$$

where A_e = effective aperture (meters^2)

I = rms terminal current (amp)

S = Poynting vector (or power density) of incident wave (watts/meter^2)

R_T = terminal resistance (ohms)

Replacing the antenna by its equivalent, or Thévenin, generator having an equivalent emf $\mathcal{V}$ and impedance Z_A ($= R_A + jX_A$), we may draw the equivalent circuit shown in Fig. 13-13b. The terminal current I is

$$I = \frac{\mathcal{V}}{Z_T + Z_A} \quad \text{amp} \qquad (13\text{-}97)$$

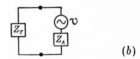

where $\mathcal{V}$ = rms emf induced by passing wave (volts)

Z_T = terminal or load impedance (ohms)

Z_A = antenna impedance (ohms)

Substituting (13-97) into (13-96), it follows that

$$A_e = \frac{\mathcal{V}^2R_T}{S[(R_A + R_T)^2 + (X_A + X_T)^2]} \qquad (13\text{-}98)$$

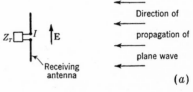

FIG. 13-13. (a) Terminated receiving antenna immersed in field of plane traveling wave and (b) equivalent circuit.

Assuming that the antenna is lossless so that R_A is entirely radiation resistance ($R_A = R_r$), the maximum power will be transferred to the load when

$$X_T = -X_A \qquad (13\text{-}99)$$

and

$$R_T = R_r \qquad (13\text{-}100)$$

Under these conditions the effective aperture is a maximum, A_{em}, as given by

$$A_{em} = \frac{\mathcal{V}^2R_T}{4SR_r{}^2} = \frac{\mathcal{V}^2}{4SR_r} \qquad (13\text{-}101)$$

The effective aperture A_e (or maximum effective aperture A_{em}) has a definite, simply defined value for all antennas.

Example 1. Find the maximum effective aperture A_{em} of a short dipole antenna.
Solution. From (13-101)

$$A_{em} = \frac{\mathcal{U}^2}{4SR_r} \tag{13-102}$$

The emf induced in the short dipole is a maximum when the dipole is parallel to the incident electric field **E**. Hence

$$\mathcal{U} = El \qquad \text{volts} \tag{13-103}$$

The Poynting vector

$$S = \frac{E^2}{Z_0} \qquad \text{watts/meter}^2 \tag{13-104}$$

where Z_0 = intrinsic impedance of medium (air or vacuum) $(= \sqrt{\mu_0/\epsilon_0})$. From (13-77) the radiation resistance

$$R_r = \sqrt{\frac{\mu_0}{\epsilon_0}} \frac{(\beta l)^2}{6\pi} \qquad \text{ohms} \tag{13-105}$$

Substituting these values for $\mathcal{U}$, S, and R_r into (13-102), the maximum effective aperture of a short dipole is

$$A_{em} = \frac{3}{8\pi} \lambda^2 = 0.119\lambda^2 \tag{13-106}$$

Thus, regardless of how small the dipole is, it can collect power over an aperture of 0.119 wavelength^2 and deliver it to its terminal impedance or load. It is assumed here that the dipole is lossless. However, in practice, losses are present due to the finite conductivity of the dipole conductor so that the actual effective aperture is less than A_{em}.

There is an interesting relation between the maximum effective aperture and the directivity of an antenna. If the directivity of an antenna is increased, the aperture is increased in direct proportion. It follows that the directivities, D_1 and D_2, of two antennas are in the same proportion as their maximum effective apertures, A_{em1} and A_{em2}. Thus

$$\frac{D_1}{D_2} = \frac{A_{em1}}{A_{em2}} \tag{13-107}$$

or

$$A_{em1} = \frac{A_{em2}}{D_2} D_1 \tag{13-108}$$

If antenna 1 is isotropic, $D_1 = 1$ and the maximum effective aperture of an isotropic antenna is then given by the ratio of the maximum effective aperture to the directivity of any antenna (antenna 2). We have previously calculated the maximum effective aperture and the directivity of a short dipole. Introducing these values into (13-108) gives

$$A_{em1} = \frac{6\lambda^2}{24\pi} = \frac{\lambda^2}{4\pi} \tag{13-109}$$

Substituting this back in (13-108), we obtain the relation that the directivity of any antenna is equal to $4\pi/\lambda^2$ times its maximum effective aperture. That is,

$$D = \frac{4\pi}{\lambda^2} A_{em} \tag{13-110}$$

Or the maximum effective aperture of any antenna is equal to $\lambda^2/4\pi$ times its directivity. That is,

$$A_{em} = \frac{\lambda^2}{4\pi} D = \frac{D}{4\pi} \lambda^2 \tag{13-111}$$

Example 2. An antenna operating at a wavelength of 2 meters has a directivity of 100. Find the maximum effective aperture of the antenna.

Solution. From (13-111) the maximum effective aperture of the antenna is

$$A_{em} = \frac{100 \times 4}{4\pi} = 31.8 \text{ meters}^2$$

13-9. The Antenna as a Terminated Transmission Line. In this section it is shown that an antenna behaves in certain respects like a section of transmission line. Consider, for instance, the coaxial transmission line shown in longitudinal section in Fig. 13-14a. This line has

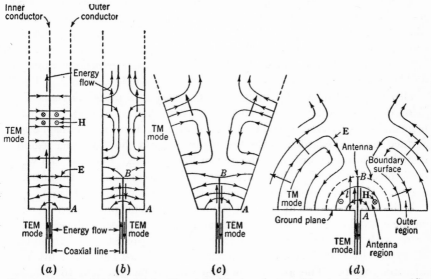

FIG. 13-14. Coaxial transmission line (a) with steps in transition to stub antenna (d).

an abrupt discontinuity at the point A, the diameter of the outer conductor being increased at this point. As a result, energy fed into the line from the bottom is partially reflected at A, producing a standing wave below A. This is suggested in the figure by the arrows, which indicate the direction of energy flow. Thus, below A there is energy flowing upward and also reflected energy flowing downward (away from A). Above A the energy flow is only upward, it being assumed that the line is infinitely long. Above and below A the field in the line is of the TEM (transverse electromagnetic) type, the direction of the electric and magnetic field lines **E** and **H** being as suggested in Fig. 13-14a.

Suppose now that the inner conductor of the coaxial line is ended at the point B, as shown in Fig. 13-14b. If the line is energized from the bottom as before, there will now be a reflection not only at A but also at B. Furthermore, there will be no transmission of energy above B unless the conductor diameter is sufficient to accommodate a higher-order mode. Assuming that the conductor diameter is sufficient, the mode excited is of the TM (transverse magnetic) type as portrayed in Fig. 13-14b. Below A the mode is still of the TEM type. This is also the predominant mode between A and B.

Let us now proceed a step further and consider the situation portrayed by the longitudinal section in Fig. 13-14c, where the outer conductor flares out into a conical, or funnel-shaped, surface. Here the situation is much as in Fig. 13-14b except that the wave above B spreads out into a larger region as it moves upward.

Finally, suppose that the outer conductor is formed at A into an infinite flat sheet, as indicated in Fig. 13-14d. We have here arrived at a familiar antenna arrangement which may be described as a stub (or unipole) antenna of length l with ground plane, the antenna being energized by a coaxial transmission line. The wave spreads out above A and is radiated into half of space. There is still a reflection at A. There is also a reflection at B although in this case it is more convenient to think of the reflection as occurring in varying amounts over an imaginary hemispherical surface of radius l with center at A. This hemispherical surface may be regarded as the boundary between the "antenna region" and the "outer region" as indicated in Fig. 13-14d. Below A the wave is of the TEM type. This is also the predominant mode in the antenna region. However, in the outer region the wave is of the TM type.[1]

If the wave reflected at B (or at the boundary hemisphere) arrives back on the coaxial line at A with equal magnitude but opposite phase as compared with the wave reflected at A, the net reflection at A is zero and all of the energy traveling up the coaxial line continues beyond A into the antenna region. The antenna is then said to be matched to the line (SWR = 1 below A). In order that the reflections be in opposite phase at A, the antenna length l may be adjusted to $\frac{1}{4}$ wavelength.[2] With l

---

[1] In a coaxial transmission line energy is conveyed in the dielectric medium between the conductors. The conductors serve only to guide the energy. Likewise, the conducting structure of an antenna guides the energy in the surrounding dielectric medium during its transition from a transmission-line mode to a radiated mode.

[2] In going from A to B and back to A the wave travels $\frac{1}{2}$ wavelength and hence is in opposite phase with respect to the wave reflected at A. Owing to end effects the length required is actually a few per cent less than $\frac{1}{4}$ wavelength.

fixed, even a slight change in frequency puts the reflections in other than phase opposition. Thus, although the standing-wave ratio may be unity at some frequency F, it tends to increase as the frequency departs from F. However, there may be a certain frequency band over which the SWR remains below some acceptable value. This is called the impedance *band width* of the antenna. The band width of a thin-stub antenna, as in Fig. 13-14d, is small. By increasing the thickness of the stub the band width may be increased. This is discussed further in the next section.

Referring again to Fig. 13-14d, we may imagine that the space outside the boundary sphere acts like a terminating impedance Z_L placed between the end of the antenna and the flat conducting sheet, as suggested in Fig. 13-15a. Proceeding a step further, the antenna itself may be regarded as a transmission line of length l, the equivalent circuit being as indicated in Fig. 13-15b. A stub of uniform cross section has a nonuniform characteristic impedance. Hence, the equivalent transmission line is drawn as a diverging (nonuniform) line. A conical-stub antenna, as in Fig. 13-16a,

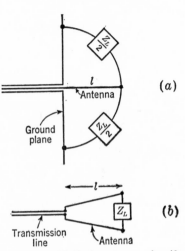

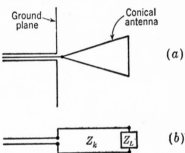

FIG. 13-15. (a) Stub antenna of uniform cross section and (b) equivalent transmission line.

FIG. 13-16. (a) Conical antenna and (b) equivalent transmission line.

however, has a uniform characteristic impedance as indicated by the equivalent line in Fig. 13-16b. If the terminating or load impedance Z_L (equivalent to the boundary hemisphere) and the characteristic impedance Z_k of the antenna are known, the input impedance of the antenna at A may be calculated using ordinary transmission-line relations, such as (11-71).[1]

Referring to Figs. 13-15b and 13-16b, the antenna has been replaced by an equivalent transmission line which acts as a transformer or match-

---

[1] This procedure has been used by Schelkunoff to calculate the input impedance of conical antennas; S. A. Schelkunoff, "Electromagnetic Waves," D. Van Nostrand Company, Inc., New York, 1943, Chap. 11.

ing section between the terminals and space as represented by a load Z_L. Thus, *the antenna itself may be regarded as a transformer (or matching section) between a two-terminal input and space* or, in the receiving case, as a transformer between space and the terminals.

13-10. Shape-Impedance Considerations. The calculation of the input (or terminal) impedance of antennas of even the simplest shape is tedious at best, while for antennas of complex shape the calculation may be of prohibitive difficulty. Fortunately it is possible in many cases to

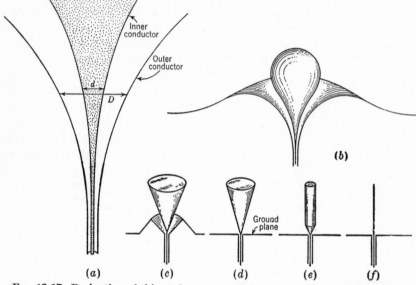

Fig. 13-17. Derivation of thin-stub antenna (f) from basic broad-band type (a).

obtain a good qualitative idea of the impedance characteristics of an antenna from its shape. This morphological approach may be illustrated with the aid of the antennas portrayed in Fig. 13-17. At (a) a coaxial transmission line (shown in longitudinal section) is flared out, with the ratio D/d of the conductor diameters maintained constant. Thus the characteristic impedance of the line is constant. If the taper is gradual and D is large where the line ends, this device radiates with little or no reflection on the line at frequencies ranging from some lower or cutoff frequency to an indefinitely high frequency. This is the ultimate in band width. At frequencies above the cutoff frequency the impedance tends to approach a constant value equal to the characteristic resistance R_0 of the transmission line as indicated by the point (R_0, 0) on the impedance diagram in Fig. 13-18.

By bending the outer conductor into a ground plane having the shape of a volcanic crater, shown cut away in Fig. 13-17b, with inner conductor of inverted teardrop form, the band width is somewhat reduced, but above the cutoff frequency the input impedance still tends to remain close to the characteristic resistance of the feed line.

Modifying the antenna further to the form of Fig. 13-17c, the impedance shows greater variation with frequency, with an impedance frequency curve as suggested by curve C in Fig. 13-18.[1] Below the lowest frequency (F) at which the impedance is a pure resistance the curve tends rapidly toward a small resistance and large negative reactance. The

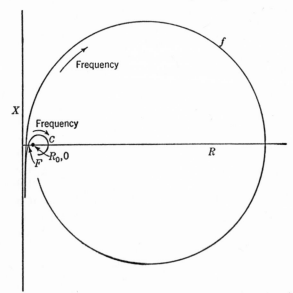

FIG. 13-18. Terminal-impedance diagram. A point on the diagram gives the resistance R and reactance X of the terminal impedance Z ($= R + jX$) at a particular frequency.

frequency F, or one somewhat below it, may be regarded as the cutoff frequency for the antenna. As the frequency is increased above F the impedance frequency curve spirals in toward the characteristic resistance value of the transmission line. This impedance frequency behavior is very similar to that for an open-circuited transmission line having considerable loss.

With each further modification of the antenna to the forms of Fig. 13-17d, e, and f the impedance variation with frequency increases, the impedance of the thin stub of Fig. 13-17f varying with frequency over a wide range as suggested by the curve f (Fig. 13-18).[2] This impedance frequency behavior is very similar to that for an open-circuited transmission line having but small loss.

[1] The maximum resistance may be a few hundred ohms.
[2] The maximum resistance may be many thousands of ohms.

If the gradually flared antenna of Fig. 13-17a is regarded as the basic form (widest band type), the thin stub of Fig. 13-17f represents the most degenerate form (narrowest band type). As we depart more from the basic form, the discontinuity in the line becomes more abrupt at what eventually is the junction of the ground plane and transmission line. This discontinuity causes some energy to be reflected back into the line. The discontinuity and reflection at the end of the antenna also increase for thinner antennas. At some frequency the two reflections may compensate, as discussed in Sec. 13-9, but the band width of compensation is narrow. Antennas with large and abrupt discontinuities have large reflections and act as reflectionless transformers or matching sections only over narrow frequency bands, where the reflections cancel. Antennas with discontinuities that are small and gradual have small reflections and are, in general, relatively reflectionless transformers over wide frequency bands.

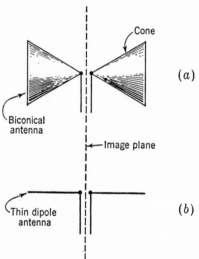

Fig. 13-19. Biconical and thin dipole antennas.

The antennas of Fig. 13-17 are of the unbalanced (unipole) type. However, the conclusions reached are also applicable to balanced or symmetrical (dipole) types. For instance, the biconical dipole antenna of Fig. 13-19a has a greater band width than the thin dipole type of Fig. 13-19b. It is to be noted that if a conducting sheet (or ground plane) is placed coincident with the image plane (plane of symmetry) one cone in Fig. 13-19a is equivalent to a conical antenna as in Fig. 13-17d except for details of the method of feed. Similarly one-half of the dipole antenna of Fig. 13-19b (with ground sheet at the image plane) is equivalent to the stub (unipole) antenna of Fig. 13-17f. It should be noted that the terminal impedance of a dipole antenna is twice the terminal impedance of the corresponding unipole type.

13-11. Receiving-Transmitting Considerations. In the foregoing sections we have discussed both transmitting antennas that radiate energy and receiving antennas that collect energy. In this section it is shown that the pattern, directivity, aperture, and impedance of an antenna are the same when it is used for either transmission or reception. However, it is also pointed out that the current distribution on the antenna is, in general, not the same when transmitting as it is when receiving.

In order to demonstrate that the pattern, directivity, etc., are the same for both transmission and reception, it is necessary to show that reciprocity applies to antennas. Thus, consider two antennas 1 and 2, as in Fig. 13-20, with media everywhere that are linear, passive, and isotropic. Since the antennas have terminals and reciprocity is to be demonstrated with respect to the two sets of terminals, let the antennas and the linear, passive, and isotropic media be replaced by an equivalent network of linear, passive, and bilateral impedances. This network may then be reduced to an equivalent T network, as in Fig. 13-21. Finally, reciprocity is easily

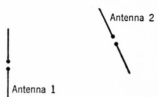

Fig. 13-20. Two antennas used in discussion of reciprocity theorem.

demonstrated for this network by simple circuit analysis[1] and it follows that if *an emf* $\mathcal{V}_1$ *applied at the terminals of antenna* 1 (see Fig. 13-20) *produces a current* I_{12} *at the terminals of antenna* 2, *then a current* I_{21} *equal*

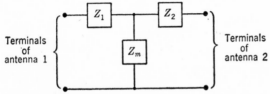

Fig. 13-21. Equivalent T network for two coupled antennas.

to I_{12} (*in both magnitude and phase*) *will be obtained at the terminals of antenna* 1 *when an emf* $\mathcal{V}_2$ *equal to* $\mathcal{V}_1$ *is applied at the terminals of antenna* 2.[2] This is the *reciprocity relation or theorem* for antennas. In symbols it states that

$$\frac{\mathcal{V}_1}{I_{12}} = \frac{\mathcal{V}_2}{I_{21}} \tag{13-112}$$

The ratio $\mathcal{V}_1/I_{12}$ is a *transfer impedance*, being the ratio of the emf applied at antenna 1 to the resulting current at antenna 2. Thus,

$$\frac{\mathcal{V}_1}{I_{12}} = Z_{12} \tag{13-113}$$

Likewise, the ratio $\mathcal{V}_2/I_{21}$ is a transfer impedance, being the ratio of the emf applied at antenna 2 to the resulting current at antenna 1. Thus,

$$\frac{\mathcal{V}_2}{I_{21}} = Z_{21} \tag{13-114}$$

[1] See, for example, J. D. Kraus, "Antennas," McGraw-Hill Book Company, Inc., New York, 1950, p. 253.
[2] It is assumed that the emfs are of the same frequency.

From the reciprocity relation (13-112) it follows that

$$Z_{12} = Z_{21} \qquad\qquad \text{(13-115)}$$

It is to be noted that, in general, the transfer impedances are complex.

Pattern. If all media involved are linear, passive, and isotropic, reciprocity holds, and it follows directly that under these conditions *the transmitting and receiving patterns of an antenna are identical.* Pattern here may refer either to the field pattern or to the power pattern, which is proportional to the square of the field pattern. Confining our attention to the field pattern, this is measured for a transmitting antenna, as antenna

Fig. 13-22. Pattern measurement on observation circle.

A in Fig. 13-22, by observing its field intensity with a receiving antenna B at points around an observation circle having antenna A at its center.[1] The reading of the current meter at the terminals of antenna B is a measure of the field intensity at the observation circle. If the measurement procedure is reversed by interchanging the generator and current meter (Fig. 13-22) so that antenna B on the observation circle transmits and antenna A receives, it follows from the reciprocity theorem that the field pattern of antenna A, observed by moving antenna B as before, will be identical to that obtained when antenna A is transmitting.

Directivity and Aperture. Directivity was discussed in Sec. 13-7 for a transmitting antenna. In general, the directivity is equal to

$$D = \frac{4\pi U_m}{\iint U \, d\Omega} \qquad\qquad \text{(13-116)}$$

[1] The same result is obtained by keeping the position of antenna B fixed and rotating antenna A about its center point.

where U_m = maximum radiation intensity
$\quad\;\; U$ = radiation intensity
$\quad\;\; d\Omega = \sin\theta\, d\theta\, d\phi$ = element of solid angle

Now U is a function of angle (θ and ϕ, see Fig. 13-7) so that we can write

$$U = U_m f(\theta,\ \phi) \tag{13-117}$$

where $f(\theta,\ \phi)$ = normalized relative space (three-dimensional) power pattern of antenna (equal to field pattern squared). Introducing (13-117) into (13-116), the directivity is

$$D = \frac{4\pi}{\iint f(\theta,\ \phi)\, d\Omega} \tag{13-118}$$

Hence, D is dependent only on the shape of the power pattern. As shown in the preceding subsection, an antenna has the same pattern for both transmission and reception. Hence, the directivity determined with an antenna's transmitting pattern is identical with the directivity determined with the antenna's receiving pattern. Accordingly, the term directivity can be applied to both transmitting and receiving antennas, the directivity of an antenna being the same for both situations.

According to (13-111) the maximum effective aperture A_{em} of an antenna is equal to the directivity of the antenna times a constant. Hence, the term maximum effective aperture may be applied to both transmitting and receiving antennas, it being understood that the maximum effective aperture of a transmitting antenna is the same as its maximum effective aperture when receiving.

Impedance. When an antenna is transmitting, it may be excited at only one point. However, when used for reception the antenna is excited over its entire extent by the received wave.[1] As a consequence the current distribution on the antenna is, in general, not the same for transmission and reception. However, the antenna always behaves as the same circuit regardless of the mode of excitation, so that *the impedance of an antenna is the same for transmission and reception.* This means that if the terminal impedance of a transmitting antenna is Z_T, the load impedance required for maximum power transfer when the antenna is receiving is equal to its complex conjugate Z_T^*.

That Z_T must be the same for transmission and reception may also be seen by considering a circuit or network of many meshes. Although the currents in the network are dependent on the location or locations of the emfs, the circuit impedances are independent of the distribution of the emfs.

13-12. Network Representation. In this section the usefulness of the four-terminal network representation of Fig. 13-21 is illustrated in

---

[1] Furthermore, the manner in which the receiving antenna is excited depends on the direction of the incident wave.

connection with the development of an equation for the effect of one antenna on the terminal impedance of another antenna.

Let us consider the case of any two antennas. The impedance Z_m in Fig. 13-21 represents the *mutual impedance*[1] of the antennas. Further, let the current at the terminals of antenna 1 be I_1 (flowing upward at the terminals, to the right into the network, and back through Z_m) and the current at the terminals of antenna 2 be I_2 (flowing upward at the terminals, to the left into the network, and back through Z_m). Also let

$$Z_1 = Z_{11} - Z_m \qquad (13\text{-}119)$$

and

$$Z_2 = Z_{22} - Z_m \qquad (13\text{-}120)$$

where Z_{11} = self-impedance of antenna 1 (that is, the impedance of antenna 1 when located remote from other antennas or objects)

Z_{22} = self-impedance of antenna 2

Then, from Kirchhoff's law we have

$$\mathcal{V}_1 = I_1 Z_{11} + I_2 Z_m \qquad (13\text{-}121)$$

and

$$\mathcal{V}_2 = I_2 Z_{22} + I_1 Z_m \qquad (13\text{-}122)$$

where $\mathcal{V}_1$ = emf applied at the terminals of antenna 1

$\mathcal{V}_2$ = emf applied at the terminals of antenna 2

Dividing (13-121) by I_1 we obtain for the terminal impedance of antenna 1

$$Z_{T1} = \frac{\mathcal{V}_1}{I_1} = Z_{11} + \frac{I_2}{I_1} Z_m \qquad (13\text{-}123)$$

Thus, if $I_2 Z_m / I_1$ is appreciable compared to Z_{11} the presence of antenna 2 produces an appreciable effect on the terminal impedance of antenna 1.

Similarly, dividing (13-122) by I_2 we have for the terminal impedance of antenna 2

$$Z_{T2} = \frac{\mathcal{V}_2}{I_2} = Z_{22} + \frac{I_1}{I_2} Z_m \qquad (13\text{-}124)$$

If antenna 2 is short circuited ($\mathcal{V}_2 = 0$) it follows that

$$Z_{T1} = Z_{11} - \frac{Z_m{}^2}{Z_{22}} \qquad (13\text{-}125)$$

Now the mutual impedance of two antennas becomes less as the distance between the antennas is increased. Hence, it follows from (13-125) that if antenna 2 is moved far away from antenna 1, Z_m approaches zero and

---

[1] The mutual impedance equals the negative of the ratio of the emf at the terminals of antenna 2 (when it is open circuited) to the terminal current of antenna 1 (that is, $Z_m = -\mathcal{V}_2/I_1$ with antenna 2 open circuited).

the input impedance of antenna 1 approaches its own self-impedance. If losses are zero the real part of the self-impedance is then equal to the radiation resistance of the antenna (that is, Re Z_{11} = radiation resistance).

The mutual impedance Z_m of two antennas is usually a complicated expression involving the size, separation, and orientation of the antennas. However, in the case of two short dipole antennas the relation is relatively simple and illustrates clearly the effect of these variables. Thus, as indicated in Prob. 13-10, the mutual impedance of two short dipoles can be resolved into three factors. The first is a magnitude factor involving the length of the dipoles and their separation, the second is an orientation factor, and the third is a periodic or complex factor (with real and imaginary parts) involving the separation of the dipoles.

PROBLEMS

13-1. Show that the far-field pattern of a small square loop is given by

$$E = \frac{120\pi^2[I]\sin\theta}{r}\frac{A}{\lambda^2}$$

where $[I]$ = retarded current on loop, θ = angle from axis of loop, A = area of loop, and λ = wavelength. Consider that the loop is made of four short dipoles as in Fig. 13-4. The axis of the loop coincides with the z axis (normal to the plane of the loop). The pattern to be obtained is that in the x-z plane.

13-2. Using a Poynting-vector integration, show that the radiation resistance of a small loop is equal to

$$320\pi^4\left(\frac{A}{\lambda^2}\right)^2 \quad \text{ohms}$$

where A = area of loop and λ = wavelength.

13-3. Show that the instantaneous value of the far electric field of a short dipole is

$$E_\theta = j\frac{60\pi I_0}{r}l_\lambda\sin\theta\cos(\omega t - \beta r) \quad \text{volts/meter}$$

where l_λ = length of dipole in wavelengths ($= l/\lambda$).

13-4. Develop the expression for the far-field pattern of a thin linear dipole antenna $\frac{1}{2}$ wavelength long with the current in phase over the entire length of the antenna but with a sinusoidal variation in magnitude. The current is a maximum at the center of the antenna and zero at the ends. Calculate and plot the relative field pattern.

13-5. An antenna has a unidirectional power pattern given by $U = \cos\theta$, where θ is as in Fig. 13-7. U has a value only for $0 \leq \theta \leq \pi/2$ and is zero elsewhere. Find the directivity of the antenna.   *Ans.:* $D = 4$.

13-6. An antenna has a far-field pattern expressed by $E = \cos 2\theta\cos\theta$. Find the directivity of the antenna.

13-7. An antenna that is a 90 per cent efficient radiator has a gain of 250. Find the maximum effective aperture of the antenna.

13-8. Show that the ratio of the maximum power P_r in the load of a receiving antenna to the power P_t radiated by a transmitting antenna is equal to

$$\frac{P_r}{P_t} = \frac{A_{emr}A_{emt}}{r^2\lambda^2}$$

where A_{emr} = maximum effective aperture of receiving antenna, A_{emt} = maximum effective aperture of transmitting antenna, r = distance from receiving antenna to transmitting antenna, and λ = wavelength. This is the *Friis transmission formula*. It is assumed that both antennas are situated in free space and are remote from other objects.

13-9. Show that the maximum mutual impedance Z_m of two antennas separated by a large distance is $Z_m = (\sqrt{D_1 D_2} \sqrt{R_1 R_2})/2\pi r_\lambda$, where D_1 = directivity of antenna 1, D_2 = directivity of antenna 2, R_1 = radiation resistance of antenna 1, R_2 = radiation resistance of antenna 2, and $r_\lambda = r/\lambda$ = separation of antennas (wavelengths). It is assumed that the receiving antenna is terminated for maximum power transfer.

13-10. Demonstrate that the mutual impedance of two short dipoles of length l separated by a distance r (Fig. 13-23) is equal to

$$Z_m = \left(\frac{60\pi l^2}{r\lambda}\right)(\sin \theta \sin \theta')(\sin \beta r + j \cos \beta r)$$

Note that the first factor on the right-hand side is a *magnitude factor*, the second an *orientation factor*, and the third a *periodic*, or *complex*, *factor* with real and imaginary

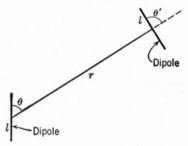

FIG. 13-23. Two short dipole antennas of length l and separation r for Prob. 13-10.

parts. Note also that when $r = n\lambda/4$, where $n = 1, 3, 5 \ldots$, Z_m is real, while if $r = n\lambda/4$, where $n = 2, 4, 6 \ldots$, Z_m is imaginary. The angles θ and θ' are as in Fig. 13-23. Both dipoles lie in the same plane. It is assumed that $\lambda \gg l$ and $r \gg l$ and also that the current is of uniform magnitude and constant phase on each dipole.

13-11. The variation with angle and time of the far-field components from an antenna is given by $E_\phi = \sin \theta \cos \phi \sin \omega t$ and $E_\theta = \sin \theta \sin \phi \cos \omega t$. Find the directivity of the antenna.

13-12. Show by means of an equivalent network that at the terminals of a receiving antenna the equivalent or Thévenin generator has an impedance $Z_{22} - (Z_m^2/Z_{11})$ and an emf $\mathcal{V}_1 Z_m/Z_{11}$, where Z_{11} = self-impedance of transmitting antenna, Z_{22} = self-impedance of receiving antenna, Z_m = mutual impedance, and $\mathcal{V}_1$ = emf applied to terminals of transmitting antenna. What load impedance connected to the terminals of the receiving antenna results in maximum power transfer?

CHAPTER 14

BOUNDARY-VALUE PROBLEMS

14-1. Introduction. The solution of an electromagnetic field problem consists, in general, of finding the space and time variation of the electric and magnetic fields appropriate to the particular configuration of dielectric and conducting objects under consideration. More specifically a solution is obtained to Maxwell's equations or the wave equation, and the arbitrary constants of the solution are then evaluated so as to satisfy the boundary conditions imposed by the dielectric and conducting objects involved. Because of the important part that the boundary conditions play, the problems are often called *boundary-value problems.*

The solution of a boundary-value problem is usually facilitated if it is set up in a coordinate system in which the boundaries can be specified in a simple manner. For instance, a problem involving a rectangular object is usually most readily handled with rectangular coordinates, a cylindrical object by cylindrical coordinates, a spherical object by spherical coordinates, an ellipsoidal object by elliptical-hyperbolic coordinates, etc. The boundaries in many practical problems are not simply expressed in any coordinate system, and often in such cases resort must be made to methods that are not purely analytical. (See the second from the last paragraph of Sec. 14-5.)

In this chapter we shall consider a number of electrostatic field problems and their solution. In the examples given it is assumed that space is free from charge ($\rho = 0$) so that the problem becomes one of finding a solution to Laplace's equation that satisfies the boundary conditions. Since Laplace's equation may be regarded as a special case of a wave equation (where $\omega = 0$), it is instructive, before proceeding to the static cases, to consider methods of solution for the more general wave-equation case where ω is not zero. This is done in Secs. 14-2 through 14-4, solutions to the scalar wave equation being obtained in rectangular, cylindrical, and spherical coordinates. Then in the sections that follow we consider the static case ($\omega = 0$), where the wave equation reduces to Laplace's equation, and work through a number of examples. The use of complex functions and conformal transformations for two-dimensional problems are also considered.

14-2. Solution of Wave Equation in Rectangular Coordinates. In Chaps. 9 to 12 we have dealt with wave equations of various forms, the most general type considered being the vector wave equation for a conducting medium (10-83c). For the problems of this chapter the wave equation of interest is the scalar wave equation in the electric scalar potential V. Assuming that the medium is lossless, this is (see Prob. 14-1),

$$\nabla^2 V + \beta^2 V = 0 \qquad (14\text{-}1)$$

where $\beta^2 = \omega^2\mu\epsilon$

$\omega = 2\pi f$ (where f = frequency)

μ = permeability of medium

ϵ = permittivity of medium

Harmonic variation of V with time is assumed. In static situations $\beta = 0$ so that (14-1) reduces to Laplace's equation

$$\nabla^2 V = 0 \qquad (14\text{-}1a)$$

Equation (14-1) is a second-order linear partial differential equation. Expanding it in terms of *rectangular coordinates*, we have

$$\frac{\partial^2 V}{\partial x^2} + \frac{\partial^2 V}{\partial y^2} + \frac{\partial^2 V}{\partial z^2} = -\beta^2 V \qquad (14\text{-}2)$$

Using the method of separation of variables to solve (14-2), let

$$V = XYZ \qquad (14\text{-}3)$$

where X = a function of x only

Y = a function of y only

Z = a function of z only

Substituting (14-3) in (14-2) yields

$$YZ\frac{d^2X}{dx^2} + XZ\frac{d^2Y}{dy^2} + XY\frac{d^2Z}{dz^2} = -\beta^2 XYZ \qquad (14\text{-}4)$$

Dividing by XYZ, to separate the variables

$$\frac{1}{X}\frac{d^2X}{dx^2} + \frac{1}{Y}\frac{d^2Y}{dy^2} + \frac{1}{Z}\frac{d^2Z}{dz^2} = -\beta^2 \qquad (14\text{-}5)$$

Since the sum of the three terms on the left-hand side is a constant and each variable is independent, each term must equal a constant. That is, we may write

$$\frac{1}{X}\frac{d^2X}{dx^2} = a_1{}^2 \qquad (14\text{-}6)$$

or

$$\frac{d^2X}{dx^2} = a_1{}^2 X \qquad (14\text{-}7)$$

and similarly

$$\frac{d^2Y}{dy^2} = a_2{}^2 Y \tag{14-8}$$

and

$$\frac{d^2Z}{dz^2} = a_3{}^2 Z \tag{14-9}$$

where

$$a_1{}^2 + a_2{}^2 + a_3{}^2 = -\beta^2 \tag{14-10}$$

A solution of (14-7) is

$$X = C_1 e^{a_1 x} + C_2 e^{-a_1 x} \tag{14-11}$$

where C_1 and C_2 are arbitrary constants that must be evaluated from the boundary conditions. Either term in (14-11) is a solution, or the sum is a solution as may be verified by substituting the solution in (14-7).

It follows that a general solution of (14-2) is

$$V = (C_1 e^{a_1 x} + C_2 e^{-a_1 x})(C_3 e^{a_2 y} + C_4 e^{-a_2 y})(C_5 e^{a_3 z} + C_6 e^{-a_3 z}) \tag{14-12}$$

where C_1, C_2, etc., are constants.

14-3. Solution of Wave Equation in Cylindrical Coordinates.[1] Let the wave equation of the scalar potential (14-1) be expanded in terms of cylindrical coordinates (see Fig. 14-1). That is,

$$\frac{\partial^2 V}{\partial \rho^2} + \frac{1}{\rho}\frac{\partial V}{\partial \rho} + \frac{1}{\rho^2}\frac{\partial^2 V}{\partial \phi^2} + \frac{\partial^2 V}{\partial z^2}$$
$$= -\beta^2 V \quad (14\text{-}13)$$

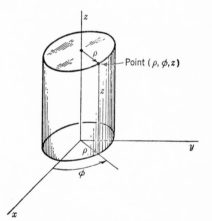

Point (ρ, ϕ, z)

Using the method of the separation of variables, let

$$V = R\Phi Z \tag{14-14}$$

where R = a function of ρ only
Φ = a function of ϕ only
Z = a function of z only

Substituting (14-14) in (14-13) yields

FIG. 14-1. Cylindrical coordinates.

$$\frac{1}{R}\frac{d^2R}{d\rho^2} + \frac{1}{\rho R}\frac{dR}{d\rho} + \frac{1}{\Phi\rho^2}\frac{d^2\Phi}{d\phi^2} + \frac{1}{Z}\frac{d^2Z}{dz^2} = -\beta^2 \tag{14-15}$$

The last term on the left-hand side is a function of z only; so we can write

$$\frac{1}{Z}\frac{d^2Z}{dz^2} = a_z{}^2 \tag{14-16}$$

---

[1] See, for example, A. B. Bronwell and R. E. Beam, "Theory and Application of Microwaves," McGraw-Hill Book Company, Inc., New York, 1948, p. 301.

or

$$\frac{d^2Z}{dz^2} = a_z{}^2 Z \tag{14-17}$$

where a_z = a constant. A solution of (14-17) is

$$Z = C_1 e^{a_z z} + C_2 e^{-a_z z} \tag{14-18}$$

where C_1 and C_2 are arbitrary constants. Substituting $a_z{}^2$ for the last term on the left-hand side of (14-15) and multiplying by ρ^2, we have

$$\frac{\rho^2}{R}\frac{d^2R}{d\rho^2} + \frac{\rho}{R}\frac{dR}{d\rho} + \frac{1}{\Phi}\frac{d^2\Phi}{d\phi^2} + (a_z{}^2 + \beta^2)\rho^2 = 0 \tag{14-19}$$

The third term on the left-hand side is a function only of ϕ; so we can write

$$\frac{d^2\Phi}{d\phi^2} = -\nu^2\Phi \tag{14-20}$$

where ν = a constant. A solution of (14-20) is

$$\Phi = C_3 \cos \nu\phi + C_4 \sin \nu\phi \tag{14-21}$$

Now substituting $-\nu^2$ for the third term on the left-hand side of (14-19) and multiplying by R yields

$$\rho^2 \frac{d^2R}{d\rho^2} + \rho\frac{dR}{d\rho} + [(a_z{}^2 + \beta^2)\rho^2 - \nu^2]R = 0 \tag{14-22}$$

This is a form of *Bessel's equation.* Let

$$k^2 = (a_z{}^2 + \beta^2) \tag{14-23}$$

and

$$u = k\rho \tag{14-24}$$

Using these relations, (14-22) becomes

$$u^2 \frac{d^2R}{du^2} + u\frac{dR}{du} + (u^2 - \nu^2)R = 0 \tag{14-25}$$

This is the *standard form of Bessel's equation.* A solution is

$$R = C_5 J_\nu(k\rho) + C_6 J_{-\nu}(k\rho) \tag{14-26}$$

where ν has nonintegral values, or

$$R = C_5 J_n(k\rho) + C_6 N_n(k\rho) \tag{14-27}$$

where[1] $\nu = n$ = integer

$J_n(k\rho)$ = Bessel function of first kind and of order n, with argument $k\rho$

$N_n(k\rho)$ = Bessel function of second kind and of order n, with argument $k\rho$

---

[1] See Appendix, Sec. A-11, for a discussion of Bessel functions; also Prob. 14-12 for an application.

It follows that a general solution of (14-13) (for $\nu = n$) is

$$V = Z\Phi R = (C_1 e^{a_z z} + C_2 e^{-a_z z})(C_3 \cos n\phi + C_4 \sin n\phi)[C_5 J_n(k\rho) \\ + C_6 N_n(k\rho)] \quad (14\text{-}28)$$

where C_1, C_2, etc., are constants.

14-4. Solution of Wave Equation in Spherical Coordinates.[1] Starting once more with the wave equation of the scalar potential (14-1), let us expand this relation in terms of spherical coordinates (see Fig. 14-2). That is,

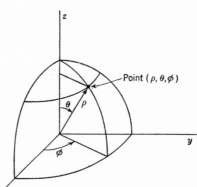

$$\frac{\partial^2 V}{\partial \rho^2} + \frac{1}{\rho^2} \frac{\partial^2 V}{\partial \theta^2} + \frac{1}{\rho^2 \sin^2 \theta} \frac{\partial^2 V}{\partial \phi^2} \\ + \frac{2}{\rho} \frac{\partial V}{\partial \rho} + \frac{\cot \theta}{\rho^2} \frac{\partial V}{\partial \theta} \\ = -\beta^2 V \quad (14\text{-}29)$$

Using again the method of separation of variables, let

$$V = RP\Phi \quad (14\text{-}30)$$

where $R =$ a function of ρ only
$\quad\ P =$ a function of θ only
$\quad\ \Phi =$ a function of ϕ only

FIG. 14-2. Spherical coordinates.

Substituting (14-30) in (14-29), we obtain

$$\frac{1}{\rho^2 R} \frac{d}{d\rho}\left(\rho^2 \frac{dR}{d\rho}\right) + \frac{1}{P\rho^2 \sin \theta} \frac{d}{d\theta}\left[\sin \theta \left(\frac{dP}{d\theta}\right)\right] \\ + \frac{1}{\rho^2 \Phi \sin^2 \theta} \frac{d^2\Phi}{d\phi^2} = -\beta^2 \quad (14\text{-}31)$$

Multiplying by ρ^2 and setting terms that are a function only of ρ equal to $a_\rho{}^2$, we have

$$\frac{d}{d\rho}\left(\rho^2 \frac{dR}{d\rho}\right) - (a_\rho{}^2 - \beta^2 \rho^2)R = 0 \quad (14\text{-}32)$$

Let

$$a_\rho{}^2 = n(n+1) \quad (14\text{-}33)$$
$$x = \beta\rho \quad (14\text{-}34)$$

where $a_\rho =$ a constant and $n =$ an integer.

Using these relations, (14-32) becomes

$$x^2 \frac{d^2 R}{dx^2} + 2x \frac{dR}{dx} + [x^2 - n(n+1)]R = 0 \quad (14\text{-}35)$$

---

[1] A. B. Bronwell and R. E. Beam, "Theory and Application of Microwaves," McGraw-Hill Book Company, Inc., New York, 1947, p. 311. J. A. Stratton, "Electromagnetic Theory," McGraw-Hill Book Company, Inc., New York, 1941, p. 399.

Let

$$R = x^{-\frac{1}{2}}W \qquad (14\text{-}36)$$

Then

$$x^2 \frac{d^2W}{dx^2} + x \frac{dW}{dx} + \left[x^2 - n(n+1) - \frac{1}{4} \right] W = 0 \qquad (14\text{-}37)$$

This is *Bessel's equation* of order $n + \frac{1}{2}$. A solution is

$$W = C_1 J_{n+\frac{1}{2}}(x) + C_2 J_{-(n+\frac{1}{2})}(x) \qquad (14\text{-}38)$$

But $R = W/\sqrt{x}$, and $x = \beta\rho$; so $R = W/\sqrt{\beta\rho}$. Therefore

$$R = C_3 \sqrt{\frac{\pi}{2\beta\rho}} \, J_{n+\frac{1}{2}}(\beta\rho) + (-1)^{-(n-1)} C_4 \sqrt{\frac{\pi}{2\beta\rho}} \, N_{n+\frac{1}{2}}(\beta\rho) \qquad (14\text{-}39)$$

and

$$R = C_3 j_n(\beta\rho) + (-1)^{-(n-1)} C_4 n_n(\beta\rho) \qquad (14\text{-}40)$$

where j_n and n_n are *spherical Bessel functions.*[1]

Now introducing $a_\rho{}^2$ for terms which are a function of ρ only and multiplying by $\sin^2 \theta$, (14-31) reduces to

$$\frac{\sin\theta}{P} \frac{d}{d\theta} \left[\sin\theta \left(\frac{dP}{d\theta} \right) \right] + \frac{1}{\Phi} \frac{d^2\Phi}{d\phi^2} + \sin^2\theta \, a_\rho{}^2 = 0 \qquad (14\text{-}41)$$

The second term is a function of ϕ only. Thus we can write

$$\frac{d^2\Phi}{d\phi^2} = -m^2\Phi \qquad (14\text{-}42)$$

where $m = $ a constant. A solution of (14-42) is

$$\Phi = C_5 \cos m\phi + C_6 \sin m\phi \qquad (14\text{-}43)$$

where m is an integer if V repeats every 2π as a function of ϕ. Substituting $-m^2$ for the second term of (14-41), multiplying by P, and dividing by $\sin^2 \theta$ yields

$$\frac{d^2P}{d\theta^2} + \frac{1}{\tan\theta} \frac{dP}{d\theta} + \left(a_\rho{}^2 - \frac{m^2}{\sin^2\theta} \right) P = 0 \qquad (14\text{-}44)$$

This is called the *associated Legendre equation.* If we put

$$a_\rho{}^2 = n(n+1) \qquad (14\text{-}45)$$

where $n = $ integer and

$$x = \cos\theta \qquad (14\text{-}46)$$

Eq. (14-44) can be written

$$(1 - x^2) \frac{d^2P}{dx^2} - 2x \frac{dP}{dx} + \left[n(n+1) - \frac{m^2}{1 - x^2} \right] P = 0 \qquad (14\text{-}47)$$

[1] See Appendix, Sec. A-13.

If V is independent of ϕ, $m = 0$ and we have

$$(1 - x^2) \frac{d^2P}{dx^2} - 2x \frac{dP}{dx} + n(n + 1)P = 0 \qquad (14\text{-}48)$$

This is *Legendre's equation*.

A solution of the associated Legendre equation (14-44) (for m = integer) is

$$P = C_7 P_n{}^m(\cos \theta) + C_8 Q_n{}^m(\cos \theta) \qquad (14\text{-}49)$$

where[1] $P_n{}^m(\cos \theta)$ = associated Legendre function of the first kind
$Q_n{}^m(\cos \theta)$ = associated Legendre function of the second kind
n = integer

A solution of Legendre's equation (14-48) (for n = integer) is

$$P = C_7' P_n(\cos \theta) + C_8' Q_n(\cos \theta) \qquad (14\text{-}50)$$

where[2] $P_n(\cos \theta)$ = Legendre function of the first kind
$Q_n(\cos \theta)$ = Legendre function of the second kind

It follows that a general solution of (14-29) is

$$V = R\Phi P = [C_3 j_n(\beta\rho) + C_4 n_n(\beta\rho)](C_5 \cos m\phi \\ + C_6 \sin m\phi)[C_7 P_n{}^m(\cos \theta) + C_8 Q_n{}^m(\cos \theta)] \quad (14\text{-}51)$$

where C_3, C_4, etc., are constants.

The above general solution of the wave equation in spherical coordinates and the solutions of the preceding sections in rectangular and cylindrical coordinates are not directly applicable in many special problems. However, they illustrate the method of analysis for the most general type of problem.

In the next four sections examples are given to illustrate the methods of solution of some typical boundary-value problems involving static fields ($\omega = \beta = 0$). One problem is handled in rectangular coordinates, two in cylindrical coordinates, and one in spherical coordinates.

14-5. Example 1. Conducting Sheet between Two Conducting Planes.[3] Referring to Fig. 14-3, two infinite parallel conducting plates are spaced a distance a. An infinitely long conducting strip is placed between the plates and normal to them, as shown in the figure.

The width of the strip is only very slightly less than the spacing between the plates. The strip is insulated from the plates. Let the two plates be

---

[1] $P_n{}^m$ (cos θ) is also called a solid zonal harmonic of the first kind. $Q_n{}^m$ (cos θ) is also called a solid zonal harmonic of the second kind. See Appendix, Sec. A-14.

[2] P_n (cos θ) is also called a surface zonal harmonic of the first kind. Q_n (cos θ) is also called a surface zonal harmonic of the second kind. See Appendix, Sec. A-14.

[3] W. E. Byerly, "Fourier Series and Spherical Harmonics," Ginn & Company, Boston, 1893, p. 4.

connected together and a constant potential V be applied between the plates and the conducting strip. The medium between the plates is air. Suppose that the plates are at zero potential and that the strip is at a positive potential of 1 volt ($V = 1$). The problem is to find the potential distribution in the region M between the plates to the right of the strip, as indicated in the cross section of Fig. 14-3b.

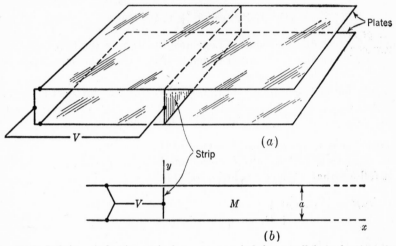

FIG. 14-3. Infinite conducting strip between two infinite parallel conducting plates in perspective view (a) and cross section (b).

Since this is a static problem $\beta = 0$ and the wave equation reduces to Laplace's equation

$$\nabla^2 V = 0 \qquad (14\text{-}52)$$

it should be possible to find the potential distribution by solving this equation subject to the boundary conditions. The analytical procedure for doing this will now be discussed.[1]

It is most convenient to handle this problem in rectangular coordinates, the relation of the conductor boundaries to the coordinate axes being as in Fig. 14-4a. Expanding (14-52) in the two rectangular coordinates of the problem (x and y), we have

$$\frac{\partial^2 V}{\partial x^2} + \frac{\partial^2 V}{\partial y^2} = 0 \qquad (14\text{-}53)$$

This differential equation is the most general way of expressing the variation of potential with respect to x and y. It is a partial differential equation of the second order and first degree. However, this equation

[1] The problem is 2-dimensional (V independent of z, normal to the page) so that a solution could also be obtained by graphical field-mapping methods.

does not tell us anything about the particular potential distribution in the problem.   For this we must obtain a solution of the differential equation which is appropriate to the boundary conditions of the problem.   These

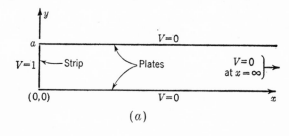

(a)

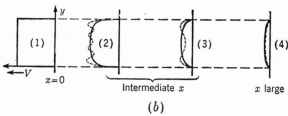

(b)

Fig. 14-4. (a) Boundary conditions for potential-distribution problem of Fig. 14-3. (b) Potential variation between plates as obtained from solution of Laplace's equation.

boundary conditions are

$$\left. \begin{array}{lll} V = 0 & \text{at } y = 0 \\ V = 0 & \text{at } y = a \\ V = 1 & \text{at } x = 0 \\ V = 0 & \text{at } x = \infty \end{array} \right\} \tag{14-54}$$

Proceeding now to find a solution of (14-53) by the method of separation of variables, let us assume that a solution for V can be expressed as

$$V = XY \tag{14-55}$$

where X = a function of x alone
      Y = a function of y alone
Substituting (14-55) into (14-53) and dividing by XY, we have

$$\frac{1}{X} \frac{d^2X}{dx^2} + \frac{1}{Y} \frac{d^2Y}{dy^2} = 0 \tag{14-56}$$

In (14-56) the variables are separated.   Since X and Y are independent and the sum of the two terms is a constant (zero), each term alone must equal a constant.   Thus, we can write

$$\frac{1}{X} \frac{d^2X}{dx^2} = k^2 \tag{14-57}$$

and

$$\frac{1}{Y}\frac{d^2Y}{dy^2} = -k^2 \tag{14-58}$$

where k equals a constant and $k^2 - k^2 = 0$.

These equations may be rearranged to the form

$$\frac{d^2X}{dx^2} - k^2X = 0 \tag{14-59}$$

and

$$\frac{d^2Y}{dy^2} + k^2Y = 0 \tag{14-60}$$

Thus, the second-order partial differential equation of (14-53) has been reduced to two second-order ordinary differential equations, each involving but one variable. These equations, (14-59) and (14-60), have the solutions

$$X = C_1e^{kx} + C_2e^{-kx} \tag{14-61}$$

and

$$Y = C_3e^{jky} + C_4e^{-jky} \tag{14-62}$$

One may readily confirm that these are solutions by substituting them into (14-59) and (14-60), in each case obtaining an identity. Introducing (14-61) and (14-62) into (14-55) yields the general solution

$$V = C_1C_3e^{kx}e^{jky} + C_2C_3e^{-kx}e^{jky} + C_1C_4e^{kx}e^{-jky} + C_2C_4e^{-kx}e^{-jky} \tag{14-63}$$

which reduces to

$$V = C_1'e^{k(x\pm jy)} + C_2'e^{-k(x\pm jy)} \tag{14-64}$$

where $C_1' = C_1C_3$ or C_1C_4 and $C_2' = C_2C_3$ or C_2C_4, depending on which sign is chosen in $x \pm jy$.

Because of the boundary condition $V = 0$ at $x = \infty$, $C_1' = 0$ so that only the second term of (14-64) applies in our problem.[1] Also, using de Moivre's theorem, (14-64) then becomes

$$V = C_2'e^{-kx}(\cos ky \pm j \sin ky) \tag{14-65}$$

To satisfy the boundary condition $V = 0$ at $y = 0$, we should retain only the imaginary part of (14-65). That is,

$$V = C_2''e^{-kx}\sin ky \tag{14-66}$$

This is a particular solution of Laplace's equation appropriate to our problem. It indicates that the potential V falls off exponentially with x and also that it varies as a sine function of y. To satisfy the boundary

---

[1] If we were interested in the potential distribution to the *left* instead of to the right of the strip (Fig. 14-3), the boundary condition is $V = 0$ at $x = -\infty$ so that $C_2' = 0$.

condition $V = 0$ at $y = a$ requires that

$$k = \frac{n\pi}{a} \qquad (14\text{-}67)$$

where $n = $ positive integer $(1, 2, 3, \ldots)$. Introducing (14-67) into (14-66) yields

$$V = C_2'' e^{-n\pi x/a} \sin \frac{n\pi y}{a} \qquad (14\text{-}68)$$

All of the boundary conditions of (14-54) are now satisfied except for the condition that $V = 1$ at $x = 0$, that is, $V = 1$ at $x = 0$ for all values of y between 0 and a. Obviously (14-68) does not satisfy this requirement, and hence a more general solution is required. Since Laplace's equation is linear, a more general solution can be obtained by taking the sum of expressions like (14-68) for different integral values of n. We then have

$$V = C_1 e^{-\pi x/a} \sin \frac{\pi y}{a} + C_2 e^{-2\pi x/a} \sin \frac{2\pi y}{a}$$
$$+ C_3 e^{-3\pi x/a} \sin \frac{3\pi y}{a} + \cdots \qquad (14\text{-}69)$$

where C_1, C_2, etc., are new constants.

Equation (14-69) may be expressed more concisely by

$$V = \sum_{n=1}^{n=\infty} C_n e^{-n\pi x/a} \sin \frac{n\pi y}{a} \qquad (14\text{-}70)$$

The solution for V given by (14-69) or (14-70) is still incomplete since the coefficients C_1, C_2, etc., are not evaluated. To find their values, we impose the boundary condition that $V = 1$ at $x = 0$ so that (14-69) reduces to

$$1 = C_1 \sin \frac{\pi y}{a} + C_2 \sin \frac{2\pi y}{a} + C_3 \sin \frac{3\pi y}{a} + \cdots \qquad (14\text{-}71)$$

Now by the Fourier sine expansion

$$f(y) = a_1 \sin y + a_2 \sin 2y + a_3 \sin 3y + \cdots + a_n \sin ny \qquad (14\text{-}72)$$

where $a_n = \frac{2}{\pi} \int_0^\pi f(y) \sin ny \, dy$. It follows that for $f(y) = 1$

$$a_n = \frac{4}{n\pi} \qquad \text{for } n \text{ odd}$$

and

$$a_n = 0 \qquad \text{for } n \text{ even}$$

Therefore, for $f(y) = 1$, (14-72) reduces to

$$1 = \frac{4}{\pi}\left(\sin y + \frac{1}{3}\sin 3y + \frac{1}{5}\sin 5y + \cdots\right) \qquad (14\text{-}73)$$

Comparing (14-73) with (14-71), it follows that

$$C_1 = \frac{4}{\pi}, \ C_2 = 0, \ C_3 = \frac{4}{3\pi}, \ C_4 = 0, \ C_5 = \frac{4}{5\pi}, \ \text{etc.}$$

Introducing these values into (14-69), we have

$$V = \frac{4}{\pi} e^{-\pi x/a} \sin \frac{\pi y}{a} + \frac{4}{3\pi} e^{-3\pi x/a} \sin \frac{3\pi y}{a}$$

$$+ \frac{4}{5\pi} e^{-5\pi x/a} \sin \frac{5\pi y}{a} + \cdots \qquad (14\text{-}74)$$

This is the complete solution of Laplace's equation for the potential V appropriate to the boundary conditions of the problem. It gives the potential V as a function of position between the plates and to the right of the strip (Fig. 14-3).

Although an infinite number of terms is required for an exact representation of the potential distribution as a function of x and y, an approximate solution of practical value may be obtained with a finite number of terms. Each term attenuates at a different rate. Since the higher terms fall off more rapidly with x, only a few terms are needed to give a good approximation except where x is small. At $x = 0$, $V = 1$ for all values of y between 0 and a. When x is very large, the distribution is very nearly equal to $\sin \pi y/a$, since the contribution of the harmonics higher than the first may be neglected. The variation of V as a function of y at $x = 0$ and at a large value of x is shown at (1) and (4) in Fig. 14-4b. The distributions at two intermediate values of x are presented at (2) and (3). The actual distribution is shown by the solid curves, the dashed curves giving the approximate distribution as obtained by four terms ($n = 1, 3, 5, 7$) of the series at (2) and by two terms ($n = 1$ and 3) at (3). It is apparent that as x decreases the effect of the higher terms becomes more important.

The potential distribution can also be presented by means of equipotential contours with orthogonal field lines as suggested in Fig. 14-5. It is apparent that graphical field-mapping methods could have been used instead of the above analytical method to obtain an engineering solution for the potential distribution. Both are procedures for solving Laplace's equation. In general, two-dimensional problems can be solved by either the graphical or the analytical approach. The analytical method is also applicable to three-dimensional problems. However, the graphical method is not, without modifications.　Experimental methods are applicable to both two- and three-dimensional problems.[1]

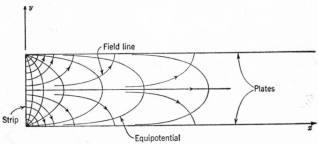

FIG. 14-5. Electric field lines (with arrows) and equipotentials in space between conducting plates.

To measure the potential distribution of the above problem in a simple experimental manner the setup shown in Fig. 14-6 can be used.　Here the plates are replaced by heavy copper bars and the conducting strip by a heavy copper bar insulated from the side bars.　A resistance strip of width a is clamped to the bars as shown.　The side bars are grounded so that the edges of the strip are at zero potential.　A generator or battery supplies a constant emf between the end bar and the ground.　The potential distribution can then be mapped with the aid of a probe and a high-resistance (vacuum-tube) voltmeter.　To avoid end effects, the

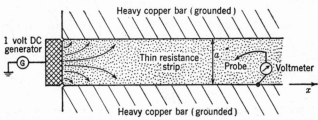

FIG. 14-6. Experimental method for determining potential distribution.

length (x dimension) of the side bars and resistance strip should be large compared with the width a.　The curved lines with arrows in Fig. 14-6 suggest the paths of the electric field (and current) between the end bar and the side bars.　As mentioned in Sec. 3-17, a solution of Laplace's equation for a steady current distribution (as obtained here experimentally) constitutes a solution for the analogous static field problem of Fig. 14-3.

If any function V satisfies Laplace's equation ($\nabla^2 V = 0$) and the

[1] Ernst Weber, "Electromagnetic Fields," John Wiley & Sons, Inc., New York, 1950, Chap. 5.

boundary conditions, it is a *unique solution*.[1] No other function will satisfy the conditions, with the possible exception of functions differing from V by an additive constant. Hence, (14-74) must be a unique solution. An experimental verification of a solution, such as (14-74), is a verification of Laplace's equation as well as of the solution.

14-6. Example 2. Coaxial Line. Consider the section of coaxial transmission line shown in Fig. 14-7a. One end (at the origin) is short-

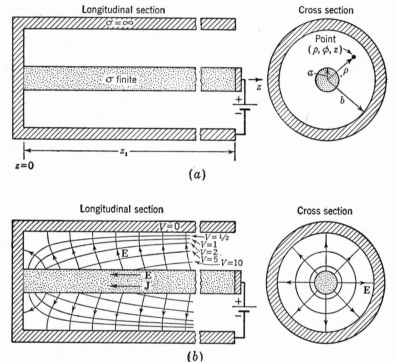

Fig. 14-7. (a) Section of coaxial transmission line. (b) Field distribution showing field lines (with arrows) and equipotentials.

circuited, and the other end is open. The outside radius of the inner conductor is a, and the inside radius of the outer conductor is b. The conductivity of the inner conductor is finite, but the conductivity of the outer conductor and of the short-circuiting disc is assumed to be infinite. A constant voltage V_1 is applied between the inner and outer conductor at the open end of the line. The length z_1 of the line is long compared with its radius ($z_1 \gg b$). The problem is to find the potential V everywhere inside the line, except near the open end.

[1] A graphically obtained field map of a two-dimensional problem is likewise a unique solution.

The boundary conditions for this problem are

(1) $V = 0$ at $z = 0$ (and $a \leq \rho \leq b$)
(2) $V = 0$ at $\rho = b$ (and $0 \leq z \leq z_1$)
(3) $V = V_1$ at $z = z_1$ (and $\rho = a$)

There is also the condition that at any distance z from the origin the electric field inside the inner conductor and also along its surface ($\rho = a$) is given by

$$\frac{\partial V}{\partial z} = \frac{V_1}{z_1} \tag{14-75a}$$

from which we have on integration that

$$V = \frac{V_1}{z_1} z \tag{14-75b}$$

At $z = z_1$ (14-75b) reduces to the third boundary condition above.

This is a static problem ($\omega = 0$) so that the wave equation reduces to Laplace's equation $\nabla^2 V = 0$. We wish to find a solution of this equation that satisfies the boundary conditions. By symmetry V is independent of ϕ; so expanding Laplace's equation in the other two cylindrical coordinates of the problem (ρ and z), we have[1]

$$\frac{\partial^2 V}{\partial \rho^2} + \frac{1}{\rho} \frac{\partial V}{\partial \rho} + \frac{\partial^2 V}{\partial z^2} = 0 \tag{14-76}$$

Using the method of separation of variables, let

$$V = RZ \tag{14-77}$$

where R = a function only of ρ
Z = a function only of z
Introducing (14-77) into (14-76) and dividing by RZ yields

$$\frac{1}{R} \frac{d^2 R}{d\rho^2} + \frac{1}{\rho R} \frac{dR}{d\rho} + \frac{1}{Z} \frac{d^2 Z}{dz^2} = 0 \tag{14-78}$$

The last term is a function only of z. Thus we can write

$$\frac{d^2 Z}{dz^2} = a_z^2 Z \tag{14-79}$$

where a_z = a constant. From (14-75a) it follows that since V_1/z_1 is a constant the second derivative in (14-79) must be zero and, hence, a_z

---

[1] Although V is dependent only on ρ and z, this problem is not two-dimensional in the sense that the problem of Example 1 is two-dimensional. Here the potential distribution for a longitudinal plane through the axis differs from the distribution for all planes parallel to it.

must be zero.   A solution of (14-79) for $a_z = 0$ is

$$Z = C_1 z + C_2 \tag{14-80}$$

The last term of (14-78) may now be set equal to zero so that the equation reduces to

$$\rho \frac{d^2 R}{d\rho^2} + \frac{dR}{d\rho} = 0 \tag{14-81}$$

A solution is

$$R = C_3 \ln \rho + C_4 \tag{14-81a}$$

Introducing (14-81a) for R and (14-80) for Z in (14-77), the solution for the potential is

$$V = (C_1 z + C_2)(C_3 \ln \rho + C_4) \tag{14-81b}$$

or

$$V = C_5 z \ln \rho + C_6 z + C_7 \ln \rho + C_8 \tag{14-81c}$$

where C_5, C_6, etc., are new constants.   To evaluate these constants, we introduce the boundary conditions.   Introducing the first condition $V = 0$ at $z = 0$, (14-81c) becomes

$$0 = C_7 \ln \rho + C_8 \tag{14-81d}$$

For (14-81d) to be satisfied for all values of ρ requires that $C_7 = C_8 = 0$. Thus our solution reduces to

$$V = C_5 z \ln \rho + C_6 z \tag{14-81e}$$

Introducing now the second boundary condition that $V = 0$ at $\rho = b$, we have

$$0 = C_5 z \ln b + C_6 z \tag{14-81f}$$

As the third boundary condition, $V = V_1$ at $z = z_1$ and $\rho = a$, which yields

$$V_1 = C_5 z_1 \ln a + C_6 z_1 \tag{14-81g}$$

From (14-81f) and (14-81g) we find that

$$C_5 = \frac{V_1}{z_1 \ln (a/b)}$$

and

$$C_6 = - \frac{V_1 \ln b}{z_1 \ln (a/b)}$$

Introducing the values for these constants into (14-81e), the complete solution for the problem is

$$V = V_1 \frac{z}{z_1} \frac{\ln (b/\rho)}{\ln (b/a)} \tag{14-81h}$$

This solution satisfies Laplace's equation and the boundary conditions and, hence, must represent the potential distribution at all points between the inner and outer conductors $(a \leq \rho \leq b)$ except near the open end. This potential distribution is portrayed in Fig. 14-7b, the relative potential being indicated for the equipotential lines. Electric field lines (with arrows) are also shown, being normal to the equipotentials.

It is interesting to note in Fig. 14-7b that although the field lines are normal to the perfectly conducting surfaces (outer conductor and short-circuiting disc) they are not normal to the finitely conducting inner conductor. The current and field direction in the inner conductor is to the left ($-z$ direction). Comparison of Fig. 14-7b should be made with Figs. 3-17 and 3-19. In Figs. 3-17 and 3-19 both inner and outer conductors are assumed to have finite conductivity.

14-7. Example 3. Uncharged Conducting Cylinder in Originally Uniform Field. Consider an infinitely long conducting cylinder of radius a as shown in Fig. 14-8a. The cylinder is at zero potential and is situated in a field that had a uniform static field intensity E_0 before the cylinder was introduced. That is, the original potential distribution is given by

$$V = E_0 \rho \cos \phi \qquad (14\text{-}82)$$

This must also be the distribution for large ρ after the cylinder is introduced. Hence (14-82) for large ρ and also the fact that $V = 0$ at $\rho = a$ constitute the boundary conditions. The problem, then, is to find V everywhere outside the cylinder, the potential and field being zero inside the cylinder.

There is no z variation of potential so that the problem is two-dimensional. It is also a static problem ($\omega = 0$) so that the wave equation reduces to Laplace's equation. Expanding Laplace's equation in the two cylindrical coordinates of the problem (ρ and ϕ), we have

$$\rho^2 \frac{\partial^2 V}{\partial \rho^2} + \rho \frac{\partial V}{\partial \rho} + \frac{\partial^2 V}{\partial \phi^2} = 0 \qquad (14\text{-}83)$$

Proceeding now to find a solution of (14-83) by the method of separation of variables, let

$$V = R\Phi \qquad (14\text{-}84)$$

where R = a function only of ρ
Φ = a function only of ϕ

Substituting (14-84) into (14-83) and dividing by $R\Phi$, we have

$$\frac{\rho^2}{R} \frac{d^2 R}{d\rho^2} + \frac{\rho}{R} \frac{dR}{d\rho} + \frac{1}{\Phi} \frac{d^2 \Phi}{d\phi^2} = 0 \qquad (14\text{-}85)$$

The first two terms are a function of ρ only so that we can write

$$\frac{\rho^2}{R} \frac{d^2 R}{d\rho^2} + \frac{\rho}{R} \frac{dR}{d\rho} = a_\rho{}^2 \qquad (14\text{-}86)$$

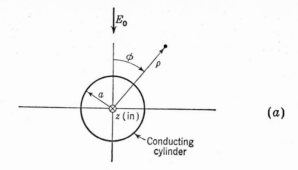

(a)

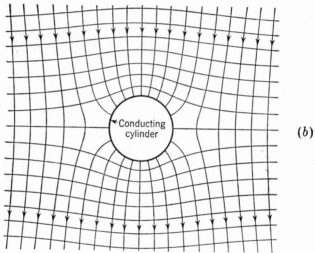

(b)

FIG. 14-8. (a) Cross section of conducting cylinder. (b) Field distribution showing field lines (with arrows) and equipotentials.

or

$$\rho^2 \frac{d^2R}{d\rho^2} + \rho \frac{dR}{d\rho} - a_\rho^2 R = 0 \tag{14-87}$$

A solution of (14-87) is

$$R = C_1 \rho^{\pm n} \tag{14-88}$$

provided

$$a_\rho^2 = n^2 \tag{14-89}$$

where n is an integer. From (14-86) and (14-89), (14-85) reduces to

$$n^2 + \frac{1}{\Phi} \frac{d^2\Phi}{d\phi^2} = 0 \tag{14-90}$$

or

$$\frac{d^2\Phi}{d\phi^2} = -n^2\Phi \tag{14-91}$$

A solution of (14-91) is

$$\Phi = C_2 \cos n\phi + C_3 \sin n\phi \qquad (14\text{-}92)$$

For V to vary as in (14-82) at large values of ρ, where the field is undisturbed by the presence of the cylinder, requires that C_3 be zero. Since Laplace's equation is linear, the solution may be written as the sum of an infinite number of particular solutions given by the product of R from (14-88) and Φ from (14-92) with $C_3 = 0$, each for a different value of n. Thus a general solution for the potential is

$$V = R\Phi = \sum_{n=0}^{\infty} A_n \rho^n \cos n\phi + \sum_{n=0}^{\infty} B_n \rho^{-n} \cos n\phi \qquad (14\text{-}93)$$

where A_n and B_n are new constants. When ρ is large, the field is undisturbed and must be as in (14-82). Thus for large values of ρ (14-93) must reduce to the form

$$V = A_1 \rho \cos \phi \qquad (14\text{-}94)$$

By comparison with (14-82) it follows that

$$A_1 = E_0 \qquad (14\text{-}95)$$

Furthermore, for V to vary as in (14-82) when ρ is large requires that $A_n = 0$ for all values of n except $n = 1$. Thus (14-93) reduces to

$$V = E_0 \rho \cos \phi + \sum_{n=0}^{\infty} B_n \rho^{-n} \cos n\phi \qquad (14\text{-}96)$$

Introducing the last boundary condition that

$$V = 0 \qquad (14\text{-}97)$$

at

$$\rho = a \qquad (14\text{-}98)$$

we have from (14-96) that

$$0 = E_0 a \cos \phi + B_0 + \frac{B_1}{a} \cos \phi + \frac{B_2}{a^2} \cos 2\phi + \cdots \qquad (14\text{-}99)$$

For (14-99) to be satisfied for all values of ϕ requires that $B_n = 0$ for all values of n except $n = 1$ and also that

$$B_1 = -E_0 a^2 \qquad (14\text{-}100)$$

The complete solution for the potential is then

$$V = \left(E_0 \rho - \frac{E_0 a^2}{\rho} \right) \cos \phi \qquad (14\text{-}101)$$

or

$$V = \left[1 - \left(\frac{a}{\rho} \right)^2 \right] E_0 \rho \cos \phi \qquad (14\text{-}102)$$

The potential V equals zero at the cylinder and also inside the cylinder. This solution satisfies Laplace's equation and also the boundary conditions and, hence, must represent the potential distribution at all points on and outside of the cylinder ($a \leq \rho \leq \infty$). This potential distribution is shown in Fig. 14-8b. Field lines (with arrows) are also shown. These lines are normal to the equipotentials. All squares in this map are either true or curvilinear squares.

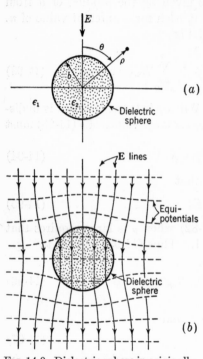

(a)

(b)

FIG. 14-9. Dielectric sphere in originally uniform field.

14-8. Example 4. Dielectric Sphere in Originally Uniform Field. Consider a dielectric sphere of permittivity ϵ_2 and radius b as in Fig. 14-9a. This is a three-dimensional problem. The sphere is situated in a field that had a uniform static electric field intensity E_0 before the sphere was introduced. That is, the original potential distribution is given by

$$V = E_0 \rho \cos \theta \qquad (14\text{-}103)$$

The medium outside the sphere has a permittivity ϵ_1. The problem is to find V everywhere, both outside and inside the sphere.

The boundary conditions are that V must be as in (14-103) at large ρ and also that the tangential component of $\mathbf{E}$ and normal component of $\mathbf{D}$ are continuous at any point on the surface of the sphere ($\rho = b$).

The problem is a static one ($\omega = 0$) so that the wave equation reduces to Laplace's equation. By symmetry the distribution is independent of ϕ. Expanding Laplace's equation in the other two spherical coordinates (ρ and θ), we have

$$\frac{\partial^2 V}{\partial \rho^2} + \frac{1}{\rho^2}\frac{\partial^2 V}{\partial \theta^2} + \frac{2}{\rho}\frac{\partial V}{\partial \rho} + \frac{\cot \theta}{\rho^2}\frac{\partial V}{\partial \theta} = 0 \qquad (14\text{-}104)$$

Using the method of separation of variables, let

$$V = RP \qquad (14\text{-}105)$$

where R = a function only of ρ

P = a function only of θ

Introducing (14-105) into (14-104) and dividing by RP yields

$$\frac{1}{R}\frac{d}{d\rho}\left(\rho^2\frac{dR}{d\rho}\right) + \frac{1}{P\sin\theta}\frac{d}{d\theta}\left(\sin\theta\frac{dP}{d\theta}\right) = 0 \qquad (14\text{-}106)$$

The first term is a function only of ρ. Thus we may write

$$\frac{d}{d\rho}\left(\rho^2\frac{dR}{d\rho}\right) = Ra_\rho{}^2 \qquad (14\text{-}107)$$

where a_ρ = constant. Letting $a_\rho{}^2 = n(n+1)$, where n is an integer, (14-107) becomes

$$\rho^2\frac{d^2R}{d\rho^2} + 2\rho\frac{dR}{d\rho} - n(n+1)R = 0 \qquad (14\text{-}108)$$

A solution of (14-108) is

$$R = C_1\rho^n + C_2\rho^{-(n+1)} \qquad (14\text{-}109)$$

Introducing $a_\rho{}^2$ into (14-106) for the first term and multiplying by P, we have

$$\frac{d^2P}{d\theta^2} + \frac{1}{\tan\theta}\frac{dP}{d\theta} + a_\rho{}^2P = 0 \qquad (14\text{-}110)$$

A solution is that of Legendre's equation, or

$$P = C_3P_n(\cos\theta) + C_4Q_n(\cos\theta) \qquad (14\text{-}111)$$

At $\theta = 0$ and $\theta = \pi$, $Q_n(\cos\theta)$ becomes infinite. Since V remains finite, $C_4 = 0$ and

$$P = C_3P_n(\cos\theta) \qquad (14\text{-}112)$$

Thus, the solution for the potential is

$$V = RP = (C_1\rho^n + C_2\rho^{-(n+1)})C_3P_n(\cos\theta) \qquad (14\text{-}113)$$

or

$$V = (C_4\rho^n + C_5\rho^{-(n+1)})P_n(\cos\theta) \qquad (14\text{-}114)$$

where C_4 and C_5 are new constants. To make $V = E_0\rho\cos\theta$ as in (14-103) when ρ is large requires that $n = 1$† and $C_4 = E_0$. Thus, external to the sphere $(\rho \geq b)$, the potential is apparently given by

$$V_e = \left(E_0\rho + \frac{C_5}{\rho^2}\right)\cos\theta \qquad (14\text{-}115)$$

Inside the sphere V must remain finite so that $C_5 = 0$ and the potential inside $(0 \leq \rho \leq b)$ is apparently of the form

$$V_i = C_6\rho\cos\theta \qquad (14\text{-}116)$$

The constants C_5 and C_6 must satisfy the boundary condition at the surface of the sphere that the tangential component of $\mathbf{E}$ and normal com-

† For $n = 1$, $P_n(\cos\theta) = P_1(\cos\theta) = \cos\theta$ (see Appendix, Sec. A-14).

ponent of $\mathbf{D}$ are continuous. That is,[1]

$$E_{t1} = E_{t2} \tag{14-117}$$

or

$$\frac{\partial V_e}{\rho \, \partial \theta} = \frac{\partial V_i}{\rho \, \partial \theta} \qquad \text{at } \rho = b \tag{14-118}$$

and

$$D_{n1} = D_{n2} \tag{14-119}$$

or

$$\epsilon_1 \frac{\partial V_e}{\partial \rho} = \epsilon_2 \frac{\partial V_i}{\partial \rho} \qquad \text{at } \rho = b \tag{14-120}$$

Substituting (14-115) and (14-116) in (14-118), we have

$$b^3 = \frac{C_5}{C_6 - E_0} \tag{14-121}$$

Substituting (14-115) and (14-116) in (14-120), we have

$$C_6 = \frac{\epsilon_1}{\epsilon_2}\left(E_0 - \frac{2C_5}{b^3}\right) \tag{14-122}$$

Introducing b^3 from (14-121) into (14-122) yields

$$C_6 = \frac{3\epsilon_1 E_0}{2\epsilon_1 + \epsilon_2} \tag{14-123}$$

Putting this value for C_6 in (14-121), we obtain

$$C_5 = b^3 E_0\left(\frac{\epsilon_1 - \epsilon_2}{2\epsilon_1 + \epsilon_2}\right) \tag{14-124}$$

Hence, the potential distribution outside the sphere ($\rho \geq b$) is

$$V_e = E_0\left[\rho + \frac{b^3}{\rho^2}\left(\frac{\epsilon_{r1} - \epsilon_{r2}}{2\epsilon_{r1} + \epsilon_{r2}}\right)\right]\cos\theta \tag{14-125}$$

and the potential distribution inside the sphere ($0 \leq \rho \leq b$) is

$$V_i = \frac{3\epsilon_{r1}E_0\rho\,\cos\theta}{2\epsilon_{r1} + \epsilon_{r2}} \tag{14-126}$$

where ϵ_{r1} = relative permittivity of medium outside of sphere = ϵ_1/ϵ_0
ϵ_{r2} = relative permittivity of medium inside of sphere = ϵ_2/ϵ_0
b = radius of sphere
E_0 = original value of electric field (or value at a large distance from sphere)

[1] In place of the boundary condition $E_{t1} = E_{t2}$ we could use the boundary condition that $V_e = V_i$ at any point on the surface of the sphere since if $V_e = V_i$ is satisfied $E_{t1} = E_{t2}$ is also satisfied.

These solutions satisfy Laplace's equation and the boundary conditions and, hence, must represent the potential distribution in the presence of the dielectric sphere.

The equipotentials, as given by (14-125) and (14-126), are shown by dashed lines in Fig. 14-9b. The field lines (solid) are everywhere normal to the equipotentials. Note that because this is a three-dimensional problem the areas are, in general, not curvilinear squares.

14-9. Conformal Transformations. Introduction. The solution of many two-dimensional field problems is greatly facilitated by the use of complex function theory with which one can transform the geometry of a problem into a simpler geometry or one for which the field and potential distribution is known. Because the shape or form of an *infinitesimal area* is preserved, these transformations are called *conformal transformations*. When this method can be applied, we may obtain an exact solution.

Any point in a plane is specified by two coordinate values. Thus the point P in the x-y plane is specified if x and y are given. In complex notation the position is designated by $x + jy$. Now $x + jy$ is a *complex* quantity. Calling this quantity z (that is, $z = x + jy$) we may refer to the x-y plane as the z plane.[1]

Let us begin by considering some relations between two complex functions z and w where

$$z = x + jy \qquad (14\text{-}127)$$

and

$$w = u + jv \qquad (14\text{-}128)$$

If $w = z$, then $u = x$ and $v = y$. It follows that any point on the z plane (coordinates x and y) transforms to the same point on the w plane (coordinates u and v). Thus, as shown in Fig. 14-10, the square $ABCD$ in the z plane transforms to the same square in the w plane. Hence there

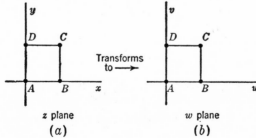

z plane   w plane
(a)   (b)

FIG. 14-10. Conformal transformation for $w = z$ (no change).

[1] The absolute value (magnitude) of z is

$$|z| = \sqrt{x^2 + y^2} = \sqrt{(x + jy)(x - jy)}$$

where $(x - jy) = z^*$ is called the complex conjugate of z.

is no change ($w = z$). It is assumed that the scales for the z and w planes are the same.

Consider next the case where

$$w = 2z \qquad (14\text{-}129)$$

Then

$$u = 2x \qquad (14\text{-}130)$$

and

$$v = 2y \qquad (14\text{-}131)$$

For this case there is a magnification of 2, the square $ABCD$ in the z plane transforming, as shown in Fig. 14-11, to the square $ABCD$ of twice the side length in the w plane.

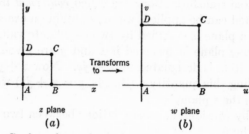

FIG. 14-11. Conformal transformation for $w = 2z$ (linear magnification).

Consider now the case where

$$w = z^{\frac{1}{2}} \qquad \text{or} \qquad z = w^2 \qquad (14\text{-}132)$$

Then

$$w^2 = (u + jv)^2 = u^2 + j2uv - v^2 \qquad (14\text{-}133)$$

and

$$z = x + jy \qquad (14\text{-}134)$$

so that, equating real parts,

$$x = u^2 - v^2 \qquad (14\text{-}135)$$

and equating imaginary parts,

$$y = 2uv \qquad (14\text{-}136)$$

It follows that

$$u^2 = v^2 + x = \frac{y^2}{4u^2} + x \qquad (14\text{-}137)$$

or

$$4u^4 - 4xu^2 - y^2 = 0 \qquad (14\text{-}138)$$

so that

$$u = \sqrt{\frac{x \pm \sqrt{x^2 + y^2}}{2}} \qquad (14\text{-}139)$$

and

$$v = \frac{y}{2u} = \sqrt{u^2 - x} \qquad (14\text{-}140)$$

In this case ($w = z^{\frac{1}{2}}$) the square $ABCD$ in the z plane transforms, as portrayed in Fig. 14-12, to the figure $ABCD$ in the w plane. Here the figure shown has been compressed from a 90° sector into a 45° sector. It is to be noted that except at A the angles are preserved.

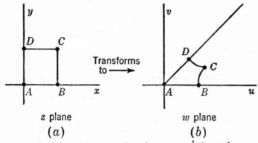

z plane

(a)

w plane

(b)

FIG. 14-12. Conformal transformation for $w = z^{\frac{1}{2}}$ (angular compression).

Thus far we have considered the cases

$w = z$ (no change)

$w = 2z$ (linear magnification)

$w = z^{\frac{1}{2}}$ (angular compression of first quadrant)

Let us now proceed to the general case where w is some arbitrary function of z. That is,

$$w = f(z) \tag{14-141}$$

As we have seen, this relation defines a transformation of a certain figure or geometry in the z plane to another figure when mapped in the w plane. Of the many functions possible those which produce a conformal transformation[1] are those for which w is an *analytic function* of z. The real and imaginary parts of an analytic function satisfy Laplace's two-dimensional equation, and hence such functions are useful in solving many two-dimensional field problems. Thus, before using a function, we must determine that it is analytic. The necessary criteria for doing this will now be developed.

Let the derivative of a complex function w be defined as follows,

$$\frac{dw}{dz} = \lim_{\Delta z \to 0} \frac{\Delta w}{\Delta z} = \lim_{\Delta z \to 0} \frac{f(z + \Delta z) - f(z)}{\Delta z} \tag{14-142}$$

where $\Delta z = \Delta x + j\,\Delta y$. For dw/dz to have a unique value for a given argument requires that

$$\lim_{\Delta z \to 0} \frac{\Delta w}{\Delta z}$$

[1] In a conformal transformation the angles and hence the shape of an infinitesimal area are preserved except at certain points. That is, the presentation in one plane is a map of the other.

be independent of the path by which Δz approaches zero. That is, it is necessary that

$$\lim_{\Delta z \to 0} \frac{\Delta w}{\Delta z} = \lim_{\Delta x \to 0} \frac{\Delta w}{\Delta x} = \lim_{\Delta y \to 0} \frac{\Delta w}{j \, \Delta y} \tag{14-143}$$

or that

$$\frac{dw}{dz} = \frac{\partial w}{\partial x} = -j \frac{\partial w}{\partial y} \tag{14-144}$$

Thus, if w has a unique derivative with respect to z,

$$\frac{\partial w}{\partial x} = \frac{dw}{dz}\frac{\partial z}{\partial x} = \frac{dw}{dz} = \frac{\partial u}{\partial x} + j \frac{\partial v}{\partial x} \tag{14-145}$$

and

$$\frac{\partial w}{\partial y} = \frac{dw}{dz}\frac{\partial z}{\partial y} = j \frac{dw}{dz} = \frac{\partial u}{\partial y} + j \frac{\partial v}{\partial y} \tag{14-146}$$

From (14-145) and (14-146) we have

$$\frac{dw}{dz} = \frac{\partial u}{\partial x} + j \frac{\partial v}{\partial x} \tag{14-147}$$

and

$$\frac{dw}{dz} = -j \frac{\partial u}{\partial y} + \frac{\partial v}{\partial y} = \frac{\partial v}{\partial y} - j \frac{\partial u}{\partial y} \tag{14-148}$$

It follows from (14-147) and (14-148) that

$$\frac{\partial u}{\partial x} = \frac{\partial v}{\partial y} \tag{14-149}$$

and

$$\frac{\partial v}{\partial x} = -\frac{\partial u}{\partial y} \tag{14-150}$$

Equations (14-149) and (14-150) are known as the *Cauchy-Riemann conditions*. A complex function $w = u + jv$ whose partial derivatives are continuous and satisfy these conditions is analytic, that is, it has a unique derivative with respect to z.† For example, $w = C_1 z^2$ and $w = 2(x + jy)$ are analytic, but $w = 2x + jy$ is not, as may be noted by applying the Cauchy-Riemann conditions to these functions.

Eliminating v from the Cauchy-Riemann conditions by taking the partial derivative of (14-149) with respect to x and the partial derivative of (14-150) with respect to y, we obtain

$$\frac{\partial^2 u}{\partial x^2} + \frac{\partial^2 u}{\partial y^2} = \nabla^2 u = 0 \tag{14-151}$$

† Such a function w that possesses a derivative at every point of a region is said to be analytic over that region. It turns out that simple functions of the algebraic, trigonometric, or exponential type are analytic. Thus, the functions $w = z$, $w = 2z$, and $w = z^{\frac{1}{2}}$, considered at the beginning of this section, are all analytic.

In like manner we have, on eliminating u,

$$\frac{\partial^2 v}{\partial x^2} + \frac{\partial^2 v}{\partial y^2} = \nabla^2 v = 0 \qquad (14\text{-}152)$$

Both (14-151) and (14-152) have the form of Laplace's equation. Hence every analytic function automatically yields two functions each of which is a solution of Laplace's equation.

Since angles are preserved, the constant x and constant y lines are orthogonal not only in the z plane but also when mapped in the w plane. Therefore, if the constant x lines represent the electric field and the constant y lines the equipotentials of a uniform field distribution they continue to represent field and equipotential lines when mapped in the w plane. It is this property which makes conformal transformations so useful in solving two-dimensional field problems.

Example. Two perfectly conducting sheets intersect at right angles, forming a corner as shown in cross section in Fig. 14-13. If a potential difference is applied between the sheets and another conductor at a large distance in the direction of the bisector of the corner, find the field and potential distribution in the vicinity of the corner.

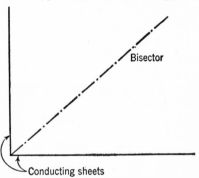

FIG. 14-13. Ninety-degree corner.

Solution. The field distribution in a 90° corner was solved graphically in Sec. 2-28 (see Fig. 2-27a). A solution may also be obtained by means of a conformal transformation, the solution in this case being exact.[1] Proceeding to obtain a solution by the conformal-transformation method, we recall (see Fig. 14-12) that the transformation $w = z^{\frac{1}{2}}$ transformed a 90° sector into 45° or a 180° sector into 90°. Hence this transformation can be applied to our problem.

In the z plane let the line $y = 0$ represent a flat conducting sheet. Then a potential difference applied between this sheet and another parallel one a large distance above it will produce a uniform field distribution as shown in Fig. 14-14a. The dashed lines (y = constant) are equipotentials, and the solid lines (x = constant) are field lines.

The transformation $w = z^{\frac{1}{2}}$ was discussed earlier in this section, and it was shown in (14-139) and (14-140) that $u = \sqrt{(x \pm \sqrt{x^2 + y^2})/2}$ and $v = y/2u = \sqrt{u^2 - x}$. By means of these relations we can obtain the coordinates (u, v) in the w plane for any point (x, y) in the z plane. In this way the uniform field (Fig. 14-14a) may be transformed point by point to the nonuniform field in the 90° corner, as shown in Fig. 14-14b, the dashed lines being equipotentials and the solid lines electric field lines.

The transformation used in the above example is of the exponential type. Other transformations of this type are listed in Fig. 14-15, with the nature of the transformation shown graphically. In all cases the

---

[1] However, in many applications a graphical solution may be equally satisfactory.

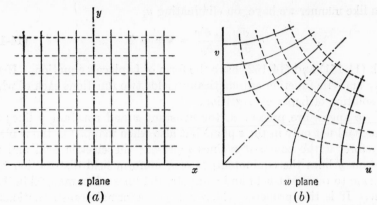

FIG. 14-14. Uniform field in z plane (a) transforms into nonuniform field of 90° corner (b).

upper half of the z plane undergoes either an angular compression or an angular expansion when mapped in the w plane. When the exponent is less than 1, there is angular compression and when the exponent is greater than 1, there is angular expansion. It follows, in general, that to bend the x axis so as to make an angle α in the w plane requires a transformation of the form

$$w = C_1 z^{\alpha/\pi} + C_2 \qquad (14\text{-}153)$$

where C_1 is a magnification factor and C_2 involves displacement.

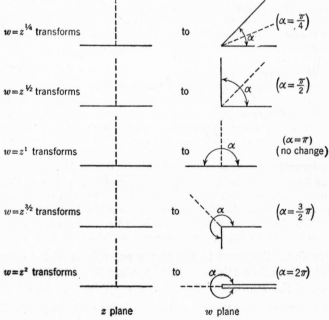

FIG. 14-15. Transformations of exponential type.

More generally the function

$$w = (z - x_1)^{\alpha/\pi} + u_1 \qquad (14\text{-}154)$$

results in a transformation of the z plane, when mapped in the w plane, as suggested in Fig. 14-16. Taking the z derivative of (14-154) to obtain

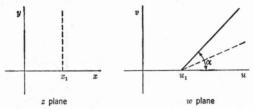

FIG. 14-16. Conformal transformation for $w = (z - x_1)^{\alpha/\pi} + u_1$.

the w variation with respect to z yields

$$\frac{dw}{dz} = \frac{\alpha}{\pi} (z - x_1)^{(\alpha/\pi)-1} \qquad (14\text{-}155)$$

In the more general situation where the x axis is bent so as to form a polygon with n angles $(\alpha_1, \alpha_2, \alpha_3, \ldots, \alpha_n)$, when mapped in the w plane, we have

$$\frac{dw}{dz} = C_1(z - x_1)^{(\alpha_1/\pi)-1}(z - x_2)^{(\alpha_2/\pi)-1}(z - x_3)^{(\alpha_3/\pi)-1} \cdots$$
$$(z - x_n)^{(\alpha_n/\pi)-1} \qquad (14\text{-}156)$$

Integrating (14-156),

$$w = C_1 \int [(z - x_1)^{(\alpha_1/\pi)-1}(z - x_2)^{(\alpha_2/\pi)-1} \cdots (z - x_n)^{(\alpha_n/\pi)-1}]\, dz \qquad (14\text{-}157)$$

This is the Schwarz-Christoffel transformation. For a single positive angle α_1 and $x_1 = 0$, (14-157) reduces to the same form as (14-153). That is,

$$w = C_1 \int z^{(\alpha_1/\pi)-1}\, dz = C_1' z^{\alpha_1/\pi} + C_2' \qquad (14\text{-}158)$$

14-10. Example 5. Slot in Infinite Flat Sheet. Consider the uniform field in a parallel-plate capacitor with plates of infinite extent. If a slot is cut in the lower plate as shown in Fig. 14-17, the resulting field

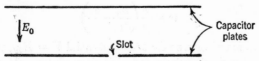

FIG. 14-17. Capacitor with slot in lower plate.

distribution may be found by an application of the Schwarz-Christoffel transformation. It is assumed that the spacing between the capacitor plates is large compared with the width of the slot.

We wish to find a function that transforms the uniform (z-plane) field in such a manner that its map in the w plane is the field with the slotted plate. As illustrated in Fig. 14-18a, let the x axis represent the unslotted lower plate of the capacitor. The slot is to be introduced between the points x_1 and x_3. By an appropriate transformation a map can be obtained in the w plane in which that part of the x axis between x_1 and x_3

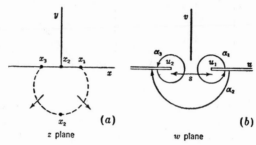

(a)   *(b)*

z plane   w plane

FIG. 14-18. z plane partially transformed, as shown by dashed lines (a), and completely transformed (b).

is stretched downward, as suggested by the dashed lines in Fig. 14-18a, until the point x_2 is at $v = -\infty$ and the x axis is folded back on itself, leaving a gap of width s, as in Fig. 14-18b. As mapped in the w plane, the point x_1 appears at u_1 and the point x_3 at u_2.

The appropriate function is obtained from (14-157) by noting that $\alpha_1 = 2\pi$, $\alpha_2 = -\pi$, $\alpha_3 = 2\pi$ and also that $x_3 = -x_1$ and $x_2 = 0$. Therefore, in this case (14-157) becomes

$$w = C_1 \int [(z - x_1)^{(2\pi/\pi)-1} z^{-(\pi/\pi)-1} (z + x_1)^{(2\pi/\pi)-1}] \, dz \quad (14\text{-}159)$$

or

$$w = C_1 \int \frac{z^2 - x_1{}^2}{z^2} \, dz = C_1 \left(z + \frac{x_1{}^2}{z} \right) + C_2 \quad (14\text{-}160)$$

When $z = \pm x_1 + j0$, it is required that $w = \pm (s/2) + j0$, where s is the slot width. Therefore

$$\pm \frac{s}{2} = C_1(\pm x_1 \pm x_1) + C_2 \quad (14\text{-}161)$$

and we have for $C_2 = 0$ that $C_1 = s/4x_1$, or

$$w = \frac{s}{4} \left(\frac{z}{x_1} + \frac{x_1}{z} \right) \quad (14\text{-}162)$$

The z-plane field is uniform so that the potential $V = E_0 y$, where E_0 is the uniform field between the unslotted capacitor plates. Now if $x_1 = s/4$; (14-162) becomes

$$w = \frac{s}{4} \left(\frac{z}{s/4} + \frac{s/4}{z} \right) = \left[z + \frac{(s/4)^2}{z} \right] \quad (14\text{-}163)$$

or

$$z = \frac{1}{2}\left[w \pm \sqrt{w^2 - \left(\frac{s}{2}\right)^2} \right] \tag{14-164}$$

The potential in the z plane is given by

$$V = E_0 y = E_0 \operatorname{Im} z \tag{14-165}$$

Therefore, the potential distribution as a function of position in the w plane is

$$V = \frac{E_0}{2}\left[v + \operatorname{Im} \sqrt{u^2 + j2uv - v^2 - \left(\frac{s}{2}\right)^2} \right] \tag{14-166}$$

This is the solution to the problem. Introducing particular values of u and v into (14-166), the potential at these points is found. Connecting

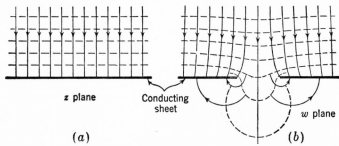

$$z \text{ plane} \qquad \text{Conducting} \atop \text{sheet} \qquad w \text{ plane}$$

(a)   (b)

FIG. 14-19. Conformal transformation of uniform field (z plane) above continuous flat sheet (a) to field for slotted sheet (w plane)(b).

points of equal potential with dashed lines yields the equipotential contours of Fig. 14-19b. The solid lines represent the electric field.

14-11. Other Conformal Transformations. *The Transformation $w = e^z$.* Consider the function

$$w = e^z \tag{14-167}$$

where $w = u + jv$
  $z = x + jy$
By de Moivre's theorem (14-167) becomes

$$w = u + jv = e^x(\cos y + j \sin y) \tag{14-168}$$

It follows that

$$u = e^x \cos y \tag{14-169}$$

and

$$v = e^x \sin y \tag{14-170}$$

Dividing (14-170) by (14-169) yields

$$v = u \tan y \tag{14-171}$$

Thus, a constant y line transforms to a radial line when mapped in the w plane. Squaring (14-169) and (14-170) and adding, we have

$$u = \sqrt{e^{2x} - v^2} \qquad (14\text{-}172)$$

Hence, a constant x line transforms to a circle when mapped in the w plane. The transformation by this function (14-167) of the z plane when mapped in the w plane is suggested in Fig. 14-20. The rectangle

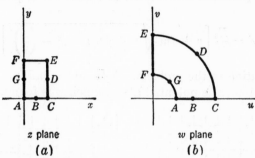

z plane   w plane
(a)   (b)

Fig. 14-20. Conformal transformation of rectangle to sector.

$ABCDEFGA$ in the z plane appears as a sector $ABCDEFGA$ in the w plane.

The Transformation $z = e^w$. The inverse of (14-167) is

$$z = e^w \qquad (14\text{-}173)$$

or

$$w = \ln z \qquad (14\text{-}174)$$

where $w = u + jv$
$\quad z = \rho e^{j\theta}$
$\quad \rho$ = radial distance
$\quad \theta$ = angle with respect to x axis

Now

$$\ln z = \ln \rho + j\theta \qquad (14\text{-}175)$$

It follows that

$$u = \ln \rho = \tfrac{1}{2} \ln (x^2 + y^2) \qquad (14\text{-}176)$$

and

$$v = \theta = \arctan \frac{y}{x} \qquad (14\text{-}177)$$

Hence (14-173) transforms a sector in the z plane to a rectangle when mapped in the w plane.

The Transformation $w = \tan z$. Consider the function

$$w = \tan z = \tan (x + jy) \qquad (14\text{-}178)$$

where $w = u + jv$. Since

$$\tan (x + jy) = \frac{\tan x + j \tanh y}{1 - j \tan x \tanh y} \tag{14-179}$$

It follows that

$$u = \frac{\tan x \, (1 - \tanh^2 y)}{1 + \tan^2 x \tanh^2 y} \tag{14-180}$$

and

$$v = \frac{\tanh y \, (1 + \tan^2 x)}{1 + \tan^2 x \tanh^2 y} \tag{14-181}$$

Adding u^2 and v^2 yields the radius ρ^2. That is,

$$u^2 + v^2 = \rho^2 = \frac{\tan^2 x + \tanh^2 y}{1 + \tan^2 x \tanh^2 y} \tag{14-182}$$

Hence, a coaxial transmission line in the w plane as shown in cross section by Fig. 14-21a is transformed, when mapped in the z plane, into a slab transmission line as in Fig. 14-21b.[1] This line has two flat parallel sheets

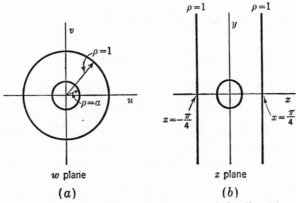

w plane

(a)

z plane

(b)

Fig. 14-21. Conformal transformation of coaxial transmission line (a) to slab line (b).

of infinite extent (corresponding to the outer conductor) and an elliptical inner conductor.

If the radius ρ of the outer conductor is unity (see Fig. 14-21a), then at $y = 0$ the outer conductor is at $\pm \pi/4$, while at $x = 0$, it is at $y = \pm \infty$. It follows that the $\rho = 1$ circle in the w plane (outer conductor) is transformed, when mapped in the z plane, into the two constant x lines $x = \pm \pi/4$. If the radius of the inner conductor is a, then at $y = 0$ the inner conductor is at $x = \pm \arctan a$, while at $x = 0$ it is at $y = \pm \operatorname{arctanh} a$. It follows that the $\rho = a$ circle (inner conductor) in the w plane is transformed, when mapped in the z plane, into an elliptically shaped figure.

[1] W. B. Wholey and W. N. Eldred, A New Type of Slotted Line Section, *Proc. I.R.E.*, **38**, 244–248, March, 1950.

Conformal transformations are applicable to *static* two-dimensional fields, but, in general, they cannot be used for time-changing fields (Laplace's equation no longer holds). However, conformal transformations can be employed to find the fields of waves traveling on a two-conductor transmission line *provided* the wave is of the TEM type, the line has a constant cross section, and there is negligible conductor and radiation loss. Under these conditions the transverse electric field configuration is identical with the static field distribution. Hence a solution of Laplace's equation via conformal transformations can be used to design a high-frequency transmission line where the above conditions are met. This has been done in the case of the slab line by Wholey and Eldred.

The Transformation $w = (h/\pi)(e^z - z + j\pi)$. Consider finally the function

$$w = \frac{h}{\pi}(e^z - z + j\pi) \tag{14-183}$$

from which

$$u = \frac{h}{\pi}(e^x \cos y - x) \tag{14-184}$$

and

$$v = \frac{h}{\pi}(e^x \sin y - y + \pi) \tag{14-185}$$

For $y = 0$, $u = (h/\pi)(e^x - x)$, and $v = h$, while for $y = \pi$,

$$u = (h/\pi)(-e^x - x)$$

and $v = 0$. Thus the $y = 0$ line, when mapped in the w plane, is folded back on itself and turned around so as to lie at $v = h$ and at u values equal to or greater than h/π. The $y = \pi$ line is transformed so as to lie along the u axis ($v = 0$). It undergoes also a scale change and reversal of direction. This transformation is illustrated in Fig. 14-22. The rectangle $ABCDEFA$ in the z plane is transformed to the figure $ABCDEFA$ when mapped in the w plane.

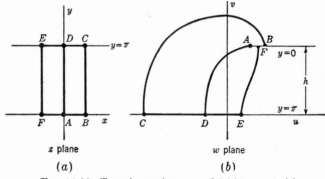

FIG. 14-22. Transformation $w = (h/\pi)(e^z - z + j\pi)$.

This transformation is useful for mapping the field at the edge of a capacitor plate situated above a ground plane, the field distribution being as portrayed in Fig. 14-23. The dashed lines are equipotentials, and the

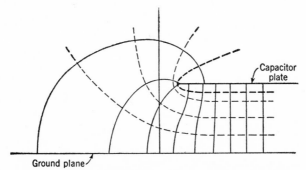

FIG. 14-23. Fringing field at edge of capacitor plate.

solid lines are field lines. (Applying the method of images to this figure we can obtain the field at the edge of a two-plate capacitor.)

For $y = 0$ we have, on taking the x derivative of u,

$$\frac{du}{dx} = \frac{h}{\pi}(e^x - 1) \qquad (14\text{-}186)$$

It follows that the relative electric field intensity E_v normal to the top capacitor plate is expressed by

$$E_v = \frac{1}{du/dx} = \frac{\pi}{h(e^x - 1)} \qquad (14\text{-}187)$$

The relative surface charge density on the top plate is

$$\rho_s = D_v = \epsilon_0 E_v = \frac{\pi\epsilon_0}{h(e^x - 1)} \qquad (14\text{-}188)$$

where ϵ_0 = permittivity of the medium (air). We note from (14-187) and (14-188) that the electric field intensity and the surface charge density are infinite at the edge of the capacitor plate (point A in Fig. 14-22b) since $x = 0$ at this point. The infinite charge density results, of course, from the implicit assumption that the plate is infinitesimally thick. If a thick plate is used and its surface coincides with one of the equipotentials in Fig. 14-23 (for example, the heavy dashed contour), the field configuration outside of the plate is undisturbed and it is apparent that the surface charge density remains finite since the edge is no longer perfectly sharp.

PROBLEMS

14-1. Show that the relations $\nabla \cdot \mathbf{D} = 0$, $\mathbf{E} = -\nabla V - j\omega\mathbf{A}$, and $\nabla \cdot \mathbf{A} = -j\omega\mu\epsilon V$ may be combined to yield the scalar wave equation $\nabla^2 V + \omega^2\mu\epsilon V = 0$. Note that when $\omega = 0$, $\nabla \cdot \mathbf{A} = 0$, as assumed in (4-169) for static fields.

14-2. A conducting wire of radius a is placed in air in an originally uniform field E_0. The wire is coated with an insulating layer of outer radius b and permittivity ϵ_1, as

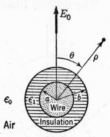

Fig. 14-24. Cross section of insulated wire for Prob. 14-2.

shown in Fig. 14-24. Find the potential V_0 everywhere outside the insulating layer and the potential V_d everywhere inside the insulating layer.

14-3. The electric field is uniform and equal to E_0 above an infinite plane sheet conductor and zero below the sheet. If a slot of width s is cut in the conductor find the surface charge density on both sides of the sheet. The medium above and below the sheet is air.

$$Ans.: \rho_s = (\epsilon_0 E_0/2)\{1 + u/[u^2 - (s/2)^2]^{\frac{1}{2}}\} \text{ above sheet.}$$
$$\rho_s = (\epsilon_0 E_0/2)\{1 - u/[u^2 - (s/2)^2]^{\frac{1}{2}}\} \text{ below sheet.}$$

14-4. Using a Schwarz-Christoffel transformation, map the field in a 60° conducting corner formed by two flat conducting sheets if a potential difference is applied between the corner and another conductor at a large distance in the direction of the corner bisector.

14-5. A conducting hemisphere is placed on a flat conducting infinite sheet, as shown in Fig. 14-25. Before the hemisphere was introduced, the electric field everywhere above the sheet was normal to it and equal to E_0. The radius of the hemisphere

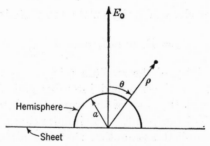

Fig. 14-25. Hemisphere for Prob. 14-5.

is a. The angle θ is measured from the normal to the sheet. The medium above the sheet is air. Assume the potential V of the hemisphere and sheet to be zero. (a) Find V everywhere above the sheet and hemisphere. (b) Find the surface charge density at all points on the hemisphere and flat sheet. (c) Plot a graph of the surface charge density along the hemisphere and flat sheet to a distance of $5a$.

$Ans.:$ (a) $V = -[1 - (a^3/\rho^3)] E_0\rho \cos \theta$; (b) $\rho_s = 3\epsilon_0 E_0 \cos \theta$ on sphere and $\rho_s = \epsilon_0 E_0[1 - (a^3/\rho^3)]$ on sheet.

14-6. A uniformly charged linear wire is situated at a distance d from two flat conducting sheets of infinite extent which intersect to form a square corner. The wire runs parallel to the corner.   (a) Find the potential V everywhere in the corner, and draw a map of the equipotential contours.   (b) Find the surface charge density along the sheets, and plot a graph of this variation to a distance of $5d$ from the corner.

14-7. What spacing D is required between the plates of a transmission line consisting of two infinite parallel plates with a symmetrically located center conductor of radius r_1 in order that the characteristic impedance of the line be 100 ohms?   The parallel plates are at the same potential.

14-8. A thin conducting spherical shell of radius r_1 is cut into two hemispheres separated by a very small air gap.   If one hemisphere is charged to a potential V_1 and the other hemisphere to a potential V_2, derive the expression of the potential at any point outside of the sphere.

14-9. A slot of width s is cut in an infinite flat conducting sheet.   Before the slot was made, the electric field above the sheet was everywhere perpendicular to the sheet and of intensity E_0, while the field below the sheet was zero.   At what distance below the center of the slot (and normal to the sheet) is the electric potential equal to one one-hundredth of its value at a distance s above the sheet and remote from the slot?

14-10. The electric field intensity in the uniform field region between the two horizontal plates of a large parallel-plate capacitor is 10,000 volts/meter.   Find the field intensity at a point in the fringing field halfway between the plates and at a horizontal distance d from the edges of the plates, where d is the plate spacing.   It is assumed that the plates are infinitesimally thick and that they are located in air.

14-11. The reflection coefficient for voltage on a line of characteristic impedance Z_0 is

$$\rho_v = \frac{Z - Z_0}{Z + Z_0} = \frac{(Z/Z_0) - 1}{(Z/Z_0) + 1} = \frac{Z_n - 1}{Z_n + 1}$$

where Z = load impedance (ohms) and Z_n = normalized impedance (dimensionless) ($= R_n + jX_n$).   It follows that

$$Z_n = \frac{1 + \rho_v}{1 - \rho_v}$$

Show that if R_n and X_n are obtained as functions of the real and imaginary parts of ρ_v a map of R_n and X_n in the ρ_v plane yields the *Smith impedance chart* (see Sec. 11-7).

14-12. A half-cylindrical metal tube of radius a, as shown in Fig. 14-26, is at zero

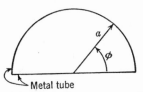

FIG. 14-26. Cross section of half-cylindrical tube for Prob. 14-12.

potential.   If a plate at a constant potential greater than zero is placed across one end of the tube, but not in contact with it, show that the potential inside the tube at a large distance z from the plate is of the form

$$V = Ce^{-\frac{R_{11}}{a}z} \sin \phi \, J_1\left(\frac{R_{11}}{a}\rho\right)$$

where C = a constant, ρ = radius of point inside of tube, J_1 = first-order Bessel function (of first kind), and $R_{11} = 3.832$ = first root of J_1 [that is, first value of u after $u = 0$ for which $J_1(u) = 0$].   Assume that the tube is infinitely long.

APPENDIX

A-1. Table of Units. In the following table dimensions or quantities commonly used in electromagnetics are listed alphabetically under the headings Fundamental, Mechanical, Electrical, and Magnetic. In the *first* column the name of the dimension or quantity is given and in the *second* column the common symbol for designating it. In the *third* column (Description) the dimension is described in terms of the fundamental dimensions (mass, length, time, and electric charge) or other secondary dimensions. The *fourth* column (Mksc unit) lists the rationalized mksc unit for the dimension, and the *fifth* column gives equivalent units. The *last* column indicates the fundamental dimensions by means of the symbols M (mass), L (length), T (time), and Q (electric charge).

For a discussion of dimensions and units see Secs. 1-1 to 1-3, inclusive.

FUNDAMENTAL UNITS

Name of dimension or quantity	Symbol	Description	Mksc unit	Equivalent units	Fundamental dimensions
Charge (electric)	Q, q	current $\times$ time	coulomb	6.25×10^{18} electron charges = ampere-second = 3×10^{9} cgs esu† = 0.1 cgs emu‡	Q
Length	L, l		meter	100 centimeters	L
Mass	M, m		kilogram	1,000 grams	M
Time	T, t		second	$\frac{1}{60}$ minute = $\frac{1}{3,600}$ hour = $\frac{1}{86,400}$ day	T

MECHANICAL UNITS

Acceleration	a	velocity/time = $\frac{\text{length}}{\text{time}^2}$	$\frac{\text{meter}}{\text{second}^2}$		$\frac{L}{T^2}$
Area	A, a, s	length^2	meter^2		L^2
Energy or work	W	force $\times$ length = power $\times$ time	joule	newton-meter = watt-second = volt-coulomb = 10^7 ergs = 10^7 dyne-centimeters	$\frac{ML^2}{T^2}$
Energy density	w	$\frac{\text{energy}}{\text{volume}}$	$\frac{\text{joule}}{\text{meter}^3}$	10 ergs/centimeter^3	$\frac{M}{LT^2}$

† cgs esu = centimeter-gram-second electrostatic unit (stat unit).

‡ cgs emu = centimeter-gram-second electromagnetic unit (ab unit).

MECHANICAL UNITS.—*(Continued)*

Name of dimension or quantity	Symbol	Description	Mksc unit	Equivalent units	Fundamental dimensions
Force	**F**	mass × acceleration	newton	$\dfrac{\text{kilogram-meters}}{\text{second}^2} = \dfrac{\text{joule}}{\text{meter}}$ $= 10^5$ dynes	$\dfrac{ML}{T^2}$
Frequency	f	cycles/second	cps (hertz)		$\dfrac{1}{T}$
Length	L, l		meter	100 centimeters	L
Mass	M, m		kilogram	1,000 grams	M
Moment (torque)		force × length	newton-meter	$\dfrac{\text{kilogram-meter}^2}{\text{second}} = \text{joule}$	$\dfrac{ML^2}{T^2}$
Momentum	$m\mathbf{v}$	mass × velocity = force × time = $\dfrac{\text{energy}}{\text{velocity}}$	newton-second	$\dfrac{\text{kilogram-meter}}{\text{second}}$ $= \dfrac{\text{joule-second}}{\text{meter}}$	$\dfrac{ML}{T}$
Period	T	$\dfrac{1}{\text{frequency}}$	second		T
Power	P	$\dfrac{\text{force} \times \text{length}}{\text{time}}$ = $\dfrac{\text{energy}}{\text{time}}$	watt	$\dfrac{\text{joule}}{\text{second}} = \dfrac{\text{newton-meter}}{\text{second}}$ $= \dfrac{\text{kilogram-meter}^2}{\text{second}^3}$	$\dfrac{ML^2}{T^3}$

MECHANICAL UNITS.—(Continued)

Name of dimension or quantity	Symbol	Description	Mksc unit	Equivalent units	Fundamental dimensions
Time	T, t		second	$\frac{1}{60}$ minute $= \frac{1}{3,600}$ hour $= \frac{1}{86,400}$ day	T
Velocity (velocity of light in vacuum $= 3 \times 10^8$ meters/sec)	$\mathbf{v}$	$\frac{\text{length}}{\text{time}}$	$\frac{\text{meter}}{\text{second}}$		$\frac{L}{T}$
Volume	v	length³	meter³		L^3

ELECTRICAL UNITS

Name of dimension or quantity	Symbol	Description	Mksc unit	Equivalent units	Fundamental dimensions
Admittance	Y	$\frac{1}{\text{impedance}}$	mho (siemens)	$\frac{\text{ampere}}{\text{volt}} = \frac{\text{coulomb}^2}{\text{joule-second}}$	$\frac{TQ^2}{ML^2}$
Capacitance	C	$\frac{\text{charge}}{\text{potential}}$	farad	$\frac{\text{coulomb}}{\text{volt}} = \frac{\text{coulomb}^2}{\text{joule}} = \frac{\text{ampere-second}}{\text{volt}} = 9 \times 10^{11}$ cm (cgs esu)	$\frac{T^2Q^2}{ML^2}$
Charge	Q, q	current $\times$ time	coulomb	6.25×10^{18} electron charges $=$ ampere-second $= 3 \times 10^9$ cgs esu $= 0.1$ cgs emu	Q

ELECTRICAL UNITS.—(Continued)

Name of dimension or quantity	Symbol	Description	Mksc unit	Equivalent units	Fundamental dimensions
Charge (volume) density	ρ	$\dfrac{\text{charge}}{\text{volume}} = \nabla \cdot \mathbf{D}$	$\dfrac{\text{coulomb}}{\text{meter}^3}$	$\dfrac{\text{ampere-second}}{\text{meter}^3}$	$\dfrac{Q}{L^3}$
Conductance	G	$\dfrac{1}{\text{resistance}}$	mho (siemens)	$\dfrac{\text{ampere}}{\text{volt}} = \dfrac{\text{coulomb}^2}{\text{joule-second}}$	$\dfrac{TQ^2}{ML^2}$
Conductivity	σ	$\dfrac{1}{\text{resistivity}}$	$\dfrac{\text{mho}}{\text{meter}}$	$\dfrac{1}{\text{ohm-meter}} = \dfrac{1}{100}\dfrac{\text{mho}}{\text{centimeter}}$	$\dfrac{TQ^2}{ML^3}$
Current	I, i	$\dfrac{\text{charge}}{\text{time}}$	ampere	$\dfrac{\text{coulomb}}{\text{second}} = 3 \times 10^9 \text{ cgs esu}$ $= 0.1 \text{ cgs emu}$	$\dfrac{Q}{T}$
Current density	J	$\dfrac{\text{current}}{\text{area}}$	$\dfrac{\text{ampere}}{\text{meter}^2}$	$\dfrac{\text{coulomb}}{\text{second-meter}^2}$	$\dfrac{Q}{TL^2}$
Dipole moment	$\mathbf{p}\ (= q\mathbf{l})$	charge × length	coulomb-meter	ampere-second-meter	LQ
Emf	$\mathcal{V}$	$\int \mathbf{E}_e \cdot d\mathbf{l}$	volt	$\dfrac{\text{weber}}{\text{second}} = \dfrac{\text{joule}}{\text{coulomb}}$	$\dfrac{ML^2}{T^2Q}$
Energy density (electric)	w_e	$\dfrac{\text{energy}}{\text{volume}}$	$\dfrac{\text{joule}}{\text{meter}^3}$	10 ergs/centimeter³	$\dfrac{M}{LT^2}$
Field intensity (E vector)	$\mathbf{E}$	$\dfrac{\text{potential}}{\text{length}} = \dfrac{\text{force}}{\text{charge}}$	$\dfrac{\text{volt}}{\text{meter}}$	$\dfrac{\text{newton}}{\text{coulomb}} = \dfrac{\text{joule}}{\text{coulomb-meter}}$ $= \tfrac{1}{3} \times 10^{-4} \text{ cgs esu}$ $= 10^6 \text{ cgs emu}$	$\dfrac{ML}{T^2Q}$

ELECTRICAL UNITS.—(Continued)

Name of dimension or quantity	Symbol	Description	Mksc unit	Equivalent units	Fundamental dimensions
Flux	ψ	charge $= \int\int \mathbf{D} \cdot d\mathbf{s}$	coulomb	ampere-second	Q
Flux density (displacement) (D vector)	$\mathbf{D}$	$\dfrac{\text{charge}}{\text{area}}$	$\dfrac{\text{coulomb}}{\text{meter}^2}$	$\dfrac{\text{ampere-second}}{\text{meter}^2} = \dfrac{\text{ampere}}{\text{meter}^2/\text{second}}$	$\dfrac{Q}{L^2}$
Impedance	Z	$\dfrac{\text{potential}}{\text{current}}$	ohm	$\dfrac{\text{volt}}{\text{ampere}}$	$\dfrac{ML^2}{TQ^2}$
Linear charge density	ρ_L	$\dfrac{\text{charge}}{\text{length}}$	$\dfrac{\text{coulomb}}{\text{meter}}$	$\dfrac{\text{ampere-second}}{\text{meter}}$	$\dfrac{Q}{L}$
Permittivity (dielectric constant) (for vacuum, $\epsilon_0 = 8.85 \times 10^{-12}$ $= 10^{-9}/36\pi$ farad/meter)	ϵ	$\dfrac{\text{capacitance}}{\text{length}}$	$\dfrac{\text{farad}}{\text{meter}}$	$\dfrac{\text{coulomb}}{\text{volt-meter}}$	$\dfrac{T^2 Q^2}{ML^3}$
Polarization	$\mathbf{P}$	$\dfrac{\text{dipole moment}}{\text{volume}}$	$\dfrac{\text{coulomb}}{\text{meter}^2}$	$\dfrac{\text{ampere-second}}{\text{meter}^2}$	$\dfrac{Q}{L^2}$
Potential	V	$\dfrac{\text{work}}{\text{charge}}$	volt	$\dfrac{\text{joule}}{\text{coulomb}} = \dfrac{\text{newton-meter}}{\text{coulomb}}$ $= \dfrac{\text{watt-second}}{\text{coulomb}} = \dfrac{\text{watt}}{\text{ampere}}$ $= \dfrac{\text{weber}}{\text{second}} = \dfrac{1}{300}$ cgs esu $= 10^8$ cgs emu	$\dfrac{ML^2}{T^2 Q}$

ELECTRICAL UNITS.—(*Continued*)

Name of dimension or quantity	Symbol	Description	Mksc unit	Equivalent units	Fundamental dimensions
Poynting vector (power surface density)	**S**	$\dfrac{power}{area}$	$\dfrac{watt}{meter^2}$	$\dfrac{joule}{second\text{-}meter^2}$	$\dfrac{M}{T^3}$
Radiation intensity	U	$\dfrac{power}{unit\ solid\ angle\dagger}$	$\dfrac{watts}{steradian}$		$\dfrac{ML^2}{T^3}$
Reactance	X	$\dfrac{potential}{current}$	ohm	$\dfrac{volt}{ampere}$	$\dfrac{ML^2}{TQ^2}$
Relative permittivity (relative dielectric constant)	ϵ_r	ratio $\dfrac{\epsilon}{\epsilon_0}$			dimensionless
Resistance	R	$\dfrac{potential}{current}$	ohm	$\dfrac{volt}{ampere} = \dfrac{joule\text{-}second}{coulomb^2}$ $= \tfrac{1}{9} \times 10^{-11}$ egs esu $= 10^{-9}$ cgs emu	$\dfrac{ML^2}{TQ^2}$
Resistivity (specific resistance)	S	resistance $\times$ length $= 1/$conductivity	ohm-meter	$\dfrac{volt\text{-}meter}{ampere}$	$\dfrac{ML^3}{TQ^2}$
Sheet current density	**K**	$\dfrac{current}{length}$	$\dfrac{ampere}{meter}$	$\dfrac{ampere}{meter^2} \times meter$	$\dfrac{Q}{TL}$
Susceptance	B	$\dfrac{1}{reactance}$	mho	$\dfrac{ampere}{volt}$	$\dfrac{TQ^2}{ML^2}$
Wavelength	λ	length	meter		L

† Solid angle is dimensionless.

MAGNETIC UNITS

Name of dimension or quantity	Symbol	Description	Mksc unit	Equivalent units	Fundamental dimensions
Dipole moment (magnetic)	$m\ (=Q_m l)$	pole strength $\times$ length $=$ current $\times$ area $=\dfrac{\text{torque}}{\text{magnetic flux density}}$	$\dfrac{\text{ampere-}}{\text{meter}^2}$	$\dfrac{\text{coulomb-meter}^2}{\text{second}}$	$\dfrac{QL^2}{T}$
Energy density (magnetic)	w_m	$\dfrac{\text{energy}}{\text{volume}}$	$\dfrac{\text{joule}}{\text{meter}^3}$	10 ergs/centimeter³	$\dfrac{M}{LT^2}$
Flux (magnetic)	ψ_m	$\iint \mathbf{B}\cdot d\mathbf{s}$	weber	volt-second $= 10^8$ maxwells (cgs emu) $= \dfrac{\text{newton-meter}}{\text{ampere}}$	$\dfrac{ML^2}{TQ}$
Flux density (B vector)	$\mathbf{B}$	$\dfrac{\text{force}}{\text{pole}} = \dfrac{\text{current moment}}{\text{magnetic flux}} = \dfrac{}{\text{area}}$	$\dfrac{\text{weber}}{\text{meter}^2}$	$\dfrac{\text{volt-second}}{\text{meter}^2} = 10^4$ gauss (cgs emu) $= \dfrac{\text{newton}}{\text{ampere-meter}}$	$\dfrac{M}{TQ}$
Flux linkage	Λ	flux $\times$ turns†	weber-turn		$\dfrac{ML^2}{TQ}$
H field (H vector) (magnetizing force)	$\mathbf{H}$	$\dfrac{\text{mmf}}{\text{length}}$	$\dfrac{\text{ampere}}{\text{meter}}$	$\dfrac{\text{newton}}{\text{weber}} = \dfrac{\text{watt}}{\text{volt-meter}}$ $= 4\pi \times 10^{-3}$ oersted (cgs emu) $= 400\pi$ gammas	$\dfrac{Q}{TL}$

† Turns are dimensionless.

MAGNETIC UNITS.—*(Continued)*

Name of dimension or quantity	Symbol	Description	Mksc unit	Equivalent units	Fundamental dimensions
Inductance	L	$\dfrac{\text{magnetic flux linkage}}{\text{current}}$	henry	$\dfrac{\text{weber}}{\text{ampere}} = \dfrac{\text{joule}}{\text{ampere}^2} = \text{ohm-second}$ $= \tfrac{1}{9} \times 10^{-11}$ cgs esu $= 10^9$ centimeters (cgs emu)	$\dfrac{ML^2}{Q^2}$
Magnetization (magnetic polarization)	$\mathbf{M}$	$\dfrac{\text{magnetic moment}}{\text{volume}}$	$\dfrac{\text{ampere}}{\text{meter}}$	$\dfrac{\text{ampere-meter}^2}{\text{meter}^3} = \dfrac{\text{ampere-meter}}{\text{meter}^2}$	$\dfrac{Q}{TL}$
Mmf	F	$\int \mathbf{H} \cdot d\mathbf{l}$	ampere-(turn)	$\dfrac{\text{coulomb}}{\text{second}}$	$\dfrac{Q}{T}$
Permeability (for vacuum μ_0 $= 4\pi \times 10^{-7}$ $= 1.257 \times 10^{-6}$ henry/meter)	μ	$\dfrac{\text{inductance}}{\text{length}}$	$\dfrac{\text{henry}}{\text{meter}}$	$\dfrac{\text{weber}}{\text{ampere-meter}} = \dfrac{\text{volt-second}}{\text{ampere-meter}}$	$\dfrac{ML}{Q^2}$
Permeance	$\mathscr{P}$	$\dfrac{\text{magnetic flux}}{\text{mmf}} = \dfrac{1}{\text{reluctance}}$	henry	$\dfrac{\text{weber}}{\text{ampere}}$	$\dfrac{ML^2}{Q^2}$
Pole density	ρ_m	$\dfrac{\text{pole strength}}{\text{volume}}$ $= \dfrac{\text{current}}{\text{area}}$ $= \nabla \cdot \mathbf{H} = -\nabla \cdot \mathbf{M}$	$\dfrac{\text{ampere}}{\text{meter}^2}$		$\dfrac{Q}{TL^2}$

MAGNETIC UNITS.—(*Continued*)

Name of dimension or quantity	Symbol	Description	Mksc unit	Equivalent units	Fundamental dimensions
Pole strength	Q_m, q_m	current × length $= \iint \rho_m \, dv$	ampere-meter	$\dfrac{\text{coulomb-meter}}{\text{second}}$	$\dfrac{QL}{T}$
Potential (magnetic) (for **H**)	U	$\dfrac{\text{work}}{\text{pole} \times \text{permeability}}$ $= \int \mathbf{H} \cdot dl$	ampere	$\dfrac{\text{joule}}{\text{weber}} = \dfrac{\text{watt}}{\text{volt}} = \dfrac{\text{coulomb}}{\text{second}}$ $= \dfrac{4\pi}{10}$ gilberts (cgs emu)	$\dfrac{Q}{T}$
Relative permeability	μ_r	ratio $\dfrac{\mu}{\mu_0}$			Dimensionless
Reluctance	$\mathcal{R}$	$\dfrac{\text{mmf}}{\text{magnetic flux}}$ $= \dfrac{1}{\text{permeance}}$	$\dfrac{1}{\text{henry}}$	$\dfrac{\text{ampere}}{\text{weber}}$	$\dfrac{Q^2}{ML^2}$
Vector potential	$\mathbf{A}$	current × permeability	$\dfrac{\text{weber}}{\text{meter}}$	$\dfrac{\text{henry-ampere}}{\text{meter}} = \dfrac{\text{newton}}{\text{ampere}}$	$\dfrac{ML}{TQ}$

A-2. Graphical Field-mapping Techniques. Some further techniques[1] of graphical field mapping may be illustrated by considering an example. Let the problem be to map the electric field in a square corner. It is assumed that the sides of the corner consist of two flat, perfectly conducting sheets of infinite extent intersecting at 90° and that a potential difference is applied between the corner and another conductor at a very large distance in the direction of the corner bisector.

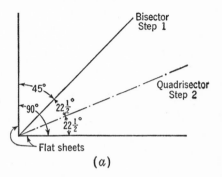

Step 1 in the procedure is to construct the corner bisector (Fig. A-1a). By symmetry the field above the bisector is a mirror image of the field below so that it suffices to map only the field below the bisector.

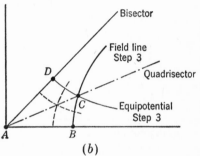

Step 2 is to construct the quadrisector as shown in Fig. A-1a. This is also a line of symmetry but differs from the bisector in that, although the field in the $22\frac{1}{2}°$ sector above the quadrisector is a mirror image of the field in the $22\frac{1}{2}°$ sector below, equipotentials are mirrored as field lines and field lines as equipotentials. This property, however, is very useful in constructing the map.

Step 3 is to sketch a field and an equipotential line intersecting at right angles at the quadrisector as indicated by the solid lines in Fig. A-1b. The starting points B and D for these lines should be chosen so as to make the figure $ABCDA$ as

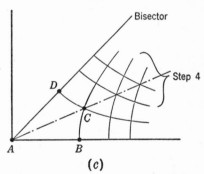

Fig. A-1. Steps in mapping field in a square corner.

nearly a curvilinear square as possible. To test whether or not $ABCDA$ is a curvilinear square,[2] it can be subdivided as shown by the dashed lines in Fig. A-1b into four areas, each of which should be a curvilinear square. If the subdivided areas appear to depart from curvilinear squares, the field

[1] See Secs. 2-27 and 2-28.
[2] For definition of *curvilinear square* see Sec. 2-27.

and equipotential lines, including if necessary their starting points B and D, should be relocated.

Assuming we are satisfied that $ABCDA$ is a true curvilinear square or very nearly one, step 4 is to sketch in more field and equipotentials as in Fig. A-$1c$. It is to be noted that the equipotentials and field lines should always intersect normally, with one set of intersections falling on the quadrisector. Also the equipotentials should be normal to the bisector and the field lines normal to the side of the corner. As an aid in determining whether or not these requirements have been met, it is frequently desirable to turn the drawing and look at it from different directions. It is particularly helpful to sight along the bisector or quadrisector. If any of the areas do not appear to be curvilinear squares or if any of the intersections are not orthogonal, the map should be revised. It is often better under such circumstances to erase the entire map and start afresh than to try and correct only those areas where inaccuracies appear to exist.

Proceeding in the above manner, it should be possible after several attempts to arrive at an accurate field map. The making of accurate field maps is an art that requires long practice. One who has acquired such skill can produce field maps of very good accuracy that are satisfactory for many engineering applications. Practice in graphical field mapping is valuable experience, if for no other reason, because it develops a sense of how fields should flow or be shaped in problems involving various geometries. Even if the field can be calculated analytically, the number of field points that need to be calculated can be minimized by utilizing graphical mapping methods to complete the map.

As described above, graphical field mapping is to a large extent a freehand art. It may be largely transformed, however, into a precise drafting technique by a *circle method* introduced by Moore.[1] In this method a circle is used to ensure that an area departs but little from a true curvilinear square. For instance, consider the two field lines and equipotential shown in Fig. A-$2a$. A circle is drawn that touches both field

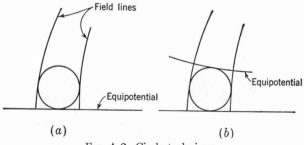

FIG. A-2. Circle technique.

[1] A. D. Moore, Mapping Techniques Applied to Fluid-mapper Patterns, *Proc. AIEE,* **71,** 1952.

lines and the equipotential as indicated. The curvilinear square is then completed by fairing in another equipotential tangent to the circle, as in Fig. A-2b. It has been shown by Moore that an area with right-angle intersections which is fitted by a circle in this way is very nearly an exact curvilinear square provided that the sides of the area do not diverge too rapidly. Thus in Fig. A-3 the distance AA' along the mid-line of the area that fits the circle is less than about $\frac{1}{2}$ per cent longer than the value AA'' along the mid-line of an exact curvilinear square provided the angle of divergence δ is less than 20°. The error is less for smaller divergence angles but is more for larger angles, being about 1.5 per cent for $\delta = 30°$. To avoid excessive error on areas having sides with a large divergence angle or areas which are otherwise highly distorted, further subdivision into smaller areas is advisable. An exception, however, is an area with diagonal symmetry such as $ABCDA$ in Fig. A-1c, in which case a perfect fit is possible.

Applying the circle technique to the

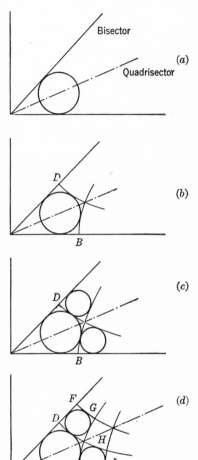

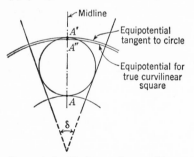

Fig. A-3. Circle and curvilinear square.

Fig. A-4. Circle method of mapping field in square corner.

square corner discussed above, steps 1 and 2 are the same as previously. That is, step 1 is to construct the bisector and step 2 the quadrisector. Step 3 is to draw a circle of convenient size as in Fig. A-4a. Although the circle may be drawn with a compass, the circle method is greatly facilitated by the use of a "circle guide," consisting of a sheet of celluloid punched with holes that differ in diameter by small increments. Several makes are commercially available. Since the holes differ in diameter by finite increments, it is sometimes necessary to use a hole that is too small, in which case the circle is spaced by the same amount from all sides of the area.

Step 4 is to draw a field line starting from B and an equipotential from D, each tangent to the circle and intersecting normally at the quadrisector, as in Fig. A-4b. Step 5 is to draw the smaller circles as in Fig. A-4c. Step 6 is to fair in an equipotential starting from F and a field line starting from E as in Fig. A-4d. The other equipotential and field line are also extended and then circles drawn at G, H, and I. This process is continued until the map extends over the area desired.

In field-mapping work where one set of lines, such as the field lines, is given the circle method is particularly valuable. Consider, for example, the fluid-mapper pattern in Fig. A-5 as obtained by Moore.[1] This pattern shows the flow or field lines that may be regarded as extending from a circular inner conductor to a rectangular outer conductor of a transmission line. Here the field lines are provided by the fluid mapper, and it is necessary only to draw in the equipotentials. The technique for handling this map differs from that described above in that each flux tube can be treated independently of all others so that equipotentials need not be continuous. Take tube A as an example. Circles are drawn as indicated, and the equipotentials extend only the width of the tube. Assuming that the line is filled with a medium of permittivity ϵ, the capacitance of tube A is $\epsilon/4.18$ farads per meter depth of line (into the page). For tube B it is $\epsilon/3.13$ farads per meter, and for tube C it is $\epsilon/4.33$ farads per meter. Mapping all tubes, the total capacitance per unit depth of line is equal to the sum of the capacitances of the individual tubes.[2] Owing to symmetry a vertical center line YY' may be drawn dividing the diagram in half as indicated and only those tubes mapped in either the left or the right half. The total capacitance is then twice the value obtained for either half. However, higher accuracy is usually obtained by completing the map for the entire diagram.

The above procedure is somewhat simplified if we imagine that the region between the inner and outer conductor (Fig. A-5) is conducting. If the resistance per unit depth of a cell is R_0, then the *normalized* resistance R_n of a cell is unity or

$$R_n = \frac{R_0}{R_0} = 1 \qquad \text{(dimensionless)}$$

[1] A. D. Moore, Fields from Fluid Flow Mappers, *J. Applied Phys.*, **20**, 790–804, August, 1949; Mapping Techniques Applied to Fluid-mapper Patterns, *Proc. AIEE*, **71**, 1952.

[2] Or the characteristic impedance of tube A is 376.7×4.18 ohms (assuming that the medium is air), and the characteristic impedance of the entire transmission line is equal to the reciprocal of the sum of the reciprocals of the characteristic impedances of all the individual tubes.

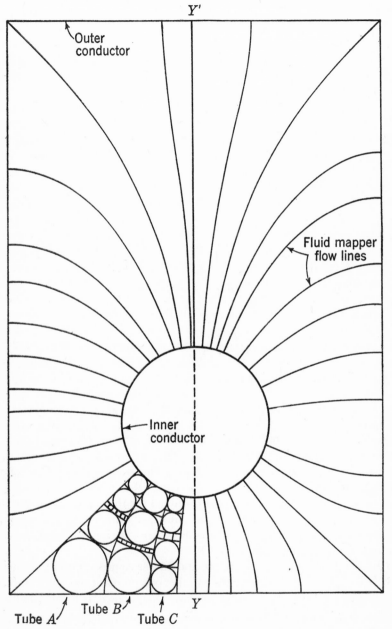

FIG. A-5. Circle method applied to fluid-mapper pattern (*after A. D. Moore*).   Tube *A* has 4.18 cells in series, tube *B* 3.13 cells in series, and tube *C* 4.33 cells in series.

Thus the total normalized resistance R_{nt} of the transmission line is

$$R_{nt} = \frac{1}{(1/R_{na}) + (1/R_{nb}) + (1/R_{nc}) + \cdots}. \qquad \text{(dimensionless)}$$

where R_{na} = normalized resistance of tube A (Fig. A-5) = 4.18
$\quad\ \ R_{nb}$ = normalized resistance of tube B = 3.13
$\quad\ \ R_{nc}$ = normalized resistance of tube C = 4.33

The reader should check these values by counting the cells in Fig. A-5. The total actual resistance per unit depth of the transmission line (if it were filled with a conducting medium) is then $R_t = R_0 R_{nt}$ ohms/meter. If the transmission line is filled with a lossless medium having a permittivity ϵ and permeability μ_0, the *capacitance per unit depth* of the line is given by

$$C = \frac{\epsilon}{R_{nt}} \qquad \text{farads/meter}$$

the *inductance per unit depth* of the line is given by

$$L = \mu_0 R_{nt} \qquad \text{henrys/meter}$$

and the *characteristic impedance*[1] of the line is given by

$$Z = \sqrt{\frac{L}{C}} = \sqrt{\frac{\mu_0}{\epsilon}} R_{nt} \qquad \text{ohms}$$

For an air-filled line this becomes

$$Z = \sqrt{\frac{\mu_0}{\epsilon_0}} R_{nt} = 376.7 R_{nt} \qquad \text{ohms}$$

Problem A-1.   Assuming that Fig. A-5 is a cross section of an air-filled transmission line, complete the map, and determine the characteristic impedance of the line. Something of a check on the accuracy of the determination is afforded by comparing the normalized resistance obtained for the left half with that obtained for the right half of the line.

Problem A-2.   What is the capacitance per unit length and also the inductance per unit length of an air-filled transmission line with the cross section shown in Fig. A-5.

Problem A-3.   Locate the 25, 50, and 75 per cent equipotential lines in Fig. A-5. *Hint:* By counting the number of squares of the same kind in a given tube a 50 per cent potential point, for instance, is located halfway,

---

[1] Note that by using conducting cloth or paper with a resistance per square equal to $\sqrt{\mu_0/\epsilon}$ ohms, as in Sec. 11-5, the characteristic impedance of the line is numerically equal to the measured resistance between the inner and outer conductors. Note also that if conducting paper of any resistance R_s (ohms per square) is used, the capacitance per unit depth is given by $C = \epsilon R_s/R_m$ farads per meter and the inductance per unit depth by $L = \mu_0 R_m/R_s$ henrys per meter, where R_m is the measured resistance between the inner and outer conductors ($R_m/R_s = R_{nt}$).

in terms of these squares, from the inner to the outer conductor. After locating this point on a sufficient number of tubes, the equipotential line can be sketched in.

A-3. Trigonometric Relations

$$\sin (x \pm y) = \sin x \cos y \pm \cos x \sin y$$
$$\cos (x \pm y) = \cos x \cos y \mp \sin x \sin y$$
$$\sin (x + y) + \sin (x - y) = 2 \sin x \cos y$$
$$\cos (x + y) + \cos (x - y) = 2 \cos x \cos y$$
$$\sin (x + y) - \sin (x - y) = 2 \cos x \sin y$$
$$\cos (x + y) - \cos (x - y) = -2 \sin x \sin y$$
$$\sin 2x = 2 \sin x \cos x$$
$$\cos 2x = \cos^2 x - \sin^2 x = 2 \cos^2 x - 1 = 1 - 2 \sin^2 x$$
$$\cos x = 2 \cos^2 \tfrac{1}{2}x - 1 = 1 - 2 \sin^2 \tfrac{1}{2}x$$
$$\sin x = 2 \sin \tfrac{1}{2}x \cos \tfrac{1}{2}x$$
$$\sin^2 x + \cos^2 x = 1$$
$$\tan (x + y) = \frac{\tan x + \tan y}{1 - \tan x \tan y}$$
$$\tan (x - y) = \frac{\tan x - \tan y}{1 + \tan x \tan y}$$
$$\tan 2x = \frac{2 \tan x}{1 - \tan^2 x}$$
$$\sin x = x - \frac{x^3}{3!} + \frac{x^5}{5!} - \frac{x^7}{7!} + \cdots$$
$$\cos x = 1 - \frac{x^2}{2!} + \frac{x^4}{4!} - \frac{x^6}{6!} + \cdots$$
$$\tan x = x + \frac{x^3}{3} + \frac{2x^5}{15} + \frac{17x^7}{315} + \frac{62x^9}{2,835} + \cdots$$
$$\pi = 3.1416$$
$$\pi^2 = 9.8696$$
$$1 \text{ rad} = 57.296°$$

A-4. Hyperbolic Relations

$$\sinh x = \frac{e^x - e^{-x}}{2} = x + \frac{x^3}{3!} + \frac{x^5}{5!} + \frac{x^7}{7!} + \cdots$$
$$\cosh x = \frac{e^x + e^{-x}}{2} = 1 + \frac{x^2}{2!} + \frac{x^4}{4!} + \frac{x^6}{6!} + \cdots$$
$$\tanh x = \frac{\sinh x}{\cosh x}$$
$$\coth x = \frac{\cosh x}{\sinh x} = \frac{1}{\tanh x}$$
$$\sinh (x \pm jy) = \sinh x \cos y \pm j \cosh x \sin y$$
$$\cosh (x \pm jy) = \cosh x \cos y \pm j \sinh x \sin y$$

$$\left.\begin{array}{l}\cosh (jx) = \frac{1}{2}(e^{+ix} + e^{-ix}) = \cos x \\ \sinh (jx) = \frac{1}{2}(e^{+ix} - e^{-ix}) = j \sin x\end{array}\right\} \text{de Moivre's theorem}$$

$$e^{\pm ix} = \cos x \pm j \sin x$$

$$e^{\pm ix} = 1 \pm jx - \frac{x^2}{2!} \mp j\frac{x^3}{3!} + \frac{x^4}{4!} \pm j\frac{x^5}{5!} - \cdots$$

$$\cosh x = \cos jx$$

$$j \sinh x = \sin jx$$

$$\tanh (x \pm jy) = \frac{\sinh 2x}{\cosh 2x + \cos 2y} \pm j\frac{\sin 2y}{\cosh 2x + \cos 2y}$$

$$\coth (x \pm jy) = \frac{\sinh 2x}{\cosh 2x - \cos 2y} \pm j\frac{\sin 2y}{\cosh 2x - \cos 2y}$$

A-5. Logarithmic Relations

$$\log_{10} x = \log x \qquad \text{common logarithm}$$
$$\log_e x = \ln x \qquad \text{natural logarithm}$$
$$\log_{10} x = 0.4343 \log_e x = 0.4343 \ln x$$
$$\ln x = \log_e x = 2.3026 \log_{10} x$$
$$e = 2.7183$$

A-6. Approximation Formulas for Small Quantities (δ is a small quantity compared with unity)

$$(1 \pm \delta)^2 = 1 \pm 2\delta$$
$$(1 \pm \delta)^n = 1 \pm n\delta$$
$$\sqrt{1 + \delta} = 1 + \frac{1}{2}\delta$$
$$\frac{1}{\sqrt{1 + \delta}} = 1 - \frac{1}{2}\delta$$
$$e^\delta = 1 + \delta$$
$$\ln (1 + \delta) = \delta$$
$$J_n(\delta) = \frac{\delta^n}{n!2^n} \qquad \text{for } |\delta| \ll 1$$

where J_n is Bessel function of order n.   Thus

$$J_1(\delta) = \frac{\delta}{2}$$

A-7. Series

Binomial: $(x + y)^n = x^n + nx^{n-1}y + \dfrac{n(n - 1)}{2!} x^{n-2}y^2$

$$+ \frac{n(n - 1)(n - 2)}{3!} x^{(n-3)}y^3 + \cdots$$

Taylor's: $f(x + y) = f(x) + \dfrac{df(x)}{dx}\dfrac{y}{1} + \dfrac{d^2f(x)}{dx^2}\dfrac{y^2}{2!} + \dfrac{d^3f(x)}{dx^3}\dfrac{y^3}{3!} + \cdots$

A-8. Solution of Quadratic Equation

If $ax^2 + bx + c = 0$, then

$$x = \frac{-b \pm \sqrt{b^2 - 4ac}}{2a}$$

A-9. Vector Identities (f and g are scalar functions; $\mathbf{F}$, $\mathbf{G}$, and $\mathbf{H}$ are vector functions)

$$\mathbf{F} \cdot \mathbf{G} = FG \cos \theta \qquad \text{scalar or dot product}$$

where $\theta = \arccos (\mathbf{F} \cdot \mathbf{G})/FG$.

$$\mathbf{F} \times \mathbf{G} = \mathbf{n}FG \sin \theta \qquad \text{vector or cross product}$$

where $\theta = \arcsin (\mathbf{F} \times \mathbf{G})/\mathbf{n}FG$.

$$\nabla \cdot (\nabla \times \mathbf{F}) = 0$$
$$\nabla \cdot \nabla f = \nabla^2 f$$
$$\nabla \times \nabla f = 0$$
$$\nabla(f + g) = \nabla f + \nabla g$$
$$\nabla \cdot (\mathbf{F} + \mathbf{G}) = \nabla \cdot \mathbf{F} + \nabla \cdot \mathbf{G}$$
$$\nabla \times (\mathbf{F} + \mathbf{G}) = \nabla \times \mathbf{F} + \nabla \times \mathbf{G}$$
$$\nabla(fg) = g \nabla f + f \nabla g$$
$$\nabla \cdot (f\mathbf{G}) = \mathbf{G} \cdot (\nabla f) + f(\nabla \cdot \mathbf{G})$$
$$\nabla \times (f\mathbf{G}) = (\nabla f) \times \mathbf{G} + f(\nabla \times \mathbf{G})$$
$$\nabla \times (\nabla \times \mathbf{F}) = \nabla(\nabla \cdot \mathbf{F}) - \nabla^2\mathbf{F}$$
$$\nabla \cdot (\mathbf{F} \times \mathbf{G}) = \mathbf{G} \cdot (\nabla \times \mathbf{F}) - \mathbf{F} \cdot (\nabla \times \mathbf{G})$$
$$\mathbf{F} \cdot (\mathbf{G} \times \mathbf{H}) = \mathbf{G} \cdot (\mathbf{H} \times \mathbf{F}) = \mathbf{H} \cdot (\mathbf{F} \times \mathbf{G})$$

A-10. Gradient, Divergence, Curl, and Laplacian in Rectangular, Cylindrical, and Spherical Coordinates (f is a scalar function; $\mathbf{F}$ is a vector function)

a. Rectangular Coordinates (unit vectors are $\mathbf{i}$, $\mathbf{j}$, $\mathbf{k}$; the vector $\mathbf{F} = \mathbf{i}F_x + \mathbf{j}F_y + \mathbf{k}F_z$)

$$\nabla f = \mathbf{i}\frac{\partial f}{\partial x} + \mathbf{j}\frac{\partial f}{\partial y} + \mathbf{k}\frac{\partial f}{\partial z}$$

$$\nabla \cdot \mathbf{F} = \frac{\partial F_x}{\partial x} + \frac{\partial F_y}{\partial y} + \frac{\partial F_z}{\partial z}$$

$$\nabla \times \mathbf{F} = \mathbf{i}\left(\frac{\partial F_z}{\partial y} - \frac{\partial F_y}{\partial z}\right) + \mathbf{j}\left(\frac{\partial F_x}{\partial z} - \frac{\partial F_z}{\partial x}\right) + \mathbf{k}\left(\frac{\partial F_y}{\partial x} - \frac{\partial F_x}{\partial y}\right)$$

$$= \begin{vmatrix} \mathbf{i} & \mathbf{j} & \mathbf{k} \\ \dfrac{\partial}{\partial x} & \dfrac{\partial}{\partial y} & \dfrac{\partial}{\partial z} \\ F_x & F_y & F_z \end{vmatrix}$$

$$\nabla^2 f = \frac{\partial^2 f}{\partial x^2} + \frac{\partial^2 f}{\partial y^2} + \frac{\partial^2 f}{\partial z^2}$$

$$\nabla^2\mathbf{F} = \mathbf{i} \nabla^2 F_x + \mathbf{j} \nabla^2 F_y + \mathbf{k} \nabla^2 F_z$$

b. Cylindrical Coordinates (unit vectors are $\mathbf{a}_r$, $\mathbf{a}_\theta$, $\mathbf{a}_z$; the vector $\mathbf{F} = \mathbf{a}_r F_r + \mathbf{a}_\theta F_\theta + \mathbf{a}_z F_z$) (related to rectangular coordinates by $x = r \cos \theta$, $y = r \sin \theta$, $z = z$)

$$\nabla f = \mathbf{a}_r \frac{\partial f}{\partial r} + \mathbf{a}_\theta \frac{1}{r} \frac{\partial f}{\partial \theta} + \mathbf{a}_z \frac{\partial f}{\partial z}$$

$$\nabla \cdot \mathbf{F} = \frac{1}{r} \frac{\partial}{\partial r} (rF_r) + \frac{1}{r} \frac{\partial F_\theta}{\partial \theta} + \frac{\partial F_z}{\partial z}$$

$$\nabla \times \mathbf{F} = \mathbf{a}_r \left(\frac{1}{r} \frac{\partial F_z}{\partial \theta} - \frac{\partial F_\theta}{\partial z} \right) + \mathbf{a}_\theta \left(\frac{\partial F_r}{\partial z} - \frac{\partial F_z}{\partial r} \right) + \mathbf{a}_z \left[\frac{1}{r} \frac{\partial (rF_\theta)}{\partial r} - \frac{1}{r} \frac{\partial F_r}{\partial \theta} \right]$$

$$\nabla^2 f = \frac{1}{r} \frac{\partial}{\partial r} \left(r \frac{\partial f}{\partial r} \right) + \frac{1}{r^2} \frac{\partial^2 f}{\partial \theta^2} + \frac{\partial^2 f}{\partial z^2}$$

c. Spherical Coordinates (unit vectors are $\mathbf{a}_r$, $\mathbf{a}_\theta$, $\mathbf{a}_\phi$; the vector $\mathbf{F} = \mathbf{a}_r F_r + \mathbf{a}_\theta F_\theta + \mathbf{a}_\phi F_\phi$) (related to rectangular coordinates by $x = r \sin \theta \cos \phi$, $y = r \sin \theta \sin \phi$, $z = r \cos \theta$)

$$\nabla f = \mathbf{a}_r \frac{\partial f}{\partial r} + \mathbf{a}_\theta \frac{1}{r} \frac{\partial f}{\partial \theta} + \mathbf{a}_\phi \frac{1}{r \sin \theta} \frac{\partial f}{\partial \phi}$$

$$\nabla \cdot \mathbf{F} = \frac{1}{r^2} \frac{\partial}{\partial r} (r^2 F_r) + \frac{1}{r \sin \theta} \frac{\partial}{\partial \theta} (F_\theta \sin \theta) + \frac{1}{r \sin \theta} \frac{\partial F_\phi}{\partial \phi}$$

$$\nabla \times \mathbf{F} = \mathbf{a}_r \frac{1}{r \sin \theta} \left[\frac{\partial}{\partial \theta} (F_\phi \sin \theta) - \frac{\partial F_\theta}{\partial \phi} \right] + \mathbf{a}_\theta \frac{1}{r} \left[\frac{1}{\sin \theta} \frac{\partial F_r}{\partial \phi} - \frac{\partial}{\partial r} (rF_\phi) \right]$$
$$+ \mathbf{a}_\phi \frac{1}{r} \left[\frac{\partial}{\partial r} (rF_\theta) - \frac{\partial F_r}{\partial \theta} \right]$$

$$\nabla^2 f = \frac{1}{r^2} \frac{\partial}{\partial r} \left(r^2 \frac{\partial f}{\partial r} \right) + \frac{1}{r^2 \sin \theta} \frac{\partial}{\partial \theta} \left(\sin \theta \frac{\partial f}{\partial \theta} \right) + \frac{1}{r^2 \sin^2 \theta} \frac{\partial^2 f}{\partial \phi^2}$$

A-11. Bessel Functions. Solutions of Bessel's equation (14-25) are called *Bessel functions*. One solution, known as a Bessel function of the first kind, is designated by $J_\nu(u)$. Another solution, known as a Bessel function of the second kind, or Neumann function, is designated by $N_\nu(u)$. A Bessel function of the third kind, or Hankel function, is given by a linear combination of $J_\nu(u)$ and $N_\nu(u)$. Hankel functions are designated by $H_\nu(u)$.

The subscript ν denotes the order of the function. The quantity u is the argument. The order may, in general, be integral, fractional, or complex. When this is the case, the subscript ν is used. However, if the order of the function is an integer, the subscript n is used.

Bessel Functions of the First Kind. When the order is integral,[1] the value of the Bessel function of the first kind is given by an infinite series

---

[1] This is the case when the field varies with ϕ an integral number of cycles in an angle of 2π. If there is no ϕ variation, the order is zero.

which can be expressed as

$$J_n(u) = \sum_{m=0}^{\infty} \frac{(-1)^m (u/2)^{n+2m}}{m!(m+n)!}$$

Curves for Bessel functions of orders $n = 0, 1, 2$, and 3 and also $\nu = 0.5$ are presented in Fig. A-6. The $J_0(u)$ curve is unity at $u = 0$. For increasing u it follows a periodic variation similar to that of a cosine curve with attenuation. The higher-order Bessel function curves are zero at $u = 0$. For increasing u they follow a similar periodic variation. At large values of u the interval between points at which a Bessel-function curve intersects the u axis $[J_\nu(u) = 0]$ is approximately π.

The following table gives the first few values of u for which Bessel functions of the first kind of order 0, 1, 2, and 3 are zero, a maximum, and a minimum. Following the value of u for a maximum or a minimum the corresponding value of $J_n(u)$ is given in parentheses, it being understood that the minimum values are negative.

$J_0(u)$			$J_1(u)$		
Zero	Max	Min	Zero	Max	Min
2.405	0 (1.00)	3.832(0.403)	0	1.84(0.582)	5.33(0.346)
5.520	7.016(0.300)	10.173(0.250)	3.832	8.54(0.273)	11.71(0.233)
8.654	13.323(0.218)	16.471(0.196)	7.016	14.86(0.207)	18.02(0.188)
11.792	19.616(0.180)	22.761(0.167)	10.173	21.16(0.173)	24.31(0.162)
14.931			13.323		
18.071			16.471		
21.212			19.616		
24.353			22.761		

$J_2(u)$			$J_3(u)$		
Zero	Max	Min	Zero	Max	Min
0	3.054(0.486)	6.706(0.314)	0	4.201(0.434)	8.015(0.291)
5.135	9.969(0.255)	13.170(0.221)	6.379	11.346(0.241)	14.586(0.211)
8.417	16.348(0.198)	19.513(0.181)	9.760	17.789(0.190)	20.972(0.175)
11.620			13.017		
14.796			16.224		
17.960			19.410		

For small arguments ($u \ll 1$) the Bessel functions of the first kind are given approximately by

$$J_n(u) \simeq \frac{u^n}{n!2^n}$$

For large arguments ($u \gg 1$ and also $u \gg n$) the Bessel functions of the the first kind are given approximately by

$$J_n(u) \simeq \sqrt{\frac{2}{\pi u}} \cos\left(u - \frac{2n + 1}{4}\pi\right)$$

According to this relation a Bessel function of large argument varies as a cosine function of u that is damped or attenuated as $1/\sqrt{u}$.

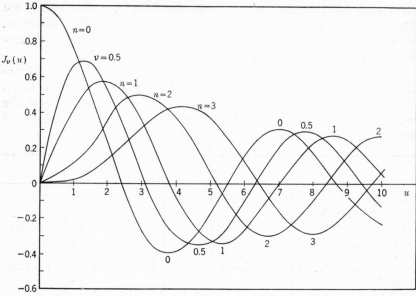

Fig. A-6. Curves for Bessel functions (of the first kind) of order 0, 0.5, 1, 2, and 3.

Bessel Functions of the Second Kind. These are often called *Neumann functions*, and when this is done, Bessel functions of the first kind can be referred to simply as Bessel functions. A Bessel function of the second kind (Neumann function) of integral order n is given (using L'Hôpital's rule) by[1]

$$N_n(u) = \lim_{\nu \to n} \frac{J_\nu(u)\cos\nu\pi - J_{-\nu}(u)}{\sin\nu\pi}$$

Curves for Neumann functions of order $n = 0$ and $n = 1$ are presented in Fig. A-7. Whereas Bessel functions of the first kind are equal to zero or unity at $u = 0$, the Neumann functions approach minus infinity as u

---

[1] This is Weber's definition of a Bessel function of the second kind. Hence it is sometimes called a Weber function. However, it is commonly called a Neumann function although Neumann's definition of a Bessel function of the second kind differs slightly from Weber's. The notation $Y_n(u)$ is used by some authors for $N_n(u)$. However, this notation may be confusing because of the existence of other Y functions.

approaches zero. At large values of u the Neumann function curves are similar to sine curves with attenuation. When u is large, the interval between zero points of a Neumann function is approximately π, the same as for a Bessel function (of the first kind).

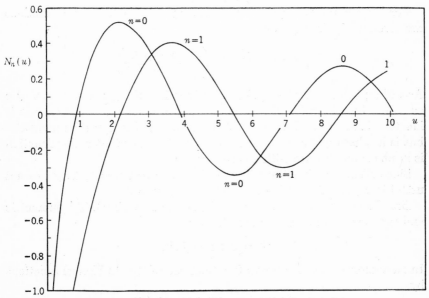

FIG. A-7. Neumann function curves of order 0 and 1.

The following table gives the first few values of u for which Neumann functions (Bessel functions of the second kind) and order 0 and 1 are zero, a maximum, and a minimum. Following the value of u for a maximum or a minimum the corresponding value of $N_n(u)$ is given in parentheses, it being understood that the minimum values are negative.

$N_0(u)$			$N_1(u)$		
Zero	Max	Min	Zero	Max	Min
0.894	2.20(0.521)	0(∞)	2.20	3.69(0.417)	0(∞)
3.958	8.60(0.272)	5.43(0.340)	5.43	10.13(0.251)	6.94(0.303)
7.086	14.90(0.207)	11.75(0.233)	8.60		13.29(0.219)
10.222			11.75		
13.361			14.90		

For small arguments ($u \ll 1$) the Neumann function of zero order is given approximately by

$$N_0(u) \simeq -\frac{2}{\pi}\ln\frac{2}{\gamma u}$$

where $\gamma = 1.781$, and for orders $n = 1$ and higher by

$$N_n(u) \simeq \frac{-(n-1)!}{\pi} \left(\frac{2}{u}\right)^n$$

For large arguments ($u \gg 1$ and also $u \gg n$) the Neumann functions are given approximately by

$$N_n(u) \simeq \sqrt{\frac{2}{\pi u}} \sin\left(u - \frac{2n+1}{4}\pi\right)$$

According to this relation a Neumann function of large argument varies as a sine function of u that is damped or attenuated as $1/\sqrt{u}$. It is identical in form to a Bessel function (of the first kind) of the same order but is in phase quadrature with it in the same way that a sine function is in phase quadrature with a cosine function.

Since Neumann functions become infinite when $u = 0$, they are not useful in representing fields that are finite at $u = 0$.

Bessel Functions of the Third Kind (Hankel Functions). Trigonometric and exponential functions are related by

$$e^{\pm ju} = \cos u \pm j \sin u$$

In an analogous manner Bessel functions are related to Hankel functions by

$$H_n^{(1)}(u) = J_n(u) + jN_n(u)$$

and

$$H_n^{(2)}(u) = J_n(u) - jN_n(u)$$

where $H_n^{(1)}(u)$ = Hankel function of type 1 and order n

$H_n^{(2)}(u)$ = Hankel function of type 2 and order n

The Hankel function of type 2 is the complex conjugate of the Hankel function of type 1.

Hankel functions may be plotted on a complex plane having $J_n(u)$ as abscissa and $N_n(u)$ as ordinate. This has been done for Hankel functions of type 1 of orders 0 and 1 in Fig. A-8. The curves are spirals with the values of u indicated along the curves. Curves for Hankel functions of type 2 would appear as mirror images of Hankel functions of type 1 with respect to the $N_n(u) = 0$ line [$J_n(u)$ axis].

For large values of u the Bessel functions of the first and second kind of the same order are in phase quadrature so that the Hankel-function curves intersect the axes normally (see Fig. A-8).

In contrast to the Hankel-function curves, which are spirals in the complex plane, a plot of the exponential function $e^{ju} = \cos u + j \sin u$ in the complex plane is a circle with center at the origin. If we imagine a three-dimensional graph of e^{ju} with $\cos u$ plotted along the x axis, $\sin u$

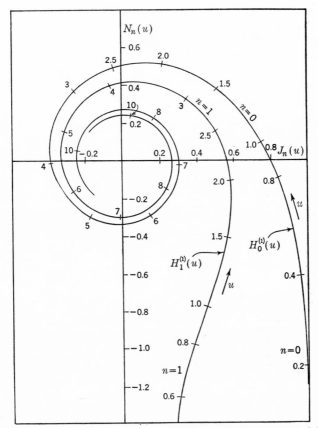

FIG. A-8. Hankel function curves of type 1 and orders 0 and 1 plotted in terms of Bessel functions of the first and second kind.

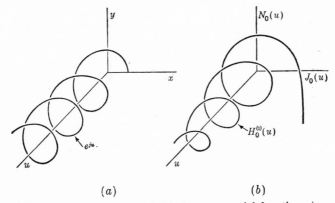

(a)   (b)

FIG. A-9. Three-dimensional graphs of (a) the exponential function e^{ju} and (b) the Hankel function $H_0^{(1)}(u)$.

along the y axis, and u along the z axis, we obtain a right-handed helix in space as indicated in Fig. A-9a. The helix has uniform diameter and pitch. The exponential function e^{-iu} yields a left-handed helix. In a similar way a three-dimensional graph of a Hankel function of type 1 yields a tapered right-handed helix as shown in Fig. A-9b for $n = 0$. The helix diameter decreases with increasing u. A Hankel function of type 2 yields a tapered left-handed helix.

A-12. Recurrence Relations for Bessel Functions. Equations expressing Bessel functions or their derivatives in terms of Bessel functions of the same or different order are called recurrence formulas, or relations. A few of these formulas are listed below for reference.[1]

$$\frac{dJ_\nu(u)}{du} = \frac{\nu}{u} J_\nu(u) - J_{\nu+1}(u) \tag{1}$$

$$\frac{dJ_\nu(u)}{du} = -\frac{\nu}{u} J_\nu(u) + J_{\nu-1}(u) \tag{2}$$

$$\frac{dJ_\nu(u)}{du} = \frac{1}{2} [J_{\nu-1}(u) - J_{\nu+1}(u)] \tag{3}$$

$$J_\nu(u) = \frac{u}{2\nu} [J_{\nu+1}(u) + J_{\nu-1}(u)] \tag{4}$$

$$J_{n+1}(u) = \frac{2n}{u} J_n(u) - J_{n-1}(u) \tag{5}$$

From (1) we have for $\nu = n = 0$,

$$\frac{dJ_0(u)}{du} = -J_1(u) \tag{6}$$

That is, the slope of the $J_0(u)$ curve is equal to $-J_1(u)$.

A-13. Spherical Bessel Functions. Bessel functions of order $n + \frac{1}{2}$ are sometimes called *spherical Bessel functions* and are designated by lower-case letters. Thus[2]

$$j_n(u) = \sqrt{\frac{\pi}{2u}} J_{n+\frac{1}{2}}(u)$$

and

$$n_n(u) = \sqrt{\frac{\pi}{2u}} N_{n+\frac{1}{2}}(u)$$

These functions are given by series involving a finite number of terms.

---

[1] All of these formulas also apply to Bessel functions of the second and third kind. See N. W. McLachlan, "Bessel Functions for Engineers," Oxford University Press, New York, 1934, p. 24.

[2] P. M. Morse, "Vibration and Sound," 2d ed., McGraw-Hill Book Company, Inc., New York, 1948, pp. 316, 446.

For orders $n = 0$ and $n = 1$ these are

$$j_0(u) = \frac{\sin u}{u} \qquad n_0(u) = -\frac{\cos u}{u}$$

$$j_1(u) = \frac{\sin u}{u^2} - \frac{\cos u}{u} \qquad n_1(u) = -\frac{\sin u}{u} - \frac{\cos u}{u^2}$$

A-14. Legendre Functions. Solutions of Legendre's equation (14-48) are called *Legendre functions* or *surface zonal harmonics*. One solution, known as a Legendre function (or surface zonal harmonic) of the first kind, is designated by $P_n(\cos\theta)$. Another solution, known as a Legendre function (or surface zonal harmonic) of the second kind, is designated by $Q_n(\cos\theta)$.

For integral values of n the Legendre functions of the first kind are given by *Rodrique's formula*

$$P_n(\cos\theta) = \frac{1}{2^n n!}\frac{d^n(\cos^2\theta - 1)^n}{d(\cos\theta)^n}$$

and of the second kind by

$$Q_n(\cos\theta) = \frac{1}{2}P_n(\cos\theta)\ln\frac{1 + \cos\theta}{1 - \cos\theta} - \sum_{m=1}^{n}\frac{1}{m}P_{m-1}(\cos\theta)P_{n-m}(\cos\theta)$$

The latter functions are infinite when $\theta = 0$ and π so that they are not useful in representing fields that are finite in these regions.

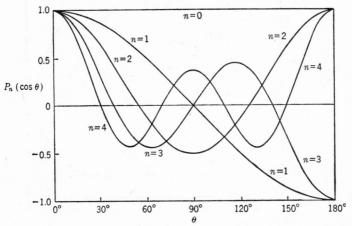

FIG. A-10. Curves for Legendre functions of orders 0, 1, 2, 3, and 4.

Curves for Legendre functions, or surface zonal harmonics, of the first kind and orders $n = 0, 1, 2, 3,$ and 4 are presented in Fig. A-10.

Legendre functions, or surface zonal harmonics, of the first kind and first few orders are listed below in polynomial form.

$$P_0(\cos\theta) = 1$$
$$P_1(\cos\theta) = \cos\theta$$
$$P_2(\cos\theta) = \tfrac{1}{2}(3\cos^2\theta - 1)$$
$$P_3(\cos\theta) = \tfrac{1}{2}(5\cos^3\theta - 3\cos\theta)$$
$$P_4(\cos\theta) = \tfrac{1}{8}(35\cos^4\theta - 30\cos^2\theta + 3)$$
$$P_5(\cos\theta) = \tfrac{1}{8}(63\cos^5\theta - 70\cos^3\theta + 15\cos\theta)$$

Solutions of the associated Legendre equation (14–44) are called *associated Legendre functions* or *solid zonal harmonics* of the first and second kind. Associated Legendre functions (or solid zonal harmonics) of the first kind are designated by $P_n{}^m$ (cos θ) and of the second kind by $Q_n{}^m$ (cos θ).

For integral values of n and m the associated Legendre functions of the first kind are given by

$$P_n{}^m(\cos\theta) = (1 - \cos^2\theta)^{m/2}\frac{d^mP_n(\cos\theta)}{d(\cos\theta)^m}$$

and of the second kind by

$$Q_n{}^m(\cos\theta) = (1 - \cos^2\theta)^{m/2}\frac{d^mQ_n(\cos\theta)}{d(\cos\theta)^m}$$

The latter functions are infinite at $\theta = 0$ and π so that they are not useful in representing fields that are finite in these regions. When $m = 0$ (no

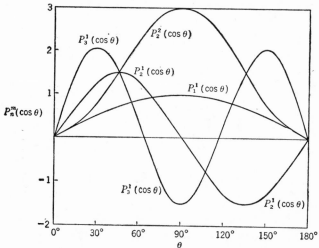

FIG. A-11. Curves for associated Legendre functions.

variation with ϕ) the associated Legendre functions reduce to the ordinary Legendre functions, or surface zonal harmonics.

Curves for a few associated Legendre functions of the first kind are shown in Fig. A-11.

A number of associated Legendre functions (or solid zonal harmonics) of the first kind are listed below in polynomial form.

$$P_1{}^1(\cos\theta) = \sin\theta$$
$$P_2{}^1(\cos\theta) = 3\sin\theta\cos\theta$$
$$P_3{}^1(\cos\theta) = \tfrac{3}{2}\sin\theta\,(5\cos^2\theta - 1)$$
$$P_4{}^1(\cos\theta) = \tfrac{5}{2}\sin\theta\,(7\cos^3\theta - 3\cos\theta)$$
$$P_2{}^2(\cos\theta) = 3\sin^2\theta$$
$$P_3{}^2(\cos\theta) = 15\sin^2\theta\cos\theta$$
$$P_4{}^2(\cos\theta) = \tfrac{15}{2}\sin^2\theta\,(7\cos^2\theta - 1)$$
$$P_3{}^3(\cos\theta) = 15\sin^3\theta$$
$$P_4{}^3(\cos\theta) = 105\sin^3\theta\cos\theta$$
$$P_4{}^4(\cos\theta) = 105\sin^4\theta$$

A-15. Table of Dielectric Materials. The following table presents data on the relative permittivity, dielectric strength, power factor, and resistivity of a number of common dielectric materials. The power factor is given in per cent at three frequencies 60 cps, 1 Mc per sec ($= 10^6$ cps), and 100 Mc per sec ($= 10^8$ cps).

TABLE OF DIELECTRIC MATERIALS

Material	Relative permittivity (relative dielectric constant)	Dielectric strength, megavolts/meter	Power factor, per cent			Resistivity, ohm-meters
			60 cps	1 Mc/sec	100 Mc/sec	
Air (atmospheric pressure)	1.0006	3				
Amber	3	...	....	0.2	....	10^{14}
Ammonia (liquid)	22					
Bakelite	5	25	2	1	....	10^{14}
Cellulose acetate	7	12	7	5	5	10^8
Cellulose nitrate	5	...	7	5		
Glass (plate)	6	30	....	0.5	....	10^{13}
Glycerine	50					
Halowax	4	...	0.2	0.2	10	10^{11}
Mica	6	200	0.5	0.03	0.03	10^{15}
Oil (mineral)	2.2	15	0.01	0.01	0.04	10^{14}
Paper (impregnated)	3	50				
Paraffin	2.1	10	0.02	0.02	0.02	10^{15}
Polyethylene	2.2	40	0.03	0.03	0.03	10^{13}
Polystyrene	2.7	20	0.02	0.02	0.03	10^{15}
Quartz	5	40	0.09	0.02	0.02	10^{17}
Rubber	3	21	1	1	....	10^{15}
Rutile† (titanium dioxide, TiO₂)	89–173	...	....	0.06		
Sulfur	4	...	....	....	....	10^{15}
Water (distilled)	81	...	....	....	....	10^4

† See footnote for Table 2-1, p. 49.

BIBLIOGRAPHY[1]

ANTENNAS

AHARONI, J., "Antennae," Oxford University Press, London, 1946.

BRUECKMANN, H., "Antennen, Ihre Theorie und Technik," S. Hirzel, Leipzig, 1939.

FRY, D. W., and F. K. GOWARD, "Aerials for Centimetre Wavelengths," Cambridge University Press, London, 1950.

JORDAN, E. C., "Electromagnetic Waves and Radiating Systems," Prentice-Hall, Inc., New York, 1950.

KING, R. W. P., H. R. MIMNO, and A. H. WING, "Transmission Lines, Antennas, and Wave Guides," McGraw-Hill Book Company, Inc., New York, 1945.

KRAUS, J. D., "Antennas," McGraw-Hill Book Company, Inc., New York, 1950.

MOULLIN, E. B., "Radio Aerials," Oxford University Press, London, 1949.

PIDDUCK, F. B., "Currents in Aerials and High-frequency Networks," Oxford University Press, London, 1946.

RAMO, S., and J. R. WHINNERY, "Fields and Waves in Modern Radio," John Wiley & Sons, Inc., New York, 1946.

SCHELKUNOFF, S. A., "Electromagnetic Waves," D. Van Nostrand Company, Inc., New York, 1943.

SILVER, S. (ed.), "Microwave Antenna Theory and Design," McGraw-Hill Book Company, Inc., New York, 1949.

SMITH, R. A., "Aerials for Metre and Decimetre Wavelengths," Cambridge University Press, London, 1950.

TERMAN, F. E., "Radio Engineering," 3d ed., McGraw-Hill Book Company, Inc., New York, 1947.

WATSON, W. H., "The Physical Principles of Wave Guide Transmission and Antenna Systems," Oxford University Press, New York, 1947.

WILLIAMS, H. Paul, "Antenna Theory and Design," Sir Isaac Pitman & Sons, Ltd., London, 1950.

BOUNDARY-VALUE PROBLEMS

BYERLY, W. E., "An Elementary Treatise on Fourier Series," Ginn & Company, Boston, 1893.

CHURCHILL, R. V., "Fourier Series and Boundary Value Problems," McGraw-Hill Book Company, Inc., New York, 1941.

SMYTHE, W. R., "Static and Dynamic Electricity," 2d ed., McGraw-Hill Book Company, Inc., New York, 1950.

STRATTON, J. A., "Electromagnetic Theory," McGraw-Hill Book Company, Inc., New York, 1941.

WEBER, E., "Electromagnetic Fields," John Wiley & Sons, Inc., New York, 1950.

[1] In general, the references in this bibliography are in addition to those in the text. The classification of a book under a particular subject does not necessarily imply that it is restricted in coverage to this subject.

ELECTROMAGNETIC THEORY (HISTORICAL)

FARADAY, MICHAEL, "Experimental Researches in Electricity," B. Quaritch, London, 1839, 1855.

HEAVISIDE, O., "Electromagnetic Theory," Ernest Benn, Ltd., London, 1893, 3 vols.; lithoreprint by Dover Publications, Inc., New York, 1950.

HERTZ, H. R., "Electric Waves," Macmillan & Co., Ltd., London, 1900.

MAXWELL, J. C., "A Treatise on Electricity and Magnetism," Oxford University Press, New York, 1873, 2 vols., 3d ed., 1904.

ELECTROMAGNETIC THEORY (INTRODUCTORY)

ATTWOOD, S. S., "Electric and Magnetic Fields," 3d ed., John Wiley & Sons, Inc., New York, 1949.

BOAST, W. B., "Principles of Electric and Magnetic Fields," Harper & Brothers, New York, 1948.

COHN, G. I., Electromagnetic Induction, *Elec. Eng.*, May, 1949.

COULSON, C. A., "Electricity," Interscience Pub., Inc., New York, 1948.

CULLWICK, E. G., "The Fundamentals of Electro-magnetism," The Macmillan Company, New York, 1939.

HARNWELL, G. P., "Principles of Electricity and Electromagnetism," 2d ed., McGraw-Hill Book Company, Inc., New York, 1949.

KELLY, H. C., "Textbook in Electricity and Magnetism," John Wiley & Sons, Inc., New York, 1941.

LIVENS, G. H., "Theory of Electricity," Cambridge University Press, London, 1926.

LOEB, L. B., "Fundamentals of Electricity and Magnetism," 3d ed., John Wiley & Sons, Inc., New York, 1947.

MOULLIN, E. B., "Principles of Electromagnetism," Oxford University Press, London, 1937.

PAGE, L., and N. 1. ADAMS, JR., "Principles of Electricity," D. Van Nostrand Company, Inc., New York, 1931.

POHL, R. W., "Electricity and Magnetism," D. Van Nostrand Company, Inc., New York, 1930.

POOR, V. C., "Electricity and Magnetism," John Wiley & Sons, Inc., New York, 1931.

POYNTING, J. H., and SIR J. J. THOMSON, "Textbook of Physics, Electricity and Magnetism," Charles Griffin & Co., Ltd., London, 1932.

RAMSEY, A. S., "Electricity and Magnetism," Cambridge University Press, London, 1937.

SKILLING, H. H., "Fundamentals of Electric Waves," 2d ed., John Wiley & Sons, Inc., New York, 1948.

STARLING, S. G., "Electricity and Magnetism," 6th ed., Longmans, Green & Co., Inc., New York, 1937.

SUYDAM, V. A., "Fundamentals of Electricity and Electromagnetism," D. Van Nostrand Company, Inc., New York, 1940.

THOMSON, J. J., "Elements of Electricity and Magnetism," Cambridge University Press, London, 1909.

WARE, L. A., "Elements of Electromagnetic Waves," Pitman Publishing Corp., New York, 1949.

WEBER, E., Ultrashort Electromagnetic Waves, *Elec. Eng.*, March, 1943, pp. 103–112.

WHITE, F. W. G., "Electromagnetic Waves," John Wiley & Sons, Inc., New York, 1934.

WHITEHEAD, J. B., "Electricity and Magnetism," McGraw-Hill Book Company, Inc., New York, 1939.

ELECTROMAGNETIC THEORY (ADVANCED)

ABRAHAM, M., and R. BECKER, "Electricity and Magnetism," G. E. Stechert & Company, New York, 1932.

BRONWELL, A. B., and R. E. BEAM, "Theory and Application of Microwaves," McGraw-Hill Book Company, Inc., New York, 1947.

HALLÉN, ERIK, "Teoretisk Electricitetslära," Skrivbyran Standard, Stockholm, 1947.

HOUSTON, W. V., "Principles of Mathematical Physics," 2d ed., McGraw-Hill Book Company, Inc., New York, 1948.

JEANS, SIR JAMES, "The Mathematical Theory of Electricity and Magnetism," Cambridge University Press, London, 1933.

JORDAN, E. C., "Electromagnetic Waves and Radiating Systems," Prentice-Hall, Inc., New York, 1950.

KING, R. W. P., "Electromagnetic Engineering," McGraw-Hill Book Company, Inc., New York, 1945.

MASON, M., and W. WEAVER, "The Electromagnetic Field," University of Chicago Press, Chicago, 1929.

PAGE, L., and N. I. ADAMS, Jr., "Electrodynamics," D. Van Nostrand Company, Inc., New York, 1940.

RAMO, S., and J. R. WHINNERY, "Fields and Waves in Modern Radio," John Wiley & Sons, Inc., New York, 1946.

SARBACHER, R. I., and W. A. EDSON, "Hyper and Ultrahigh Frequency Engineering," John Wiley & Sons, Inc., New York, 1943.

SCHELKUNOFF, S. A., "Electromagnetic Waves," D. Van Nostrand Company, Inc., New York, 1943.

SCHUMANN, W. O., "Elektrische Wellen," Carl Hanser Verlag, Munich, 1948.

SLATER, J. C., and N. H. FRANK, "Electromagnetism," McGraw-Hill Book Company, Inc., New York, 1947.

SMYTHE, W. R., "Static and Dynamic Electricity," 2d ed., McGraw-Hill Book Company, Inc., New York, 1950.

STRATTON, J. A., "Electromagnetic Theory," McGraw-Hill Book Company, Inc., New York, 1941.

VAN VLECK, J. H., "Theory of Electric and Magnetic Susceptibilities," Oxford University Press, New York, 1932.

WEBER, ERNST, "Electromagnetic Fields," John Wiley & Sons, Inc., New York, 1950.

FERROMAGNETISM

BECKER, R., and W. DÖRING, "Ferromagnetismus," Verlag Julius Springer, Berlin, 1939; lithoreprint by Edwards Bros., Inc., Ann Arbor, Mich., 1943.

BITTER, F., "Introduction to Ferromagnetism," McGraw-Hill Book Company, Inc., New York, 1937.

BOZORTH, R. M., Magnetism, Rev. Mod. Phys., 19, 29–86, January, 1947.

BOZORTH, R. M., "Ferromagnetism," D. Van Nostrand Company, Inc., New York, 1951.

ROTERS, H. C., "Electromagnetic Devices," John Wiley & Sons, Inc., New York, 1941.

SANFORD, R. L., "Permanent Magnets" (monograph), Natl. Bur. Standards (U.S.) Circ. C 448.

WILLIAMS, S. R., "Magnetic Phenomena," McGraw-Hill Book Company, Inc.,
New York, 1931.

MATHEMATICS (BESSEL AND LEGENDRE FUNCTIONS)

"Associated Legendre Functions, Tables of," Columbia University Press, New York,
1945.
"Bessel Functions of First Kind, Orders Zero and One (and Higher), Tables of,"
Harvard University Press, Cambridge, 1947. These tables, when completed,
will give orders from 0 to 100. The argument increment is 0.001 for arguments
from 0 to 25 and 0.01 for arguments from 25 to 100. Values are given to 18
decimal places.
"Bessel Functions of Fractional Order, Tables of," Columbia University Press,
New York, 1948.
BOWMAN, F., "Introduction to Bessel Functions," Longmans, Green & Co., Inc.,
New York, 1938.
FLETCHER, A., J. C. P. MILLER, and L. ROSENHEAD, "An Index of Mathematical
Tables," McGraw-Hill Book Company, Inc., New York, 1946.
GRAY, A., G. B. MATHEWS, and T. M. MACROBERT, "A Treatise on Bessel Functions,"
Macmillan & Co., Ltd., London, 1931.
JAHNKE, E., and F. EMDE, "Tables of Functions," B. G. Teubner, Leipzig, 1933;
lithoreprint by Dover Publications, Inc., New York, 1943.
MACROBERT, T. M., "Spherical Harmonics," 2d ed., Methuen & Co., Ltd.,London,
1947.
MCLACHLAN, N. W., "Bessel Functions for Engineers," Oxford University Press,
New York, 1934.
RELTON, F. E., "Applied Bessel Functions," Blackie & Son, Ltd., Glasgow, 1946.
"Spherical Bessel Functions, Tables of," Columbia University Press, 1947.
WATSON, G. N., "Theory of Bessel Functions," Cambridge University Press, London,
1944.

MATHEMATICS (GENERAL)

BYERLY, W. E., "An Elementary Treatise on Fourier Series," Ginn & Company,
Boston, 1893.
CHURCHILL, R. V., "Introduction to Complex Variables and Applications," McGraw-
Hill Book Company, Inc., New York, 1948.
CHURCHILL, R. V., "Modern Operational Mathematics in Engineering," McGraw-
Hill Book Company, Inc., New York, 1944.
COFFIN, J. G., "Vector Analysis," John Wiley & Sons, Inc., New York, 1911.
COHEN, A., "An Elementary Treatise on Differential Equations," D. C. Heath and
Company, Boston, 1906.
COPSON, E. T., "Theory of Functions of a Complex Variable," Oxford University
Press, London, 1935.
FRANK, P., and R. VON MISES (eds.), "Die Differential und Integralgleichungen der
Mechanik und Physik," Friedrich Vieweg & Sohn, Brunswick, 1930, 1935;
M. S. Rosenberg, New York, 1943.
FRANKLIN, P., "Differential Equations for Electrical Engineers," John Wiley & Sons,
Inc., New York, 1933.
LOVITT, W. V., "Linear Integral Equations," McGraw-Hill Book Company, Inc.,
New York, 1924; lithoreprint by Dover Publications, Inc., New York, 1950.
MACROBERT, T. M., "Functions of a Complex Variable," 3d ed., Macmillan & Co.,
Ltd., London, 1947.

MARGENAU, H., and G. M. MURPHY, "The Mathematics of Physics and Chemistry,"
D. Van Nostrand Company, Inc., New York, 1943.

MELLOR, J. W., "Higher Mathematics for Students of Chemistry and Physics," 4th
ed., Longmans, Green & Co., Inc., New York, 1931; lithoreprint by Dover Publications, Inc., New York, 1947. Excellent introduction to higher mathematics.

PHILLIPS, E. G., "Functions of a Complex Variable," Interscience Pub., New York,
1940.

PHILLIPS, H. B., "Vector Analysis," John Wiley & Sons, Inc., New York, 1933.

PIERPONT, J., "Functions of a Complex Variable," Ginn & Company, Boston, 1914.

REDDICK, H. W., and F. H. MILLER, "Advanced Mathematics for Engineers," John
Wiley & Sons, Inc., New York, 1947.

ROTHE, R., F. OLLENDORFF, and K. POHLHAUSEN, "Theory of Functions as Applied
to Engineering Problems," Technology Press (M.I.T.), Cambridge, 1933.

SCHELKUNOFF, S. A., "Applied Mathematics for Engineers and Scientists," D. Van
Nostrand Company, Inc., New York, 1948.

SOKOLNIKOFF, I. S., and E. S. SOKOLNIKOFF, "Higher Mathematics for Engineers and
Physicists," McGraw-Hill Book Company, Inc., New York, 1941.

SOMMERFELD, A., "Partial Differential Equations in Physics," Academic Press Inc.,
New York, 1949.

WHITTAKER, E. T., and G. N. WATSON, "A Course of Modern Analysis," The Macmillan Company, New York, 1944.

WILSON, E. B., "Gibbs' Vector Analysis," Yale University Press, New Haven, 1901.

POLARIZATION

BOHNERT, J. I., Measurements on Elliptically Polarized Antennas, *Proc. I.R.E.*, **39**,
549–552, May, 1951.

BORN, MAX, "Optik," Verlag Julius Springer, Berlin, 1933; lithoreprint by Edwards
Bros., Inc., Ann Arbor, Mich., 1943.

DESCHAMPS, G. A., Geometrical Representation of the Polarization of a Plane Electromagnetic Wave, *Proc. I.R.E.*, **39**, 540–544, May, 1951.

KALES, M. L., Elliptically Polarized Waves and Antennas, *Proc. I.R.E.*, **39**, 544–549,
May, 1951.

RUMSEY, V. H., Transmission between Elliptically Polarized Antennas, *Proc. I.R.E.*,
39, 535–540, May, 1951.

SINCLAIR, GEORGE, The Transmission and Reception of Elliptically Polarized Waves,
Proc. I.R.E., **38**, 148–151, February, 1950.

TRANSMISSION LINES

CONDON, E. U., Principles of Microwave Radio, *Revs. Modern Phys.*, **14**, 341–389,
October, 1942.

EVERITT, W. L., "Communication Engineering," McGraw-Hill Book Company, Inc.,
New York, 1937.

GUILLEMIN, E. A., "Communication Networks," John Wiley & Sons, Inc., New York,
1935.

JOHNSON, W. C., "Transmission Lines and Networks," McGraw-Hill Book Company,
Inc., New York, 1950.

KIMBARK, E. W., "Electrical Transmission of Power and Signals," John Wiley & Sons,
Inc., New York, 1949.

KING, R. W. P., H. R. MIMNO, and A. H. WING, "Transmission Lines, Antennas, and
Wave Guides," McGraw-Hill Book Company, Inc., New York, 1945.

MARCHAND, N., "Ultrahigh Frequency Transmission and Radiation," John Wiley & Sons, Inc., New York, 1947.

SKILLING, H. H., "Electric Transmission Lines," McGraw-Hill Book Company, Inc., New York, 1951.

SLATER, J. C., "Microwave Transmission," McGraw-Hill Book Company, Inc., New York, 1942.

TERMAN, F. E., "Radio Engineers' Handbook," McGraw-Hill Book Co., Inc., New York, 1943.

TERMAN, F. E., "Radio Engineering," 3d ed., McGraw-Hill Book Company, Inc., New York, 1947.

UNITS

HALLÉN, ERIK, "Some Units in the Giorgi System and the C.G.S. System," *Trans. Roy. Inst. Tech.* (Stockholm), *Mono.* No. 6, 1947.

WAVE GUIDES

ATTWOOD, S. S., Surface Wave Propagation over a Coated Plane Conductor, *J. Applied Phys.*, **22**, 504–509, April, 1951.

BARROW, W. L., Transmission of Electromagnetic Waves in Hollow Tubes of Metal, *Proc. I.R.E.*, **24**, 1298–1328, October, 1936.

BRILLOUIN, LEON, Propagation d'ondes électromagnétique dans un tuyau, *Rev. gén. élec.*, **40**, 227–239, August, 1936.

CARSON, J. R., S. P. MEAD, and S. A. SCHELKUNOFF, Hyper-frequency Wave Guides— Mathematical Theory, *Bell System Tech. J.*, **15**, 310–333, April, 1936.

CHANDLER, C. M., An Investigation of the Dielectric Rod as Wave Guide, *J. Applied Phys.*, **20**, 1188–1192, December, 1949.

CHU, L. J., and W. L. BARROW, Electromagnetic Waves in Hollow Metal Tubes of Rectangular Cross Section, *Proc. I.R.E.*, **26**, 1520–1555, December, 1938.

ELSASSER, W. M., Attenuation in a Dielectric Circular Rod, *J. Applied Phys.*, **20**, 1193–1196, December, 1949.

GOUBAU, G., Single-conductor Surface-wave Transmission Lines, *Proc. I.R.E.*, **39**, 619–624, June, 1951.

HONDROS, D., and P. DEBYE, Elektromagnetische Wellen an dielektrischen Drahten, *Ann. Physik.*, **32**, 465–476, June, 1910.

JORDAN, E. C., "Electromagnetic Waves and Radiating Systems," Prentice-Hall, Inc., New York, 1950.

KING, R. W. P., H. R. MIMNO, and A. H. WING, "Transmission Lines, Antennas, and Wave Guides," McGraw-Hill Book Company, Inc., New York, 1945.

MARCHAND, N., "Ultrahigh Frequency Transmission and Radiation," John Wiley & Sons, Inc., New York, 1947.

MUELLER, G. E., and W. A. TYRRELL, Polyrod Antennas, *Bell System Tech. J.*, **26**, 837–851, October, 1947.

RAMO, S., and J. R. WHINNERY, "Fields and Waves in Modern Radio," John Wiley & Sons, Inc., New York, 1946.

RAYLEIGH, LORD, On the Passage of Electric Waves through Tubes or the Vibrations of Dielectric Cylinders, *Phil. Mag.*, **43**, 125–132, February, 1897.

ROTMAN, W., A Study of Single-surface Corrugated Guides, *Proc. I.R.E.*, **39**, 952–959, August, 1951.

SARBACHER, R. I., and W. A. EDSON, "Hyper and Ultrahigh Frequency Engineering," John Wiley & Sons, Inc., New York, 1943.

SCHELKUNOFF, S. A., "Electromagnetic Waves," D. Van Nostrand Company, Inc., New York, 1943.

SLATER, J. C., "Microwave Electronics," D. Van Nostrand Company, Inc., New York, 1950.

SLATER, J. C., "Microwave Transmission," McGraw-Hill Book Company, Inc., New York, 1942.

SOUTHWORTH, G. C., Hyper-frequency Wave Guides—General Considerations and Experimental Results, *Bell System Tech. J.*, **15**, 284–309, April, 1936.

SOUTHWORTH, G. C., "Principles and Applications of Waveguide Transmission," D. Van Nostrand Company, Inc., New York, 1950.

TERMAN, F. E., "Radio Engineers' Handbook," McGraw-Hill Book Company, Inc., New York, 1943.

TERMAN, F. E., "Radio Engineering," 3d ed., McGraw-Hill Book Company, Inc., New York, 1947.

WATSON, W. H., "The Physical Principles of Wave Guide Transmission and Antenna Systems," Oxford University Press, New York, 1947.

WHITMER, R. H., Fields in Non-metallic Guides, *Proc. I.R.E.*, **36**, 1105–1109, September, 1948.

INDEX

Where an entire section or chapter is devoted to a subject, the reference is usually only to the first page of the section or chapter.

A

Absolute value, 430
Air gap, 263
Air-iron boundary, 258
Alford, A., 383
A-c behavior of materials, 312
A-c generator, 294
Ampere-turns, 172
Ampère's law, 168, 171
Analogous transmission line, 404
Analytic function, 543
Anomalous dispersion, 356
Antenna, definition, 484
  equivalent circuit, 505
  impedance of, 515
    mutual, 516
  network representation of, 515
  shape of, 510
  as transmission line, 507
  (See also specific types of antennas)
Aperture, 504, 514
Approximation formulas, 574
Artificial dielectrics, 56
Attenuation, above cutoff frequency, 471
  below cutoff frequency, 469
  in wave guide, 469
Attenuation constant, 422, 423
  in wave guide, 472
Attenuation factor, 396, 423
Attenuator, wave-guide, 471
Attwood, S. S., 261
Axial ratio (AR), 380

B

B vector, 146
Ballistic galvanometer, 315
Bar magnets, 206, 208
Barkhausen steps, 235, 236

Barkofsky, E. C., 383
Barrier surface, 174
Barrow, W. L., 452
Battery, 122
Beam, R. E., 521, 523
Bessel functions, 522, 576
  spherical, 524, 582
    table, 582–583
  table, 577
Bessel's equation, 522
Betatron, 296
  injection in, 299
  removal time, 300
Beverage antenna, 477
Bibliography, 587
Biconical antenna, 512
Binomial series, 574
Block, notched, 136, 140
Boldface letters, meaning of, 4, 323
Bound charges, 109
Bound wave, 479
Boundary relations, at conducting surface, 42
  at conductor-conductor boundary, 131
  at conductor-insulator boundary, 128
  electric field, 52, 56
  magnetic, 226, 230
  tables of, 56, 230, 325
Boundary-value problems, 519
Braun, C. F., 276
Braun tube, 276
Brillouin, L., 355
Broad-band antenna, 510
Broad-band transformer, 441
Bronwell, A. B., 521, 523
Bushing, capacitor, 105
Byerlay, W. E., 525

C

Capacitance, 59
Capacitivity, 4

595